23rd World Hydrogen Energy Conference (WHEC 2022)

Istanbul, Turkey
26 – 30 June 2022

ISBN: 978-1-7138-5770-9

Printed from e-media with permission by:

Curran Associates, Inc.
57 Morehouse Lane
Red Hook, NY 12571

Some format issues inherent in the e-media version may also appear in this print version.

International Association for Hydrogen Energy (IAHE)
5794 SW 40 St. #303
Miami, FL 33155, USA

Phone: (305) 284-4666
Fax: (305) 284-2580

www.iahe.org

Additional copies of this publication are available from:

Curran Associates, Inc.
57 Morehouse Lane
Red Hook, NY 12571 USA
Phone: 845-758-0400
Fax: 845-758-2633
Email: curran@proceedings.com
Web: www.proceedings.com

NATIONAL HYDROGEN ASSOCIATION TURKEY

OntarioTech UNIVERSITY

International Association for Hydrogen Energy

ABSTRACT BOOK

Bridging Continents by H_2

WHEC-2022

23rd World Hydrogen Energy Conference

Onsite and Online

June 26-30, 2022

Istanbul Congress Center, Istanbul, Turkey

www.whecistanbul.org

info@whecistanbul.org

TABLE OF CONTENTS

MESSAGE FROM CONFERENCE CHAIRMAN

Due to the unexpected COVID-19 pandemic, the entire humanity has faced many devastating challenges. As a consequence, we had to postpone our 23rd WHEC from July 2020 to June 2022 with the hope that we will successfully organize the conference. Its format will this time be hybrid to cover both onsite and online presentations along with the exhibitions in both manners.

WHEC is a unique scientific event, as initiated by Prof. T. Nejat Veziroglu and his Colleagues back in 1974, and it aims to bring all researchers, scientists, academicians and professionals working in the field of hydrogen energy systems; ranging from production to storage and end-use options, such as fuel cells for a common goal to hydrogen civilization. This time I have the privilege to chair this conference which provides both online and onsite platforms for contributions to the development and enhancement of hydrogen energy systems; as well as a place to interact with researchers from all around the world to gain a better understanding of the use of hydrogen energy systems for a sustainable future. Much like past WHECs, WHEC-2022 does not only provide an outlook on the current research activities, but also helps in shaping the future of hydrogen energy technologies.

Furthermore, Istanbul, as an ancient city that connects two continents of Asia and Europe, has always been strategically very important, and hosting such a conference in Istanbul will attract researchers from every part of the world to promote hydrogen energy systems and share their innovative ideas and future plans. Moreover, one has to keep in mind that Turkey is dedicated to increase the share of renewables in its energy supply and consider hydrogen energy systems as potential solutions. In conjunction with this, Turkey has expanded its research, innovation, and technology development activities to produce, store, and use hydrogen in an affordable, reliable, safe, clean, and sustainable manner. Given these activities as well as the financial investment and dedication to hydrogen energy systems in Turkey, Istanbul is undoubtedly the perfect host city for this event. Under the shelters of the prestigious International Association for Hydrogen Energy (IAHE) and Turkish National Hydrogen Association, we are now ready to host you for the 23rd WHEC in Istanbul and make it a success story with the strongest online and onsite participations. In this regard, I would like to take this opportunity to warmly thank everyone who has contributed to this success story.

Enjoy the Conference and enjoy your stay in Istanbul.

Prof. Dr. Ibrahim Dincer

Conference Chairman, WHEC-2022

President, National Hydrogen Association

MESSAGE FROM HONORARY CHAIRS

Welcome to the 23rd World Hydrogen Energy Conference (WHEC-2022) held from 26-30 June 2022 in Istanbul, Turkey.

Fossil fuels (i.e., petroleum, natural gas and coal), which meet most of the world's energy demand today, are being depleted fast. Also, their combustion products are causing global problems, such as global warming, climate change, ozone layer depletion, acid rain, oxygen depletion and pollution, which pose a great danger for our environment and, eventually, for life on our planet. Many engineers and scientists agree that the solution to these global problems would be to replace the existing fossil fuel system with the Hydrogen Energy System. Hydrogen is the lightest, most efficient and cleanest fuel. Its use will produce no greenhouse gases, no ozone layer depleting chemicals, no acid rain ingredients, no oxygen depletion and no pollution.

Around the world, there is extensive Research and Development work on Hydrogen Energy. Internal combustion engines are being modified for hydrogen fuel. Many types of fuel cells – to convert hydrogen efficiently to electricity – are being developed. Hyundai, Toyota, Honda and Mercedes started selling hydrogen fueled cars. Many bus companies are selling hydrogen fueled buses. Siemens is selling hydrogen fuel cell powered submarines. Hydrogen fueled appliances based on catalytic combustion have been built. There is research and development work on hydrogen hydride refrigeration and air conditioning systems. Aircraft manufacturers are working on hydrogen fueled subsonic and supersonic transport planes.

Scientists and Engineers from many countries of the world will gather at the 23rd WHEC-2022 Conference to present their papers covering the recent advances in hydrogen energy and technologies. All these will no doubt speed up the conversion to a hydrogen economy eliminate global environmental problems and provide the humankind with higher living standards. I congratulate the organizers of this conference and wish all the participants a very fruitful meeting and pleasant days in the historic capital of two world empires, Istanbul, Turkey.

T. Nejat Veziroğlu

Honorary Chair, 23rd WHEC-2022

Founding President, International Association for Hydrogen Energy

MESSAGE FROM HONORARY CHAIRS

Welcome to the 23rd World Hydrogen Energy Conference.

The demand for hydrogen is predicted to increase fivefold by 2050, driven primarily by the transport, maritime and aviation sectors, according to the recent Global Energy Perspective report developed by Energy Insights, the global market intelligence and analytics group of McKinsey & Company. This report predicts the role of electricity in the global consumption of energy to grow from approximately 20% today to 40% by 2050. Renewable energy is predicted to account for 80 to 90% of the global electric power generation by 2050.

As a result, green hydrogen is predicted to account for approximately 28% of the electric power demand by 2050. Despite creating additional electric demand, dispatchable electrolyzers will permit the integration of intermittent renewable energy sources resulting in more resilient and sustainable energy systems. Green hydrogen is predicted to serve as an energy storage for electric power generation. Gas turbines and compression-ignition, internal combustion engines converted to hydrogen can provide additional flexibility when integrated with power-to-power smart grids, especially stand-alone microgrids.

Finally, three fundamental enablers will be needed for the development of our hydrogen economy: the timely deployment of infrastructure and supply chain; cost reduction from technology advancement and manufacturing scale-up; and government support and targeted actions.

I wish you Godspeed in your endeavors for a bright and sustainable future.

John W. Sheffield, Ph.D.

President – International Association for Hydrogen Energy

ORGANIZING COMMITTEE

HONORARY CHAIRS

T. Nejat Veziroglu
John Sheffield

CONFERENCE CHAIR

Ibrahim Dincer

EXECUTIVE ORGANIZING COMMITTEE

Can Ozgur Colpan
Inci Eroglu
Aysel Kanturk Figen
Filiz Karaosmanoğlu
Adnan Midilli
Murat Ozturk
Bestami Ozkaya
Ramazan Solmaz
Ayfer Veziroglu
Emre Veziroglu

ORGANIZING COMMITTEE

Technical Co-Chairs

Can Ozgur Colpan
Mehmet Akif Ezan

Track Coordinators

Canan Acar, Coordinator of Track 1. Hydrogen Production: Thermochemical and Photonic Methods
Ankica Kovac, Coordinator of Track 2. Hydrogen Production: Electrolysis
İlgi Karapınar, Coordinator of Track 3. Hydrogen Production: Biological Methods and Biohydrogen
Rami El-Emam, Coordinator of Track 4. Hydrogen Production: Nuclear
Adolfo Iulianelli, Coordinator of Track 5. Hydrogen Separation and Purification
Tayfur Ozturk, Coordinator of Track 6. Hydrogen Storage
Selmiye Alkan Gürsel, Coordinator of Track 7. Fuel Cells: PEMFC
Meng Ni, Coordinator of Track 8. Fuel Cells: SOFC and other types
Yusuf Biçer, Coordinator of Track 9. Integrated Hydrogen Energy Systems
Benedetto Nastasi, Coordinator of Track 10. Power to Gas
Tahir A.H. Ratlamwala, Coordinator of Track 11. Hydrogen Safety
Nader Javani, Coordinator of Track 12. Codes, Standards and Regulations
Adnan Midilli, Coordinator of Track 13. Hydrogen Strategies and Policies
Yılser Devrim, Coordinator of Track 14. Hydrogen Industry, Commercialization and Marketing, Applications
Wei-Hsin Chen, Coordinator of Track 15. Hydrogen Economy, Logistics, Infrastructure
Farrukh Khalid, Coordinator of Track 16. Environmental Impact and Sustainable Development
C. Ozgur Colpan, Coordinator of Track 17. Social Dimensions

Conference Planning Coordinators

Yusuf Biçer, Communications Coordinator
Mehmet Karakılçık, Financial Coordinator
Adnan Midilli, Sponsorship and Exhibitions Coordinator
Kaan Baltacıoğlu, Social Media Co-Coordinator
Hüseyin Turan Arat, Social Media Co-Coordinator

Graduate Student Volunteers

Yağmur Nalbant Atak
Sera Ayten Çetinkaya
Tacettin Dişli
Beyza Dursun
Anıl Erdoğan
Feride Cansu İskenderoğlu
Aykut Korkmaz
Fatih Sorgulu

INTERNATIONAL ADVISORY BOARD

Frano Barbir, Croatia & USA
Juan Carlos Bolcich, Argentina
Eniya Listiani Dewi, Indonesia
Ibrahim Dincer, Canada
Gibril S. Eljrushi, Libya
İnci Eroglu, Turkey
Chiara Fiori, Italy
Patrick Hallenbeck, Canada
David Hart, Switzerland
Yun Hang Hu, USA
Ioan Iordache, Romania
Terry Kimmel, Canada
Vladimir Linkov, South Africa
Zong Qiang Mao, China
Cesare Marchetti, Italy
Elisa Marrasso, Italy
Matthew M. Mench, USA
Paulo Emílio de Miranda, Brazil
Nazim Muradov, Azerbaijan & USA
Byeong Soo Oh, South Korea
Alexander Y. Ramenskiy, Russia
Jacques Saint-Just, France
John W. Sheffield, USA
Giuseppe Spazzafumo, Italy
Detlef Stolten, Germany
Andrei V. Tchouvelev, Canada
Hirohisa Uchida, Japan
Ayfer Veziroglu, USA
Emre A. Veziroglu, USA

INTERNATIONAL SCIENTIFIC COMMITTEE

Angelo Basile, Italy
Sema Baykara, Turkey
Fanglin (Frank) Chen, USA
Marcos Vera Coello, Spain
Debabrata Das, India
Umit B. Demirci, France
Nedjib Djilali, Canada
Daniel Fruchart, France
Jürgen Garche, Germany
Maximilian Gorensek, USA
Makoto R. Harada, Japan
Alfredo Iranzo, Spain
Arunachalanadar M. Kannan, USA
Ilgi Karapinar, Turkey
Kevin Kendall, UK
Umit O. Koylu, USA
Gurkan Kumbaroglu, Turkey
E. Caglan Kumbur, USA
Xianguo Li, Canada
Hongtan Liu, USA
Matthew M. Mench, USA
Greg F. Naterer, Canada
Meng Ni, Hong Kong – China
Sandro Nizetic, Croatia
Ken-ichiro Ota, Japan
Tayfur Ozturk, Turkey
Bestami Ozkaya, Turkey
Vicenzo Palma, Italy
Sumer Sahin, Turkey
Oumarou Savadogo, Canada
David S. Scott, Canada
P Joseph Sebastian, Mexico
S. A. Sherif, USA
Patrick Takahashi, USA
Armen Trchounian, Armenia
Alexander Vorontsov, Russia
Chao-Yang Wang, USA

FORMAT OF THE CONFERENCE

WHEC-2022 will include both inspiring technical programs as well as enjoyable social events. The technical part of the WHEC-2022 will include sessions where plenary, keynote, invited and general speakers will deliver talks on their work and research in hydrogen energy. The conference will also include several specialized sessions and panel discussion sessions. There will also be numerous poster sessions where the poster presenters will have an opportunity to directly discuss their research outcomes with the conference participants. The social events will include a welcome reception, a gala dinner, and an optional tour of historical places. The conference will also include many other opportunities to socialize and connect with participants. The conference will offer both onsite and online presentations and exhibitions. The official language of the event is English. All papers must be presented in English. There will not be simultaneous translations.

PRESENTATIONS

Papers are to be presented in “Oral” or “Poster” Sessions. Speakers are requested report to the session chair 10 minutes before the start of the session. During the Oral Sessions each speaker is allocated for her/his presentation an estimated time of 12 minutes + 2-3 minutes for questions and answers. All posters will be shown on digital boards. Onsite presenters should be near the digital boards for taking any comments or questions at the break following the session scheduled in the conference program. Both online and onsite presenters should include an e-mail address on the poster. We will ask the participants to ask the questions by e-mail or via the conference website to the online presenters. Online participants may post questions to onsite participants via the conference website. So, we kindly encourage onsite/online poster presenters to visit the conference website regularly to follow up on the possible questions. There will be technical assistant in each room in case you have technical issues.

PUBLICATIONS

WHEC-2022 conference proceedings will be available for download right after the conference. The short papers of the authors who presented their papers in the conference will be included. The authors will have a chance to extend their papers and submit extended versions of their papers to special issues in prestigious journals associated with the conference. The selection and invitation process of the special issues will start after the conference ends. The authors will be informed of this process via e-mail.

The support received from the following sponsors is highly appreciated:

Main Sponsors

REPUBLIC OF TURKEY MINISTRY OF ENERGY AND NATURAL RESOURCES

TENMAK
TURKISH ENERGY, NUCLEAR AND MINERAL RESEARCH AGENCY

TURKISH AIRLINES
A STAR ALLIANCE MEMBER

Platinum Sponsors

BAU
Bahçeşehir University

FuelPositive
Fuel For A Mindful World

INOGEN
ENERJİ TEKNOLOJİLERİ
ENERGY TECHNOLOGIES

Gold Sponsors

ENERJİSA ÜRETİM

TEMSA
MOTORLU ARAÇLAR

Sabancı Üniversitesi

ÜSKÜDAR BELEDİYESİ

Silver Sponsors

Kawasaki
Kawasaki Gas Turbine Europe GmbH

TEKSIS

WHTC 2023

Bronze Sponsors

BCS MÜHENDİSLİK

Fakir
HAUSGERÄTE

İTÜ

Sistem AI
ALÜMİNYUM

Westfälische Hochschule
Gelsenkirchen Bocholt Recklinghausen
University of Applied Sciences

Other Sponsors

KUTEM

OZ
Energy

WHEC-2022

23rd World Hydrogen Energy Conference

PLENARY SPEAKERS

Kazunari Domen

The University of Tokyo/Shinshu University

domen@chemsys.t.u-tokyo.ac.jp

PHOTOCATALYTIC WATER SPLITTING FOR LARGE SCALE SOLAR HYDROGEN PRODUCTION

Water splitting to hydrogen and oxygen using particulate photocatalysts is one of the potential candidates to produce green hydrogen at low cost and on a large scale. To achieve solar hydrogen production based on such systems in a near future, there are several problems that need to be solved, such as development of efficient and durable photocatalysts, cost effective reactors, efficient hydrogen separation systems, ensuring safety issues, and so on. In this talk, recently developed photocatalysts, water splitting reactors and hydrogen separation systems being developed in our project will be introduced. In addition, safety issues of the total solar hydrogen production system based on particulate photocatalysts for water splitting will be discussed.

Stuart Hawksworth

Head of Centre for Energy, HSE, UK &
President of International Association for
Hydrogen Safety, HySafe

SafetyStuart.hawksworth@hse.gov.uk

SAFETY OF HYDROGEN IN THE ENERGY SYSTEM

This presentation will give an overview of the activities of the International Association for Hydrogen Safety (IAHYSAFE) and their impact in the hydrogen safety space. It will also provide an overview of current hydrogen safety projects and how their outputs will be applied in Regulations, Codes and Standards. The presentation will then:

- describe current priorities addressing transport, heat and power applications in the hydrogen
- discuss future technical challenges in hydrogen safety and the importance of addressing them to enable future progress and innovation in hydrogen technologies.
- discuss broader challenges around education and training in hydrogen safety as uptake in technologies grows.

The presentation will draw on inputs such as IAHYSAFE Research Priorities Workshop.

Bruce E Logan

Penn State University, USA

blogan@psu.edu

GREEN HYDROGEN PRODUCTION USING BIOMASS IN NEXT GENERATION MICROBIAL ELECTROLYSIS CELLS AND IMPAIRED WATER IN NOVEL WATER ELECTROLYZER SYSTEMS

The promise of widespread use of H_2 for heavy duty transport and many other applications will depend on developing both green (no net carbon dioxide emissions) and inexpensive methods to produce H_2. The US DOE has set a goal of 1:1:1 (1 kg for $1 USD, within 1 decade) for green H_2. In this talk I examine two of the main methods being examined by the DOE: microbial electrolysis cells (MECs), and novel water electrolyzer systems (WEs). My laboratory is developing next-generation MECs based on using zero-gap architectures incorporating an anion exchange membrane and a vapor gas phase cathode chamber for electrochemical H_2 evolution. We have recently achieved an order of magnitude increase in volumetric production rates. MECs have the advantage of using a favorable anode reaction (biomass utilization by exoelectrogenic bacteria) and therefore they have lower power requirements than WEs. WEs can achieve much higher current densities than MECs but they currently require ultra-pure water, and the cost, process intensification, and potential impacts of brine production for making this water could impact overall WE costs. Therefore, we are looking at novel architectures and materials that could enable the use of impaired (slightly salty) water in WEs. One approach is to use thin film membranes, such as those used for reverse osmosis (RO) desalination. RO membranes are $1/10^{th}$ the price of proton exchange membranes (PEMs), they can withstand high pressures, and unlike PEMs there is no use of PFAS chemicals to make RO membranes. Another WE approach is to use a vapor phase anolyte for water splitting to minimize salt crossover to the anode that can result in unwanted reactions such as chlorine gas production. Innovations in MECs and WEs such as those presented here have great promise to provide new and green methods of H_2 generation in many different locations around the world.

Peter Strasser

Technical University of Berlin, Germany

pstrasser@tu-berlin.de

ELECTROCATALYSIS OF HYDROGEN TECHNOLOGIES

Electrified solid-liquid interfaces of catalytic materials orchestrate the conversion of free electrons to molecular bonds and back. That is why they play such a key role for the performance of electrochemical energy conversion devices such as water electrolyzers and hydrogen fuel cells.

This talk will highlight advances, challenges and prospects in the quest and development of ever improved electrocatalysts and electrodes for hydrogen-based electrolysis and fuel cell technologies.

WHEC-2022

23rd World Hydrogen Energy Conference

KEYNOTE SPEAKERS

Shannon Bragg-Sitton

Idaho National Laboratory, USA

shannon.bragg-sitton@inl.gov

THE ESSENTIAL ROLE OF NUCLEAR-GENERATED CLEAN HYDROGEN IN ACHIEVING A NET-ZERO ECONOMY

We are faced with an unparalleled challenge as we plan our future energy systems. Various studies have painted a rather bleak future, calling on all of us to take action to change our habits to reduce temperature rise, or to face the dire consequences to our ecosystems and way of life. All of this comes as we are also working to provide many communities greater access to electricity, clean water, and other resources that many of us in developed nations take for granted every day. Those communities can't be denied the opportunity to improve their quality of life, which means that energy demands will continue to increase, even as developed nations flatten or reduce energy demands through energy efficiency measures.

In light of these challenges, numerous decarbonization commitments have been announced by nation states, municipalities, and private companies, with many seeking to decarbonize the electricity sector by 2035 and to achieve net-zero emissions economy-wide by 2050. Traditionally, electricity generation and management and meeting energy demands for industry and transportation are considered independently. As we seek to achieve net-zero, we need to reassess energy demands, and energy carriers. When we consider overall energy use, only one-third is in the form of electricity. Additional energy demands are in the form of heat or steam for industrial processes, as well as transportation. These sectors are much harder to abate, and electrification may not be the best option—hydrogen, when produced without concurrent emissions, is an enabler to many clean energy solutions. Reducing environmental emissions at an affordable cost, while maintaining grid reliability and resilience, will require all clean energy resources available. That means coordinating the use of nuclear, renewables, and fossil fuels with carbon capture to meet growing demands for electricity, industrial applications, and mobility.

The DOE Office of Nuclear Energy (DOE-NE) Program on Integrated Energy Systems (IES) is led by researchers at Idaho National Laboratory (INL) and work is conducted in partnership with an array of other DOE laboratories, industry, and academia. The primary focus of IES research is to assess the technical and economic potential of IES to enhance the flexibility and utilization of nuclear reactors working alongside renewable generators to meet an array of energy demands—thereby maximizing the utilization of clean energy resources across all energy sectors. Various energy applications and product streams beyond electricity are being evaluated, ranging from generation of potable water to production of hydrogen and hydrogen-based products such as fertilizers, synthetic fuels, steel, and various chemicals. This presentation will highlight the wide array of R&D being conducted across multiple DOE-funded programs to develop and deploy nuclear-based IES that will be key to achieving our net zero goals. By working with key collaborators in the nuclear industry, analytical studies are now becoming a reality in nuclear-generated hydrogen demonstration projects.

Xianguo Li

University of Waterloo, Canada

Xianguo.Li@uwaterloo.ca

THE DEGRADATION AND DURABILITY OF HYDROGEN PEM FUEL CELLS

Hydrogen PEM (proton exchange membrane) fuel cells have made significant technical progress and have reached early stage of commercial applications. However, cost reduction and durability improvement, the two interrelated technical challenges, are required for widespread commercial adoption. In this presentation, the degradation mechanism leading to the durability reduction is summarized, including thermal degradation, chemical degradation and mechanical degradation; efforts for their analyses and simulations are described, interactions between the different degradation mechanisms are outlined for accelerated degradation. Various test protocols for the accelerated stress tests (ASTs) will be previewed, and methods to mitigate the various degradation mechanisms will be discussed. Finally, some of our own efforts in the field will be shared. The current effort will be presented with the objective of achieving low cost, highly performing and durable hydrogen fuel cells with high power density. To achieve this technical target, it is necessary to combine the efforts in the development of low cost, highly performing and durable fuel cell materials, fuel cell manufacturing/processing techniques and design optimization, with a good understanding of fundamentals and command of applied aspects for the technology development, involving phenomena at the nano-, micro-, and macro-scales.

Hirohisa Uchida

Tokai University / KSP Inc., Japan

uchida@se.kanazawa-u.ac.jp

HYDROGEN STORAGE BY HYDROGEN STORAGE ALLOYS – FUNDAMENTALS AND APPLICATION

With the development of FC technology, hydrogen technology is spreading rapidly. The development and establishment of large-scale hydrogen generation, transportation and storage technology are very important issues. In the growing awareness of the global environment, clean hydrogen from renewable energy is attracting high attention. However, on the other hand, hydrogen production from fossil fuels such as LNG and lignite is also practical at present. For example, Japan, which aims to realize a hydrogen society, plans to produce a large amount of hydrogen from Uruguay's LNG, and from Australian lignite and transport it to Japan using tankers. A large amount of hydrogen on land is mainly stored as liquid hydrogen or high-pressure hydrogen gas.

As a project of Japan's Ministry of the Environment, we have developed a mass production technology of nanostructured FeFi hydrogen storage alloy and succeeded in reducing the price to one-third compared with those of conventional alloys. As a result, renewable energy such as wind or solar energy can be stored easily with hydrogen, and output/input fluctuation can be controlled well using the developed alloy.

In this lecture, at first, the basic reaction mechanisms between hydrogen gas and metal, and then the surface or bulk process controlling the rate of hydrogen absorption/storage will be explained. In applications of hydrogen storage alloys, the reaction rate is determined by the surface process and heat transfer factors depending upon density of alloy in a tank and materials contacting alloy. Secondly, the application of hydrogen storage alloys will be mentioned; (1) the application of the exothermic / endothermic heat reaction that occurs during hydrogen absorption / desorption reactions to agriculture and fish breeding, and (2) the renewable energy storage and fluctuation control by the nanostructured FeTi alloy will be reported.

WHEC-2022

23rd World Hydrogen Energy Conference

INVITED SPEAKERS

Frano Barbir

Faculty of Electrical Engineering, Mechanical Engineering and Naval Architecture (FESB), Center of Excellence for Science and Technology – Integration of Mediterranean Region (STIM), University of Split

fbarbir@fesb.hr

COMMON MISCONCEPTIONS ABOUT HYDROGEN AND HOW TO DEBUNK THEM

Hydrogen is now in a focus of interest, not only in EU, and mass deployment of hydrogen from production to applications is being planned on the highest level. However, there are still skeptics that need to be convinced that hydrogen is not only a viable but the key technology for full or deep decarbonization of energy supply. Some people, even experts, usually focus just one aspect, such as efficiency or storage size or perceived danger, and jump to conclusions without considering a wider picture. Common misconceptions about hydrogen typically include:

- Hydrogen is not an energy source. Indeed, hydrogen is an energy carrier like electricity.
- Hydrogen is (mainly) produced from fossil fuels (natural gas). That is true today, however in a decarbonized energy system hydrogen will be produced exclusively from renewable energy sources
- There is no hydrogen infrastructure. That is true today, it needs to be built. There was no infrastructure when the first cars appeared or when the first power plants were built.
- There is no hope for hydrogen fuel cell electric vehicles – BEV are so much better. This is true for light vehicles and relatively short distances. Hydrogen storage onboard is at least two times lighter than the batteries and hydrogen refueling takes a fraction of time that batteries charging takes.
- It is inefficient to produce hydrogen and then to convert it back to electricity. Compared to batteries that is inefficient indeed. However, for storing large amount of energy for relatively long time (seasonally) we do not have a better option.
- Hydrogen is bulky. Compared to gasoline or diesel hydrogen is indeed bulky. However, car manufacturers managed to fit bulky hydrogen tanks in vehicles without sacrifices
- Hydrogen does not create pollution, but its use will produce huge amounts of water. Use of hydrogen, combustion or electrochemical conversion creates exactly the same amount of water as it was used for its generation.
- Hydrogen is extremely flammable and explosive, thus dangerous. Many safety studies and use records have shown that hydrogen is not more dangerous than other fuels.

Hydrogen should not be judged by these individual properties, but by its ability to decarbonize those energy sectors that would be hard to decarbonize otherwise.

Wei-Hsin Chen

National Cheng Kung University, Taiwan

chenwh@mail.ncku.edu.tw

OPERATION AND SYSTEM OPTIMIZATION FOR HYDROGEN PRODUCTION AND SEPARATION

Over the last several decades, hydrogen has been considered as a promising green fuel to substitute fossil fuels for heat and power generation. In recent years, the development of hydrogen technology and economy has attracted a great deal of attention because it is a promising route to achieve deep decarbonization of the global energy system. Hydrogen is a non-carbon fuel; therefore, no air pollutants are emitted when hydrogen is burned. Meanwhile, hydrogen is a potential energy carrier, so it can be delivered to the appropriate places for its usage. In recent years, significant progress in proton exchange membrane fuel cell (PEMFC) has been made. Accordingly, hydrogen can be applied in the transportation sector through the applications of PEMFC. On account of a foreseeable hydrogen-based society in the future, hydrogen production and separation with high-efficiency routes become a crucial task in the implementation of hydrogen technology. In this study, a number of operation and system optimization methods for hydrogen production from thermochemical methods (such as gasification, catalytic partial oxidation, and autothermal reforming) and for hydrogen separation using palladium membranes will be illustrated. The introduced optimization methods include the Taguchi method, response surface method (RSM), and Nelder-Mead method. From these methods, the influences of operating conditions (e.g., temperature, steam-to-carbon ratio, oxygen-to-carbon ratio, and GHSV) on hydrogen yield and recovery can be figured out. The performances of the optimization methods will also be addressed.

Francesco Ganda

International Atomic Energy Agency (IAEA)

Vienna International Centre, Austria

WORLDWIDE NUCLEAR HYDROGEN DEVELOPMENT PLANS AND HYDROGEN-RELATED SERVICES OFFERED BY THE IAEA

An overview will be provided of plans by several countries related to the development of nuclear hydrogen.

In addition, a high-level description will be provided of the tools and services offered by the IAEA to all Member States, including techno-economic assessment tools and models, recent nuclear hydrogen related publications, a new coordinated research project on "Role of Nuclear Cogeneration within the Context of Sustainable Development", and technical and consultancy meetings related to the field of hydrogen.

Yun Hang Hu

Department of Materials Science and Engineering, Michigan Technological University, USA

yunhangh@mtu.edu

THERMO-PHOTO CATALYTICAL HYDROGEN PRODUCTION

The critical issues of fossil fuels are their limited natural sources and their contribution to the increase of atmospheric greenhouse gases. To solve those issues, hydrogen is being developed as a promising alternative fuel. Furthermore, solar energy is the largest energy source and technologies are being developed to exploit solar energy efficiently. Visible-light photocatalytic splitting of water to hydrogen is attractive, but its efficiency is poor due to insufficient driving force. In recent years, Prof. Hu's group demonstrated a new strategy by introducing thermal energy as kinetic energy to increase the driving force for the visible light photocatalytic process, leading to 100 times increase in efficiency. Actually, this created a new type of catalysis, "Thermo-Photo Catalysis". In this talk, he will discuss the thermo-photo catalytic hydrogen production from water with emphasis on the reaction mechanism and the synergetic effect of thermal/photo energies.

Nafiz Arica

Bahcesehir University, Turkey

nafiz.arica@eng.bau.edu.tr

ARTIFICIAL INTELLIGENCE IN SUSTAINABLE ENERGY

Artificial Intelligence (AI) has a significant impact on achieving sustainable development goals. Shaping many sectors, AI is one of the most important technologies in the transformation of the energy sector for sustainable development. Intelligent software is used in many areas from energy production to supply and demand management, from integration of renewable resources to price estimation. As sustainable energy is predicted to become the essential provider of global energy demand, the role of AI is paramount in accelerating, maintaining and expanding this adoption on which civilization is run on clean and dependable energy with minimal impact on the environment. In this presentation, the applications of Artificial Intelligence, especially for sustainable energy purposes, how AI techniques outperform the classical models and the future directions will be discussed.

Michaela Kendall

Adelan, UK

THE UK HYDROGEN STRATEGY AND TECHNOLOGY SUPPLY CHAINS

In 2017, Dr Kendall published the first UK Fuel Cell and Hydrogen Strategy devised by colleagues that created the Midlands Hydrogen and Fuel Cell Network, a regional trade association representing the pioneers of the early hydrogen economy. In August 2021, Minister Kwarteng published the second Hydrogen Strategy committing to a 5 GW hydrogen production target for the UK; only 8 months later, the target doubled to 10 GW.

The UK Hydrogen Strategy has been in the making for several decades, and the history of fuel cells and hydrogen globally is depicted in the Adelan book "Hystory". The story is one of remarkable serendipity and chance for such an important topic as low carbon energy, driven by pioneering characters inspired by international events and coincidences. The UK is a key nation in the innovation narrative, but other countries namely the USA and China have been much more successful at clustering expertise, supporting infrastructure investments, commercializing technologies, and creating momentum in the growing global hydrogen economy. Turkey played an incredibly important role in the story of hydrogen by hosting the UN Hydrogen Centre in Istanbul, forming a global nucleus of scientists, engineers, businesses and international agencies to build critical networks that remain today, especially in Europe.

This talk will examine the history of hydrogen to predict the net-zero technologies and fuels of the future. Important top-down lessons have been learned to date related to the role of hydrogen technology policy, early market clustering, market barriers, accelerating scale-up, and investment bottlenecks. Reflecting on past successes and failures will support the creation of a more resilient global hydrogen economy from the ground up.

Saim Özkar

Department of Chemistry

Middle East Technical University, Turkey

sozkar@metu.edu.tr

NOBLE METAL NANOCATALYSTS FOR HYDROGEN GENERATION FROM THE HYDROLYSIS OF AMMONIA BORANE

Ammonia borane (AB) is the most promising solid hydrogen storage materials, and its catalytic hydrolysis is the best way of releasing H_2 at ambient conditions. Noble metal nanoparticles (NPs) are the most active catalysts providing high TOF for hydrogen generation from the hydrolysis of AB. However, high price of the precious noble metals hampers their large-scale applications in catalysis. Achieving high catalytic performance with the smallest amount of metal is critical for any catalytic applications of noble metals. While continuous efforts have been devoted to improve the catalytic activity of non-noble metals in hydrolytic dehydrogenation of AB, an immense challenge is the enhancement of utilization efficiency and thus, ultimately lowering the cost of noble metal catalysts. The following approaches can be used for increasing the catalytic efficacy of noble metal nanocatalysts. (i) Reducing the particle size from macroregime to nanoregime increases the surface area and thus, the number of active sites. For example, using the colloidal NPs can increase the catalytic activity tremendously compared to the bulk metals. However, colloidal NPs are unstable and tend to aggregate to larger particles, which greatly hampers their recyclability/reusability and catalytic performance. (ii) Adding a suitable ligand into the suspension can stabilize the colloidal NPs though the activity may decrease as well. (iii) Another way of stabilizing noble metal NPs is to support them on the surface of solid materials such as metal oxide or carbonaceous materials whereby catalytic activity is expectedly enhanced by the large surface area. The catalytic activity and stability of supported noble metal NPs depend on the particle size distribution, surface area of support, and strength of metal-support interaction. Selecting suitable supports is of paramount importance in obtaining NPs which are stable and still catalytically active. (iv) Downsizing the NPs can also increase the catalytic activity of supported noble metal nanocatalysts. (v) Using reducible oxide as support is found to enhance the catalytic activity of noble metal NPs significantly. (vi) Increasing the lifetime and reusability of nanocatalysts can certainly help to improve the atom efficiency of noble metal nanocatalysts. (vii) Making the NPs magnetically separable significantly improves the reusability of noble metal nanocatalysts. The results on rhodium and platinum nanoparticles will be discussed for each approach to demonstrate that the catalytic efficiency of noble metal nanocatalysts in hydrolytic dehydrogenation of ammonia borane can be increased by a suitable combination of all the available methods.

Joris Proost

Division of Materials and Process Engineering,
Université catholique de Louvain (UCLouvain),
Belgium

joris.proost@uclouvain.be

CRITICAL ASSESSMENT OF THE PRODUCTION SCALE REQUIRED FOR FOSSIL PARITY OF GREEN ELECTROLYTIC HYDROGEN

Hydrogen produced from renewable electricity through Power-to-Hydrogen can facilitate the integration of high levels of variable renewable electricity into the energy system. An electrolyser is a device that splits water into hydrogen and oxygen using electricity. When electricity is produced from renewable energy sources, electrolytic hydrogen can be considered to be green. Key green hydrogen production technologies, mostly PEM and alkaline electrolysers, are still further maturing, both in technical (efficiency), economical (CAPEX), and durability (lifetime) performance. Nonetheless, we will show in this contribution how fossil parity for green hydrogen, i.e., a Total Cost of Ownership (TCO) similar to grey H_2 coming from CO_2 intensive SMR processes, can already be achieved today. Moreover, this can be realised at a scale which corresponds to the basic units of renewable electricity generation, i.e. a few MW.

Karen Quackenbush

Fuel Cell and Hydrogen Energy Association (FCHEA)

CODES AND STANDARDS FOR HYDROGEN ENERGY SYSTEMS

Codes and standards enable widescale commercialization of hydrogen energy systems. FCHEA facilitates industry participation to ensure that developing requirements reflect industry best practices and facilitates harmonization of technical requirements throughout national and international codes and standards. This presentation will describe current efforts and explore the importance of interdisciplinary collaboration on technical requirements for hydrogen energy systems in emerging markets.

S.A. Sherif

Department of Mechanical and Aerospace Engineering, University of Florida, USA

LIQUID HYDROGEN STORAGE IN MICROGRAVITY

Cryogens such as liquid hydrogen are frequently stored over long periods of time particularly in space applications. The operating conditions of cryogenic storage systems are strongly influenced by several factors including heat leak. Cryogens are stored at temperatures close to their respective boiling points. As a result, any addition of energy could lead to the vaporization of a portion of the liquid cryogen. In the absence of gravity, gaseous cryogens could form a vapor bubble, the shape and location of which are not known a priori. The boil-off losses associated with the storage, handling, and transportation of cryogens can result in severe losses. Heat leak causes an increase in the internal pressure of the dewar. Several mechanisms influence the size and position of the vapor bubble in the dewar. Understanding these mechanisms is important to designing storage vessels under optimum conditions and also to the development of cryogenic transfer systems. The work upon which this presentation partially reports aimed at investigating some of the fluid physics observed in a cryogenic dewar under microgravity. The objective is to quantify changes in the storage pressure and temperature and the amount of boil-off observed in a typical dewar under microgravity conditions.

S. Vasudevan

CSIR-Central Electrochemical Research Institute

Karaikudi, India

HYDROGEN PRODUCTION BY ELECTROLYSIS TO CLEAN REALITY

Alternative energy sources like solar, wind, thermal, ocean, geothermal, thermonuclear, hydrogen etc., are being considered as possible sources of energy to meet the growing demand. However, none of these energy sources except hydrogen has all the desirable qualities to replace petroleum and natural gas. For example, some are only intermittently available; others are available away from the consumption centers and cannot be used as fuel for transportation. Therefore, out of the above alternative energy sources, hydrogen is considered the best option, which could form the link between the new energy sources and the user. Hydrogen is the clean fuel and when used as a fuel, produces only water. In the hydrogen energy system, it is envisaged that hydrogen will be produced from non-fossil energy sources and will be used in every applications where fossil fuels are used today. Over the last decade there have been increasing research efforts to investigate the various aspects of the hydrogen energy systems like production, storage and transport and its applications.

Generation of hydrogen via electrolysis is a well-known and established technology. There are two main types of electrolyser [Alkaline and Proton Exchange Membrane (PEM)] and both are well proven and long-lived. Electrolysis has been traditionally based on an alkaline technology, but Proton Exchange Membrane (PEM) electrolysers are now coming to the forefront. However, due to the high cost of both electricity and material, only a small proportion (4 -5%) of the worldwide hydrogen production comes from electrolysis. Yet electrolyser costs are expected to drop within the few years as a consequence of standardization, mass-production, and a greater competitiveness. The demand for clean-produced hydrogen and its storage potential spell enormous possibilities for renewable electrolysis in the future. Even non-renewable electrolysis is bound to play an important role in the short-term as a source of moderate amounts of hydrogen for small fuelling stations and domestic applications.

In future low-carbon economics, electrolyser technology could provide a central solution to meeting both the power management needs of the electricity sector and the needs of the transport and industrial sectors for low/zero carbon fuels. Electrolytic hydrogen could thereby displace large proportions of non-electricity fuel consumption. Hence, the new market potential for electrolyser dwarfs the existing market potential and on a global scale it is truly vast.

In this talk some of the important and recent developments in the electrochemical alternatives with newer materials for hydrogen generation are discussed. The talk also covers hydrogen-based technologies developed at CSIR-CECRI.

WHEC-2022

23rd World Hydrogen Energy Conference

ORAL & POSTER SESSIONS

Track 1. Hydrogen Production: Thermochemical and Photonic Methods
Track 2. Hydrogen Production: Electrolysis
Track 3. Hydrogen Production: Biological Methods and Biohydrogen
Track 4. Hydrogen Production: Nuclear
Track 5. Hydrogen Separation and Purification
Track 6. Hydrogen Storage
Track 7. Fuel Cells: PEMFC
Track 8. Fuel Cells: SOFC and other types
Track 9. Integrated Hydrogen Energy Systems
Track 10. Power to Gas
Track 11. Hydrogen Safety
Track 12. Codes, Standards and Regulations
Track 13. Hydrogen Strategies and Policies
Track 14. Hydrogen Industry, Commercialization and Marketing, Applications
Track 15. Hydrogen Economy, Logistics, Infrastructure
Track 16. Environmental Impact and Sustainable Development
Track 17. Social Dimensions

This page intentionally left blank.

Track 1.

Hydrogen Production: Thermochemical and Photonic Methods

#11

ASSESSMENT OF HYDROGEN PRODUCTION SYSTEMS BASED ON BIOGAS CATALYTIC REFORMING WITH CARBON CAPTURE

Calin-Cristian Cormos, Ana-Maria Cormos, Letitia Petrescu, Simion Dragan
Babes-Bolyai University, Faculty of Chemistry and Chemical Engineering, Arany Janos 11, Cluj-Napoca, Romania
*Corresponding author e-mail: calin.cormos@ubbcluj.ro

ABSTRACT

Hydrogen is considered one of the most promising energy carriers for the future. Increasing the share of renewable energy and large-scale deployment of carbon capture, utilization and storage (CCUS) technologies are also important for reducing the greenhouse gas emissions to combat climate change actively. This work is aimed to evaluate the hydrogen production by biogas catalytic reforming processes equipped with CO_2 capture feature. The size of evaluated designs is 100,000 Nm^3/h hydrogen with purity higher than 99.95% (vol.). The assessed carbon capture options involved conventional gas-liquid absorption and innovative chemical looping cycle using iron oxide as an oxygen carrier. The evaluated schemes were modeled and simulated using the process flow modeling software ChemCAD. The mass & energy balances were used to quantify the key plant performance indicators. As the results show, the chemical looping option is very promising in term of increasing the overall energy efficiency (61.02% vs. 54.53%) and the carbon capture rate (95 vs. 70%) as well as reducing specific CO2 emissions (29.42 kg/MWh vs. 206.89 kg/MWh) than the reactive gas-liquid absorption.

Keywords: Hydrogen production, Biogas catalytic reforming, Carbon capture, utilization and storage (CCUS).

#29

AMMONIA DECOMPOSITION OVER Ru-COATED METAL STRUCTURED CATALYSTS FOR CO_x-FREE HYDROGEN PRODUCTION

[1,2] Kee Young Koo, [1] Hyo Been Im, [1] Dahye Song, [1] Unho Jung*
[1] Hydrogen Research Department, Korea Institute of Energy Research (KIER), 152 Gajeong-ro, Yuseong-gu, Daejeon 34129, Republic of Korea
[2] Advanced Energy and System Engineering, University of Science and Technology (UST), 217 Gajeong-ro, Yuseong-gu, Daejeon, 34113, Republic of Korea
*Corresponding author e-mail: uhjung@kier.re.kr

ABSTRACT

Ammonia decomposition reaction produces green hydrogen without CO_x emission and has a simple process without post treatment like water-gas shift reaction unlike the conventional natural gas reforming reaction. At the point of end use, ammonia has been considered as a promising hydrogen carrier due to a high volumetric energy density and gravimetric energy density. Liquid hydrogen makes it difficult to handle and store due to cryogenic temperature (-253°C) and boil-off loss (2-3% per day), while ammonia is feasible to liquefy at room temperature (8-10 bar) and utilize established infrastructures for storage and transport. Herein, we present the results about the catalytic performance of Ru-coated metal structured catalysts (monolith, foam) in ammonia decomposition. Metal structured catalyst has been highlighted as an alternative to ceramic pellet catalyst which causes some problems such as pressure drop, low thermal conductivity, and slow response in fixed bed reactor. We tested the metal structured catalysts at various temperatures (550-700°C) and gas hourly space velocities (GHSV=3,000-10,000 h^{-1}) in ammonia decomposition reaction. It was confirmed that the monolith catalysts with large geometric surface area showed a high NH_3 conversion at low temperature below 650°C, while the foam catalysts showed good catalytic performance at high GHSV.

Keywords: Ammonia decomposition, Hydrogen, Ru catalyst, Metal structured catalyst

#42

EXPERIMENTAL INVESTIGATION OF A PHOTOELECTROCHEMICAL REACTOR FOR HYDROGEN PRODUCTION AND WASTEWATER TREATMENT

*[1,2]*Murat Emre Demir*, [1,3]*Ibrahim Dincer*
[1]Clean Energy Research Laboratory, University of Ontario Institute of Technology, Faculty of Engineering and Applied Science, 2000 Simcoe Street North, Oshawa, Ontario L1H 7K4, Canada
[2] Faculty of Naval Architecture and Ocean Engineering, Istanbul Technical University, Maslak-Sariyer, Istanbul, 34469, Turkey
[3] Yildiz Technical University, Faculty of Mechanical Engineering, Istanbul, 34349 Turkey
*Corresponding author e-mail: medemir@itu.edu.tr

ABSTRACT

In this study, a novel photoelectrochemical reactor for hydrogen and clean water production is designed, constructed, and experimentally investigated. TiO_2 photocatalyst is used in a photoelectrochemical (PEC) reactor, which cleans the water via Fenton-like process and produces hydrogen. A novel dual anode structure is used in the experiments. The TiO_2 nanoparticle deposited photoanode induces electro currents for hydrogen production and produces hydroxyl ions, which assist the removal of chemical oxygen demand (COD) process. The second anode is a stainless-steel plate, which is used as a sacrificial anode to electrogenerated iron ions for the Fenton process. It is aimed to reduce the anode cell half potential and energy consumption by replacing oxygen evaluation with the iron oxidation process. The overall energy and exergy efficiencies of the system are 81% and 80% respectively. After 40 minutes of the operation time of the PEC reactor under 2.3 V and 60°C of cell potential and temperature, the reactor produces 22.6 mg of hydrogen and removes 87% of the COD.

Keywords: Hydrogen, Electrolysis, Photoelectrochemistry, Effluent treatment, Titanium dioxide, Fenton reagent, Energy, Exergy, Efficiency

#58

IMPROVING CATALYTIC ACTIVITY OF SUPPORTED PRECIOUS METAL CATALYSTS FOR HYDROGEN PRODUCTION BY HYDROTHERMAL CONVERSION PROCESSES

Sibel Irmak
Pennsylvania State University, Agricultural and Biological Engineering Department,
227 Agricultural Engineering Building, Shortlidge Road University Park, PA 16802 USA
*Corresponding author e-mail: sji5137@psu.edu

ABSTRACT

Development of highly active and robust catalysts for hydrothermal conversion of biomass-derived compounds to hydrogen is the most effective way for economically feasible hydrogen production. Precious metal catalysts have been known to be active catalysts for hydrogen production. Since precious metals are expensive these catalysts are widely used in the supported form for recycling.

In the present study, following strategies were applied to increase and improve activity of supported Pt catalysts to be used in hydrothermal conditions for hydrogen production from organic-rich biomass-derived feeds: (i) integrating non-expensive metals into catalyst system, (ii) using different precursors for metals, and (iii) evaluating various carbon supportive materials with enhanced properties. The catalysts were prepared by wet impregnation method that followed by chemical reduction and thermal activation processes.

The results showed that use of different precursors for Pt did not change activity of the catalysts. Co-deposition of W or Ni with Pt showed promising activity. Catalytic performance of the catalyst considerably improved by changing the type of carbons used as support for metal deposition. However, each carbon studied brought its own drawback that indicates there is a need to develop new carbons with unique properties to maximize catalytic activity of the supported metal catalysts.

Keywords: Precious metal supported catalysts, Carbon, Hydrogen, Biomass.

#81

THERMODYNAMIC ANALYSIS OF BIOGAS-TO-SYNGAS CONVERSION WITH DRY OXIDATIVE REFORMING AND CH_4 RECYCLING USING ASPEN HYSYS

*Pali Rosha and *Hussameldin Ibrahim*

Clean Energy Technologies Research Institute, Process Systems Engineering, Faculty of Engineering and Applied Science, University of Regina, 3737 Wascana Parkway, Regina, SK, Canada

*Corresponding author e-mail: hussameldin.ibrahim@uregina.ca

ABSTRACT

Syngas synthesis from biogas through the dry oxidative reforming route was studied using an Aspen Hysys simulator. This study dealt with the biogas-to-syngas conversion process's feasibility; initially, the simulation outcomes concerning O_2 effects in dry oxidative reforming, followed by their parametric optimization w.r.t. temperature and O_2/CH_4 ratio, were studied. The simulation outcomes of reported work revealed that the CH_4 conversion influenced primarily by O_2 injecting, particularly at lower temperature range. At all temperatures, CO_2 conversion was found to be less in dry oxidative reforming when compared to dry reforming, but the conversion rate improved at 0.20 O_2/CH_4 ratio. Further, the CH_4 recycling loop showed positive effects in CH_4 conversion and CO_2 emission reduction. For model validation, the simulated outcomes were compared with the previous experimental study in biogas reforming was carried out using pure nickel nanoparticles. Overall, the study infers that the dry oxidative reforming integrated with CH_4 recycling can be an enviro-friendly route for syngas production.

Keywords: Biogas, Hydrogen, CH_4 recycling, Hydrocarbon reforming, Aspen HYSYS

#82

H_2-ENRICHED SYNGAS PRODUCTION BY ALGAE-PLASTIC WASTE CO-GASIFICATION USING ASPEN PLUS

*Pali Rosha and *Hussameldin Ibrahim*

Clean Energy Technologies Research Institute, Process Systems Engineering, Faculty of Engineering and Applied Science, University of Regina, 3737 Wascana Parkway, Regina, SK, Canada

*Corresponding author e-mail: hussameldin.ibrahim@uregina.ca

ABSTRACT

Fluidized bed gasification is considered one of the most well-known methods in the thermochemical conversion route for renewable fuel production. Several experimental studies were reported in the open literature on downdraft gasification using different biomass feedstocks. In this study, an initiative was made to assess the feasibility of co-gasifying algae-plastic waste mixtures using an Aspen Plus simulator. Simulation results demonstrated that the algae-plastic waste co-gasification enhances H_2 content in the gaseous product distribution. The effect of gasifier temperature is more prominent in energy-efficient product formation; moreover, plastic loading enhanced H_2 production to a greater extent. At the same time, CO_2 formation increased due to more carbon conversion after improving O_2 content in the gasifier. Hence, the findings can produce energy-efficient renewable fuel that simultaneously addresses the waste disposal concern. Also, the study can serve as a guideline for future experimental studies.

Keywords: Co-gasification, Algae, Plastic waste, Hydrogen, Aspen Plus.

#83

MODELING CATALYST POISONING DURING METHANE REFORMING FOR THE PRODUCTION OF HYDROGEN

[1] Michael Fabrik, [1] Amgad Salama, [1*] Hussameldin Ibrahim*

[1]Faculty of Engineering and Applied Science, University of Regina, 3737 Wascana Parkway, Regina, Saskatchewan, Canada

*Corresponding author e-mail: hussameldin.ibrahim@uregina.ca, amgad.salama@uregina.ca

ABSTRACT

A one-dimensional simplified heterogeneous reactor model is used to simulate both steam methane reforming and dry methane reforming (i.e., using methane and carbon dioxide) under hydrogen sulfide poisoning conditions – a key challenge to this method of hydrogen production. The proposed simulation utilizes the Temkin sulfur adsorption isotherm of Alstrup et al. [1] and a Maxted-type catalyst activity expression. The reactor model is solved using the finite volume method, and the complete simulation is written and optimized in MATLAB. The simulation is validated against the numerical results of Rout & Jakobsen [2] and the experimental data of Koningen & Sjörström [3]. It was found that the deactivation order for methane reforming, based on the results of Koningen & Sjörström, was $n = 1$ versus the order of $n = 3$ proposed by Rostrup-Nielsen [4]. Discussion is provided concerning differences in expected deactivation orders observed both in this study and in other investigations, and potential influences of sulfur coverage isotherms on estimated deactivation order.

Keywords: Catalyst Deactivation, Sulfur poisoning, Hydrogen, Methane reforming, Reactor simulation

#84

MECHANISTIC KINETIC MODELING FRAMEWORK FOR THE CONVERSION OF WASTE CRUDE GLYCEROL TO VALUE-ADDED HYDROGEN-RICH GAS

[1] *Anita Odoom,* [1] *Michael Fabrik,* [1] *Amgad Salama,* [1*] *Hussameldin Ibrahim*
[1]Faculty of Engineering and Applied Science, University of Regina, 3737 Wascana Parkway, Regina, Saskatchewan, Canada
*Corresponding author e-mail: hussameldin.ibrahim@uregina.ca

ABSTRACT

The kinetics for crude glycerol autothermal reforming over 5% Ni/CeZrCa catalyst were studied using previous experimental work. An overall power law model was developed for autothermal crude glycerol reforming, with a frequency factor of 4.3×10^{10} (mol/min)/g_{cat}, an activation energy of 8.78×10^{4} kJ/mol, and orders of reaction for crude glycerol, water, and oxygen of 1.04, 0.54, and 1.78, respectively. The power law model featured an average absolute error (AAE) of 5.8%. Additionally, mechanistic models describing autothermal crude glycerol reforming were also developed for three primary sub-reactions: steam reforming of crude glycerol, total oxidation of crude glycerol, and carbon dioxide methanation. An Eley-Rideal (ER) type expression best described steam reforming of crude glycerol, featuring an AAE of 9.7%. A Langmuir Hinshelwood Hougen Watson (LHHW) type expression best described total oxidation, presenting an AAE of 14.6%. Lastly, carbon dioxide methanation was best represented by an ER type expression, featuring an AAE of 5.8%.

Keywords: Glycerol, Hydrogen, Kinetics, Reactor modeling, Autothermal reforming

#85

APPLICATION OF DFT AND MACHINE LEARNING TO PREDICT OPTIMUM OPERATING CONDITIONS FOR METHANE PYROLYSIS USING MOLTEN METALS FOR CARBON-FREE HYDROGEN PRODUCTION

[1*] *Lord Ugwu,* [1] *Hussameldin Ibrahim,* [2] *Yasser Morgan*
[1]Clean Energy Technologies Research Institute (CETRI), Process Systems Engineering, Faculty of Engineering and Applied Science, University of Regina, 3737 Wascana Parkway Regina, SK, S4S 0A2, Canada.
[2]Software Systems Engineering, Faculty of Engineering and Applied Science, University of Regina, 3737 Wascana Parkway Regina, SK, S4S 0A2, Canada.
*Corresponding Author: E-mail address: hussameldin.ibrahim@uregina.ca

ABSTRACT

The production of hydrogen from various feedstock involves the catalyzation of various reactions for the generation of the desired product. Experimental studies provide an understanding of the reaction mechanism and the nature of the reactants and products of the reaction. Computational studies involving DFT provide even greater insights into these reactions. The pyrolysis of methane over various catalysts requires an efficient means of screening catalysts for the reaction. The reaction is an endothermic reaction that is associated with a high demand for energy to drive the reaction. A process associated with a reduced demand for energy and increased yield of hydrogen will make the pyrolysis reaction more efficient and more industrially applicable. A combination of DFT and ML provides a means of establishing catalytic descriptor-based predictions for the reaction. The prediction of the relaxation energies of doped group 10, 11 and 12 transition elements from their initial structures with the adsorbate ions at the different stages of the reactions provides a predictable path for the calculation of the Turnover Frequency of the reactions, suggesting the preferred catalyst for the reaction. This study seeks to establish a model for predicting catalytic activity in methane pyrolysis reactions at various operational conditions.

Keywords: Heterogeneous catalysis, Hydrogen, Density functional theory, Machine learning, Pyrolysis

#106

PHOTOCATALYTIC HYDROGEN PRODUCTION BY TiO_2/CdTe QUANTUM DOTS

[1]*Maria J. Rivero,* [1] *Juan Corredor,* [1]*Clara Rodriguez-Tezanos,* [1*] *Inmaculada Ortiz*
[1] University of Cantabria, ETSIIT, Department of Chemical and Biomolecular Engineering, Avda. de los Castros s/n, 39005, Santander, Spain
*Corresponding author e-mail: riveromj@unican.es

ABSTRACT

In a current global context with the necessity of reducing the greenhouse gas emissions, hydrogen arises as an energy source with the advantage that the only product of its combustion is water. Photocatalytic hydrogen production is an alternative to generate directly green energy driven by solar light. TiO_2 is one of the most commonly used semiconductors in photocatalysis due to its great properties. However, its wide bandgap and electron-hole recombination limit its application. A strategy to avoid these limitations consists of using another semiconductor material leading to a constructed heterojunction. A possible mechanism consisting of photo-generated electron transfer from CdTe quantum dots (QDs) to TiO_2 has been considered with great potential to increase hydrogen production. CdTe QDs were prepared by a facile one-step synthesis method. Several variables were studied during the synthesis such as temperature, CD:Te weight ratio, and reaction time. 100°C and Cd:Te weight ratio of 1:0.2 were the best conditions to achieve a homogeneous size distribution of QDs. TiO_2/CdTe QDs 5% photocatalyst was prepared by a one-step method by mechanical mixing. The composite was used for hydrogen production from a 20% methanol solution using visible and UVA light sources. The composite produced almost 10-fold more hydrogen than bare TiO_2.

Keywords: CdTe QDs, TiO_2/CdTe, Photocatalysis, Hydrogen production

#116

IN-SITU DEVELOPMENT OF AMORPHOUS NiPi CO-CATALYST LAYER ON HEMATITE SURFACE FOR ENHANCED OXYGEN-EVOLUTION IN SOLAR WATER SPLITTING

Aditya Singh [1], *Satirth Sarma* [1], *Sujay Karmakar* [2] *Suddhasatwa Basu* * [1,3]
[1]Department of Chemical Engineering, Indian Institute of Technology, Delhi, 110016, India
[2]NTPC Energy Technology Research Alliance, NTPC, Greater Noida, 201306, India
[3]CSIR-Institute of Minerals and Materials Technology, Bhubaneswar, 751013, India
*Corresponding author: sbasu@iitd.ac.in

ABSTRACT

Hematite (α-Fe_2O_3) is an attractive semiconductor due to its favourable bandgap (~2.1 eV), stability, nontoxicity, abundance, and economic viability. The poor water oxidation activity of the α-Fe_2O_3, which limits the PEC water splitting, can be overcome by surface modification with OER co-catalyst [1]. α-Fe_2O_3 has been synthesized by the electrodeposition method, and a thin amorphous layer of nickel phosphate (NiPi) OER co-catalyst is in-situ derived from Ni_3N nanoflakes via oxidative polarization in PBS buffer. The α-Fe_2O_3/Ni_3N/NiPi photoanode has been characterized by XRD, SEM, XPS, HR-TEM, UV-Vis optical absorption, linear sweep voltammetry, and electrochemical impedance spectroscopy to assess the phase purity, morphology, and elemental composition, amorphous nature, phase identification, visible light photoactivity, photocurrent and charge transfer resistance respectively. NiPi decorated α-Fe_2O_3 photoanode showed enhanced photocurrent density of 2.5 mA cm^{-2} at potential of 1.23 V vs. RHE in 1 M NaOH, 8 times higher than pristine α-Fe_2O_3. The increased PEC performance of NiPi decorated α-Fe_2O_3 photoanode is due to the combined effect of enhanced separation of photogenerated electron-hole pairs and improved water oxidation on the hematite surface. All these features declare its use as an attractive low-cost photoanode in solar water splitting devices for hydrogen production under environment-friendly conditions.

Keywords: Oxygen evolution reaction, Photoelectrochemical, Photoanode, Electron-hole separation, Co-catalyst

#130

PHOTOCATALYTIC GLYCEROL REFORMING ON GOLD - COPPER NANO METALLIC TiO_2

[1*] *Ramazan Yıldırım,* [1] *Pınar Özdemir*
[1]Department of Chemical Engineering, Boğaziçi University, 34342, Istanbul, Turkey
*Corresponding author e-mail: yildirra@boun.edu.tr

ABSTRACT

The photocatalytic reforming of glycerol was studied on gold-copper (Au-Cu) loaded titanium dioxide (TiO_2) photocatalyst with the aim of utilizing glycerol, which is the main by-product of biodiesel production, to produce hydrogen using solar energy. 0.2 wt. % Au, 1 wt.% Cu as well as 0.2 % Au and 0.8 wt.% Cu containing photocatalysts were tested. The monometallic and bimetallic photocatalysts were synthesized by deposition precipitation with urea (DPU) and sequential deposition precipitation with urea (S-DPU) respectively and calcined in air at 400°C for 4h. Then the photocatalysts were tested in a photoreactor, equipped with 300 W xenon lamp, at ambient condition using 20 wt.% aqueous glycerol mixture. 0.2 wt.% Au loaded on TiO_2 produced H_2 with 1085 µmol/h.gcat production rate, which is comparable to that of 1 wt.% platinum (Pt) loaded on TiO_2. Then, it was concluded that Au/TiO_2 could be a more economical alternative for Pt considering that it produced the same results even though its loading was five times lower.

Keywords: Glycerol, Au/TiO_2, Hydrogen production, Photocatalysis, Photocatalytic reforming

#138

NOVEL DESIGN CONCEPT FOR THERMOLYSIS REACTOR IN THE THERMOCHEMICAL COPPER-CHLORINE CYCLE OF HYDROGEN PRODUCTION

[1*] *Ehsan Armoudli,* [1] *Ofelia A. Jianu*
[1] Mechanical Automotive and Materials Engineering, University of Windsor, 401 Sunset Avenue, Windsor, Canada
*Corresponding author e-mail: armoudl@uwindsor.ca

ABSTRACT

Hydrogen is considered one of the most promising solutions for renewable energy storage and decoupling generation from demand for large-scale implementation in the near future. The copper-chlorine (Cu-Cl) cycle for clean hydrogen production is known to be the most feasible thermochemical cycle due to its low energy requirements. Nonetheless, there are difficulties in scaling up and enhancing the efficiency of the Cu-Cl cycle for its commercialization. One of the most challenging sections to design is the thermolysis reactor in which the decomposition of copper oxychloride ($CuO.CuCl_2$) into molten CuCl(l) and O_2(g) occurs at approximately 530°C. To address this challenge, this study presents a novel design concept for the thermolysis reactor in a 4-step Cu-Cl cycle with the principal objective of improving the temperature distribution on the reactant side. The results of the flow and heat transfer analysis of the reactant side in the heat exchanger showed a decrease of 61% in temperature standard deviation in the upward direction, which shows an improved temperature distribution.

Keywords: Thermochemical Cu-Cl cycle for hydrogen production, Continuous thermolysis reactor, Molten salt heat exchanger, Solar salt.

#158

CHEMICAL KINETICS OF TWO-STEP THERMOCHEMICAL DECOMPOSITION OF H_2S OVER NICKEL SULFIDE

Asma Al Blooshi,[1] *Ahmed Al-Hajaj,*[1&3] *Mohammad Abu Zahra,*[1&3] *Giovanni Palmisano,*[1&3] *Khalid Al-Ali*[*1,2&3]
[1] Department of Chemical Engineering, Khalifa University, P.O. Box 127788, Abu Dhabi, United Arab Emirates
[2] Center for Catalysis and Separations, Khalifa University, P.O. Box 127788, Abu Dhabi, United Arab Emirates
[3] Research and Innovation on CO_2 and H_2 (RICH) Center, Khalifa University, P.O. Box 127788, Abu Dhabi, United Arab Emirates

*Corresponding author e-mail: khalid.alali@ku.ac.ae

ABSTRACT

The conversion of Hydrogen Sulfide into H_2 and Sulfur ($H_2S \rightarrow H_2 + S$) is beneficial from both environmental and energy perspectives. The two-step thermochemical decomposition of H_2S is considered one of the most promising technologies for Hydrogen production. This work investigates the chemical kinetics of the two-step thermochemical decomposition of H_2S using Nickel Sulfide and studies the key parameters that affect the overall cycling process and H_2S conversion efficiency. Gas-phase and surface-phase kinetics of the two-step thermochemical decomposition of H_2S models were developed in CHEMKIN software. The formulated model results were found to be consistent with the experimental results.

Keywords: Solar thermochemical cycle, H_2S splitting, Hydrogen, Nickel sulfide

#160

EFFECTS OF PREPARATION CONDITIONS ON THE EFFICIENCY OF HYDROGEN GENERATION OF Ni-MODIFIED $Zn_{0.75}Cd_{0.25}S$ PHOTOCATALYSTS

[1*] *Maali-Amel Mersel,* [1] *Lajos Fodor,* [1] *Ottó Horváth*
[1] University of Pannonia, Faculty of Engineering, Center for Natural Sciences, Research Group of Environmental and Inorganic Photochemistry, 8200, Egyetem u. 10, Veszprém, Hungary
*Corresponding author e-mail: sam003miloo@gmail.com

ABSTRACT

The photocatalytic hydrogen production on ZnS-CdS catalysts prepared from ammine complexes was investigated in previous works. It was shown that the preparation conditions of this catalyst have a high influence on its H_2 generation efficiency. In this study, we compared the effects of the use of a co-catalyst and the hydrothermal treatment; It was found that an increase in the temperature and duration of hydrothermal treatment could improve the photoactivity of ZnS-CdS. In addition, a higher rate of H_2 production was observed when 0.1 to 0.3% NiS was used as a co-catalyst on the surface of this semiconductor before hydrothermal treatment.

Keywords: Photocatalytic H_2 production, Ammine complexes, ZnS-CdS

#162

APPLYING ARTIFICIAL INTELLIGENCE ON STEAM GASIFICATION OF WASTE PLASTIC TO GENERATE HYDROGEN

[1*] *Serap Özmen,* [1] *Peter T. Clough*
[1]Cranfield University, Cranfield, Bedfordshire, MK43 0AL, UK
*Corresponding author e-mail: s.ozmen@cranfield.ac.uk

ABSTRACT

Global warming is a major environmental threat, and the demand of renewable energy sources has been increased significantly. Hydrogen has been proposed as a key future energy carrier for the low carbon energy systems owing to its cleanliness and high-energy yield. Meanwhile another significant global threat is plastic pollution and waste plastic management is a major concern in many countries. Consequently, hydrogen production from waste plastic has become one of the most demanding research topics. One of the most promising techniques to produce hydrogen from waste plastic is gasification. However, there is a lack of understanding for the plastic gasification process since the plastic samples are mostly used as a side feedstock with biomass and coal for the gasification studies. In this study, Artificial Neural Network (ANN) modelling will be employed to provide insights of plastic gasification process. Different types of plastics will be gasified under different reaction conditions within a lab scale fluidized bed reactor and the data will be collected to train the ANN model with the data collected from literature. Thus, the impact of the input materials on the hydrogen production will be investigated.

Keywords: Plastic gasification, Hydrogen production, Artificial neural network, Process modelling, Waste to Hydrogen

#165

WASTE TO VALUE

Mustafa Rauf Kabakcioglu, Kagan Cicekdag, Soner Ureden, Selin Kahya, Bilge Altınay Uzuner
Bursa Uludag University, Engineering Faculty, Mechanical Engineering, Görükle Kampusu 16059 Nilüfer, Bursa,
*Corresponding author e-mail: **Mustafarauf50@gmail.com*

ABSTRACT

In this study, we aimed to use a fuel cell to convert the renewable hydrogen we produce under the Green Deal into electrical energy produced with domestic and national resources by reacting the waste metals and acids that end up in the soil and ocean and affect the health of the environment. The green hydrogen was produced by a reaction between aluminum and hydrochloric acid, which we obtain from industrial waste. The coagulant aluminum chloride was also obtained as a residue at the end of the reaction.

Keywords; Green hydrogen, Waste metals, Aluminum chloride, Renewable energy, Generating energy

#174

DESIGN OF GREEN HYDROGEN PRODUCTION SYSTEM IN CONTEXT OF COLLABORATIVE INTERNATIONAL ONLINE LEARNING (COIL)

[1] *Enzo Ochoa,* [2] *Patricio Alarcon,* [3] *James Gonzales,* [4] *Abrahan Malpartida,* [5] *Marlis Campos,* [6] *Gabriel Bancayan,* [7] *Luis Machaca,* [8] *Daniel Tafur,* [9] *Ignacio De-La-Puente,* [10] *Jose Gamarra,* [11] *Hector Bravo,* [12] *John Sheffield,* [13] *Stewart Bauserman,* [14] *Johnny Nahui,* [15*] *Jose Ramos-Saravia*
[1,2,3,4,5,6,7,8,9,15] University of Engineering & Technology, Department of Energy & Mechanical Engineering, Jr. Medrano Silva 165 (Barranco), Lima, Peru
[10, 14] National University of Engineering, Lima, Peru
[11] National University of San Agustín, Arequipa, Peru
[12, 13] Purdue University, West Lafayette, Indiana, USA
*Corresponding author e-mail: enzo.ochoa@utec.edu.pe

ABSTRACT
This work is about the collaboration between Purdue University (Purdue) and University of Engineering & Technology (UTEC). Both are educational institutions located in the USA and Peru, respectively. This work presents the results of the implementation of a Collaborative Online International Learning (COIL) Program. Students from different engineering careers and cultures participated in the development of a COIL Project on the hydrogen production by water splitting using high temperature heat from a concentrating solar plant. Students formed working groups to carry out the different research activities. It was found that the objective of the COIL Project were achieved in a short period of time, evidencing the academic growth of the students and, at the same time, students gained international experience.
Keywords: Collaborative online international learning (COIL) program, Transformative pedagogy, Green hydrogen.

#177

TECHNICAL AND ECONOMIC ASSESSMENT OF A SOLAR HYDROGEN PRODUCTION PLANT IN A PERUVIAN MINING COMPANY

[1] *Enzo Ochoa,* [2] *Patricio Alarcon,* [3] *James Gonzales,* [4] *Abrahan Malpartida,* [5] *Marlis Campos,* [6] *Gabriel Bancayan,* [7] *Luis Machaca,* [8] *Daniel Tafur,* [9] *Ignacio De-La-Puente,* [10] *Jose Gamarra,* [11] *Hector Bravo,* [12] *John Sheffield,* [13] *Stewart Bauserman,* [14] *Johnny Nahui,* [15*] *Jose Ramos-Saravia*
[1,2,3,4,5,6,7,8,9,15] University of Engineering & Technology, Department of Energy & Mechanical Engineering, Jr. Medrano Silva 165 (Barranco), Lima, Peru
[10, 14] National University of Engineering, Lima, Peru
[11] National University of San Agustín, Arequipa, Peru
[12, 13] Purdue University, West Lafayette, Indiana, USA
*Corresponding author e-mail jramos@utec.edu.pe

ABSTRACT
The basic engineering of a hydrogen production plant has been developed. In this work, the results of the technical and economic assessment of a green hydrogen production plant with renewable energy in Peru, is presented. The hydrogen production plant employs a water splitting technology based on thermochemical cycles [1-2] powered by a concentrating solar plant and a photovoltaic power plant. This plant includes a hydrogen storage and hydrogen transportation systems to replace diesel fuel (1,15 millions of liters per year) by hydrogen within a truck fleet from a mining company in Peru.
Keywords: Green hydrogen, Green mining, Concentrating solar plant, Replacement of diesel by hydrogen, Renewable energy, Sulfur-iodine thermochemical cycle.

#195

HYDROGEN PRODUCTION BY OXIDATION OF ALUMINUM NANOPOWDER IN WATER UNDER THE ACTION OF LASER PULSES

[1*] *Boris Aduev,* [1] *Denis Nurmukhametov,* [1] *Gennadiy Belokurov,* [1] *Yaroslav Kraft,* [1,2] *Zinfer Ismagilov*
[1] Federal Research Center of Coal and Coal-Chemistry of Siberian Branch of the Russian Academy of Sciences, Kemerovo, Russia
[2] Federal Research Center «Boreskov Institute of Catalysis SB RAS», Novosibirsk, Russia
*Corresponding author e-mail: lesinko-iuxm@yandex.ru

ABSTRACT

The possibility of hydrogen production by the action of laser pulses on a suspension containing aluminum nanoparticles in water is shown. The mechanism of interaction of laser radiation with aluminum nanoparticles is proposed. Laser radiation is selectively absorbed by aluminum nanoparticles, which leads to their heating to a high temperature. As a result, the volume of the metal core of the nanoparticle increases, the continuity of the outer oxide shell is disrupted, and water interacts with metallic aluminum to form green hydrogen. We have demonstrated 100% conversion of metallic aluminum into products. The time of complete transformation of metallic aluminum depends on the energy density of the laser radiation. To obtain hydrogen by the proposed method, an energy density is sufficient 0.5 Дж/см^2.

Keywords: Green hydrogen, Laser, Nanoparticles, Aluminum

#199

PHOTOELECTROCHEMICAL WATER SPLITTING: SHORT REVIEW ON CURRENT DENSITY AND STABILITY OF PHOTOELECTRODES

[1] Dinko Brezak, [1] Doria Marciuš, [1] Ankica Kovač*
[1] University of Zagreb, Faculty of Mechanical Engineering and Naval Architecture, Zagreb Croatia
*Corresponding author e-mail: dinko.brezak@fsb.hr

ABSTRACT
Direct conversion of water to hydrogen via solar energy encounters multiple obstacles in practical operation - the most important ones being low current density and short-term stability. If photoelectrochemical water splitting is expected to ever compete with a solar panel system in tandem with electrolyzers, it is necessary to develop photoelectrodes with higher current densities using certain nanostructures and a combination of materials that meet a wide range of requirements. The limited stability of photoelectrodes becomes more pronounced with the rise of their efficiency and in photoelectrochemical water splitting is one of the biggest challenges hindering the commercialization of this technology. For this reason, it is of utmost importance to find materials that could fulfill both aforementioned requirements to bring the photoelectrochemical water splitting to the level of competitiveness. This review seeks to provide insight into what has been researched so far, as well as to propose the perspective future directions for the technology development regarding mentioned drawbacks.

Keywords: Photoelectrodes, Photoelectrolysis, Efficiency, Stability

#202

THERMODYNAMIC ANALYSIS OF BIOGAS-TO-METHANOL CONVERSION WITH CH_4 RECYCLING USING ASPEN HYSYS

*Pali Rosha, * Hussameldin Ibrahim*
Clean Energy Technologies Research Institute, Process Systems Engineering, Faculty of Engineering and Applied Science, University of Regina, 3737 Wascana Parkway, Regina, SK, Canada
*Corresponding author e-mail: hussameldin.ibrahim@uregina.ca

ABSTRACT
The methanol synthesis from syngas derived through dry reforming of biogas was studied using an Aspen HYSYS simulator. Studies revealed that hydrocarbon reforming is a practical approach to produce energy-efficient renewable fuels. In this simulation study, an initiative was made to utilize biogas for renewable methanol production using Aspen Hysys simulator. In the biogas dry reforming process, it was observed that the reactant (CH_4 and CO_2) conversions are largely favoured at elevated temperature (900 °C) and ambient pressure (1 bar). Moreover, at optimal parametric conditions, i.e., 200 °C (temperature) and 100 bar (pressure), the methanol production rate of 24.7 kg/h was assessed. However, the variation in syngas product distribution was observed w.r.t. temperature and pressure in the water gas shift reactor. Hence, based on the above observations, it can be stated that the biogas-to-methanol process is eco-friendlier, and might be used to mitigate greenhouse gases.
Keywords: Biogas, Syngas, CH4 recycling, Renewable methanol, Aspen HYSYS

#208

ENHANCED HYDROGEN-RICH SYNGAS PRODUCED BY DEVELOPED PLASMA REFORMER SYSTEM

[1] Ahmed Alharbi, [1] Naif Alqahtani, [1]Abdullah Alkhedhair, [1] Abdullah Alabduly, [1] Ahmed Almaleki, [1] Mustafa Almadih, [1] Miqad Albishi, [1] Abdullah Almayeef*
[1]King Abdulaziz City for Science and Technology (KACST), P.O. Box 6086, Riyadh 11442, Saudi Arabia
* Corresponding author e-mail: ahalharbi@kacst.edu.sa

ABSTRACT
The wide use of internal combustion engines significantly affects the environment, human health and global warming due to their exhausts, while spark ignition engine is considered as one of the main pollution sources globally. Therefore, In order to create a clean environment, achieve higher efficiency, and comply with strict regulations aimed at protecting the globe, many methods have been used to enhance SI engine performance and reduce emissions. Possible solution for emission reduction are the use of alternative fuels such hydrus ethanol or synthesis gas under lean conditions. In this study, a developed design of plasma fuel reformer was used to enhance generation of hydrogen-rich synthesis gas mixing with gasoline. Four modifications of the anode design, two modifications of the swirl ring, and two cathode materials were tested to decide the most efficient configuration of the plasma torch assembly in terms of syngas (or hydrogen) yield. The experimental results revealed that the anode design with smooth funnel shape of the gas inlet anode 1 in ring 1 at air:fuel flow rate of 30:5 was the most effective in terms of hydrogen concentrations in the reformate syngas, by about 46% increment comparing to plasmatron old design.
Keywords: Plasma, Fuel reforming, Syngas production, Plasma torch

#216

A NOVEL NANOPOROUS Mg-Li MATERIAL FOR EFFICIENT HYDROGEN GENERATION

*Xiping Song**
University of Science and Technology Beijing, State Key Laboratory for Advanced Metals and Materials, No.30, Xueyuan Road, Haidian District, Beijing, China
*Corresponding author e-mail: xpsong@skl.ustb.edu.cn

ABSTRACT
Hydrogen generation material is a new kind of energy material that can supply hydrogen by reacting with water and is drawing more and more attention with the development of hydrogen economy. In this study, a novel nanoporous magnesium-lithium material prepared by a physical vapor deposition method exhibits brilliant hydrogen generation properties. It generates hydrogen efficiently and quickly with saltwater, reaching a hydrogen generation amount of 965 mlg^{-1} (100%) and rates of 60 $mlg^{-1}min^{-1}$, 109 $mlg^{-1}min^{-1}$, 256 $mlg^{-1}min^{-1}$ and 367 $mlg^{-1}min^{-1}$ at 0°C, 25°C, 35°C and 50°C, respectively. The nanoporous magnesium-lithium material is a solid solution phase with magnesium atom and lithium atom ratio of 17:3. By synchrotron radiation analysis, its porosity is about 42.4% and its pore size is 200~400 nm. The improved hydrogen generation property is attributed to its nanoporous structure with a high specific surface area, and the addition of lithium element which acts as active sites in hydrogen generation process. As a result, the nanoporous magnesium-lithium alloy shows a remarkable hydrogen generation property.

Keywords: Nanoporous Mg-Li material, Physical vapor deposition, Hydrogen generation

#219

PERFORMANCE OF MICROWAVE AND CONVENTIONALLY HEATED REACTOR SYSTEMS IN STEAM REFORMING OF ETHANOL OVER NICKEL IMPREGNATED MESOPOROUS CARBON

*Merve Sarıyer, *Naime Aslı Sezgi, Timur Doğu*
Middle East Technical University, Department of Chemical Engineering, Ankara, Turkey
*Corresponding author e-mail: sezgi@metu.edu.tr

ABSTRACT

Hydrogen production via steam reforming of ethanol reaction was investigated over nickel impregnated commercial mesoporous carbon catalyst (10Ni-MC) in conventionally and microwave heated reactor systems. The characterization results of the catalyst revealed that according to UIPAC classification, nickel impregnated mesoporous carbon showed Type IV isotherm with H_2 hysteresis. Highly stable product distributions for steam reforming of ethanol were obtained with the 10Ni-MC catalyst. With an increase in the reaction temperature, the hydrogen yield and the hydrogen concentration were increased in both reactor systems. Higher hydrogen yield and higher concentration of hydrogen were observed in the microwave heated reactor system compared to the conventionally heated reactor system.

Keywords: Hydrogen, Ethanol steam reforming, Microwave heating, Mesoporous carbon, Nickel

#220

PRODUCTION OF "GREEN" HYDROGEN IN THE PROCESS OF LOW-TEMPERATURE CATALYTIC H_2S DECOMPOSITION

Anatolii Startsev
Pensioner, 630090 Novosibirsk, Russia
*Corresponding author e-mail: anatolii.startsev@gmail.com

ABSTRACT

The possibilities of the recently discovered reaction of the low-temperature catalytic decomposition of hydrogen sulfide to produce hydrogen and elemental sulfur with H_2S conversion close to 100% are considered. Since this process is carried out at room temperature without the supply of thermal energy from the outside, the main attention is paid to the thermodynamic aspect of the implementation of this chemical transformation. The reaction mechanisms on sulfide and metal catalysts are considered within the framework of non-equilibrium thermodynamics of irreversible processes for open systems, since this reaction is carried out due to the internal chemical energy of the substrate molecules - hydrogen sulfide. The concept of the crucial role of catalysts in the process of low-temperature catalytic decomposition of H_2S is advanced. This method can be easily adapted to the existing industrial processes of H_2S utilization by the Claus method, when instead of high - temperature, metal- and energy-intensive processes of H_2S utilization, the catalytic low-temperature decomposition processes will come to obtain the target product - hydrogen. This method can be especially in demand for the processing H_2S in the Black Sea, where it can be used in coupling with the methane conversion to produce hydrogen.

Keywords: Hydrogen production, Catalytic H_2S decomposition, Non-equilibrium thermodynamics

#223

STRUCTURE REGULATION OF ULTRATHIN GRAPHITIC CARBON NITRIDE FOR SIGNIFICANTLY ENHANCED PHOTOCATALYTIC H_2 EVOLUTION UNDER VISIBLE-LIGHT IRRADIATION

Jinwen Shi, Cheng Cheng, Liejin Guo*
State Key Laboratory of Multiphase Flow in Power Engineering, Xi'an Jiaotong University, Xi'an, 710049, China
*Corresponding author e-mail: jinwen_shi@mail.xjtu.edu.cn

ABSTRACT

Graphitic carbon nitride (g-C_3N_4) emerges as a promising candidate for achieving high-efficiency photocatalytic H_2 production. The molecular configuration, element content and crystal size of the precursor can significantly affect the polymerization degree and micro-nano structure of g-C_3N_4. Based on our previous work, biuret was developed to prepare high-efficiency g-C_3N_4 for the first time. Herein, proper treatment on biuret was employed as an effective way to improve the photocatalytic performance of g-C_3N_4. Biuret underwent hydrothermal treatment for recrystallization to form biuret hydrate, which had higher content of O element and regular morphology compared with biuret. These traits for biuret hydrate could promote the polymerization of heptazine for the formation of g-C_3N_4 network, resulting in higher polymerization degree of biuret hydrate-derived g-C_3N_4 than that of biuret-derived g-C_3N_4. In addition, biuret hydrate-derived g-C_3N_4 showed ultrathin nanosheet structure with large surface area and vast pores, which provided abundant reactive sites and was beneficial for the diffusion and accumulation of reactants. Biuret hydrate-derived g-C_3N_4 behaved high-efficiency photocatalytic H_2-production activity, with an AQY of 52.4% at 425 nm. This work provides a meaningful reference for structural regulation of g-C_3N_4 to achieve efficient solar energy conversion and storage into hydrogen.

Keywords: Polymerization degree, Hydrogen, Photocatalysis

#227

PERFORMANCE COMPARISON OF Ru AND Ru-Ni BASED CATALYSTS IN AUTOTHERMAL AND STEAM REFORMING OF DIESEL FUEL

[1] Arzu Arslan Bozdağ, [2] Arife Derya Deniz Kaynar, [1] Naime Aslı Sezgi, [1] Timur Doğu*
[1] Chemical Engineering Department, Middle East Technical University, Ankara, Turkey
[2] Vestel Defense Industry, Ankara, Turkey
*Corresponding author e-mail: sezgi@metu.edu.tr

ABSTRACT

On-site and on-demand hydrogen production through diesel autothermal and steam reforming reactions are attractive routes for both stationary and mobile auxiliary power unit applications. This study focuses on catalyst investigation for both steam and autothermal reforming reactions of diesel, which require high operating temperatures (~800°C). The scope of this study was to analyze the effect of ruthenium and ceria incorporation into Ni/Al_2O_3 catalysts in terms of their reforming reaction performance and hydrogen production capabilities. Activity tests in both reactions showed the most successful catalyst in terms of hydrogen production capability as 0.5 wt.% ruthenium loaded Ni/Al_2O_3 catalyst due to easier reducibility of nickel and the higher surface area of the material compared to the ones with higher ruthenium and ruthenium/ceria loading. Ruthenium and ceria-loaded Al_2O_3 catalyst showed weak activity in terms of hydrogen production and lead to the highest coke deposition, which presented the significant role played by nickel in reforming catalysts. Long-term activity test of 0.5 wt.% ruthenium loaded Ni/Al_2O_3 catalyst towards diesel steam reforming reaction also showed the stability of the catalyst besides its high activity. Characterization of the used catalyst presented no structure change except for carbon deposition.

Keywords: Hydrogen, Diesel, Steam Reforming, Ruthenium, Nickel

#232

THE EFFECT OF HEATING PROFILE ON HYDROGEN PRODUCTION IN A MEMBRANE-INTEGRATED STEAM-METHANE REFORMER (MISMR)

[1,2*]*Rached Ben-Mansour,* [1,3]*Mohamed Haque, ,*[1,3]*Mohamed Habib,* [4]*Stephen Paglieri,* [4]*Aadesh Harale,* [1,5]*Esmail Mokheimer*
[1] Mechanical Engineering Department, KFUPM, Dhahran 31261, Saudi Arabia
[2] IRC for Smart Mobility & Logistics, KFUPM, Dhahran 31261, Saudi Arabia
[3] Researcher at K.A. CARE Energy Research & Innovation Center at Dhahran, Saudi Arabia
[4]Carbon Management R&D Division, R&D Center, Saudi Arabian Oil Company, Dhahran, 31311, Saudi Arabia
[5]IRC for Renewable Energy and Power Systems, KFUPM, Dhahran 31261, Saudi Arabia
*Corresponding author e-mail: rmansour@kfupm.ed.sa

ABSTRACT

In order to operate reforming plants at maximum efficiency it is important to investigate their operation under various conditions. This study aims to perform a computational analysis to examine the effect of thermal boundary conditions on Steam Methane Reforming and hydrogen recovery. The studied thermal boundary conditions include constant and variable inlet temperature, outer wall temperature, and heat flux on outer wall of the reactor. A constant total inlet flow rate of 0.001 kg/s with steam-to-methane ratio (S/C) of 4 is considered in the reformer side for all the cases. Furthermore, the pressure difference on both sides of the membrane is kept constant. Sweeping flow is incorporated to further raise the hydrogen partial pressure difference. About 1.7 times increase in methane conversion is observed as the reformer temperature is increased from 500 to 700 °C. The hydrogen recovery is found to decrease with the increase in temperature. Around 57% and 56% decrease in methane conversion and 42% and 11.5% rise in hydrogen recovery is observed with segmented case as compared to the constant heat flux and constant temperature cases, respectively.

Keywords: Reforming, Methane, Membrane, Heating, Conversion

#242

HYDROGEN PRODUCTION BY GLYCEROL STEAM REFORMING

[1*] *Mirela Draghia,* [1] *Gheorghe Pasca,* [2] *Tudor Marinescu* [3]*Diana Mariana Cocârță*
[1]I.S. TECH, Take Ionescu 69, Timisoara, Romania
[2] INOVECO Expert, 6-8 Eroilor Bvd., Voluntari, Romania
[3] University POLITEHNICA of Bucharest, Faculty of Energy Engineering, Department of Energy Production and Use, Splaiul Independenței 313, Bucharest, Romania
*Corresponding author e-mail: mirela.draghia@istech-ro.com

ABSTRACT

During the last decade, petroleum-based industry and the exploitation of non-renewable resources for energy supply and production of chemicals have been continuously developed. Consequently, fossil fuel consumption has increased significantly, with large impact on climate change. Thus, finding alternatives for non-renewable reserves and developing of the new technologies for processing renewable resources are required. During the production of biodiesel, a large amount of glycerol is produced as by-product. The main objective of the paper is to develop the process diagram of a facility for hydrogen production from glycerol and to establish the optimal configuration for minimizing the conventional energy consumption. The paper introduces the developed configuration of the experimental facility aiming to investigate the chemical reactions involved in the process and the assessment of the results related to the output streams composition. The experimental data allow evaluation of the process performances of various components based on the amount of generated hydrogen versus to the molar amount of glycerol fed in the process. As far as long-term operation is concerned, the plant will be used to test the reliability of the catalysts used in the conversion process and also the reliability of the hydrogen permeation membrane used to separate/purify the hydrogen.

Keywords: Glycerol conversion, Steam reforming, Hydrogen, Biodiesel, By-product

#244

PSEUDO-DYNAMIC MODELING AND OPTIMIZATION OF HEAVY PARAFFIN DEHYDROGENATION PROCESS FOR SELECTIVE OLEFIN AND HYDROGEN PRODUCTION IN CONVENTIONAL REACTORS

[1] *M. Dehdashti*, [2*] *M. Farsi*, [3] *M. Binazadeh*
[a] Department of Chemical Engineering, School of chemical and Petroleum Engineering, Shiraz University, Shiraz 71345, Iran
*Corresponding author e-mail: farsi@shirazu.ac.ir

ABSTRACT
Hydrogen has emerged as a clean novel energy carrier. Catalytic dehydrogenation of hydrocarbons such as paraffin is a reliable method for hydrogen production. In this study, a radial flow conventional tubular fixed bed reactor is pseudo-dynamically modeled, and the operating conditions are optimized using genetic algorithm to maximize olefin and hydrogen production. The model accuracy is validated by industrial data and the model output is optimized using multi-objective genetic algorithm method. Validated model reveals that paraffin conversion and selectivity are enhanced by 3.6% and 0.12% in the optimized process compared to the conventional process, respectively.
Keywords: Heavy paraffin dehydrogenation, Radial flow conventional tubular reactor, Pseudo-Dynamic model, Genetic algorithm

#248

HYDROGEN PRODUCTION BY STEAM-CARBON DIOXIDE CONVERSION OF METHANE: CREATING AN EFFECTIVE CATALYST USING THE EX-SOLUTION APPROACH

[1*] *Ekaterina Matus*, [1] *Ilyas Ismagilov*, [1] *Olga Sukhova*, [1] *Mikhail Kerzhentsev*, [1] *Vladimir Ushakov*, [1] *Svetlana Yashnik*, [1] *Eugenie Gerasimov*, [1] *Olga Stonkus*, [2] *Andrey Nikitin*, [2] *Zinfer Ismagilov*
[1] Boreskov Institute of Catalysis SB RAS, Lavrentiev Ave. 5, Novosibirsk, Russia
[2] Federal State Budget Scientific Centre «The Federal Research Center of Coal and Coal-Chemistry of Siberian Branch of the Russian Academy of Sciences», Sovetsky Ave. 18, Kemerovo, Russia
*Corresponding author e-mail: matus@catalysis.ru

ABSTRACT
Hydrogen production by steam-carbon dioxide conversion of methane was studied over advanced Ni catalysts. The ex-solution approach at catalyst synthesis was implemented to create highly active and stable to deactivation supported Ni-containing catalysts. The highly dispersed state of Ni^{o} active component is realized due to the strong metal-support interaction, achieved by targeted synthesis of complex oxides $(CeM)_{1-x}Ni_xO_y$, catalyst precursors, followed by their thermal activation. The textural, structural, redox, and functional properties of samples were tuned by regulating the Ni/M/Ce molar ratio (M = Al, La, Mg) and conditions of activation. With an increase in M/Ce, the size of crystallites decreases, the reducibility decreases, and the thermal stability of the material increases. This ensures high rates of the process of joint conversion of methane and carbon dioxide into a hydrogen-containing gas. The catalyst of the optimal composition was developed $(Ce_{0.8}Mg_{0.2})_{0.8}Ni_{0.2}O_{1.4}$. It is resistant to carburization and provides stable performance of the steam-carbon dioxide conversion of methane: the hydrogen yield is 90% with a conversion of reagents of 85% at 800°C.
Keywords: Hydrogen, Methane, Combined reforming, Catalyst, Ex-solution

#256

INTEGRATION OF CATALYTIC HYDROCARBON DECOMPOSITION AND SUBSEQUENT USE OF CARBON NANOMATERIALS PRODUCED FOR PURE HYDROGEN FORMATION

[1*] *Olga Podyacheva*, [1] *Sergey Khairulin*, [1,2] *Zinfer Ismagilov*
[1] Boreskov Institute of Catalysis, Lavrentieva, 5, Novosibirsk, Russia
[2] Federal State Budget Scientific Centre «The Federal Research Center of Coal and Coal-Chemistry of Siberian Branch of the Russian Academy of Sciences», Sovetskiy Ave. 18, Kemerovo, Russia
*Corresponding author e-mail: pod@catalysis.ru

ABSTRACT
The results of the decomposition of methane, ethane and ethylene on Fe-containing and Ni-containing catalysts resulting in carbon nanomaterials production and pure hydrogen formation are presented. The physicochemical properties of carbon nanomaterials produced (nanotubes and nanofibers) are described in detail. The carbon nanotubes and nanofibers were successfully used as supports for the deposition of active gold and palladium species for formic acid decomposition in the gas phase. The designed catalysts demonstrate high selectivity towards hydrogen production (99.4-99.8%) at 90% formic acid conversion and stability in the reaction.
Keywords: Hydrogen, Catalytic decomposition, Formic acid, Catalyst, Selectivity

#272

STATIONARY METHANOL STEAM REFORMING TO HYDROGEN FUEL FOR FUEL-CELL FILLING STATIONS

[1] *Athanasios A. Tountas*, [2] *Geoffrey A. Ozin*, [*1,3] *Mohini M. Sain*
[1] University of Toronto, Faculty of Engineering, Department of Chemical Engineering and Applied Chemistry, 200 College St., Toronto, Canada
[2] University of Toronto, Faculty of Arts & Science, Department of Chemistry, 80 St. George St., Toronto, Canada
[3] University of Toronto, Faculty of Engineering, Department of Mechanical and Industrial Engineering, 5 King's College Circle, Toronto, Canada
*Corresponding author e-mail: m.sain@utoronto.ca

ABSTRACT
Renewable hydrogen (H_2) carriers such as methanol (MeOH), dimethyl ether (DME), oxymethylene dimethyl ethers (OMEs) and conceivably ammonia (NH_3) can be reformed back into H_2 and are fundamental chemical conversions for the long-term viability of the H_2 economy due to their higher densities and ease of transportability compared to H_2. MeOH is an especially important carrier as it is a simple C1 chemical that can be produced from green solar-PV-generated H_2 and direct-air-captured CO_2 with a current commercially practical solar-to-fuel efficiency of 10% from renewable solar energy. MeOH steam reforming (MSR) in stationary systems next to H_2 fuel-cell filling stations can eliminate the need for on-board mobile reformers and the former systems can be more robust in terms of attaining strict H_2 product specifications and MeOH is a safe, lossless and a compact medium for long-term H_2 storage. Both thermal- and photo-catalysts are viable options for achieving stable, long-term performance of stationary MSR systems.
Keywords: Fuel-cell vehicle filling stations, Methanol steam reforming, Hydrogen transport and storage, Stationary reformer, Liquid hydrogen carriers

#281

HYDROGEN SYNTHESIS BY HYDROGEN SULFIDE DECOMPOSITION IN CATALYTIC MEMBRANE REACTOR

[1*] *Sergei Khairulin*, [1] *Anton Salnikov*, [1] *Mikhail Kerzhentsev*, [2] *Zinfer Ismagilov*
[1] Boreskov Institute of Catalysis SB RAS, Lavrentiev Ave. 5, Novosibirsk, Russia
[2] Federal State Budget Scientific Centre «The Federal Research Center of Coal and Coal-Chemistry of Siberian Branch of the Russian Academy of Sciences», Sovetsky Ave. 18, Kemerovo, Russia
*Corresponding author e-mail: sergk@catalysis.ru

ABSTRACT
A number of ceramic membrane reactors (CMR) of various designs and compositions for high-temperature hydrogen sulfide decomposition were studied. Two CMR types with the layered structure were used: the first type included catalyst layer, membrane support, and membrane layer, while the second one was composed of the catalyst layer, membrane support, an intermediate layer, and membrane layer. It is demonstrated that the pore structure and the thickness of the membrane layer have a significant effect on permeability for H_2 and H_2S. Due to the high H_2/H_2S separation coefficient (more than 2.5), a significant improvement of the parameters of H_2S decomposition in CMR in comparison with the flow reactor with a granulated catalyst is observed. The H_2S conversion (with the formation of H_2) reaches 87 % at 900°C in the CMR of the optimal composition prepared using the optimal method.
Keywords: Reactor, Catalytic membrane, Hydrogen sulfide, Decomposition

#284

EXPERIMENTAL INVESTIGATION OF A Fe_2O_3 CARBOTHERMIC REDUCTION CYCLE FOR HYDROGEN PRODUCTION

[1*] *Lina Maria Varon Cardona*, [1,2] *Beethoven Narváez-Romo*, [3] *Marcelo Mourão* [1] *José Roberto Simões-Moreira*
[1] Renewable and Alternative Energy Systems Laboratory (SISEA), Escola Politécnica at University of São Paulo, São Paulo, Brazil
[2] Grupo de Energía y Termodinámica, Facultad de Ingeniería Mecánica, Universidad Pontificia Bolivariana, Medellín, Colombia
[3] Department of Metallurgical and Materials Engineering, Escola Politécnica at University of São Paulo, Brazil
*Corresponding author e-mail: varon@usp.br

ABSTRACT
The use of thermochemical water-splitting cycles to produce hydrogen gas is considered a promising low-carbon technology if they are powered by solar energy. This work presents an experimental study of a two-stage thermochemical cycle for hydrogen production. It is based on the carbothermic reduction of iron ore (Fe_2O_3) and the re-oxidation of it with steam, being the whole process powered by concentrated solar energy. Samples studied were self-reducing pellets The first stage of the proposed cycle consists in the reduction of hematitic iron oxide into its own metal at temperatures above 1173 K. The second phase of the cycle consists of iron metal oxidation by steam, which produces hydrogen gas. The rate of hydrogen gas production was measured using the gas chromatography methodology. After carbothermic reduction the samples showed a high specific surface area of 35.05 m^2/g measured by the BET method.
Keywords: Hydrogen production, Solar fuels, Carbothermic reduction, Iron oxide (Fe_2O_3), Catastrophic swelling,

#287

ON-SOLAR SIMULATOR DATA FOR KINETIC STUDIES OF CdSZnS-Pt WATERS SPLITTING

[1] *Tayseir Mohammed and [1,2]* Konstantinos Kakosimos,*
[1]Chemical Engineering Department, Texas A&M University at Qatar, PO Box 23874, Doha, Qatar
[2]Chemical Process & Energy Resources Institute, Centre for Research & Technology Hellas (CPERI/CERTH), Greece
Corresponding author e-mail:k.kakosimos@qatar.tamu.edu

ABSTRACT

Water splitting via solar energy to generate hydrogen represents a promising energy resource to address the emission and the environmental climate change. Cadmium Sulfide (CdS), with its specific characteristics, attracts significant attention as a promising photocatalyst for water splitting. However, most experimental studies do not provide adequate data to perform kinetic studies and develop kinetic models that are necessary for reactor and process design. Therefore, in this study, the binary photocatalyst CdS-ZnS/Pt was employed for water splitting using simulated solar energy to produce Hydrogen. In addition, it was necessary to design and fabricate a fully automated experimental lab-apparatus (cylindrical reactor with 70 mm ID and 10 mm depth; top-down illumination) to conduct unattended and long-duration experiments while collecting data continuously. At first, the crystallinity of the catalyst, the particle size distribution of the particles, and the band gap of the catalyst were checked given their critical role in the hydrogen evolution rate. The XRD results verified the hexagonal structure (of CdS), the FESEM images showed particles' size from 150 nm to 2 µm, and the solid-state UV-Vis yielded a band gap of 2.3 eV. Toward the collection of the kinetic data, various ranges of the catalyst loading, the concentration of the sacrificial reagent, the temperature, and the light intensity were studied. In parallel, the photo-deposition of Pt cocatalyst proved as another critical factor; herein conducted for 30 min under 1-sun intensity. The so far data showed that the optimum hydrogen evolution rate at one-sun is 37 µmol/h or (2507 µmol/g-h) at 50°C and 0.2 M ascorbic acid. At completion, the experimental dataset will be one of the few appropriate ones for kinetic studies' and comprehensive design of photocatalytic reactors.

Keywords: Kinetic Data, Experimental, PhotoReactor, Water Splitting

#291

ECONOMICALLY VIABLE LOW TEMPERATURE HYDROGEN PRODUCTION USING ALUMINUM-WATER SPLITTING METHODS

[1]Jayaraman Kandasamy, [1] Rasiha Nefise Mutlu, [1,3] Esra Eroğlu, [2] Mehmet Karaca, [3] Hande Toffoli, [1] İskender Gökalp*
Middle East Technical University, 06800, Ankara, Turkey
[1]Department of Mechanical Engineering
[2] Department of Aerospace Engineering
[3] Department of Physics
*Corresponding author e-mail: jayaraman_mit@yahoo.com

ABSTRACT

Hydrogen can be produced as a thermochemical by-product from the reactions involving metals such as Na, Al, And Fe with water in tbe gas or liquid phase. The effectiveness of the splitting of hydrogen from water molecule can be increased using activators or catalysts. The faster chemical reaction rate is demanding to meet the industry needs. The process controlling should be implemented in this reaction, since, metal reaction with water is exothermic in nature. In this work, cylindrical aluminum wires are activated using a NaOH solution and hydrogen production rate is studied experimentally as a function of several parameters including temperature and wire diameter. To provide an atomistic insight into our experimental results, first-principles total energy calculations were carried out using density functional theory (DFT). Activation barriers calculated by DFT are compared with experimental results and validate our theoretically proposed reaction mechanism.

Keywords: Hydrogen generation, Aluminum activation, Density Functional Theory, Clean energy.

#311

UTILIZATION OF Al_2O_3 AND MgO AS STRUCTURAL PROMOTERS OF Fe INTO 2 AND 3 STEPS CHEMICAL LOOPING HYDROGEN PROCESS: PURE AND GREEN H_2 PRODUCTION

[1] Martina Damizia, [1] Benedetta de Caprariis, [1] Maria Paola Bracciale, [1] Francesco Anania, [2] Livio D'Alvia, [2] Zaccaria Del Prete, [1]Paolo De Filippis*

[1] SAPIENZA University of Rome, Department of Chemical Materials Environment Engineering, Via Eudossiana 18, Rome

[2] SAPIENZA University of Rome, Department of Mechanical and Aerospace Engineering, Via Eudossiana 18, Rome

*Corresponding author e-mail: martina.damizia@uniroma1.it

ABSTRACT

The use of H_2 as alternative fuel in the transportation sector is one of the most promising solutions to reduce global warming. Chemical looping hydrogen processes (CLH) allow the production of high purity H_2, suitable for powering PEM fuel cells. This work focuses on the production of pure and renewable H_2 by CLH process using iron as redox material and ethanol as renewable reductant. To scale up the technology, the thermal stability of Fe for repeated redox cycles is a key point and still needs improvement. The addition of structural promoters can be an effective solution. Experiments at 3 different reaction temperatures (675°C-750°C) are conducted to evaluate the effect of the addition of Al_2O_3 and MgO on Fe_xO_y redox performances. The particles' thermal stability is evaluated for 10 redox cycles. The results show that the presence of Al_2O_3 led to a completely deactivation of iron oxides after few cycles at all the conditions due to the formation of Hercynite ($FeAl_2O_4$), which cannot be oxidized by water. However, introducing an air oxidation step in the system (3 steps CLH) makes this material suitable for this application. The addition of MgO guarantees stable H_2 yields at the lowest temperature tested (675°C, E=35%).

Keywords: Hydrogen, Chemical looping, Structural Promoters, Water Splitting, Iron Oxide

#319

GLYCEROL STEAM REFORMING FOR THE PRODUCTION OF HYDROGEN OVER REMARKABLY ACTIVE AND STABLE PEROVSKITE SUPPORTED Ni CATALYSTS

[1] Igor Luisetto, [2] Anastasios I. Tsiotsias, [2] Nikolaos D. Charisiou, [2] Andreas Beka, [3] Kyriaki Polychronopoulou, [2*] Maria A. Goula*

[1] ENEA Research Center, Department of Energy Technologies, Process and Energy Systems Engineering Laboratory, Casaccia, Via Anguillarese, 301, 00123, S.M. di Galeria, Rome, Italy

[2] Laboratory of Alternative Fuels and Environmental Catalysis (LAFEC), Department of Chemical Engineering, University of Western Macedonia, GR-50100 Kozani, Greece

[3] Department of Mechanical Engineering, Khalifa University of Science and Technology, Abu Dhabi, P.O. Box 127788, UAE

*Corresponding author e-mail: mgoula@uowm.gr and igor.luisetto@enea.it

ABSTRACT

The glycerol steam reforming (GSR) reaction for hydrogen production, was investigated over Ni catalysts supported on perovskite-type oxides (Ni/$BaZrO_3$, Ni/$CaZrO_3$ and Ni/$SrZrO_3$) synthesized via the auto-combustion method. The prepared catalysts were characterized via XRD and H_2-TPR, showing a high phase purity (limited formation of alkaline earth carbonate impurity phases) and reducibility. Catalytic activity evaluation revealed that Ni/$CaZrO_3$ (CaZ-Ni7) and Ni/$SrZrO_3$ (SrZ-Ni7) were remarkably active for the conversion of glycerol towards gaseous products, yielding high amounts of H_2 and preventing its consumption via side-reactions, like CO_x hydrogenation. Ni/$BaZrO_3$ (BaZ-Ni7) was found to be less effective for the gasification of glycerol, providing an overall lower H_2 yield. Ni/$SrZrO_3$ (SrZ-Ni7) was shown to be the best-performing and most resilient catalyst, exhibiting a remarkably stable performance during 20h time-on-stream at 600 °C, as it outperforms many of the employed catalysts in the literature. The produced gas has a very high H_2/CO ratio (> 20) and thus, could be fed into fuel cell stacks without extensive downstream processing.

Keywords: Glycerol steam reforming, Hydrogen production, Nickel catalysts, Perovskite oxides, Catalytic stability

#380

A BRIEF OVERVIEW OF RENEWABLE HYDROGEN PRODUCTION: PROSPECTS AND CHALLENGES

Robina Maihan[1,2], Selma Yarligan Uysal[3]
[1] Eskişehir Technic University, Faculty of Art and science, Department of chemistry, Gazipaşa Mahallesi, İki Eylül Kampüsü 26555, Tepebaşı, Eskişehir, Turkey
[2] Kabul Polytechnic University, Faculty of Industrial Chemical Engineering, Department of Chemical Engineering, Karta-e-Mamorin Kabul/5th district, Kabul, Afghanistan
[3] Eskişehir Osmangazi University, Faculty of Art and science, Department of chemistry, Büyükdere Meşelik Yerleşkesi, 26040 Odunpazarı, Eskişehir, Turkey
*Corresponding author e-mail: r.maihan@kpu.edu.af

ABSTRACT

Fuels such as oil, natural gas, and coal are electrolyzed to create hydrogen energy, which is used to power electric vehicles. Renewable energy sources like solar, wind, and hydropower could also be used to make it. This would help cut down on the amount of greenhouse gas emissions. Even though this approach has been extensively studied, it is still being used to create a practical and cost-effective way to produce hydrogen domestically. Hydrogen, on the other hand, is abundant on Earth. It is often found as an element in another compound, such as H_2O or CH_4, and must be processed into pure hydrogen before being utilized in fuel cell electric vehicles. H_2 fuel is combined with O_2 from the air in a fuel cell via an electrochemical reaction to generate electricity and H_2O.

Keywords: Renewable energy, Hydrogen production, Storage, Distribution

#381

COMBINED AUTOTHERMAL AND SORPTION-ENHANCED REFORMING OF OLIVE MILL WASTEWATER FOR THE PRODUCTION OF HYDROGEN: THERMALLY NEUTRAL CONDITIONS ANALYSIS

[1,2]P. Cerqueira, [1,2]M.A. Soria, [1,2]L. M. Madeira*
1. LEPABE, Department of Chemical Engineering, Faculty of Engineering, University of Porto, Rua Dr. Roberto Frias s/n, 4200-465 Porto, Portugal.
2. ALiCE - Associate Laboratory in Chemical Engineering, Faculty of Engineering, University of Porto, Rua Dr. Roberto Frias, 4200-465 Porto, Portugal
*Corresponding author e-mail: up201505213@up.pt

ABSTRACT

In this work a thermodynamic study and an energy analysis are performed on the autothermal and sorption-enhanced reforming of olive mill wastewater (OMW), to produce green hydrogen. The thermodynamic equilibrium compositions are calculated by using the Gibbs free energy minimization method. The effect of different parameters is assessed for the different reactor configurations. The results show hydrogen yields close to the theoretical maximum for the sorption-enhanced autothermal reforming of OMW whilst operating in thermally neutral conditions.

Keywords: Thermally neutral, Sorption, Autothermal, Olive mill wastewater, Hydrogen

#383

HYDROGEN PRODUCTION VIA STEAM REFORMING OF GLYCEROL OVER CE-LA-CU-O TERNARY OXIDE CATALYSTS

[1] Angeliki Latsiou, [1] Nikolaos D. Charisiou, [2,3] Aasif A. Dabbawala, ,[2,3*] Kyriaki Polychronopoulou, [1*] Maria A. Goula

[1] Laboratory of Alternative Fuels and Environmental Catalysis (LAFEC), Department of Chemical Engineering, University of Western Macedonia, GR-50100 Kozani, Greece

[2] Department of Mechanical Engineering, Khalifa University of Science and Technology, Abu Dhabi, P.O. Box 127788, UAE

[3] Center for Catalysis and Separation, Khalifa University of Science and Technology, Abu Dhabi, P.O. Box 127788, UAE

*Corresponding author e-mail: mgoula@uowm.gr (Maria A. Goula); kyriaki.polychrono@ku.ac.ae (Kyriaki Polychronopoulou)

ABSTRACT

In the work presented herein, Ce-La-xCu-O catalysts with different Cu contents were synthesised using the conventional microwave (MW) method and an enhanced microwave method where air cooling (AC) during heating was applied. The catalytic materials were then studied for the steam reforming of glycerol (GSR). It was revealed that the synthesis methods (MW and AC) had an effect mainly on the degree of Cu incorporation into the Ce-La-O fluorite lattice, leading to one or two phases system. GSR tests revealed that the Ce-La-10Cu-O (AC) catalyst showed the highest glycerol conversion, conversion to gaseous products and yield of H_2 (5.3 mol/mol of glycerol) and deactivated at slower rate. The improved performance of the AC catalyst can be correlated to a more homogeneous Cu incorporation into Ce-La-O mixed oxide thus forming more accessible active sites to reactants which overall impact on the catalytic performance.

Keywords: Ce-La-Cu oxides, Ternary oxides, Glycerol steam reforming; Hydrogen production

#396

SODIUM FORMATE FORMATION VIA IN-SITU CATALYTIC HYDROGEN PRODUCTION FOR DECARBONIZATION

[1]Özge Coşkuner, [2]Umit Bilge Demirci,* [1]Aysel Kantürk Figen*

[1]Yıldız Technical University, Department of Chemical Engineering, İstanbul, Turkey

[2]Institut Européen des Membranes, IEM – UMR 5635, Univ Montpellier, ENSCM, CNRS, Montpellier, France

*Corresponding author e-mail: akanturk@yildiz.edu.tr

ABSTRACT

Hydrogenation strategies, in which hydrogen and boron hydrides are used as hydrogen and heat carriers, draw attention to reducing the carbon footprint and creating a sustainable hydrogen-boron-carbon cycle. An alternative strategy to achieve the goal of the European Green Deal is the synthesis of synthetic fuels such as methanol (CH_3OH), methane (CH_4), and formic acid (HCOOH) from greenhouse gases.

Within this scope, the study is focused on sodium formate formation via in-situ hydrogen production for decarbonization, especially formic acid production. For this purpose, sodium borohydride ($NaBH_4$) is used as a hydrogen and heat carrier. Cobalt-catalyzed hydrolysis of $NaBH_4$ takes place, and the reaction is accelerated in the presence of CO_2. As a result, sodium formate (NaHCOO) and an HCOO group containing borate $B(OH)_2(OOCH)$ are obtained.

Keywords: Carbon dioxide reduction, Formate, Hydrolytic conditions, Sodium borohydride

#400

HYDROGEN AND METHANE PRODUCTION FROM ANAEROBICALLY DIGESTED WATER PLANT BY HYDROTHERMAL GASIFICATION

[1,2]*Fatma Gamze Bodur*, [1*] *Tülay Güngören-Madenoğlu*, [3]*Güven Özdemir*, [1]*Nalan Kabay*, [1]*Levent Ballice*
[1]Ege University, Engineering Faculty, Department of Chemical Engineering, Bornova-Izmir, Turkey
[2]Ege University, Graduate School of Natural and Applied Sciences, Biotechnology Division, Bornova-Izmir, Turkey
[3]Ege University, Science Faculty, Department of Biology, Bornova-Izmir, Turkey
*Corresponding author e-mail: tulay.madenoglu@ege.edu.tr

ABSTRACT

Previously, water hyacinth (*Eichornia crassipes*) was anaerobically digested with anaerobic sludge in batch system at varying total solid (TS) contents of 3.3 and 4.3% and at 35°C. In this study, high organic content of the digested biomass was evaluated in hydrothermal gasification in batch reactor system at different temperatures (200-500°C) to produce biofuels and biochemicals. Hydrothermal gasification was performed in sub- and super-critical water (T_c = 374°C, P_c = 221 bar) conditions. Prevailing products are biochemicals (glycolic acid, formic acid, acetic acid, furfural, 5-methyl furfural, phenols etc.) at lower temperatures (200-300°C) while biofuels (especially hydrogen and methane) are produced at higher temperatures (400-500°C). Nearly 63% of the feed was converted to gas and aqueous products at 500°C.

Keywords: Hydrothermal gasification, Water hyacinth, Hydrogen, Methane

#415

A THERMODYNAMIC EVALUATION OF BORON BASED THERMOCHEMICAL HYDROGEN PRODUCTION CYCLE

[1*] *Onur Oruc*, [2,1] *Ibrahim Dincer*
1 Faculty of Mechanical Engineering, Yildiz Technical University, Besiktas, Istanbul, Turkey
2 Faculty of Engineering and Applied Science, University of Ontario Institute of Technology, Oshawa, Ontario, Canada
*Corresponding author e-mail: onur.oruc@std.yildiz.edu.tr

ABSTRACT

In this study, thermodynamic analyses and simulations are performed via using the Aspen Plus software to examine the Boron based thermochemical hydrogen production cycle in detail. There are four main reactions in the cycle and one of them is performed in electrolyzer. Therefore, the cycle requires heat, electricity, and water to obtain hydrogen. The electrolyzer efficiency is around 60%, and the overall cycle exergy efficiency varies between 70%-85%.

Keywords: Boron cycle, Hydrogen production, Thermochemical water splitting

#420

A NOVEL SOLAR ENERGY DRIVEN THERMOCHEMICAL HYDROGEN PRODUCTION SYSTEM INTEGRATED WITH ELECTRIC VEHICLE CHARGING STATION

[1*] *Faran Razi*, [1] *Ibrahim Dincer*
[1] Clean Energy Research Laboratory (CERL), Faculty of Engineering and Applied Science Ontario Tech University 2000 Simcoe Street North, Oshawa, Ontario, L1H 7K4, Canada
*Corresponding author e-mail: faran.razi@ontariotechu.net

ABSTRACT

Due to excessive emissions contributed by transportation sector, electrification of vehicles has become extremely essential. In this regard, battery electric vehicles are a promising solution however, a downside to electrification is its impact on power grid. To reduce pressure on power grid, utilization of renewable energy sources is essential. Thus, this paper presents a novel idea of a solar energy based integrated system where a thermochemical hydrogen production system is combined with an electric vehicle charging station. The hydrogen produced through the thermochemical process is utilized for electricity generation through a proton exchange membrane fuel cell. The thermal energy requirements of the thermochemical cycle are fulfilled by both solar thermal energy and internal heat recovery while the electrical energy requirements of the entire system are met though solar photovoltaic energy.

Keywords: Solar energy, Hydrogen, Fuel cell, Charging station, Cu-Cl cycle.

#421

CFD SIMULATION AND ANALYSIS OF A NOVEL PHOTOELECTROCHEMICAL HYDROGEN GENERATING REACTOR DESIGN

[1*] *Ali M. M. I. Qureshy and [1] Ibrahim Dincer*
[1] Clean Energy Research Laboratory, Faculty of Engineering and Applied Science, Ontario Tech University, 2000 Simcoe Street North, Oshawa, Ontario L1G 0C5, Canada.
*Corresponding author e-mail: ali.ismael@ontariotechu.net

ABSTRACT
This study presents a novel photoelectrochemical apparatus configuration for producing hydrogen to maximize the light harvested by the photoelectrode. The new design of the photoelectrode can receive the maximum amount of light energy at any angle of sunlight. Two trapezoidal photoanode and cathode are immersed in potassium hydroxide alkaline solution. The photoanode, cathode, and Nafion membrane are positioned in the potassium hydroxide solution in the new reactor design. The multiphysics simulation of the novel photoelectrochemical reactor configuration for hydrogen production is conducted. The energy and Navier-Stokes equations of the photoelectrochemical apparatus design are solved for the hydrogen bubbles and the solution flow using CFD software. The fluid flow simulation results confirm that this new design can completely clean the adhered bubbles over the surface of the electrodes due to the unique configuration that leads to an exceptional flow distribution.
Keywords: Multiphysics simulation, Hydrogen production, Novel photoelectrode, Photoelectrochemical reactor, Photonic energy

#424

PHOTONIC REACTORS FOR HYDROGEN PRODUCTION AND WASTEWATER TREATMENT IN UNDERGROUND AND UNDERWATER APPLICATIONS

[1,2*] *Dogan Erdemir,* [1,3] *Ibrahim Dincer*
[1]Ontario Tech University, Clean Energy Research Laboratory, Oshawa, ON, Canada
[2] Erciyes University, Department of Mechanical Engineering, Kayseri, Turkey
[3] Yildiz Technical University, Department of Mechanical Engineering, Istanbul, Turkey
*Corresponding author e-mail: erdemir@erciyes.edu.tr and dogan.erdemir@ontariotechu.ca

ABSTRACT
This study investigates the potential use of photocatalysis and photoelectrochemical reactors in underground and underwater applications for hydrogen production and wastewater treatment. The solar photons are transmitted by fibre optic cables. At the end of the present study, it is observed that the efficiency of the system is limited to the low efficiency of photocatalysis and photoelectrochemical reactors. Today's fibre optic technology provides a satisfactory performance for solar transmission. The biggest obstacle for the proposed system is the cost of fibre optic cables. It may be more suitable for the defence industry and space technology applications.
Keywords: Hydrogen; wastewater treatment; sustainability; underground energy systems; underwater energy systems.

#430

SYNTHESIS OF SnS_2 PHOTOCATALYST FOR PHOTOCATALYTIC HYDROGEN PRODUCTION

*Alaaddin Cem Ok, *Cevat Sarıoğlu*
Marmara University, Faculty of Engineering, Metallurgical and Materials Engineering Department, TR34722, Istanbul, Turkey
*Corresponding author: cevat.sarioglu@marmara.edu.tr

ABSTRACT
Hydrogen could be generated from both renewable and non-renewable sources of energy. Using nonrenewable energy sources to produce hydrogen will result in greenhouse CO_2 gas emissions and cause global warming. Photocatalytic systems for generating hydrogen from solar energy have a great deal of potential to solve the global warming problem because of the totally renewable green source of sun and water. Because of its superior properties, such as a proper and narrow bandgap, better chemical stability, non-toxic, photo-corrosion resistance, and suitable optimum conduction and valance band potentials, the tin disulfide (SnS_2) photocatalyst has great potential to be used for producing H_2 from the splitting of water via solar energy. In this study, SnO_2 powders were successfully thermally sulfurized to SnS_2 powders at 500°C for 24 hours under an Argon (Ar) atmosphere. The XRD analysis verified the hexagonal SnS_2 crystals. UV-vis spectroscopy was used to determine the band gap value of the generated powder, which is 2.24 eV.
Keywords: Tin disulfide, Photocatalyst, Solar energy, Water splitting, Hydrogen production

#433

PROGRESS OF 5 m^3/h H_2 PRODUCTION TESTING FACILITY THROUGH IODINE-SULFUR THERMOCHEMICAL WATER-SPLITTING METHOD

[1] Bo Ling, [1] Yong He, [1] Jinxu Zhang, [1] Yanqun Zhu, [1*] Zhihua Wang
[1]Zhejiang University, State key laboratory of Clean Energy Utilization, 310027, Hangzhou, P.R. China
*Corresponding author e-mail: wangzh@zju.edu.cn

ABSTRACT

The Iodine–Sulfur (IS) thermochemical water-splitting cycle is regarded as one of the most promising hydrogen production methods with the advantages of high efficiency, low cost and zero carbon emissions. Several research institutions have done extensive studies in this field. The CEU initiated the IS research in 2004 and constructed a pilot-scale facility made of industrial structural materials with the design rate of 5 m^3/h in 2019. In this paper, the pilot-scale facility is briefly introduced, and the result of preliminary continuous test is shown.

Keywords: Thermochemical hydrogen production, Iodine sulfur cycle, Pilot-scale facility

#1512

PHOTOCATALYSIS vs PHOTOVOLTAICS: WHY NOT MAKE IT A SYMBIOSIS?

[1*] Paul Hazemann, [1] Cedric Brochier, [1] Laure Peruchon, [2] Eric Puzenat
[1] Brochier Technologies, Villeurbanne, France
[2] IRCELYON, Université UCBL Lyon1, CNRS, UMR 5256, Villeurbanne, France
*Corresponding author e-mail: paul.hazemann@brochiertechnologies.com

ABSTRACT

Photocatalytic reforming of biomass-sourced molecules is a promising method for green hydrogen production from solar energy. Current photocatalysts cannot use the entire solar spectrum efficiently, and an alternative approach is to couple photovoltaics with LED technology to convert the highest solar spectrum fraction into a monochromatic light. Such a process has yet to be energetically optimized to be competitive with conventional heliophotocatalytic processes, and numerous parameters can be tuned such as LED current intensity, carbohydrate concentration, temperature or catalyst amount. In this study, it has been shown that these parameters significantly affect the hydrogen production rate, and their optimization is necessary to maximize energy-to-hydrogen efficiency and so the hydrogen production cost. It was however observed, using the H2A tool, that the optimum of energy efficiency is not necessary the optimum of hydrogen production cost and a careful cost analysis should be carried out to design the best industrial operating point.

Keywords: Photocatalysis, Reforming, TiO_2, Woven optical fiber

#1515

PROMOTION OF COPPER-ZINC CATALYST WITH Sm AND Gd FOR STEAM REFORMING OF METHANOL

You-Sheng Lin, Kuen-Song Lin, Wang-Ting Hong, Yun Ko, Abrar Hussain, Yun-Cheng Hsieh*
Department of Chemical Engineering & Materials Science, Yuan-Ze University, Taoyuan City, Taiwan.
*Corresponding author e-mail: kslin@saturn.yzu.edu.tw

ABSTRACT

Steam reforming of methanol (SRM) is a chemical reaction in which methanol and water vapor are decomposed through a catalyst, thereby producing gas rich in hydrogen and other substances. The $CuO/ZnO/Al_2O_3$ catalysts have been synthesized, X-ray diffractometer (XRD) and temperature programmed reduction (TPR) (<200°C) have been used to characterize reduction property and catalyst structure. The catalyst was filled into the packed reactor, and the gas composition after the SRM reaction was analyzed by a gas chromatograph (GC-TCD) (WHSV=10 h^{-1}). The research shows that the catalyst activity of $CuO/ZnO/Sm_2O_3/CeO_2$ and $CuO/ZnO/Gd_2O_3/CeO_2$ promoters modified Cu-Zn catalysts have been improved, with conditions as the T_{95} is at 250 °C, and the value of Y_{H2} is close to 3.0. Compared with promoter doped $CuO/ZnO/Al_2O_3$ catalyst, bare Cu-Zn catalyst (T_{95}: 240°C, Y_{H2} < 2.7) have been considered as limited efficacy of SRM reaction. In this study, the hydrogen production from SRM reaction have been applied in self-made U-shaped tube filled reactor (filled with 2.5 g of catalyst) combined with fuel cells, which can produce 20W of electricity successfully.

Keywords: Copper-Zinc catalyst, SRM, Samarium, Gadolinium, Hydrogen.

#1527

KINETIC CHARACTERIZATION OF Pt/Al_2O_3 CATALYST FOR HYDROGEN PRODUCTION VIA METHANOL AQUEOUS-PHASE REFORMING

[1,2] *Paranjeet Lakhtaria,* [1,2] *Paulo Ribeirinha,* [1,2,3] *José Sousa,* [1,2*] *Adélio Mendes*
[1] LEPABE - Laboratory for Process Engineering, Environment, Biotechnology and Energy, Faculty of Engineering, University of Porto, Rua Dr. Roberto Frias, 4200-465 Porto, Portugal
[2] ALiCE - Associate Laboratory in Chemical Engineering, Faculty of Engineering, University of Porto, Rua Dr. Roberto Frias, 4200-465 Porto, Portugal
[3] Departamento de Química, Escola de Ciências da Vida e do Ambiente, Universidade de Trás-os-Montes e Alto Douro, Quinta de Prados, 5000-801 - Vila Real, Portugal
*Corresponding author e-mail: mendes@fe.up.pt

ABSTRACT

Methanol aqueous-phase reforming (APR) is a simpler and more energy-efficient process compared to traditional gas-phase reforming. Methanol APR is considered to be a potential technology for providing *in-situ* hydrogen (H_2) production, mainly for H_2-powered fuel cell technology. The performance evaluation of a Pt/Al_2O_3 catalyst in methanol APR under various operating conditions is reported. Studies were conducted at various temperatures, pressures, methanol concentrations, and residence times to evaluate APR performance. An increase in methanol conversion was observed with increased operating temperature and decreased system pressure. It was also noted that higher methanol concentration in the feed had an adverse effect on APR performance.

Keywords: Aqueous-phase reforming, Methanol, Hydrogen production, Catalyst, Pt/Al_2O_3

#1537

Ni-BASED CATALYSTS FOR CO_2 REFORMING OF GLYCEROL TO H_2

[1] *Ozge Selcuk,* [1*] *Ahmet K. Avci,*
[1] Department of Chemical Engineering, Bogazici University, Bebek 34342, Istanbul, Turkey
*Corresponding author e-mail: avciahme@boun.edu.tr

ABSTRACT

Dry reforming of glycerol is a recently emerging pathway for making H_2. The route is promising due to the consumption of glycerol, a side product of biodiesel synthesis, with CO_2, a major greenhouse gas. This study aims to develop Ni-based catalysts for providing insight into the role of support material on activity towards glycerol dry reforming. In this respect, Ni/La_2O_3, Ni/ZrO_2 and Ni/La_2O_3-ZrO_2, all loaded with 5% Ni by mass, are synthesized. The catalysts are tested at 750°C, molar inlet CO_2-to-glycerol ratio (CO_2/G) between 1-5 and residence time of 0.25 mg min NmL^{-1}. The results clearly showed that Ni/La_2O_3-ZrO_2 was more active than the single-oxide supported counterparts. The catalyst showed superior durability with only 12% loss in CO_2 conversion after the 72 h time-on-stream stability test. On the other hand, Ni/ZrO_2 and Ni/La_2O_3 were completely deactivated at the 47th and 63rd h of the stability tests, respectively. Superior activity and stability of the Ni/La_2O_3-ZrO_2 is attributed to the fine dispersion of the Ni nanoparticles and durability against coke deposition.

Keywords: Catalyst, CO_2, Glycerol, Hydrogen, Reforming

#1541

POTENTIAL HYDROGEN PRODUCTION AS BYPRODUCT IN CATALYTIC MICROWAVE ASSISTED PYROLYSIS OF ABS PLASTIC WASTE

[1] *Vahid Mortezaeikia,* [1*] *Omid Tavakoli*
[1] 1School of Chemical Engineering, College of Engineering, University of Tehran (UT), Tehran 14176, Iran
*Corresponding author e-mail: otavakoli@ut.ac.ir

ABSTRACT

Microwave assisted pyrolysis of ABS plastic waste is performed in a single reactor to obtain hydrogen enriched gaseous product. Experiment was carried out in the presence of neat SiC and Fe impregnated SiC as catalyst under the condition of 1.15 amps microwave power, 200 mL/min Nitrogen flow rate, final temperature of 450°C and catalyst to plastic ratio of 0.275. The results showed syngas and hydrogen content increased by Fe addition to SiC. Increasing the Fe content leads to higher hydrogen yield. Maximum hydrogen yield of 54.2% was achieved in the case of 10% Fe content in catalyst. Moreover, the obtained results also are evidence for suitability of microwave assisted technology than conventional pyrolysis towards hydrogen production.

Keywords: Microwave assisted, Pyrolysis, Catalysis, Hydrogen

#1544

WASHCOATING Cu CATALYST WITH CeO_2 SOL ONTO MICROCHANNEL REACTOR FOR STEAM REFORMING OF METHANOL

Abrar Hussain, Kuen-Song Lin, Hsiu-Ping Yeh, You-Sheng Lin, Yun Ko, Yung-Chen Hsieh**
Department of Chemical Engineering & Materials Science, Yuan Ze University, Taoyuan City, Taiwan
*Corresponding author e-mail: kslin@saturn.yzu.edu.tw

ABSTRACT
Microchannel reactors (MCR) are intended to be assembled in this study for the production of hydrogen from the steam reforming of methanol (SRM). Catalyst CuO/ZnO-γ-Al_2O_3 was prepared by the sequential precipitation method to catalyze SRM. Powders of prepared catalysts were subsequently washcoated, onto a microchannel of stainless-steel plate as an active plate for MCR, by cerium oxide sol. After a calcination treatment at 350°C, the adhesion strength of coated layers was evaluated in terms of a fraction of weight loss (F_L) during a standard erosion of ultra-sonification. Optical microscopic examination noticed that ethanol solvent substantially promoted the wetting ability of resulted slurry on S.S 304 substrate and a smooth coated layer. F_L was found to decrease on increasing the binder content (B) in coated slurries. However, the temperature required for 95% conversion of methanol (T_{95}) also increased with B. FE-SEM and ESCA characterization suggesting that particles of oxide sol tended to fill into pores among catalyst powders and partially covered active sites of the catalyst. Temperature programmed reduction also found a shift of reduction of copper oxide to high temperatures by the binder. A T_{95} =240°C was found from MCR, with an active plate coated with a slurry of B=2, at an SRM condition of WHSV=16.2 and steam to methanol ratio of 1.3. Similar T_{95} was found from a packed bed reactor (PBR) using the same binder-coated catalyst. However, high methanol conversion was generally found from MCR at low reaction temperatures. The advantage of MCR at low temperatures was attributed to its efficient transfer of heat.
Keywords: Cerium oxide, Washcoating, Microchannel reactor, Hydrogen production, Methanol steam reforming.

#1545

SHAPE DEPENDENT ELECTROCATALYTIC HYDROGEN EVOLUTION BY COPPER-ANTIMONY SULFIDE

[1*] *Emre Aslan,* [2] *Faruk Özel,* [3] *İmren Hatay Patır*
[1] Selcuk University, Department of Biochemistry, 42030, Konya, Turkey
[2] Karamanoglu Mehmetbey University, Department of Metallurgy and Materials Engineering, Karaman 70200, Turkey
[3] Selcuk University, Department of Biotechnology, 42030, Konya, Turkey
*Corresponding author e-mail: emreaslan89@gmail.com

ABSTRACT
The chalcostibite electrocatalysts are using towards energy conversion processes including hydrogen evolution reaction (HER) due to its excellent properties as low-cost and high activity. Herein, the ternary chalcostibite copper-antimony sulfides in different shapes and as nanodot (D-$CuSbS_2$) and microrod (R- $CuSbS_2$) were synthesized by hot-injection approach. These chalcostibite materials were firstly investigated on the electrocatalytic HER in alkaline media. Microrod shape of catalyst displayed enhancing catalytic activity of HER in alkaline conditions when compared to spherical shape of catalyst. This result may be explained by efficient charge separation efficiency of 1D materials, which is microrod shape.

Keywords: Electrocatalytic hydrogen evolution, Copper-antimony sulfide

#1546

CATALYTIC HYDROGEN EVOLUTION BY USING DIFFERENT CARBON-BASED NANOCOMPOSITE AT SOFT INTERFACES

[1] *Emre Aslan ,*[2*]*Imren Hatay Patir*
[1]Selcuk University, Faculty of Science, Department of Biochemistry, Konya,
[1]Selcuk University, Faculty of Science, Department of Biotechnology, Konya,
*Corresponding author e-mail: imrenhatay@gmail.com

ABSTRACT
Efficiency increment of hydrogen evolution reaction (HER) is great challenge in the literature. Nanocomposite based catalysts are significant drawn attention due to the increasing active sites for hydrogen evolution. Herein, it is reported that in situ electrodeposition of metallic nanoparticles on multi-walled carbon nanotube or reduced graphene oxide by using organic sacrificial electron donor decamethylferrocene (DMFc) at liquid/liquid interfaces. The nucleation and catalytic reactions have been tracked by using 4-electrode voltammetry and biphasic reactions. The catalytic activities of metallic nanoparticles on carbon-based nanocomposites are founded as higher activities than that of non-metallic nanocomposites for biphasic catalysis.

Keywords: Hydrogen evolution, Liquid/liquid interface, Electrodeposition

#1548

APPLICATION OF DIFFERENT CATALYSTS IN BIOMASS GASIFICATION IN UPDRAFT/DOWNDRAFT FIXED BED REACTORS

[1]Özgün Tezer, [2]Nazlıcan Karabağ, [3,4]Atakan Öngen, [5*]Azize Ayol
[1] Dokuz Eylul University, The Graduate School of Natural and Applied Sciences, Department of Environmental Engineering, 35160, Buca, Izmir, Turkey
[2] Istanbul University-Cerrahpaşa, Department of Environmental Engineering, Istanbul, Turkey
[3] Istanbul University-Cerrahpaşa, Department of Environmental Engineering, Istanbul, Turkey
[4] Istanbul University-Cerrahpaşa, Environmental and Earth Sciences Application and Research Center, Istanbul, Turkey
[5] Dokuz Eylul University, Department of Environmental Engineering, 35160, Buca, İzmir, Turkey
*Corresponding author e-mail: azize.ayol@deu.edu.tr

ABSTRACT

This study aims to investigate the effects of different catalysts on biomass gasification. Two different types of red mud (RM1, RM2), white mud (WM), and aluminum - nickel alloy were used as catalysts with biomass mixture for the lab-scale gasification studies by using an updraft and a downdraft fixed bed reactors. Green waste (GW), sewage sludge (SS) and olive pomace (OP) were used as feedstock. The results showed that the highest concentration of H_2 (47 vol.%) was observed in mixed sample with 0.05 L/min dry air at 900 °C in updraft gasifier. In downdraft gasifier, max. H_2 concentration was measured for mixed sample at 800°C while 0.1 L/min dry air was applied. In general, it has been observed that RM increases the H_2 gas in the syngas between 1-7vol.% at 900 °C in updraft gasifier. In the downdraft reactor, on the contrary, H_2 concentration in the syngas decreased by 2-6% with the addition of RM. However, when aluminum - nickel alloy was added to the samples, syngas production drastically increased and its H_2 content was found more than 65% for both reactors. This study presents the research results on the catalytic effects on the syngas composition in detail.

Keywords: Gasification, Hydrogen, Biomass, Catalyst, Renewable Energy

#1561

THE EFFECT OF THERMAL OXIDATION TIME IN AIR AND ARGON ATMOSPHERE ON PEC EFFICIENCY OF HEMATITE (Fe_2O_3) PHOTOANODE

[1,2] Fatma Betül Yılmaz, [1*] Cevat Sarıoğlu
[1]Marmara University, Faculty of Engineering, Department of Metallurgical and Materials Engineering, 34854, İstanbul, Turkey
[2]Marmara University, Graduate School of Natural and Applied Sciences, 34722, İstanbul, Turkey
* E-mail: cevat.sarioglu@marmara.edu.tr

ABSTRACT

Fe thin films electrodeposited on FTO substrate were thermally oxidized to hematite. The photocurrents values, indication of H_2 production efficiency in PEC cell were improved by optimizing thermal oxidation parameters of undoped hematite photoanode such as oxidation atmospheres (air and argon), oxidation temperatures (450°C and 550°C) and oxidation time. The effect of these parameters on the photocurrents measured in PEC cell in hematite photoanode were characterized by using LSV (the linear sweep voltammetry), Mott Schottky and, EIS analyses. The effect of oxidation time on photocurrents were studied. Photocurrents first increased and reached the maximum values and then decreased with oxidation time in both argon and air atmospheres at 450°C and 550°C. The photocurrents measured at 0.6 V vs. SCE for hematite at 450°C and 550°C in argon atmosphere were greater compared to the photocurrents measured in hematite synthesized in air. The highest photocurrent of 0.56 mA/cm^2 at 0.6 V vs. SCE was measured for the hematite synthesized in argon atmosphere at 450°C with oxidation time of 96 hours.

Keywords: Hematite, Photoanode, Water splitting, PEC, Thermal oxidation.

#1584

PRODUCTION OF HYDROGEN-RICH SYNTHESIS GAS BY GASIFICATION OF WASTE MATERIALS IN A ROTARY KILN REACTOR

[1*] *Anđelina Bubalo*, [2] *Danica Maljković*, [1] *Dražen Vouk*
[1] University of Zagreb, Faculty of Civil engineering, Water research department, Kačićeva ulica 26, 10 000 Zagreb, Croatia
[2] Dok-ing Energo Ltd., Research and development, Slavonska avenija 22, 10 000 Zagreb, Croatia
*Corresponding author e-mail: andelina.bubalo@grad.unizg.hr

ABSTRACT

The problem of today is the increasing disposal of waste materials and the increasing depletion of natural resources. Therefore, the European Commission is adapting further regulations on waste management to the principles of the circular economy. Gasification of waste materials has not yet been established as one of the methods of waste utilisation, but a considerable number of studies on the subject point to a number of advantages of this method while reducing greenhouse gas emissions. One waste whose disposal is a global problem is sewage sludge (SS). In addition to SS, plastic waste is also a major issue due to the growing problem of microplastic contamination. In this work, the following wastes were used for gasification: SS from the wastewater treatment plant (WWTP) Zagreb and mixed plastic wastes (MP) originating from one of the waste collectors on the territory of the Republic of Croatia. Gasification was carried out in a rotary reactor. SS was gasified at temperatures of 1100°C and MP at temperatures of 900°C. The syngas produced from SS has a lower heating value (LHV) of 6.1 MJm^{-3} and a volume fraction of H_2 in the syngas of 22.94%, while the syngas produced from gasification of MP has a better LHV of 14.4 MJm^{-3} and a volume fraction of H_2 of 48.56%.

Keywords: Gasification, Sewage sludge, Mixed plastic waste, Syngas, Hydrogen

#1586

$Cd_xZn_{1-x}S$ WITH BULK-TWINNED HOMOJUNCTIONS AND RICH SULFUR VACANCIES FOR EFFICIENT PHOTOCATALYTIC HYDROGEN PRODUCTION

[1*] *İsmail Boz*, [2] *Mohammed Alfatih Hamid*, [3] *Yaşar Zengin*
[1] Boğaziçi Üniversitesi, Faculty of Engineering, Chemical Engineering Department, Bebek, Istanbul, Turkey
[2] Istanbul University-Cerrahpaşa, Faculty of Engineering, Chemical Engineering Department, Avcilar, Istanbul, Turkey
[3] Istanbul University-Cerrahpaşa, Faculty of Engineering, Chemical Engineering Department, Avcilar, Istanbul, Turkey
* e-mail: Alfatiham874@gmail.com

ABSTRACT

Photocatalysts containing rich sulphur vacancies and bulk-twinned homojunctions have showed good prospects for solar hydrogen production. In this work, we synthesized photocatalysts composed of bulk-twinned homojunction $Cd_xZn_{1-x}S$ solid solutions along with rich sulphur vacancies to promote charge transfer and prevent the recombination. The photocatalysts were prepared via a simple hydrothermal method and then characterized by X-ray diffractometer to study the phase purity and crystallographic structure. UV-vis spectra were also carried out to investigate the optical properties. The achieved $Cd_xZn_{1-x}S$ photocatalysts exhibited a high solar hydrogen production activity in comparison with the sulphur vacancies free or non-twinned $Cd_xZn_{1-x}S$ solid solutions.

Keywords: Photocatalysts, Visible light, Hydrogen production

#1600

INVESTIGATION OF HYDROGEN PRODUCTION POTENTIAL FROM MEDICAL WASTE IN AN UPDRAFT PLASMA GASIFIER

[1*] *A. Alp Erdogan*, [1] *M. Zeki Yilmazoglu*
[1]Gazi University, Faculty of Engineering, Department of Mechanical Engineering, Maltepe, Ankara, Turkey
*Corresponding author e-mail: altugalp.erdogan@gazi.edu.tr

ABSTRACT

In this study, an experimental investigation is performed on the gasification characteristics and hydrogen production potential from medical waste in a novel updraft plasma gasifier. Medical waste samples are prepared with different mixture percentages of possible compositions such as face masks and plastic bags. Estimated power output for the gasifier is calculated as 4 kWh, whereas the maximum rated power of the DC arc plasma torch is 2.5 kWh. Measurements such as energy consumption of the system or hydrogen content in the syngas and performance calculations such as cold-gas efficiency or overall energy efficiency are also evaluated during the experiments.

Keywords: Plasma gasification, Medical waste, Hydrogen production, Waste-to-energy, COVID-19

#1601

SOLAR-LIGHT-DRIVEN PHOTOCATALYTIC HYDROGEN EVOLUTION *IN SITU* DEPOSITED Pt ON PEROVSKITE TYPE OXIDES

[1*] *Ali Keles,* [1] *Talha Kuru,* [2] *Emre Aslan,* [3] *İmren Hatay Patır*
[1] GKE Energy R&D Center,48200, Mugla, Turkey.
[2] Selcuk University, Department of Biochemistry, 42030, Konya, Turkey
[3] Selcuk University, Department of Biotechnology, 42030, Konya, Turkey
*Corresponding author e-mail: a.keles@gke.com.tr

ABSTRACT

Hydrogen generation through photocatalytic splitting of water, which is known as hydrogen evolution reaction (HER), is an attractive method of converting the solar energy generated from renewable sources into chemical energy stored in molecular hydrogen. perovskite oxides hold promise as functional materials for the water splitting due to its excellent properties as low-cost and high activity. Herein, platinum photodeposited onto $MTiO_3$ (M: Ba and Sr) perovskites ($MTiO_3$-Pt) have been investigated on the photocatalytic hydrogen evolution under solar light irradiation in the presence of triethanolamine (TEOA) and Eosin Y as electron donor and photosensitizer, respectively. Photocatalytic hydrogen evolution activities take place in the order of $SrTiO_3$-Pt> $BaTiO_3$-Pt> $SrTiO_3$> $BaTiO_3$.

Keywords: Photocatalytic hydrogen evolution, Perovskites, Titanates

#1605

NICKEL-BASED GRAFTED CATALYSTS FOR DRY REFORMING OF METHANE THROUGH HIGH-THROUGHPUT EXPERIMENTATION

[1,2] *Gokhan Celik,* [2*] *Magali Ferrandon,* [2*] *Massimiliano Delferro*
[1] Department of Chemical Engineering, Middle East Technical University, Ankara, 06800, Turkey
[2] Chemical Sciences and Engineering Division, Argonne National Laboratory, Lemont, IL, 60439, USA
*Corresponding author e-mail: delferro@anl.gov, ferrandon@anl.gov

ABSTRACT

High-throughput synthesis of Ni-based catalysts was performed by organometallic liquid grafting using a robotic arm. Monometallic catalysts contain Ni, whereas bimetallic catalysts contain a promoter metal such as B, Mg, V, Mn, Fe, Co, Cu, Zn, or Sn, supported on inorganic metal oxides such as magnesia, alumina, titania, silica, or ceria. The catalytic performance results showed that the support-metal-promoter choice affect catalyst activity, stability, syngas composition, and type and nature of carbon species formed under reaction conditions. Among 95 catalysts studied, NiFe/MgO and NiFe/Al_2O_3 catalysts are the most active and stable. In addition, the synthesized catalysts were characterized using several characterization methods including, but not limited to, N_2 physisorption, chemisorption, X-ray diffraction, vibrational spectroscopy, and imaging techniques. Characterization results show that (i) the best performing catalysts have metallic sites that are highly dispersed, uniform, and resistant to sintering at 800°C, (ii) reduction profile of catalysts supported on alumina exhibits important structure-activity relationships, and (iii) distinct carbon species formed on specific sites, affecting the stability. Our findings demonstrate that organometallic grafting is a successful technique for synthesizing catalytic materials with highly dispersed and uniform sites that lead to promising catalytic performance for dry reforming of methane.

Keywords: Hydrogen, Dry reforming, Methane, Grafting, Carbon dioxide

Track 2.

Hydrogen Production: Electrolysis

#13

ENHANCED WATER OXIDATION REACTION BY NICKEL OXIDE NANOROD ARRAYS ELECTROCATALYST

[1] *Khadijeh Hemmati*, [2] *Omran Moradlou*, [1,3]**Alireza Z. Moshfegh*
[1] Department of Physics, Sharif University of Technology, P. O. Box 11155-9161, Tehran, Iran
[2] Department of Chemistry, Alzahra University, P. O. Box 1993893973, Tehran, Iran
[3] Institute for Nanoscience and Nanotechnology, Sharif University of Technology, P. O. Box 14588-8969, Tehran, Iran
*Corresponding author e-mail: moshfegh@sharif.edu

ABSTRACT

Water splitting for hydrogen generation is an interesting strategy in energy technology. Hence, developing cheap and robust electrodes have received great attention in recent years. In this research, we fabricated nickel oxide (NiO) Nanorod Arrays structure coating as an anode that has a strong bonding with the Ni foam (NF) substrate to prepare NiO/NF. The electrode was prepared by using the hydrothermal method (in a temperature of 100°C and reaction time of 12 h) in a solution containing nickel nitrate and urea under the optimized experimental conditions. The electrochemical performance of the fabricated electrode was investigated in alkaline solution of 1 M KOH and revealed that only +450 mV is required to achieve a current density of 100 mA cm^{-2} for water oxidation showing an efficient electrocatalyst. The enhanced performance of the developed electrode for water splitting can be related to the morphology of the nanorod structure, high ordered array structure and high adhesion of NiO nanorod arrays on nickel foam substrate.

Keywords: Water Oxidation, NiO, Nanorod Array

#19

THE USE OF NANOSTRUCTURED NICKEL-MOLYBDENUM OXIDE AS AN EFFICIENT AND LOW-COST ELECTROCATALYST FOR THE HYDROGEN EVOLUTION REACTION IN THE ACIDIC MEDIUM

[1*] *Mahmoud Rammal*, [2] *Sasha Omanovic*
Department of Chemical Engineering, McGill University, 3610 University St., Montreal, Quebec H3A 0C5, Canada
Corresponding author email: mahmoud.rammal@mail.mcgill.ca

ABSTRACT

Due to its favorable chemical and structural properties, nanostructured nickel-molybdenum oxides produced through an environmentally benign solution combustion method were investigated as possible cathode materials for the hydrogen evolution reaction in an acidic electrolyte. Ni-Mo-oxides of different compositions were employed, leading to the identification of the equiatomic stoichiometric sample ($NiMoO_4$) as the best performing electrode composition for the HER. The promising performance of this material could be linked to the synergistic effect that is induced through the combination of metal oxides in a binary form. While the activity of $NiMoO_4$ is slightly inferior to the state-of-the-art 20% Pt/C, when the cost of the material and the stability aspect are considered, $NiMoO_4$ emerges as the more economically viable option.

Keywords: Hydrogen, Mixed-Metal Oxides, Electrocatalysis, Synergism, Acidic Electrolyte

#22

QUALIFYING TESTS AND ECONOMIC ANALYSIS OF ELECTROLYZERS FOR GRID SERVICES

[1] Regine Reissner, [1]Jörg Bürkle, [2]Stéphanie Crevon, [2]Valérie Seguin, [3]Valerian Klemenz, [3]Tanaka Mandy Mbavarira, [3]Christoph Imboden,*

[1]German Aerospace Center (DLR), Institute of Engineering Thermodynamics, Pfaffenwaldring 38, 70569 Stuttgart, Germany

[2] CEA, Energy Systems and Demonstration Lab, 17 Rue des Martyrs, 38054 Grenoble, France

[3] Lucerne University of Applied Sci. and Arts, Inst.of Innovation and Technology Management, Technikumstr. 21, Horw, Switzerland

*Corresponding author e-mail: regine.reissner@dlr.de

ABSTRACT

As part of the European project QualyGridS, drafts for standardized testing protocols for electrolyzers to perform electricity grid services are defined and elaborated. These protocols are designed to be used by alkaline and proton exchange membrane (PEM) electrolyzers up to the Megawatt scale. The protocols are being submitted for standardisation. Testing results using these protocols on a state-of-the-art PEM electrolyzer system of 50 kW with 1500 cm^2 area stack are presented with considerations of the influence of balance of plant (BOP) components. System behaviour of 50 kW and Megawatt PEM electrolyzers are compared to determine the influence of their scale in performance and response time. An economic analysis has been conducted in the scope of the project. Today's situation has been analyzed in a first part: the objective was to identify the best way to combine H_2 supply for a primary value stream and provision of grid services. A second part of the analysis studied the potential future evolutions that could change the current picture.

Keywords: PEM Electrolyser, Grid Service, Dynamics

#68

NICKEL COBALT OXIDE NANOCUBES AS AN EFFICIENT ELECTROCATALYST FOR HYDROGEN EVOLUTION IN ALKALINE SOLUTION

[1] Hossein Faraji, [2] Khadijeh Hemmati, [1] Kavoos Mirabbaszadeh*

[1] Department of Energy Engineering and Physics, Amirkabir University of Technology, 14588 Tehran, Iran

[2] Department of Physics, Sharif University of Technology, P. O. Box 11155-9161, Tehran, Iran

*Corresponding author e-mail: mirabbas@aut.ac.ir

ABSTRACT

The use of hydrogen as a promising approach to meet the impending climate change and global warming has attracted a lot of attention. Electrolysis of water is one of the best ways to produce pure H_2. However, implementing water electrolysis for large-scale applications requires robust and efficient electrocatalysts that can sustain water splitting without corrosion. Here, we reported 3D nanocubes grown on Nikel foam ($NiCo_2O_4$/NF) by a hydrothermal method that can act as an efficient hydrogen evolution reaction (HER) electrocatalyst in alkaline solution (1M KOH). We have achieved a unique structure that exhibits exceptional HER activity (overpotential of 38 and 166 mV to drive current densities (j) of 10 and 100 mA.cm^{-2}). Such superior HER catalytic performance can be derived from the rough feature of the edges and synergistic effect between Ni and Co atoms and exposure to many active sites on the nanocubes. This discovery significantly helps us to design and synthesize low-cost and highly efficient electrocatalysts for large-scale hydrogen production from water electrolysis.

Keywords: $NiCo_2O_4$/NF, Nanocubes, Hydrothermal, Hydrogen Evolution Reaction.

#70

MODELING OF H_2O AND CO_2 ELECTROLYSIS IN A MOLTEN CARBONATE ELECTROLYZER

[1]Dayan Monzer, [1] Chakib Bouallou*
(MINES ParisTech, PSL - Research University, CES - Centre d'Efficacité Energétique des Systèmes), 60 Boulevard Saint Michel, 75006 Paris, France
*Corresponding author e-mail: chakib.bouallou@mines-paristech.fr

ABSTRACT

The reversible operation as an electrolyzer of a commercialized molten carbonate fuel cell for the generation of syngas (H_2 & CO) has recently provoked the interest of researchers. In general, Electrolyzers have the benefit of storing the surplus of renewable energy. This type of electrolyzer can additionally transform CO_2 into valuable fuel due to its unique properties at dissolving and reducing carbon dioxide in its molten carbonate electrolyte. The capability of such electrolyzer represents a conceptual revolution in the energy sector with a wide range of applications. This work presents the co-electrolysis of CO_2 and H_2O model of the Molten carbonate electrolyzer (MCEC). The one-dimensional steady-state model was created by making some changes to previously published work to introduce CO_2 electrolysis. To some extent, the model findings matched the previous model, which only took H_2O electrolysis into account. The discrepancies are driven by the chemical extent of the CO_2 electrolysis reaction in conjunction with the chemical reverse water gas shift reaction. These discrepancies highlighted the necessity of considering CO_2 electrolysis as the obtained cell voltage and temperature exhibited a higher value at the limiting current density by about 65% and 40%, respectively, than when CO_2 electrolysis is ignored.

Keywords: Molten Carbonate Electrolysis Cell, Numerical Modeling, Co-Electrolysis, Syngas Production

#72

INVESTIGATION OF ELECTRICITY, HYDROGEN AND CLEAN WATER PRODUCTION WITH RENEWABLE ENERGY SYSTEM INTEGRATED ONTO A SHIP: MOBILE ENERGY PRODUCTION ON A SHIP

[1]Mustafa Erden, [2]Ayhan Atiz, [3]Hatice Karakilcik, [1*]Mehmet Karakilcik
[1]Cukurova University, Faculty of Sciences and Letters, Department of Physics, 01330 Adana, Turkey
[2]Alanya Alaaddin Keykubat University, Faculty of Education, Department of Mathematics and Science Education Alanya 07400, Antalya, Turkey
[3]Cukurova University, Faculty of Engineering, Department of Geology Engineering, 01330 Adana, Turkey
*Corresponding author e-mail: kkilcik@cu.edu.tr

ABSTRACT

In this study, sustainable portable renewable energy generation system with hydrogen production and desalination of sea water is proposed. For this purpose, a wind turbine, photovoltaic panels (PVs), parabolic through solar collectors (PTSCs), flash turbine, organic Rankine cycle (ORC), water electrolysis system, reverse osmosis unit (RO) and storage tanks are constructed on a ship. This system is suitable for coastal settlements with high solar and wind potentials which are short of drinking water and electrical energy. It is an advantageous system in that going to a place where it is needed and meet the demand there. This integrated system is conceptually modeled and simulated using Engineering Equation Solver (EES) software. Thus, the system produces 5947.20 MJ electric energy and 468.56 g of hydrogen with 38.06% and 38.87% maximum energy and exergy efficiencies, respectively.

Keywords: Wind Turbine, Photovoltaic Panels, Parabolic Collectors, Hydrogen Production, Desalination.

#74

PARABOLIC TROUGH SOLAR COLLECTOR INTEGRATED WITH SOLAR POND FOR ELECTRICITY AND HYDROGEN PRODUCTION BASED ON SOLAR ENERGY

[1]Serdal Damarseckin, [2]Ayhan Atiz, [2]Mehmet Karakilcik*
[1]Sırnak University, Faculty of Engineering, Department of Energy Systems Engineering, 73000 Sırnak, Turkey
[2]Cukurova University, Faculty of Sciences and Letters, Department of Physics, 01330 Adana, Turkey
*Corresponding author e-mail: aatiz@cu.edu.tr

ABSTRACT

In this work, electricity, hydrogen production performance of parabolic trough solar collectors (PTSCs) integrated with a solar pond is researched. The system consists of the PTSCs with the surface area of 100 m^2, a solar pond with the surface area of 100 m^2, an Organic Rankine Cycle (ORC) which is operated with n-butane for electricity production, and a proton exchange membrane (PEM). In order to improve the overall system performance, n-butane is selected as working fluid in the ORC and the waste heat of the ORC is used in the mushroom production unit. In addition, the low-temperature water coming from the solar pond was circulated to the PTSCs via a pump and the temperature of the water was increased by the PTSCs. Thus, the temperature of this preheated water is upgraded by the PTSCs, and it increase the electricity performance of the ORC. The electricity is used to produce hydrogen by PEM. The analyses of the integrated system are determined with Engineering Equation Solver (EES) for a daily solar energy in July. So, an integrated energy generation system is simulated and it is occurred entirely of renewable energy systems. As a result, it has been found that if the integrated system components are improved, the heat, electricity and hydrogen production can be increased considerably.

Keywords: Solar Pond, Parabolic trough Solar Collectors, Organic Rankine Cycle, Hydrogen Production, Exergy

#78

HYDROGEN PRODUCTION FLAT PLATE SOLAR COLLECTOR INTEGRATED WITH PV-T

[1]Ayhan Atiz, [1]Mustafa Erden, [1]Mehmet Karakilcik*
[1]Cukurova University, Faculty of Sciences and Letters, Department of Physics, 01330 Adana, Turkey
*Corresponding author e-mail: aatiz@cu.edu.tr

ABSTRACT

In this work, the electricity and hydrogen production performance of an integrated system is investigated. The system includes a flat plate solar collector (FPSC), a photovoltaic thermal (PV-T) panel, an Organic Rankine Cycle (ORC), a proton exchange membrane (PEM) and a building for fungus production. In order to improve electric production performance of the ORC is worked with n-butane. The FPSC and PV-T has 6.48 m^2 and 2.16 m^2 area for capturing efficiently solar energy. The analyses of the integrated system are found by employing Engineering Equation Solver (EES) under daily solar energy in July. So, the low-temperature water coming from the PV-T to FPSC via a pump is upgraded to higher degree. The heated water is transferred to ORC for generating electricity. Besides, electricity is produced by the PV-T. Thus, a lot of electricity is produced in the overall system, efficiently. Moreover, overall performance of the system is found for under daily solar radiation. As a result, it was found that integrated system generated much more thermal energy, electricity and hydrogen.

Keywords: Photovoltaic Thermal Panel, Flat-Plate Solar Collectors, Organic Rankine Cycle, Hydrogen Production, Energy and Exergy Analyses

#109

ANALYSIS OF EXPERIMENTAL APPLICATION OF PERMANENT NEODYMIUM MAGNETS IN ALKALINE ELECTROLYZER FOR GREEN HYDROGEN PRODUCTION

[1] Matej Paranos, [1] Ankica Kovač*
[1] University of Zagreb, Faculty of Mechanical Engineering and Naval Architecture, Zagreb Croatia
*Corresponding author e-mail: matej.paranos@fsb.hr

ABSTRACT

This paper deals with the influence of magnetic filed on water electrolysis for green hydrogen production. Experimental setup was design and experimental research conducted. Results of influence of magnetic filed on the energy efficiency of the alkaline electrolyzer is analysed. Average energy efficiency for three cases is calculated and compared. In the first case, water electrolysis was conducted without application of the magnetic field. In the second case, magnetic filed is created with one pair of permanent neodymium magnets and applied on the electrolyzer, while in the third case the same experiment is repeated, but with stronger magnetic filed created by two pairs of neodymium magnets. Each type of the experiment is repeated several times and average values are calculated. Results indicated that magnetic filed is having positive impact on the energy efficiency of the process, and that with application of stronger magnetic field, the increase of energy efficiency is higher.

Keywords: Green Hydrogen, Water Electrolysis, Alkaline Electrolyzer, Magnetic Filed, Permanent Neodymium Magnets

#127

AISI 442 AND 446 FERRITIC STAINLESS STEELS AS A SUPPORT FOR BIPOLAR PLATES IN PROTON EXCHANGE MEMBRANE WATER ELECTROLYZERS

[1] Corneliu M. Crăciunescu, [2] A. Sigrid Lædre, [1] Nicolae Vaszilcsin, [2] Thulile Khoza, [1] Mircea L. Dan, [1] Andrea Kellenberger, [1] Delia Duca, [1] Aurel Ercuţa, [1] Ion Mitelea
[1] Politehnica University Timişoara, 300006 Piata Victoriei, Timişoara, Romania
[2] SINTEF Industry, 7465 Trondheim, Norway
*Corresponding author e-mail: andrea.kellenberger@upt.ro

ABSTRACT

This paper presents the results obtained in the study of corrosion resistance of ferritic steels AISI 442 and AISI 446 with the objective of using them as substrate material for bipolar plates (BPPs) in proton exchange membrane water electrolyzers (PEMWEs). The overall objective is to reduce the cost by replacing titanium BPPs with cheaper steel alloys. Corrosion current and corrosion potential of AISI 442 and 446 steels have been determined by potentiodynamic polarization in solutions having a similar composition to the fluid from the anodic side of PEMWEs. Furthermore, to evaluate the corrosion resistance at anodic potentials, AISI 442 and 446 were subjected to a voltage stress test (VST) where the current is monitored while the samples are maintained at constant potentials of 1.5, 1.75 and 2.0 V for 8 hours. Both samples showed good corrosion resistance at 1.5 V, as indicated by the low current densities, but the current densities increased significantly at 1.75 and 2.0 V. This shows that the surface of the ferritic steels must be protected with a corrosion-resistant coating, which should also have high conductivity. After the VST the samples have also been investigated by electrochemical impedance spectroscopy (EIS) and scanning electron microscopy (SEM).

Keywords: Proton Exchange Membrane, Water Electrolyzer, Bipolar Plate, Voltage Stress Test, Tafel Plots.

#128

CHEMICALLY STABILISED SHORT SIDE CHAIN AQUIVION® MEMBRANES FOR OPERATION IN WATER ELECTROLYSIS

[1*] *Stefania Siracusano,* [1]*Antonino S. Aricò,* [2]*Claudio Oldani,* [2]*Stefano Tonella*
[1]CNR-ITAE Institute of Advanced Energy Technologies, National Research Council, Via Salita S. Lucia Sopra Contesse 5, 98126 Messina, Italy
[2] Solvay Specialty Polymers Italy S.p.A., Viale Lombardia 20, 20021 Bollate Mi, Italy
*Corresponding author e-mail: siracusano@itae.cnr.it

ABSTRACT

Membrane-electrode assemblies based on chemically stabilised short-side-chain proton exchange Aquivion® membranes, prepared by extrusion or recast methods, have been investigated for operation at high current density (3 - 4 A cm^{-2}) in water electrolysis cells. A thickness of 90 μm was selected for these perfluorosulfonic acid membranes in order to provide proper resilience to hydrogen crossover under differential pressure operation while allowing operation at high currents. The membranes showed proper mechanical strength for high pressure operation and suitable conductivity to reduce ohmic losses at high current densities. Both membranes showed excellent performance in electrolysis cells by achieving a voltage efficiency better than 85% and 80% (1.85 V) at 3 and 4 A cm^{-2}, respectively, in polarisation curves at 90 °C.

Keywords: Electrolysis, Polymer Electrolyte Membrane, Hydrogen, Extruded Membrane, Recast Membrane

#144

HYDROGEN GENERATION IN MEMBRANE-FREE MICROFLUIDIC ELECTROLYSIS CELL

[1]*Biswajit Samir De,* [2]*Neeraj Khare,* [3]*Anastasia Elias,* [4]**Suddhasatwa Basu*
[1,4] Department of Chemical Engineering, Indian Institute of Technology (IIT) Delhi, Hauz Khas, New Delhi, Delhi, India – 110016.
[2]Department of Physics, Indian Institute of Technology (IIT) Delhi, Hauz Khas, New Delhi, Delhi, India – 110016.
[4]Department of Chemical and Materials Engineering, University of Alberta, Edmonton, Alberta, Canada, T6G2R3.
*Corresponding author e-mail: sbasu@chemical.iitd.ac.in

ABSTRACT

Microfluidic membrane-free electrolysis cell for hydrogen generation marks a new electrochemical energy conversion device paradigm. The characteristic length of the microfluidic electrolysis cell is less resulting in high surface to volume ratio. The laminar flow is prevalent in the microchannel rendering the cell membrane-free. Membrane-free operation of the microfluidic electrolysis cell results in pH flexible operation. The H_2 and O_2 separation in the microchannel was attained by electrolyte flow rate optimization. The overpotential of water electrolysis was reduced by incorporating acidic catholyte and alkaline anolyte that is referred to as an asymmetric electrolyte configuration. The energy from electrochemical neutralization owing to the pH gradient of the asymmetric electrolyte configuration improves the water electrolysis kinetics drastically. The performance of the microfluidic electrolysis cell was evaluated by performing electrochemical characterization. A visualization tool allows for qualitative analysis of the bubble dynamics in the microchannel.

Keywords: Electrochemical Neutralization, Microfluidics, Hydrogen, Membrane-Free

#150

H_2BASQUE – TECHNOLOGIES FOR BOOSTING THE HYDROGEN ECONOMY IN THE BASQUE COUNTRY: GREEN HYDROGEN PRODUCTION

[1] Ekain Fernandez, [2] Beatriz Calleja Sanchez, [3] Francisco Alcaide, [4] Stefania Doppiu, [5] Mikel Oregui-Bengoechea, [6] Eva G-Berasategui, [7] Elias Unzueta, [8] Jone Irigoyen*

[1]TECNALIA, Basque Research and Technology Alliance (BRTA), Mikeletegi Pasealekua 2, 20009 Donostia-San Sebastián, Spain.

[2]TUBACEX INNOVACION AIE, Parque Científico y Tecnológico de Bizkaia, edificio nº 612, Astondo Bidea, 48160, Derio, Spain.

[3]CIDETEC, Basque Research and Technology Alliance (BRTA), Po. Miramón 196, 20014 Donostia-San Sebastián, Spain

[4]CIC energiGUNE, Basque Research and Technology Alliance (BRTA), C/Albert Einstein 48, 01510 Vitoria-Gasteiz, (Álava) Spain

[5]UPV/EHU, Plaza Ingeniero Torres Quevedo 1, 48013 Bilbao, Spain.

[6]Department of Physics of Surfaces and Materials, TEKNIKER, Basque Research and Technology Alliance (BRTA), Iñaki Goenaga 5, 20600 EIBAR, Spain.

[7]PETRONOR INNOVACIÓN, San Martín, Nº-5, 48550 Muskiz (Bizkaia) Spain.

[8]BASQUE ENERGY CLUSTER, C/ S. Vicente 8, II-4º Dcha., 48001 Bilbao, Spain.

*Corresponding author e-mail: ekain.fernandez@tecnalia.com

ABSTRACT

H_2BASQUE is a strategic project funded by the Basque Government for developing innovative technologies (and their key components) for cost-competitive green hydrogen production. The green production technologies that will be developed in H_2BASQUE are AEM electrolysis, PEM electrolysis and thermochemical cycles. In addition, this project at improving the scientific-technological and commercial positioning of the Basque Network of Science, Technology and Innovation and Basque companies in the hydrogen sector and in particular in green hydrogen generation technologies.

Keywords: Green Hydrogen Production, Electrolysis, Thermochemical Cycles

#156

ACTIVITY OF BINARY NON-PRECIOUS METAL OXIDE-BASED ELECTRODE FOR OXYGEN EVOLUTION REACTION IN ACID

[1] Koichi Matsuzawa, [2] Soma Hirayama, [2] Yuma Kohara, [3] Akimitsu Ishihara*

[1] Yokohama National University, Graduate School of Engineering, 79-5, Tokiwadai, Hodogaya-ku, Yokohama, Japan

[2] Yokohama National University, Graduate School of Engineering Science, 79-5, Tokiwadai, Hodogaya-ku, Yokohama, Japan

[3] Yokohama National University, Institute of Advanced Sciences, 79-5, Tokiwadai, Hodogaya-ku, Yokohama, Japan

*Corresponding author e-mail: matsuzawa-koichi-zs@ynu.ac.jp

ABSTRACT

In order to develop non-platinum group metals anode electrocatalyst for the proton exchange membrane water electrolysis, the catalytic activity of Ta and Mo oxide-based electrocatalyst with Mn addition for the oxygen evolution reaction (OER) have been investigated. The Ta and Mo oxide-based electrocatalyst with Mn addition (Mn-TaO_x and Mn-MoO_x) has increased current density than that Ta oxide-based electrocatalyst with Mn addition in our previous study (Mn-TaO_x(Pre)). From the slow scan voltammogram of Mn-TaO_x and Mn-MoO_x, the redox peak of Mn species was detected in both samples. Though the electric charge of redox peak and the OER current density was independent relation in Mn-TaO_x and Mn-MoO_x, the Mn content is affected on the enhancement of electrical conductivity in Mn-TaO_x and Mn-MoO_x compared to Mn-TaO_x(Pre).

Keywords: Oxide-Based Electrode, Oxygen Evolution Reaction, PEM Electrolyzers, Green Hydrogen

#157

SOEC AS ENABLER OF HIGHLY EFFICIENT HYDROGEN & E-FUEL PRODUCTION

[1*] *Juergen Rechberger,* [1] *Josef Macherhammer,* [1] *Martin Rothbart,* [1] *Rittmar von Helmolt,* [1] *Martin Hauth*
[1]AVL List GmbH, Hans List Platz 1, Graz, Austria
*Corresponding author e-mail: juergen.rechberger@avl.com

ABSTRACT

Production of green hydrogen from renewable sources shows a promising pathway for the long-term de-fossilization, now adopted by many countries in their national strategic vision. The business case hinges on widespread application in transport, stationary and industrial sectors. Cross-sectoral approach is critical, interconnection user profiles to guarantee energy security, despite intermittency. Energy efficiency of the hydrogen production process is of utmost importance to achieve hydrogen cost which are required for industry and energy applications. SOEC represents a particularly interesting technology to improve the production efficiency of hydrogen and e-fuels. This paper will discuss the technology advantages and potentials for improvement.

Keywords: SOEC, Hydrogen, e-Fuel, Production

#159

DEVELOPMENT OF Fe OVER Ni/Si-Al NANOCATALYSTS FOR THE HYDROGEN AND LIQUID FUEL GENERATION FROM PYROLYSIS-CATALYTIC STEAM REFORMING OF POLYETHYLENE TEREPHTHALATE PLASTIC WASTE DISSOLVED IN PHENOL

[1,2]*Walid Nabgan,* [1,2*]*Mohamad Wijayanuddin Ali,* [1,2]*Aishah Abdul Jalil,*[1,2]*Tuan Amran Tuan Abdullah*
[1] School of Chemical and Energy Engineering, Faculty of Engineering, Universiti Teknologi Malaysia, 81310 Skudai, Johor, Malaysia
[2] Centre for Hydrogen Energy, Institute of Future Energy, Universiti Teknologi Malaysia, 81310 Skudai, Johor, Malaysia.
*Corresponding author e-mail: mwali@utm.my

ABSTRACT

Millions of tons of plastic are created each year, however is estimated only around 10% is being recycled. This project aims to convert environmental plastic waste (polyethylene terephthalate - PET) into liquid products for high-value engineering applications, particularly to increase the financial incentive for recycling plastics. This research chose phenol as a solvent for PET for liquid fuels and hydrogen gas generation. Despite extensive studies on hydrogen production, catalysts typically suffer various issues, from poor hydrogen selectivity to rapid deactivation. In this regard, transition metal-based catalysts have attracted extensive attention from researchers due to their excellent performance and recyclability. Herein, this study aims to develop, test, and characterize promising bimetallic Fe-Ni supported on Si-Al nanocatalysts for hydrogen and liquid fuel production from steam reforming and cracking reactions of phenol and PET. Nano-sized catalysts with various loading of Fe metals over Ni/Si-Al were synthesized via hydrothermal treatment method, and their physical and chemical properties were also characterized. During tests, high phenol conversions ranged from 34-87% and high yields in hydrogen at more than 75% was achieved. According to GCMS analysis of liquid products, PET cracking and phenol steam reforming processes yielded important components such as toluene, dibenzofuran and benzene. This phenomenon is a crucial concept for resolving the problem of plastic waste recycling.

Keywords: PET, Hydrogen, Fe-Ni/Si-Al, Plastic Waste

#167

A NOVEL HYDROGEN ECONOMY BASED ON ELECTROCHEMICAL CELLS INTEGRATED WITH FOSSIL FUEL ASSETS AND WASTEWATER RESOURCES

[1*] *Lateef A Jolaoso*, [1] *Javad Asadi*, [1] *Pejman Kazempoor*

[1] School of Aerospace and Mechanical Engineering, University of Oklahoma, Norman, OK, USA

*Corresponding author e-mail: pkazempoor@ou.edu

ABSTRACT

The availability of water for hydrogen production is a fundamental challenge threatening water security and its economic sustainability. This work addresses this by focusing on the design, performance and economic estimation of a novel, highly efficient and environmentally benign hydrogen production process which can be integrated with several power production units, including coal, natural gas-fired power plants and renewable energy sources. The system uses flue gas from coal power plants and various wastewater sources as the process's feedstock to generate steam for the SOEC unit. The SOEC and the balance of plant components are designed, simulated, and integrated using Aspen Hysys Software. The SOEC model is experimentally and numerically validated, and a piece-wise performance evaluation of the system is carried out. The result of this innovative system shows high system efficiencies, which can be improved depending on the energy source and by full energy Integration. The techno-economic analysis of the system gives a Levelized hydrogen cost of $2.99/kg, which can be improved to meet the U.S. Department of Energy (DOE) targets. The study offers insights into water-energy nexus for the researchers and policymakers for decision making and technology development.

Keywords: Solid Oxide Electrolytic Cell (SOEC), Hydrogen Production, Flue Gas, Water-Energy Nexus, Techno-Economic Analysis (TEA)

#180

PREPARATION AND ANALYSIS OF MEMBRANE ELECTRODE ASSEMBLIES FOR PEM WATER ELECTROLYSERS BASED ON LASER-GENERATED IRIDIUMOXIDE NANOPARTICLES AS ELECTROCATALYSTS FOR THE OXYGEN EVOLUTION REACTION

[1*] *Norbert Kazamer*, [2] *Sven Reichenberger*, [3] *Mathias Spree*, [1,4] *Ulrich Rost*, [2]*Meike Tack*, [5]*Tejas Bopardikar*, [1]*Florian Wirkert*, [1] *Haujin Salih*, [1]*Leonard Böhm*, [1]*Maximilian Cieluch*, [1,4]*Jeffrey Roth*, [5]*Tom Zoz*, [3]*Tim Hülser*, [2]*Stephan Barcikowski*, [1]*Michael Brodmann*

[1] Westphalian University of Applied Sciences Gelsenkirchen Bocholt Recklinghausen, Westphalian Energy Institute,
Neidenburger Str. 43, 45897 Gelsenkirchen, Germany
[2] University Duisburg-Essen, Technical Chemistry I, Universitätsstr. 5, 45141, Essen, Germany
[3] Institut für Energie- und Umwelttechnik e.V. (IUTA), Bliersheimer Str. 58-60, 47229, Duisburg, Germany
[4] ProPuls GmbH, Neidenburgerstr. 10, 45897, Gelsenkichen, Germany
[5] ZOZ GmbH, Raiffeisenstr. 17, 57462, Olpe, Germany
*Corresponding author e-mail: norbert.kazamer@w-hs.de

ABSTRACT

One of the promising ways for green hydrogen production is polymer exchange membrane water electrolysis (PEMWE). To this day, precious metal electrocatalysts are necessary for high production rates in PEMWEs. Catalysts such as Ir/IrO_2 have been extensively studied for the oxygen evolution reaction, but their high costs and the scarcity of resources hinder their use on a large scale. In this work, we focussed on IrO_x nanoparticles produced by pulsed laser ablation as an electrocatalytic material with the potential of a low-cost production in large scale. Furthermore, we studied B-doped Si structures as promising support material for the IrO_x particles to enhance the precious metal utilisation. The laser-generated IrO_x and B-doped Si nanostructures were ultrasonically sprayed to achieve a homogeneous coating, that builds up the anode catalyst layer, showing a high catalytic activity and promising kinetic parameters. In-situ analysis performed in a self-developed PEMWE are planned to validate the electrochemical results.

Keywords: Polymer Exchange Membrane, Electrolysis, Synthesis, IrO_x, Si:B

#183

ELECTRODEPOSITION OF A Ni-Mo ALLOY CATALYST WITH OPTIMIZED Mo-CONTENT FOR HYDROGEN EVOLUTION REACTION IN AEM-ELECTROLYSIS

[1*] *Leonard Böhm,* [1] *Klaus Thielker,* [1] *Norbert Kazamer,* [1] *Florian Wirkert,* [1] *Ulrich Rost, Gabriela Marginean*[2], *Ulf-Peter Apfel*[3,4], *Michael Brodmann*[1]

[1]Westphalian University of Applied Sciences Gelsenkirchen Bocholt Recklinghausen, Westphalian Energy Institute,
Neidenburger Str. 43, 45897 Gelsenkirchen, Germany

[2]Westphalian University of Applied Sciences Gelsenkirchen Bocholt Recklinghausen, Department of Materials Science and Testing, Neidenburger Str. 43, 45897 Gelsenkirchen, Germany

[3]Ruhr University Bochum, Inorganic Chemistry 1, Universitätsstraße 150, 44801 Bochum, Germany

[4]Fraunhofer UMSICHT, Osterfelder Str. 3, 46047 Oberhausen

*Corresponding author e-mail: leonard.boehm@w-hs.de

ABSTRACT

Various aqueous citrate electrolyte compositions for the Ni-Mo electrodeposition are explored in order to deposit Ni-Mo alloys with Mo-content ranging from 40 wt% to 65 wt% to find an alloy composition with superior catalytic activity towards the hydrogen evolution reaction (HER). The depositions were performed on copper substrates mounted onto a rotating disc electrode (RDE) and were investigated via scanning electron microscopy (SEM), X-ray fluorescence (XRF) and X-ray diffraction (XRD) methods as well as linear sweep voltammetry (LSV) and impedance spectroscopy. Kinetic parameters were calculated via Tafel analysis. Partial deposition current densities and current efficiencies were determined by correlating XRF measurements with gravimetric results. The variation of the electrolyte composition and deposition parameters enabled the deposition of alloys with Mo-content over the range of 40-65 wt%. An increase in Mo-content in deposited alloys was recorded with an increase in rotation speed of the RDE. Current efficiency of the deposition was in the magnitude of <1%, which is characteristic for the deposition of alloys with high Mo-content. The calculated kinetic parameters were used to determine the Mo-content with the highest catalytic activity for use in the HER.

Keywords: Anion Exchange Membrane Electrolysis, Nickel, Molybdenum, Electrodeposition, Hydrogen Evolution Reaction

#187

UPSCALING HIGH PERFORMANCE 3-D ELECTRODES FOR ALKALINE WATER ELECTROLYSIS TOWARDS NEAR-INDUSTRIAL CONDITIONS

[1*] *Renaud Delmelle,* [1] *Fernando Rocha,* [1] *Christos Georgiadis,* [2] *Jonathan Lambrechts and* [1] *Joris Proost*

[1]Université catholique de Louvain (UCLouvain), Institute of Mechanics, Materials and Civil Engineering, Division of Materials and Process Engineering, Place Sainte-Barbe, 2, 1348 Louvain-la-Neuve, Belgium

[2]Université catholique de Louvain (UCLouvain), Institute of Mechanics, Materials and Civil Engineering, Division of Applied Mechanics and Mathematics, Avenue Georges Lemaître, 4-6, 1348 Louvain-la-Neuve, Belgium

*Corresponding author e-mail: renaud.delmelle@uclouvain.be

ABSTRACT

Initial laboratory results using 3-D electrodes with forced electrolyte flow indicate a significant process intensification potential. This work aims to validate this process intensification on a larger scale, using a pilot-scale alkaline water electrolyser with a 6 kW cell stack working in the ranges 5-10 bar, 20-70°C and with 30% KOH. This pilot plant is also representative of industrial electrolysers in terms of gas collection, cell stacking and current distribution. In addition, it has been modified to allow for forced electrolyte flow using KOH compatible pumps.

The pilot system was first validated using standard 2-D electrodes and showed state-of-the-art results. Various cell stacks with 3-D electrodes were then tested under conditions of forced flow, showing interesting intensification potential. However, obstacles in terms of stack design still limit the flow effect. The latter are currently being tackled using CFD simulation tools.

Keywords: 3-D Electrodes, Alkaline Water Electrolysis, Pilot Demonstration, Process Intensification.

#205

ACTIVITY OF ELECTRODEPOSITED RHODIUM IN ACIDIC AND BASIC WATER ELECTROLYSIS

[1*] *Ryan Bonifacio*, [2] *Manolo Mena*

[1,2] Department of Mining, Metallurgical and Materials Engineering, College of Engineering, University of the Philippines Diliman, Quezon City, Philippines

*Corresponding author e-mail: ryan.bonifacio@up.edu.ph

ABSTRACT

Hydrogen is increasingly seen as a future fuel and a potential alternative to fossil fuels, as it is the cleanest and ideal energy carrier. Water electrolysis is one of the easiest methods to produce hydrogen, offering the advantage of simplicity. Rhodium is considered one of the best electrocatalysts for water electrolysis. This research was conducted to investigate the activity of electrodeposited Rh for its potential electrocatalytic application in acidic and basic water electrolysis. The electrode was fabricated from a 5g/L solution of $Rh_2(SO_4)_3$ electrodeposited at 3.00V for 3mins in a 92.5% Ag alloy substrate. Electrochemical characterizations were performed using cyclic voltammetry in a three-electrode set-up. The acidic electrolyte was a H_2SO_4 solution while the basic electrolyte was a NaOH solution. Results showed onset potentials of 1.4V and -0.2V for acidic OER and HER, respectively, while 0.6V and -0.9V for basic OER and HER, respectively. Consistent absolute value of limiting current, 8.00 x 10^{-3}A was observed for both reactions of the two electrolytes.

Keywords: Water Electrolysis, Cyclic Voltammetry, OER, HER

#209

MEMBRANE ELECTRODE ASSEMBLIES FOR PEMWE BASED ON GLASS FIBRE REINFORCED PFSA/SSPS COMPOSITE MEMBRANES

[1*] *Maximilian Cieluch*, [2] *Dennis Düerkop*, [1] *Norbert Kazamer*, [1] *Florian Wirkert*, [3] *Ulrich Rost*, [1] *Michael Brodmann*, [2] *Achim Schmiemann*

[1] Westphalian University of Applied Sciences Gelsenkirchen, Westphalian Energy Institute, Neidenburgerstr. 43, 45897 Gelsenkirchen, Germany

[2] Ostfalia University of Applied Sciences, Institute of Recycling, Robert-Koch-Platz 8A, 38440 Wolfsburg, Germany

[3] ProPuls GmbH, Neidenburgerstr. 10, 45897 Gelsenkirchen, Germany

*Corresponding author e-mail: maximilian.cieluch@w-hs.de

ABSTRACT

Applied research is focussing on reducing costs for membrane electrode assemblies (MEA) and improving the performance by reducing polarization losses. The present research is investigating MEAs for proton exchange membrane water electrolysis (PEMWE) based on glass fibre reinforced composite membranes assembled with gas diffusion electrodes or processed as catalyst coated membranes. Membranes were prepared by casting a polymer suspension onto both sides of a glass fibre fabric. Subsequently, the reinforced composite membranes were ex-situ investigated showing promising proton conductivity and comparable thermo-oxidative stability compared to commercial Nafion115 membrane. In-situ tests were performed by assembling the composite membrane into an MEA either with gas diffusion electrodes prepared via electrochemical catalyst deposition or ultrasonic spray coating, or catalyst coating of the membrane by ultrasonic spay coating. Ir was used as anode catalyst, Pt as cathode catalyst, respectively. The polarization curves were recorded using a single cell, hydraulic compressed test system. Preliminary results with a slightly thicker ssPS(CL)-PPSU membrane than the used reference material, showed that the synthesized, composite membrane with the self-prepared catalyst coating reached a cell voltage of 2.4 V at a current density of 2 A*cm^{-2}, making it competitive to the reference Nafion115 sample prepared and tested the same way.

Keywords: MEA, Water Electrolysis, Composite PFSA/SSPS Membranes, Glass Fibre Reinforcement, in-situ.

#218

ELECTROCHEMICAL PERFORMANCE OF 3-D PRINTED ELECTRODE GEOMETRIES IN VIEW OF ENHANCED GAS EVACUATION DURING ALKALINE WATER ELECTROLYSIS

[1*] *Fernando Rocha,* [1] *Nathan Wauthy,* [1] *Renaud Delmelle,* [1] *Christos Georgiadis,* [1] *Joris Proost*
[1] Université catholique de Louvain (UCLouvain), Div. of Materials and Process Engineering, Louvain-la-Neuve, Belgium
*Corresponding author e-mail: fernando.rocha@uclouvain.be

ABSTRACT

Water electrolysis plays a key role in the energy transition as it can be used to store energy by the conversion of electrical energy from renewable and intermittent sources to chemical energy in the form of hydrogen gas. Currently, the most mature technology is alkaline water electrolysis. The benchmark electrolyzer configuration is a zero-gap cell with porous electrodes. Gas evacuation is a challenge when using this kind of electrode, as bubbles can get trapped within the 3-D structure. This work aims to identify parameters that can help the construction of enhanced gas evacuation periodic electrodes. It was found that electrodes that direct the flow and present a lower pressure drop are better in terms of gas removal.

Keywords: Alkaline Water Electrolysis, Bubble Removal, Forced Electrolytic Flow, 3-D Printed Electrodes

#224

EXPERIMENTAL RESEARCH ON 100-BAR HIGH PRESSURE DIFFERENTIAL PROTON EXCHANGE MEMBRANE ELECTROLYZER

[1] *Jian Dang,* [2*] *Fuyuan Yang,* [3] *Yayang Jiang*
[1] Tsinghua University, School of Vehicle and Mobility, Tsinghua University Street, Haidian District, Beijing, China
[2] Tsinghua University, School of Vehicle and Mobility, Tsinghua University Street, Haidian District, Beijing, China
[3] Tsinghua University, School of Vehicle and Mobility, Tsinghua University Street, Haidian District, Beijing, China
*Corresponding author e-mail: dangj18@mails.tsinghua.edu.cn

ABSTRACT

A proton exchange membrane (PEM) electrolysis system including electrolyzers and accessory systems has been developed to allow direct electrolysis to produce hydrogen under high pressure difference. Based on the system, the performance of the high-pressure hydrogen production electrolyzer under high pressure has been analyzed. The influence of operating parameters including current, circulating water velocity, circulating water temperature and compression force on the performance of the electrolyzer was analyzed by means of polarization curve and electrochemical impedance spectrum (EIS). The experimental results show that the temperature has the greatest effect on the electrolysis performance in the form of ohmic loss, activation loss and mass transfer loss simultaneously. The circulating water flow and the compression force have no obvious influence on the performance of the electrolyzer within the range selected in this study. The current density mainly acts on the ohmic impedance of the electrolyzer. It is worth noting that no significant change in voltage efficiency was found by gradually increasing the cathode pressure to 90 bar while the anode was kept at atmospheric pressure.

Keywords: PEM Water Electrolysis, High-Pressure Difference, Efficiency, EIS

#231

ELECTROCATALYTIC AMMONIA OXIDATION COUPLED WITH HYDROGEN PRODUCTION - MOVING TOWARDS A CARBON-NEUTRAL WATER TREATMENT CYCLE

[1*] *Egle Latvyte,* [1] *Liang Wu,* [1] *Ming Zhu,* [2] *Peter Vale,* [1] *John Graves*
[1] Institute for Clean Growth and Future Mobility, Coventry University, Priory Street, Coventry, United Kingdom
[2] Severn Trent Water Ltd., St. John's Street, Coventry, United Kingdom
*Corresponding author e-mail: latvytee@coventry.ac.uk

ABSTRACT

This study presents a non-noble metal nickel-copper catalyst, as a durable anode for alkaline ammonia electrolysis. We report that a nickel-copper catalyst can electrochemically oxidise ammonia to nitrogen at room temperature and atmospheric pressure. Cyclic voltammetry experiments in a three-electrode cell confirmed the nickel-copper anode had a lower overpotential for ammonia electrolysis when compared with other precious metal catalysts. Electrodes were prepared at a larger scale and evaluated in a membrane flow cell. Gas chromatography of the off-gases confirmed that both, nitrogen at the anode and hydrogen at the cathode, were generated with relatively high faradaic efficiencies. Anode morphology and structure before and after electrolysis were investigated by X-ray diffraction (XRD), X-ray fluorescence (XRF), X-ray Photoelectron Spectroscopy (XPS) and scanning electron microscopy (SEM-EDS). Overall, the electrode showed good stability after continuous electrolysis in an alkaline ammonia electrolyte and the nickel-copper system is a potential electrocatalyst for efficient ammonia oxidation. Morever, hydrogen can generated as a useful by-product at the cathode. The ammonia is effectively cracked into nitrogen and hydrogen without the consumption of water. The hydrogen produced can be used to power fuel cells, can be burnt in combustion engines or has the possibility to be injected into the gas grid and blended with methane.

Keywords: Ammonia, Hydrogen, Electrolysis, Electrolyser, Nickel-Copper, Wastewater

#250

POWDER METALLURGY: AN EFFICIENT AND SCALABLE PRODUCTION PROCESS OF ELECTRODES FOR THE GIGAWATT ELECTROLYSIS INDUSTRY

Thomas Rauscher[1;*], *Christian Bernäcker*[1], *Justin Albers*[1], *Martin Anders*[1], *Tilo Büttner*[1], *Stefan Loos*[1], *Thomas Weißgärber*[1], *Lars Röntzsch*[1]
[1] Fraunhofer Institute for Manufacturing Technology and Advanced Materials IFAM, Winterbergstraße 28, Dresden, Germany
*Corresponding author e-mail: Thomas.Rauscher@ifam-dd.fraunhofer.de

ABSTRACT

In this contribution a powder metallurgical (PM) production process is outlined to produce highly active electrodes for the alkaline water electrolysis. Different catalytic coatings were produced on porous substrates, including foams. The electrochemical activity of the electrodes towards the hydrogen (HER) and oxygen evolution reaction (OER) were analyzed considering technical conditions. It can be shown that the performance of the catalysts can significantly be improved by adjusting the chemical composition and the catalytic loading. Furthermore, the catalytic coating obtained by the PM production route exhibits an excellent mechanical stability on different substrates.

Keywords: Alkaline Electrolysis, Cathode, Anode, Production Process

#251

INVESTIGATION OF ELECTROLYTE FORCED FLOW FOR ALKALINE WATER ELECTROLYSIS USING COMPUTATION FLUID DYNAMICS

[1] Christos Georgiadis, [1] Fernando Rocha, [2] Jonathan Lambrechts and [1] Joris Proost*

[1]Université catholique de Louvain (UCLouvain), Institute of Mechanics, Materials and Civil Engineering, Division of Materials and Process Engineering, Place Sainte-Barbe, 2, 1348 Louvain-la-Neuve, Belgium

[2]Université catholique de Louvain (UCLouvain), Institute of Mechanics, Materials and Civil Engineering, Division of Applied Mechanics and Mathematics, Avenue Georges Lemaître, 4-6, 1348 Louvain-la-Neuve, Belgium

*Corresponding author e-mail: christos.georgiadis@uclouvain.be

ABSTRACT

Green hydrogen production by water electrolysis constitutes a fundamental process for the transition to the hydrogen economy. While alkaline water electrolysis is considered a mature technology to this end, recent work has shown that we can achieve further process intensification with forced electrolyte flow through macro-porous 3D electrodes. The objective of this work is to simulate and analyze electrolyte flow through an industrial-scale pilot and through lab-scale 3D printed electrodes using Computational Fluid Dynamics (CFD). Initial results show that our current pilot cell design is inadequate for forced flow and offer insights in order to design a cell structure that is more suited for gas removal.

Keywords: Computational Fluid Dynamics, Alkaline Water Electrolysis, Forced Flow

#307

A NUMERICAL ENERGY AND EXERGY ANALYSIS OF THE EFFECT OF PHASE CHANGE MATERIALS ON A PHOTOVOLTAIC THERMAL COLLECTOR FOR HYDROGEN PRODUCTION IN NORTH CYPRUS

[1] Ahmad Sultan, [2] Muhammad Abid, [1*] Mustafa Dagbasi*

[1]Cyprus International University, Energy Systems Engineering, Nicosia, TRNC

[2] Universiti Brunei Darussalam, Integrated Technologies, Energy Systems Engineering, Brunei Darussalam

ABSTRACT

Thermal energy storage has been accompanying energy systems the moment their full potential was realized, from these, the phase change material is a key element in increasing the efficiency of the photovoltaic thermal system, through research it was shown that phase change materials increase the efficiency by lowering the temperature of the panel which leads to a higher efficiency. In the paper, the effects of several phase change materials will be observed in Cyprus and analyzed to assess the best PCM to optimize hydrogen production. A MATLAB model that was validated will be used to assess the performance of several PCMs in the production of hydrogen in north Cyprus. The study shows that the PCM causes an increase in efficiency and the power output of the total system, in addition to that the one that shows the most significance phase change material that will cause the optimal hydrogen production as well as the range of which t chose the PCM for better hydrogen production.

Keywords: Photovoltaic Thermal System, Phase Change Materials, Hydrogen Production

#308

Ir-DECORATED Pt NANOPARTICLES AS A BIFUNCTIONAL CATALYST FOR OXYGEN EVOLUTION AND REDUCTION REACTIONS

[1]Lucinda Blanco Redondo, [1]Vladimír Matolín, [1]Yevheniia Lobko*
[1]Charles University, Faculty of Mathematics and Physics, Department of Surface and Plasma Science.
V Holesovickach 2, 180 00, Prague 8, Czech Republic
*Corresponding author e-mail: lublare93@gmail.com

ABSTRACT

The challenge of meeting the growing worldwide energy demand requires progress in using renewable energy sources and hydrogen technology. Regenerative fuel cells (URFCs) are expected to be part of this energy system shift. URFC is an electrochemical device that can operate alternately as a fuel cell (to produce electricity) or water electrolyser (to produce hydrogen). Merging of WE and FC in a unique device would decrease costs due to the reduced use of precious catalysts. However, the way to develop an efficient device is still opened. Oxygen electrode in URFC is a limiting component because of the sluggish kinetics of the oxygen reduction and oxygen evolution reaction (ORR and OER). Moreover, there is not a common material that catalyses both reactions: the most suitable materials for ORR and OER are platinum and iridium, respectively. Consequently, it is necessary to reach a compromise in the composition of a bifunctional oxygen catalyst (BOC) based on Pt and Ir to improve, or at least sustain, the activity and stability with the lowest noble metal loading possible. The present work reports the polyol synthesis of Ir-decorated Pt nanoparticles with different compositions (Ir10/Pt90, Ir20/Pt80, and Ir40/Pt60). For a good understanding of the electrochemical properties, morphological and chemical surface composition of the nanoparticles have been studied by means of XRD, EDS, TEM, XPS, and RDE techniques. The results showed that the nanoparticles with an Ir:Pt ratio 20:80 display the best results.

Keywords: PEM Unitized Regenerative Fuel Cell, Catalyst, Polyol Method, Iridium, Platinum

#334

DEVELOPMENT AND OPTIMIZATION OF SEMICONDUCTOR NS-TiO_2-In_2O_3 DOPED PHOTOELECTROCHEMICAL SOLAR CELL FOR HYDROGEN PRODUCTION

[1]Priyanka Chawla, [1]Kumari Pooja, [1]Mridula Tripathi*
[1]Department of Chemistry, CMP Degree College, University of Allahabad, Prayagraj-211002, India
*Corresponding author e-mail: ccmpau@gmail.com

ABSTRACT

In the present paper we have fabricated a photoelectrochemical solar cell (PEC) with ns-TiO_2-In_2O_3 photoelectrode for four different electrode areas. In order to determine the consequence of electrode area on the production of hydrogen by SC SEP PEC cell. In the present work we have taken several geometric areas like 1, 2, 3, 4 cm^2 for the fabrication of ns-TiO_2-In_2O_3 admixed/Ti photoanode. From the results it can be seen that the photoanode area of 3 cm^2 corresponds to optimum hydrogen production rate.

Keywords: Photoelectrochemical Solar Cell, Photoanode, Tio_2-In_2O_3, Optimization

#340

TiO_2-CeO_2 ADMIXED PHOTOELECTRODE FOR OPTIMIZATION OF HYDROGEN PRODUCTION IN REGARDS TO PHOTOELECTROCHEMICAL SOLAR CELL

[1]Mridula Tripathi, Piyanka Chawla and Kumari Pooja*
Department of Chemistry, CMP PG College, University of Allahabad, Allahabad, India
*Corresponding author e-mail: mtcmpau@gmail.com

ABSTRACT

In the present research work we have optimized ns-TiO_2-CeO_2 admixed/ TiO_2 with respect to optimum photoelectrode area for semiconductor septum photoelectrochemical solar cell. The main focus was to prepare an electrode having high effective area and hence better hydrogen production rate. The photoelectrochemical cell having ns-TiO_2-CeO_2 admixed/Ti photoanode of several geometric areas like 0.5, 1.0, 1.5, 2.0 and 2.5 cm^2 were fabricated and characterize. It was found that the photoanode area of 1.5 cm^2 showed better hydrogen production.

Keywords: Hydrogen, Solar Cell, Photoelectrode

#344

GREEN HYDROGEN FOR AMMONIA PRODUCTION – A CASE FOR THE NETHERLANDS

*Gianni Pagani, Canan Acar, Yashar Hajimolana
University of Twente, Faculty of Engineering Technology, 7500 AE Enschede, The Netherlands
*Corresponding author e-mail: g.l.paganiserrano@student.utwente.nl

ABSTRACT

An integrated system is studied to supply green hydrogen feedstock for ammonia production in the Netherlands. The system compares wind and solar resources when coupled to alkaline and PEM electrolysis with a compressed hydrogen storage system. The nominal installed capacity of the electrolysis plant is around 2.3 GW, the most suitable energy source is offshore wind, and the preferred storing technology is pressurized tubes. The levelized costs of hydrogen (LCOH) are 5.30 €/kgH_2 and 6.03 €/kgH_2, and the levelized costs of ammonia (LCOA) are 1.22€/kgNH_3 and 1.34€/kgNH_3 for alkaline and PEM technologies, respectively.

Keywords: Green Hydrogen, Green Ammonia, Levelized Cost, Renewable Energies, The Netherlands.

#382

HIGH-PRESSURE PEM WATER ELECTROLYSIS BASED ON HYDRAULIC SINGLE CELL COMPRESSION

[1*] Florian J. Wirkert, [1] Ulrich W. Rost, [1] Jeffrey Y. Roth, [1] Michael Brodmann
[1]Westfälische Hochschule University of Applied Sciences, Neidenburger Str. 43, 45897 Gelsenkirchen, Germany
*Corresponding author e-mail: florian.wirkert@w-hs.de

ABSTRACT

Hydrogen needs to be compressed, such as up to above 100 bars for seasonal storage or even 700 bars to meet pressure levels for mobile applications. Up to now, high pressure hydrogen production in combination with high operation dynamics can only be handled by proton exchange membrane water electrolysis (PEMWE). However, not only but also due to still limited outlet pressures of about 40 bars, which requires additional compressors to meet storage pressure levels, PEMWE is still subject of intensive research. In this work a novel high-pressure electrolyzer system is described that was engineered with respect to hydraulic single cell compression to meet this task. Homogeneous pressure distribution throughout the entire active area is achieved via a hydraulic medium entirely surrounding the active cell components, also providing waste heat management independent of the electrochemical operation conditions. Construction details of a near industrial scale PEMWE system for an operation at a balanced 100 bar outlet pressure level are given. Further, findings related to cell performance indicated by polarization curves that were obtained up to 6 A cm^{-2} during 100 bar operation are described. Finally, a 600-hour long-term run at 2 A cm^{-2} is presented, revealing performance degradation to be in µV h^{-1} range and hydrogen crossover to be below 50 % of the lower explosion limit on the anode side.

Keywords: PEM Water Electrolysis, High-Pressure, Hydraulic Cell Compression, Modular Stack Design

#391

EXTERNAL EFFECTS ON THE HIGH FREQUENCY EIS RESPONSE OF A PEM ELECTROLYSIS CELL

[1*] Irene Franzetti, [1] Ai-Lin Chan, [2] Artem Pushkarev, [1] Sebastian Metz
[1] Fraunhofer Institute for Solar Energy System ISE, Heidenhofstrasse 2, D-79110, Freiburg, Germany
[2] National Research University "Moscow Power Engineering Institute", Moscow, Russia
*Corresponding author e-mail: irene.franzetti@ise.fraunhofer.de

ABSTRACT

Electrochemical impedance spectroscopy (EIS) is a very useful tool to characterize and distinguish the electrochemical processes in an electrolysis cell. However, to exclude external influences on the results, a method to pre-evaluate them is suggested and its usefulness is demonstrated by a faster and better fitting of the equivalent circuit model (ECM). In fact, if not considered in the ECM, the inductance artificially increases the ohmic resistance obtained at high frequencies (HFR). This effect increases at higher current densities.

Keywords: Inductance, EIS, ECM, PEM Electrolysis, HFR

#393

EFFICIENCY OF THE PRODUCTION PROCESS AND MANAGEMENT OF GREEN HYDROGEN THROUGH SIMULATION AND BALANCE OF PLANTS (BOF)

[1]*C. Castañeda-Castañeda,* [2] *J.J. Ramos-Valencia,* [3] *M.T. Cadenas-González** *& G. Leo Avelino.*
[1]Plant engineering management. Centro de Tecnología Avanzada (CIATEQ, A.C.). Av. del Retablo 150. Col. Constituyentes FOVISSSTE. Querétaro, Qro., Mexico.
[2]Process engineering management. Centro de Tecnología Avanzada (CIATEQ, A.C.). Av. del Retablo 150. Col. Constituyentes FOVISSSTE. Querétaro, Qro., Mexico.
[3]Process engineering management. Centro de Tecnología Avanzada (CIATEQ, A.C.). 23 de agosto 213. Col. Jesús García. Villahermosa, Tabasco, Mexico.
*Corresponding author e-mail: carlos.castaneda@ciateq.mx

ABSTRACT

The research carried out presents an integrated analysis of the green hydrogen production process from water hydrolysis; and of the transformation stages from water treatment, electrolytic production, separation, drying, compression, cooling and conditioning operations to reach hydroduct injection specifications, through simulation and plant balance (BoF); considering effluent recovery; using a calculation model to determine the different energy consumptions and used; the renewable energy efficiency factor to quantify the energy demand required by the process for the target control flow, this allowed the determination of the production indices, which correspond to scaling and mass production parameters such as the overall process efficiency , hydrogen flow index and the generated power index, to achieve the operational specifications of hydrogen product delivery, these and aim to have a quick guide for the determination of capacities in scale systems.

Keywords: Green Hydrogen; Energy efficiency; Balance of Plant (BoF).

#434

PARAMETRIC ANALYSIS OF BIOMETHANOL PRODUCTION UNIT USING BIOMASS GASIFIER AND HIGH-TEMPERATURE ELECTROLYZER

[1*] *Hamed Ghiasirad,* [2] *Anna Skorek-Osikowska*
[1] Silesian University of Technology, Faculty of Energy and Environmental Engineering, 44-100 Gliwice, Poland
[2] Silesian University of Technology, Faculty of Energy and Environmental Engineering, 44-100 Gliwice, Poland
*Corresponding author e-mail: hamed.ghiasirad@polsl.pl

ABSTRACT

The so-called hydrogen economy has become particularly important in global and national energy policies. In this paper, a methanol generation system is proposed that uses a high temperature electrolysis process and biomass gasification unit to follow this trend. Biomass is subjected to gasification in the oxygen and steam atmosphere. Hydrogen is produced in solid-oxide electrolysis, to which heat is supplied from the reactor's cooling. As a result of gasification, synthesis gas is obtained, consisting mainly of CO_2, CO, H_2. The gas is cooled and cleaned, and the separated tars can be used for biofuels production. The heat from gas cooling is used in the electrolysis process, too. The purified gas is used for the production of methanol. The analysis aims to calculate the efficiencies of the proposed system and indicate the potential for optimization of the processes by pointing out strengths and bottlenecks. As a result, the proposed cycle consumes 14.2 kg/h biomass in the gasifier and 52.12 kW power in SOEC, contributing to 61.4 kg/h methanol generation. Accordingly, the total energy efficiency is found to be 42.16%. In addition, sensitivity analysis showed that higher target purity of methanol and lower syngas temperature could lead to more methanol production.

Keywords: Gasification, SOEC, Methanol Production, Hydrogen Production, Thermodynamic Modelling.

#1449

A HIGH-PERFORMANCE ELECTROLYSIS CELL PROMISES MORE COST-COMPETITIVE RENEWABLE HYDROGEN

[1]*Aaron Hodges,* [1]*Anh Linh Hoang,* [1]*George Tsekouras,* [1,2]*Klaudia Wagner,* [1,2]*Chong-Yong Lee,* [1]*Prerna Tiwari,* [1,2,*]*Gerhard F. Swiegers,* [1,2]*Gordon G. Wallace*[1,2]

[1]Intelligent Polymer Research Institute, University of Wollongong, Wollongong, NSW 2522, Australia
[2] Australian Research Council Centre of Excellence for Electromaterials Research, University of Wollongong, Wollongong, NSW 2522, Australia
*Corresponding author e-mail: swiegers@uow.edu.au

ABSTRACT

We describe a new concept in water electrolysis – a '*capillary-fed electrolysis*' (CFE) cell. In such a cell, water is supplied to the hydrogen- and oxygen-evolving electrodes by capillary-induced transport along a porous inter-electrode separator, leading to inherently *bubble-free* operation at the electrodes. An alkaline CFE cell of this type is shown to outperform commercial alkaline and PEM electrolysis cells under normal operating conditions. The CFE cell required a cell voltage of only 1.51 V, equating to 98% energy efficiency (vs the Higher Heating Value, HHV, of hydrogen), at 0.5 A cm^{-2} and 85 °C, with an energy consumption of 40.4 kWh/kg hydrogen (vs. ~47.5 kWh/kg in commercial electrolysis cells). This surpasses the target set by the *International Renewable Energy Agency* (IRENA) for 2050 to decrease the energy consumption of water electrolysis cells to <42 kWh/kg. The high energy efficiency significantly decreases the *levelized cost of the hydrogen (LCOH)* produced.

Keywords: Hydrogen, Green Hydrogen, Electrolysis

#1469

ENHANCING THE ELECTROCATALYTIC HYDROGEN EVOLUTION ACTIVITY OF BARE COPPER ELECTRODES THROUGH ULTRAFAST FEMTOSECOND LASER NANOSTRUCTURING

[1,2*] *Shahbaz Ahmad,* [1,2] *Mehmet Egilmez,* [1,3] *Mehmet F. Orhan, and* [1,2] *Ali S. Alnaser*
[1]Material Science and Engineering Program, American University of Sharjah, Sharjah, United Arab Emirates
[2] Department of Physics, American University of Sharjah, Sharjah, United Arab Emirates
[3] Department of Mechanical Engineering, American University of Sharjah, Sharjah, United Arab Emirates
*Corresponding author e-mail: sahmad19@asu.edu

ABSTRACT

In this study, we report on enhancing the surface area of bare copper electrodes via femtosecond laser processing for its application in alkaline water electrolysis. It is shown that the laser nanostructuring process creates unique and hierarchal nanostructures superimposed over spiky microstructures. Analysing the effect of various laser parameters indicate that scanning speed greatly effects the microstructures by decreasing its dimensions and increasing porosity. The results also shows that laser processing has significantly enhanced the surface area with spiky and superhydrophilic structures. Furthermore, this process is expected to improve the hydrogen evolution reaction (HER) kinetics by allowing more electrode to electrolyte interface, which can favor the enrichment and formation of protons on structured Cu cathode.

Keywords: Femtosecond Laser; Hydrogen Evolution Reaction; Electrode; Nanostructuring

#1481

THIN FILM COATING OF PLATINUM ON 3D PRINTED POLYMERIC ANODE ELECTRODES FOR PEMWE

[1,2]*Bulut Hüner*,[1,2*] *Nesrin Demir*, [1,2]*Mehmet Fatih Kaya*
[1]Erciyes University, Engineering Faculty, Energy Systems Engineering Department, Heat Engineering Division, 38039, Kayseri, Turkey
[2]Erciyes University H2FC Hydrogen Energy Research Group, 38039, Kayseri, Turkey
*Corresponding author e-mail: nkayatas@erciyes.edu.tr

ABSTRACT

Three-dimensional (3D) printing technology presents a higher flexible technique to produce different complex geometric shapes compared to conventional manufacturing. This technology is known as additive manufacturing (AM) may be also suitable for industrial production. AM method is widely used in different areas, including construction, medicine, energy, and electrochemistry, recently. Polymeric materials such as polylactic acid (PLA) and acrylonitrile butadiene styrene (ABS) filaments are used in the 3D printing process. In this study, the conductive polymeric anode electrodes are prepared using 3D printing method. Then, these electrodes are coated with Pt in different thicknesses (0.5, 1, 1.5, and 2μm) by the electron beam evaporation (EBM) method. A thin Cr adhesion layer (20nm) is used to improve the adhesion of the Pt coating on the sample surface. After the completion of the coating process, the polymeric electrodes are named as Pt-0.5, Pt-1, Pt-1.5, and Pt-2. Pt coated 3D printed polymeric electrodes have been physically characterized by using Field Emission Scanning Electron Microscopy (FE-SEM), FE-SEM/Energy Dispersive X-Ray Spectroscopy (FE-SEM/EDX), FE-SEM mapping, and X-Ray Powder Diffraction (XRD) techniques. Cycling Voltammetry (CV), Linear Sweep Voltammetry (LSV), Electrochemical Impedance Spectroscopy (EIS), and Chronoamperometry (CA) analysis of the Pt coated electrodes have been conducted to evaluate their electrochemical performance.

Keywords: Additive Manufacturing, 3D Printed Polymeric Electrode, Thin Film

#1487

IMPROVING HYDROGEN EVOLUTION CATALYTIC ACTIVITY OF 2D CARBON ALLOTROPE BIPHENYLENE WITH B, N, P DOPING: DENSITY FUNCTIONAL THEORY INVESTIGATIONS

Mukesh Singh[a*], *Alok Shukla*[a], *Brahmananda Charkroborty*[b,c,**]
[a]Department of Physics, Indian Institute of Technology Bombay, Powai, Mumbai 400076, India
[b]High Pressure and Synchrotron Radiation Physics Division, Bhabha Atomic Research Centre, Trombay, Mumbai, India
[c]Homi Bhabha National Institute, Mumbai, India
*Corresponding author e-mail: gkpmukeshsingh@gmail.com

ABSTRACT

Using the first principle calculations, we studied the hydrogen evolution reaction (HER) activity of pristine Biphenylene (BPh) and B, N, P decorated BPh sheet. HER activity of BPh sheet is not encouraging, it is similar to pristine graphene. However, doping of P on top of one carbon atom of the BPh sheet improves its activity better than Pt-catalysts. We analyzed the adsorption mechanism of dopants (B, N, P) and hydrogen adsorption with Bader charge analysis and density of states (DOS) analysis. We have compared all our best HER activity results in the reaction coordinate and volcano plots of pristine, B, N, P-doped BPh sheets, and they indicate that P doped BPh is a powerful catalyst for HER activities.

Keywords: Hydrogen production, HER, Biphenylene, first principle calculation

#1509

ANION EXCHANGE MEMBRANE (AEM) WATER ELECTROLYSERS: CURRENT STATUS AND FUTURE PERSPECTIVE

Cüneyt Karakaya, Immanuel Vincent, Ion Velasco and Ekain Fernandez
TECNALIA, Basque Research and Technology Alliance (BRTA), Mikeletegi Pasealekua 2, 20009 Donostia-San Sebastián, Spain.
Corresponding author e-mail: cuneyt.karakaya@tecnalia.com

ABSTRACT

Electrolysis using an anion exchange membrane (AEM) is a promising method for producing hydrogen on a large scale using renewable energy sources. However, the AEM electrolysis performance remains inferior to that of conventional proton exhange membrane (PEM) electrolysis technologies. This work compiles recent significant research in the creation of crucial materials (catalysts, membranes, and MEAs) and operating conditions (electrolyte composition, cell temperature, performance achievements). Additionally, we propose how to reach the optimal MEA for AEM electrolysis that maximizes performance and stability. The purpose of this study is to ascertain the present state of materials development and to identify areas for improvement in order to establish the technology's practicality. Once materials development challenges are overcome, AEM water electrolysis has the potential to accelerate the eventual usage of hydrogen as an energy storage vector on a large scale (GW), particularly in developing nations.

#1517

IRIDIUM-RUTHENIUM CATALYST ON SPUTTER-ETCHED MEMBRANE FOR PROTON EXCHANGE MEMBRANE WATER ELECTROLYZERS

[1] Tomáš Hrbek, [1]Peter Kúš, [1]Vladimír Matolín, [1]Iva Matolínová*
[1]Charles University, Faculty of Mathematics and Physics, Department of Surface and Plasma Science Holešovičkách 2, 180 00 Prague 8, Czech Republic
*Corresponding author e-mail: tomas.hrbek@mff.cuni.cz

ABSTRACT

We present an iridium-ruthenium-based catalyst (25 % Ir, 75 % Ru) for Proton Exchange Water Electrolyzers (PEM-WE) with low iridium loading (158 µg cm^{-2}), prepared by magnetron sputtering. We use no additional support for the PEM-WE's anode. The sputter-etching of the PEM replaces them – its simultaneous plasma and deposition of a cerium oxide layer during reactive magnetron sputtering leads to a pronounced fiber-like structure on its surface. The prepared catalyst is tested for 1272 hours in a single-cell PEM-WE, demonstrating excellent activity and stability. We focus on stability, which is the crux of a low-iridium-loading catalyst. We search for its origin through several electrochemical and surface analysis methods – Potential Electrochemical Impedance Spectroscopy, Energy X-Ray spectroscopy, X-ray Photoelectron Spectroscopy, and Scanning Electron Microscopy.

Keywords: Magnetron Sputtering, PEM-WE, Lateral Conductivity, Iridium-Ruthenium

#1538

EXERGETIC ANALYSIS OF A SOLAR ENERGY-BASED HYDROGEN PRODUCTION SYSTEM

[1] Hilal Akci, [2] Huseyin Gunerhan, [3] Arif Hepbasli*
[1] Ege University, Graduate School of Natural and Applied Science, Mechanical Engineering Program, 35100 Bornova, Izmir, Turkey
[2] Ege University, Faculty of Engineering, Department of Mechanical Engineering, 35100 Bornova, Izmir, Turkey
[3] Yasar University, Faculty of Engineering, Department of Energy Systems Engineering, 35100 Bornova, Izmir, Turkey
*Corresponding author e-mail: hilalakci@gmail.com

ABSTRACT

In this study, energy, exergy and sustainability analyses are performed for a solar energy-based hydrogen production system, which is modeled with TRNSYS and Engineering Equation Solver (EES) software packages. This system consists of solar photovoltaic panels (PVs), a controller, an electrolyzer, a metal hydride hydrogen tank used for hydrogen production and storage, and Proton Exchange Membrane Fuel Cell (PEMFC) for electricity storage. Dead state temperature is taken as 0 °C. The results revealed that the PEMFC had the highest energy efficiency of 53.28%. Exergy efficiencies of the solar PV panel, the electrolyzer and the PEMFC were determined to be 9.66%, 60% and 29.39%, respectively. The exergetic sustainability index of the electrolyzer had the maximum value of 2.501.

Keywords: Exergy, Hydrogen Production, Electrolyzer, Efficiency, Solar Energy

#1543

UNDERSTANDING RESEARCH EVOLUTION IN HYDROGEN PRODUCTION FROM WATER ELECTROLYSIS: A BIBLIOGRAPHIC STUDY

[1] *Ibrar Ullah,* [2,3] *Muhammad Nihal Naseer,* [4] *Joongbae Kim,* [4] *Jae-Bum Pyo,* [1,4,*] *Bumjoo Kim*
[1] Department of Future Convergence Engineering, Kongju National University, Cheonan 1223-24, Korea
[2] National University of Sciences and Technology (NUST), 44000-Islamabad, Pakistan
[3] Department of Mechanical Engineering, College of Engineering, Seoul National University, Seoul 08826, Republic of Korea
[4] Department of Mechanical Engineering and Automotive Engineering, Kongju National University, Cheonan 1223-24, Korea
*Corresponding author e-mail: bumjoo@kongju.ac.kr

ABSTRACT

Hydrogen production from water electrolysis has been a topic of keen interest for the research community. Although an exponential growth in water electrolysis was observed, conducting quantitative analysis of literature is still a novelty. Therefore, authors took an initiative to use bibliographic and content analysis techniques to quantitatively analyze literature published on this topic during last 50 years indexed in Web of Science (WoS). A total of 9,277 published articles were extracted from WoS and were analyzed. Further, research evolution and recent hot topics of this field were also highlighted using the content analysis technique. Results shows that more than half of the literature on this topic was published during last fiver years (2017-2021). China followed by USA and Germany are the main research hubs of this field. Furthermore, performance enhancement of hydrogen production from electrolysis by using nanoparticles, nanosheets and nanoarrays are the hot topics of the filed. To pave path of electrolysis to industrial sector, techno-economic analysis is becoming a pivot to research community.

Keywords: Hydrogen, Electrolysis, Research Trends, Bibliometric

#1573

DEVELOPMENT OF Pt-Cr COATED SS316L ELECTRODES FOR PEM ELECTROLYZERS BY SELECTIVE LASER MELTING METHOD

Murat Kisti[1,2], *Emre Özdoğan*[1,2,3], *Süleyman Uysal*[1,2,3], *Mehmet Fatih Kaya*[1,2,3*]
[1]*Erciyes University, Engineering Faculty, Energy Systems Engineering Department, Heat Engineering Division, 38039, Kayseri, Turkey*
[2]*Erciyes University H2FC Hydrogen Energy Research Group, 38039, Kayseri, Turkey*
[3]*BATARYASAN Enerji ve San.Tic. Ltd.Şti, Yıldırım Beyazıt Mah., Aşık Veysel Bul., ERÜ TGB İdare ve Kuluçka 4, No: 67/3/11, Melikgazi, Kayseri, Turkey*
*Corresponding author e-mail: kayamehmetfatih@erciyes.edu.tr

ABSTRACT

Proton exchange membrane (PEM) water electrolyzer (PEMWE) is used to obtain a high amount of hydrogen cleanly from water. However, to make PEMWE common in everyday life, their cost must be reduced, and the performance of these systems must be increased. Thus, alternative materials should be developed to obtain low-cost PEMWE systems. In this study, stainless steel 316L (SS316L) is used as gas diffusion electrode (GDE) materials. The selective laser melting (SLM) method is selected to produce the SS316L electrode. To enhance to SS316L electrodes' corrosion resistance and kinetic activity, SS316L electrodes are coated with Pt different thickness values using electron beam evaporation method (EBM) with a Cr interlayer film. Electrochemical properties of SS316L electrodes have been investigated by cyclic voltammetry (CV), linear sweep voltammetry (LSV), and electrochemical impedance spectroscopy (EIS) techniques. Durability of SS316L electrodes have been conducted by Tafel and chronoamperometry (CA) techniques. The surface morphologies of SS316L electrodes have been characterized by field emission scanning electron microscopy (FE-SEM), energy dispersive X-ray analysis (EDX), X-ray diffractometers (XRD), and X-ray fluorescence (XRF) analysis. As a result, electrochemical performance, kinetic activity, and corrosion resistance of the electrodes are enhanced significantly with Pt-Cr material by EBM coating.

Keywords: Proton Exchange Membrane Electrolyzers, Gas Diffusion Electrode, Selective Laser Melting, Electron Beam Evaporation, SS316L

#1576

A NEW EXPERIMENTAL INVESTIGATION ON HYDROGEN PRODUCTION OF NaCl, KCl AND $CaCl_2$ SOLUTIONS THROUGH CHLORALKALI REACTOR

[1] Mustafa Erden, [2] Mehmet Karakilcik*
[1]Cukurova University, Faculty of Sciences and Letters, Department of Physics, 01330 Adana, Turkey
*Corresponding author e-mail: mustafaerden01@hotmail.com

ABSTRACT

In this experimental study, hydrogen production performance of NaCl, KCl and $CaCl_2$ solutions via electrochemical method through a small scale chloralkali reactor are investigated. A cation exchange membrane is placed in between the anode and cathode chamber to separate the anolyte and catholyte solutions. 316 stainless steel electrodes are used in the experiment due to its economic efficiency. While the anode compartment of the reactor is fed with NaCl, KCl and $CaCl_2$ solutions one by one, the cathode compartment is fed with a low-density NaOH, KOH and $Ca(OH)_2$ base solution depending on the type of salt used in the experiment. Experiments are carried out at cell voltage range of 3 to 5 volts according to three different brine densities (30 g/L, 60 g/L and 90 g/L), three different electrolyte flow rates (0.4 g/s, 0.6 g/s and 0.8 g/s) and three different electrolyte temperatures (30 °C, 50 °C and 70 °C). While a significant amount of hydrogen gas output was observed from the cathode compartment of the reactor, the expected chlorine gas output from the anode compartment was not observed. Since the chlorine gas is very active it reacts with many metals easily. Therefore, chlorine gas produced in the anode chamber caused serious corrosion and contamination on the electrode in this chamber.

Keywords: Hydrogen Production, Electrochemical Process, Chloralkali Reactor, NaCl, Kcl, $CaCl_2$.

#1578

FLOW CHANNEL EFFECT ON PERFORMANCE OF PEM WATER ELECTROLYSIS

[1] Seong Keun Kim, [1] Sung Yong Jung*
[1]Chosun University, Department of Mechanical Engineering, 309 Pilmun-daero, Dong-gu Gwangju, Republic of Korea
*Corresponding author e-mail: syjung@chosun.ac.kr

ABSTRACT

PEMWE (proton exchange membrane water electrolyzer) can operate at a high current density with a small size to obtain a large mount of hydrogen. However, when PEMWE operate under high current density conditions, lots of air bubbles are generated which causes the reduction of water electrolysis efficiency due to the increase of mass transport loss. In this study, three types of flow channels (single serpentine, double serpentine, and parallel) were designed to reduce mass transport loss and PEMWE performances were compared. Performance was measured with a current density ranging from 0 to 2.0 A/cm^2, and water at 50 and 70 °C was supplied to the anode at 1.5 to 14.1 ml/min, and to the cathode at 1.5 ml/min. Two-phase flow patterns were analyzed using an optical high-speed imaging to understand relationship between flow channel design and cell performance. Among tested channels, the parallel channel had the worst performance because slug flows with Tayler bubbles, that could disturb the water supply, were mainly occurred. Whereas, the single serpentine channel had the best performance because annular flows with a thin liquid film could reduce mass transport loss were dominant.

Keywords: Electrolyzer, Proton Exchange Membrane Water Electrolyzer, Flow Channel Design

#1594

EFFECT OF MOLYBDENUM OXIDE ADDITION TO METAL-SUPPORTED ZEOLITE CATALYST FOR REVERSE WATER GAS SHIFT REACTION

[1,*,2] *Makoto Ryo Harada,* [2] *Atsushi Okemoto,* [2] *Norihito Hiyoshi,* [2] *Yasuhisa Hasegawa,* [2] *Koichi Sato*
[1] Tokai University, Department of Human Development, Course of Environment and Resources, 4-1-1 Kitakaname, Hiratsuka-shi, Kanagawa 259-1292, Japan
[2] National Institute of Advanced Industrial Science and Technology (AIST), 4-2-1, Nigatake, Miyagino-ku, Sendai 983-8551, Japan
*Corresponding author e-mail: MRHARADA@tsc.u-tokai.ac.jp

ABSTRACT

In this study, the effect of molybdenum oxide addition on metal catalysts in the reverse water gas shift reaction was investigated. By adding molybdenum to the copper, iron and cobalt supported catalysts, CO_2 conversion rate was improved while maintaining a high CO selectivity. In addition, it was made clear that the addition of molybdenum to ruthenium and nickel supported catalysts containing methane as the main product suppresses the production of methane and improves the selectivity for the reverse water gas shift reaction. The addition of molybdenum oxide from being presumed to suppress complete reduction of CO_2, proceeds highly selectively reverse water gas shift reaction. The addition of molybdenum oxide as a reverse shift reaction catalyst can be expected to be a useful method.

Keywords: Reverse Shift Reaction, Molybdenum Oxide, Zeolite Support, Carbon Dioxide, Selectivity

#1598

ON THE POTENTIAL OF COUPLING SOLAR CHIMNEY AND WIND ENERGY TO PRODUCE HYDROGEN AS GREEN-TO-GREEN SYSTEM

[1,2] *Mohamad Ramadan,* [2] *Ahmad Haddad,* [3] *Mohammad Alkhedher*
[1] International University of Beirut, PO Box 146404 Beirut, Lebanon
[2] Lebanese International University, Beirut, Lebanon
[3] Mechanical Engineering Department, Abu Dhabi University, United Arab Emirates
*Corresponding author e-mail: mohamad.ramadan@liu.edu.lb

ABSTRACT

The energy crisis, we are facing nowadays requires fast and efficient actions. Indeed, renewable sources are a main pillar, however storage systems are also principal pillars to overcome the intermittent nature of renewable sources. However, and to maintain a fully green system the storage should also be green and eco-friendly. Green to Green (*G2G*) are systems that gathers green sources and green storage. A typical solution is to couple renewable source to fuel cell. In this frame the present paper aims at studying the coupling of two renewable energy systems that are wind turbine and solar chimney to Fuel cell. A case study on the region of Rayak (Lebanon) is performed. Results show that in the first half of the year wind turbine-fuel cell coupling provides higher power supply whereas from June till November, solar chimney-fuel cell coupling is better.

Keywords: Green to Green, G2G, Hydrogen, Fuel Cell, Wind Turbine, Solar Chimney, Renewable Energy

#1627

ENERGY PERSPECTIVE AND ANALYSES OF SEAWATER ELECTROLYZER FOR SEA VEHICLE

[1]*Meryem Gizem Sürer,* [2*] *Hüseyin Turan Arat*
[1]Iskenderun Technical University, Faculty of Engineering and Natural Sciences, Mechanical Engineering, Central Campus, Hatay, 31200, Turkey
[2]Sinop University, Faculty of Engineering and Architecture, Mechanical Engineering, Sinop, 57000, Turkey
* Corresponding author e-mail: htarat@sinop.edu.tr

ABSTRACT

In this study, a prototype marine vehicle is designed to produce hydrogen from sea water and convert it into electricity and use it as an auxiliary power in the main propulsion, and it is provided to look at this design from an energy perspective. In the designed marine vehicle, the main propulsion power was provided by a diesel generator. In this study, first of all, the requirements were determined, a conceptual design was made and necessary evaluations were made from the energy perspective. In this study, high-weight hydrogen storage difficulties will be avoided by providing hydrogen production at any time, and costs will decrease in the long run. In addition, it will make great contributions to zero carbon dioxide studies.

Keywords: Hydrogen, Sea Vehicle, Purification, Energy Analyses, Electrolysis

#1629

THE EXPERIMENTAL STUDIES ON ELECTROLYSER MODE OPERATION OF UNITIZED REGENERATIVE PEM FUEL CELL

[1*] *Nebi Yelegen*, [1,2] *Enis Selçuk Altuntop*, [1] *Gamze Atalmis*, [1,2] *Yüksel Kaplan*
1 Nigde Omer Halisdemir University Prof. Dr. T. Nejat Veziroglu Clean Energy Research Center, 51245, Nigde, Turkey
2 Nigde Omer Halisdemir University, Mechanical Engineering Department, 51245, Nigde, Turkey
*Corresponding author e-mail: nebiyelegen@gmail.com

ABSTRACT

A unitized regenerative proton exchange membrane fuel cell (UR-PEMFC) is an electrochemical component that is capable of operating both as electrolyser and fuel cell mode. While UR-PEMFC produces hydrogen and oxygen by decomposing water in the electrolyser mode, it can also produce electricity and heat by using hydrogen as fuel in the fuel cell mode. A reversible system possesses several distinctive advantages for instance, high specific energy, pollution free, and most importantly, the decoupled energy storage capacity with rated power [1]. In this study, the performance of a unitized regenerative fuel cell and stack in electrolyser mode was investigated. The active areas of URFC are 100 cm^2, and the stack has three cell, which has a 100 cm^2 active area. The clamping pressure is optimized for cell and stack by using pressure film. Thus, the contact resistance was minimized, and optimum contact was achieved.

Keywords: Unitized Regenerative Fuel Cell, PEM Electrolyser Stack, Experimental Study

Track 3.

Hydrogen Production: Biological Methods and Biohydrogen

#6

CARBON FOOTPRINT OF HYDROGEN PRODUCED FROM SPENT COFFEE GROUNDS

[1*] *Fehmi Gorkem Uctug*, [2] *Hakan Cay*, [2] *Gozde Duman*, [2] *Jale Yanik*
[1]Izmir University of Economics, Department of Mechanical Engineering, Sakarya Caddesi No: 156 35530 Balçova, Izmir - Turkey
[2]Ege University, Department of Chemistry, Erzene Mahallesi 35040 Bornova, Izmir - Turkey
*Corresponding author e-mail: gorkem.uctug@ieu.edu.tr

ABSTRACT

Life cycle carbon footprint of producing hydrogen from spent coffee grounds was calculated. The following scenarios were compared: direct gasification; gasification of biochar produced by carbonization at 300°C and at 500°C; and gasification of hydrochar produced by hydrothermal carbonization. In each scenario, two sub-scenarios for one-step and two-step gasification were also studied, respectively. CCaLC2 software was used with CML2001 methodology, and the functional unit was defined as 1 kg of hydrogen gas produced. Material inputs and emissions were obtained based on experimental data whereas energy consumption of the process was partially adopted from the literature. Hydrogen produced via the two-step gasification of hydrochar obtained as a result of hydrothermal carbonization was found to have the lowest carbon footprint (33.0 kg CO_2eq. per kg H_2) whereas hydrogen produced via direct one-step gasification of spent coffee grounds was found to have the highest carbon footprint (87.0 kg CO_2eq. per kg H_2). The results in general were observed to be in reasonable consistency with the values reported for the carbon footprint of other hydrogen production methods. The main conclusions of the study were the necessity of adding a carbonization step prior to the gasification process, and preferring two-step gasification instead of one-step so that the carbon footprint can be reduced.

Keywords: Hydrogen Production, Carbon Footprint, Spent Coffee Grounds, Carbonization, Gasification

#10

IMPACT OF MICROBIAL INOCULUM STORAGE ON DARK FERMENTATIVE H_2 PRODUCTION

[1]*Kevin Dauptain*, [1]*Alexandre Schneider*, [1]*Marie Noguer*, [2]*Carole Barrau*, [3]*Pierre Fontanille*, [1]*Nicolas Bernet*, [1]*Hélène Carrère*, [1*]*Eric Trably*
[1] Univ Montpellier, INRAE, LBE, Narbonne, 102 avenue des Étangs, 11100 Narbonne, France
[2] Syndicat Mixte TRIFYL route de sieurac, 81300 Labessiere Candeil, France
[3] Univ Clermont Auvergne, Institut Pascal, TSA 60026, 63178 Aubière, France
*Corresponding author e-mail: eric.trably@inrae.fr

ABSTRACT

Hydrogen production by Dark Fermentation (DF) of complex organic matter is usually performed by adding a microbial inoculum issued from various natural environments. Not only the inoculum origin can significantly impact the DF performances, but also the microbial community composition that can fluctuate over time and subsequently impact the DF process. As a result, comparing experiments carried out with different inoculum storage can be controversial. The main objective of this work aims to determine whether the type and time of inoculum storage could impact the DF performances, i.e. H_2 and metabolite productions. Biochemical Hydrogen Potential (BHP) tests were carried out on three substrates: glucose, the organic fraction of municipal solid waste (OFMSW), and food waste (FW), and three different microbial inoculums were tested. For glucose, hydrogen production with the stored inoculums was significantly impacted and was dependent on the inoculum origin. For complex substrates and for all inoculums, H_2 production with the stored inoculums was not statistically different or higher than the ones of the fresh inoculums, suggesting the possibility of a microbial inoculum storage by freezing or freeze drying and preserving the DF performances over time.

Keywords: Biohydrogen, Dark Fermentation, Inoculum Storage, Freezing, Freeze-drying

#23

THE POTENTIAL OF USING MICROALGAE IN PHOTOBIOREACTORS FOR H_2 PRODUCTION

[1*]*Sergei Markov*
[1]Austin Peay State University, Biology Department, 601 College Street, Clarksville, TN, USA
*Corresponding author e-mail: markovs@apsu.edu

ABSTRACT

Many species of microalgae produce molecular hydrogen (H_2) in reactions catalyzed by the enzymes hydrogenase or nitrogenase. This H_2 production is coupled with photosynthesis. Thus, it is possible to design photobioreactors in which solar energy can be used for the production of H_2. Our research and development efforts were concentrated on designing hollow-fiber photobioreactors incorporating green algae and cyanobacteria. We have continuously for six months operated hollow-fiber photobioreactors for the photoproduction of H_2 from water using two metabolically different species of microalgae. One photobioreactor employed green alga *Chlamydomonas reinhardtii*. Hydrogen production was measured under partial vacuum at the average rate of 6.0 ml•g cell dry weight $^{-1}$•h^{-1}. Another photobioreactor utilized cyanobacterium *Anabaena variabilis* with average H_2 photoproduction rate of 20 ml•g cell dry weight $^{-1}$•h^{-1}. In both photobioreactors the duration of H_2 photoproduction was 6 months long.

Keywords: Biohydrogen, Photobioreactors, Hollow-fibers, Microalgae, Cyanobacteria

#24

A NOVEL THREE-STAGE INTEGRATED SYSTEM (DARK FERMENTATION, METHANOGENESIS AND PHOTOFERMENTATION): DIFFERENT COMBINATIONS TO MAXIMIZE H_2 AND CH_4 PRODUCTION

[1*] *Tuba Hande Erguder,* [1] *Melih Can Akman,* [1] *Engin Koç,* [1] *Ekin Güneş Tunçay,* [2] *Ufuk Gündüz,* [3] *İnci Eroğlu*
[1] Middle East Technical University, Department of Environmental Engineering, 06800, Ankara, Turkey
[2] Middle East Technical University, Department of Biology, 06800, Ankara, Turkey
[3] Middle East Technical University, Department of Chemical Engineering, 06800, Ankara, Turkey
*Corresponding author e-mail: etubahan@metu.edu.tr

ABSTRACT

A unique three-stage integrated system composed of dark fermentation (DF), methanogenesis (M) and photofermentation (PF) in series was developed to maximize the total energy production from unit organic matter (sucrose). The three-stage system aims to minimize the disadvantages of two-stage DF-PF systems and use the advantage of methanogenesis stage via CH_4 production. This study compares the total energy yields (kJ/g soluble chemical oxygen demand, sCOD) of six different reactor configurations, that is, both two-stage DF-M and DF-PF systems to three-stage DF-M-PF systems. Results revealed that three-stage configurations produced a maximum gross heat energy of 13.47-16.11 kJ/g $sCOD_{added}$ and maximum yield equivalence of 9.18-10.80 mol H_2/mol hexose. These values are 14-37% greater than 8 mol H_2/mol hexose, defined to be the economic threshold for application of two-stage DF-PF systems. A methanogenesis stage placed between DF and PF stages was the most significant stage in total energy production.

Keywords: Anaerobic Digestion, Energy, Hydrogen, Methane, Two-stage Systems

#26

INVESTIGATION OF H_2 AND CH_4 PRODUCTION FROM YARD WASTES VIA TWO-STAGE ANAEROBIC DIGESTION AT DIFFERENT PRE-TREATMENT OPTIONS AND SOLIDS CONCENTRATIONS

[1]*Nihan Nur Kalaycıoğlu*, [1*]*Tuba Hande Ergüder*
[1]Middle East Technical University, Department of Environmental Engineering, 06800, Çankaya, Ankara
* Corresponding author e-mail: etubahan@metu.edu.tr

ABSTRACT

Yard waste, an abundant lignocellulosic biomass, was used as the substrate in a two-stage anaerobic digestion system (TSAD) conducted for hydrogen and methane production. The effect of initial solids concentration (2%, 5% and 8% Total Solids, TS) and pre-treatment options (alkaline, thermal and ultrasound) on H_2 or CH_4 production yield in TSAD were investigated. Batch experiments showed that the highest hydrogen production (30.5 mL H_2/g VS) was observed in alkaline pre-treated (AP) yard waste with 2% TS in the first-stage of TSAD. Alkaline pre-treatment was the best alternative for all three initial TS contents studied in terms of H_2 yields. The highest methane yield (around 40 mL CH_4/g VS), on the other hand, was obtained with thermal pre-treated (TP) yard waste with 2% TS in the second-stage of TSAD. Thermal pre-treatment improved the methane yield for all three TS contents. Overall, this study revealed that, despite the low yield levels, alkaline pre-treatment and 2% initial TS application provided the highest total energy gain from yard wastes in TSAD (2 MJ/kg VS_{addded}) followed by thermal pre-treatment. Independent of the pre-treatment type, the increase in TS contents decreases the yield and the energy production potential from yard wastes.

Keywords: Two-stage Anaerobic Digestion, Dark Fermentation, Biohythane, Yard Waste

#51

TOWARDS SCALABLE BIO-HYDROGEN: TRANSPARENT PVA CRYOGEL AS IMMOBILISATION MATRIX FOR PHOTOFERMENTATIVE BACTERIA

[1]*Jan-Pierre du Toit*, [1*] *Robert Pott*
[1] Stellenbosch University, Department of Process Engineering, Banghoek Road, Stellenbosch, South Africa
*Corresponding author e-mail: rpott@sun.ac.za

ABSTRACT

Phototrophic bacteria have gained significant attention for their ability to produce sustainable bio-hydrogen from the degradation of a wide variety of organic wastes via photofermentation. For maturation of photofermentative bioprocesses towards industrial feasibility, development of suitable immobilisation materials is required to allow continuous production from a stable pool of catalytic biomass in which energy is not diverted towards biomass accumulation. Here the development of a transparent poly vinyl-alcohol cryogel is described, along with characterisation of favourable light transmission properties, mechanical strength, diffusion resistance and biocompatibility. Hydrogen production studies of immobilised *Rhodopseudomonas palustris* in batch photobioreactors show higher specific hydrogen production rates which continue longer than planktonic cultures. Continuous cultivation yielded stable long-term hydrogen production for at least 67 days from immobilised bacteria, demonstrating the suitability of PVA cryogel immobilisation for photofermentative bio-hydrogen production.

Keywords: Biohydrogen, Photofermentation, Bacterial Immobilisation, Purple Non-Sulfur Bacteria, PVA Cryogel

#52

A THERMOSIPHON BASED PHOTOBIOREACTOR FOR PHOTOFERMENTATIVE HYDROGEN PRODUCTION

[1] *Bovinille Anye Cho,* [1] *Calizé Bosman,* [1]*Steven Bradshaw* [1*] *Robert W. M. Pott*
[1]Department of Process Engineering, Stellenbosch University, South Africa
*Corresponding author e-mail: rpott@sun.ac.za

ABSTRACT

Photofermentation is a process driven by, primarily, anaerobic photosynthetic bacteria. Significant advances have been made in the field with regards hydrogen productivity using these organisms, however, comparatively little work has been to develop reactors optimised for photofermentation. This paper presents a novel photobioreactor, designed with anaerobic photosynthetic organisms in mind: the thermosiphon photobioreactor (TPBR). This reactor utilises absorbed light to drive passive circulation, potentially reducing operating costs, and allowing for continuous hydrogen production. The prototype reactor's thermal and hydrodynamic performance was investigated using Computational Fluid Dynamics (CFD) and validated with experimentation. Using *Rhodopsueduomonas palustris* as an exemplary photofermentative organism, the TPBR operation was demonstrated at laboratory scale. Hydrogen production and bacterial growth were shown to be in line with that seen in test bioreactors. The CFD results demonstrated good agreement with experimental data, indicating that the model has functionality in predicting fluid operation in this reactor. Further, the TPBR demonstrated excellent liquid circulation with up to 88% of the microbial cells kept in free suspension, using only passive circulation. The TPBR is demonstrated as an anaerobic photobioreactor system entirely agitated using passive circulation, which has the potential to be used as a low energy-input reactor for photosynthetic organism cultivation.

Keywords: Thermosiphon Photobioreactor (TPBR), Photosynthetic Bacteria, Biohydrogen, Photofermentation

#53

BIOLOGICAL HYDROGEN PRODUCTION BY IMMOBILIZED RHODOPSEUDOMONAS PALUSTRIS: COMPARISON OF A PACKED BED AND FLUIDIZED BED PHOTOBIOREACTOR SYSTEM.

[1] *Brandon Ross,* [1*] *Robert W.M. Pott*
[1] Department of Process Engineering at Stellenbosch University, Banghoek Rd, Stellenbosch, South Africa
*Corresponding author e-mail: rpott@sun.ac.za

ABSTRACT

Biological hydrogen production is a promising replacement for the current modes of hydrogen production. The use of photosynthetic bacteria such as the purple non sulphur bacterium (PNSB) *Rhodopseudomonas palustris* to produce hydrogen *via* photofermentation has been shown to have a low environmental impact and can be integrated into wastewater treatment systems. However, production rate, and energy conversion, require improvement before the system can be considered viable. One method of enhancement is the design and development of photobioreactor (PBR) systems to improve the hydrogen production; for instance, the use of immobilised cells in novel photobioreactor configurations. This study compares the hydrogen productivity of *R. palustris* biomass under planktonic *vs.* immobilised conditions, with the reactor operating either as a packed bed or fluidised bed. A PBR that facilitated hydrogen production by *R. palustris* either as a growing planktonic cell culture or immobilised in a polyvinyl alcohol (PVA) cryogel matrix was successfully designed and constructed. The performance of the PBR operating with planktonic cells was compared to immobilised cells operating as a fluidised bed PBR (FBPBR) and a packed bed PBR (PBPBR). The FBPBR achieved the highest maximum specific hydrogen production rate of 15.74±2.2 mL/g/h. The planktonic culture and PBPBR achieved lower production rates of 12.6±8.0 mL/g/h and 4.53±0.8 mL/g/h respectively. In terms of the substrate conversion efficiency, the FBPBR achieved a conversion of 43% which outperformed the PBPBR which only achieved a conversion of 26.7%. The conversion efficiency of the planktonic cell culture was between the two immobilised cell configurations with an efficiency of 32%.

Keywords: Hydrogen, *Rhodopseudomonas Palustris*, Cryogel, Photobioreactor.

#97

TiO_2 SUBSTRATE FOR THYLAKOID MEMBRANE WITH NEW PORE MAKING AGENT

[1*] *Voloshin R.A.*, [1] *Bozieva A.M.*, [1] *Rodionova M.V.*, [2] *Zharmukhamedov S.K.*, [1,2] *Allakhverdiev S.I.*
[1]Controlled Photobiosynthesis Laboratory, K.A.Timiryazev Institute of Plant Physiology, Russian Academy of Sciences, Botanicheskaya Street 35, Moscow 127276, Russia
[2]Institute of Basic Biological Problems, Russian Academy of Sciences, Pushchino, Moscow Region 142290, Russia
* Corresponding author e-mail: voloshinra@gmail.com

ABSTRACT

TiO_2 nanostructured films are suitable substrates capable of adsorbing the components of the photosynthetic apparatus with the following use in bio-hybrid light energy convertors and hydrogen fuel cells. The general principles of the film preparation are well known, and the commercial TiO_2 pastes are available in special shops. But most of the preparation techniques highlighted in the literature focus on the TiO_2 substrate for one-molecule dyes instead of the large pigment-protein complexes. On other hand, commercial pastes are not always suitable for the research goals and are expensive. One of the main properties of the nanostructured films is their porosity. The special compounds called pore making agents or templates are responsible for the pore formation. We used new template, hydroxyethyl cellulose (HEC), for the preparation of TiO_2 film that can adsorb thylakoid membrane. In comparison with common template, polyethylene glycol (PEG), this new compound demonstrates more suitability for the thylakoid-sensitized solar cells. Photocurrent generated by the HEC-cell was about more than three times higher than the one generated by the PEG-cell.

Keywords: Titanium Dioxide, Thylakoid, Hydroxyethyl Cellulose, Solar Cell, Photocurrent.

#114

GREEN HYDROGEN PRODUCTION FROM THE NON-CENTRIFUGAL SUGAR INDUSTRY

[1*] *Nestor Sanchez*, [1] *David Rodríguez-Fontalvo*, [1] *Nelly M. Cantillo*, [2] *Ruth Y. Ruiz-Pardo*, [1] *Martha Cobo*
[1]Group of Energy, Materials, and Environment. Universidad de La Sabana, Faculty of Engineering, Department of Chemical and Biochemical Processes. km 7 Autopista Norte Bogotá-Chía, Campus Universitario Puente del Común. Chia, Colombia
[2] Group of Agro-industrial Processes, Faculty of Engineering, Department of Chemical and Biochemical Processes. km 7 Autopista Norte Bogotá-Chía, Campus Universitario Puente del Común. Chia, Colombia
*Corresponding author e-mail: nestor.sanchez1@unisabana.edu.co

ABSTRACT

Decarbonizing the economy has become one of the main concerns in Colombia, where hydrogen (H_2) plays an outstanding role. H_2 is obtained through different pathways, including water electrolysis or by thermochemical pathways such as the ethanol steam reforming (ESR). The latter process is an interesting alternative for those areas where residual biomass is highly available. The non-centrifugal sugar agroindustry has an important role in the Colombian economy and produces different residual biomass that can be employed to produce H_2 by coupling alcoholic fermentation and ESR. Herein, the technical and environmental assessment of the conversion of sugarcane press-mud, a residual biomass of this sector, into H_2 was performed. Technical analysis revealed that sugarcane press-mud should be pretreated under hydrothermal conditions and fermented with a pH of 4.5 to decrease fusel alcohol which have a negative impact during ESR. In terms of environmental impact, H_2 could be used as energy vector to produce heat and replace sugarcane bagasse to mitigate greenhouse gases emissions. Therefore, the upgrading of sugarcane press-mud into H_2 will have a positive impact on climate change and this technology could be employed to decarbonize the Colombian economy.

Keywords: Bioethanol, HT-PEMFC, Life Cycle Assessment, Power, Steam Reforming.

#129

EVALUATION OF BIOHYDROGEN PRODUCTION VIA DARK FERMENTATION OF PALM OIL MILL EFFLUENT AT MESOPHILIC AND THERMOPHILIC TEMPERATURE IN BATCH SYSTEM

[1]*Azam Akhbari,* [1]*Farahin Mohd Jais,* [1]*Onn Chiu Chuen,* [2*] *Shaliza Ibrahim,*
[3]*Afifi Zainal,* [3]*Liyana Yahya,* [3]*Noraziah Omar*
[1]Department of Civil Engineering, Faculty of Engineering, University of Malaya, Kuala Lumpur 50603, Malaysia
[2] Institute of Ocean and Earth Sciences (IOES), University of Malaya, Kuala Lumpur 50603, Malaysia
[3]TNB Research Sdn. Bhd., Kajang, Selangor 43000, Malaysia
*Corresponding author e-mail: shaliza@um.edu.my

ABSTRACT

The present work is a comparative study of biohydrogen production from palm oil mill effluent (POME) in mesophilic and thermophilic conditions by dark fermentation in batch serum bottles. Response surface methodology (RSM) was applied to investigate the influence of the two significant parameters viz. substrate concentration (5, 12.5, and 20 g/l), and volumetric substrate to inoculum ratio (1:1, 1:1.5, and 1:2, v/v %), with inoculum concentration of 14.3 g/l. All the experiments including 13 runs were analyzed at 37˚C and 55˚C at incubation time 24 h. The highest chemical oxygen demand (COD) removal, hydrogen content (H2%), and hydrogen yield (HY) were obtained at substrate concentration 12.5 g/l and S:I ratio1.5; (27.3, 24.2%), (57.92, 66.24%), and (6.43, 12.27 ml H_2/g COD_{rem}), in mesophilic and thermophilic condition, respectively. The results showed that thermophilic temperature in terms of COD removal was more effective for higher COD concentration than lower concentration compared to mesophilic temperature. Moreover, higher hydrogen content was obtained under thermophilic conditions (66.24%). It is generally recognized that more biohydrogen can be produced under thermophilic conditions compared to mesophilic. Nevertheless, the data obtained in this study does not continuously support this assumption and seems to be dependant on substrate concentration.

Keywords: Biohydrogen Production, Mesophilic, Thermophilic, Dark fermentation, Palm Oil Mill Effluent

#136

A PRELIMINARY TECHNO-ECONOMIC ANALYSIS OF PHOTOBIOLOGICAL HYDROGEN PRODUCTION

[1*] *Şehnaz Genç,* [2] *Harun Koku*
[1]Eskişehir Technical University, Department of Chemical Engineering, İki Eylül Kampüsü, Tepebaşı, 26555 Eskişehir, Turkey
[2] Middle East Technical University, Department of Chemical Engineering, Dumlupınar Bulv. No. 1, 06800 Ankara, Turkey
*Corresponding author e-mail: harunk@metu.edu.tr

ABSTRACT

Photofermentation of cheap feedstock using sunlight is a promising route for sustainable hydrogen production. While successful laboratory and pilot-scale hydrogen production examples have been demonstrated, the economic feasibility remains to be improved. In this study, a preliminary techno-economic analysis of photobiological hydrogen production was performed, taking into consideration current production technologies.

First, several hydrogen production technologies were investigated and their costs were compiled from literature. The results show that conventional steam reforming of natural gas still offers the least cost. Future trajectories and prices for natural gas were investigated worldwide and for Turkey. In view of the fact that natural gas is a fossil-fuel, predictions show a continuously increasing unit price.

The cost of photobiological hydrogen production was based on an existing outdoor, pilot-scale photobioreactor design. The annual capital cost and operating costs of the plant were calculated as 195 USD/year and 33 USD/year, respectively. Overall, the specific hydrogen production cost was found as 3.8 USD/mol (1890 USD/kg H_2). While this cost is currently unfeasible, it can be decreased via the use of more productive strains combined with valorization of side-products and concurrent treatment of waste.

Keywords: Photofermentation, Biohydrogen, Economic Analysis

#154

COMPARISON OF WILD TYPE AND UPTAKE HYDROGENASE DEFICIENT MUTANT STRAINS OF *RHODOBACTER CAPSULATUS* FOR HYDROGEN AND PHB PRODUCTION

[1] *Etkin Tarlan,* [2] *Ertan Hoşafcı,* [2] *Tuba Hande Ergüder,* [1*] *Harun Koku*
[1] Middle East Technical University, Department of Chemical Engineering, 06800 Ankara, Turkey
[2] Middle East Technical University, Department of Environmental Engineering, 06800 Ankara, Turkey
*Corresponding author e-mail: harunk@metu.edu.tr mailto:

ABSTRACT

In this study two strains of *Rhodobacter capsulatus* were compared in terms of efficiency of hydrogen (H_2) and poly-β-hydroxybutyrate (PHB) synthesis. One strain of *R. capsulatus* (YO3 (*hup*$^-$)) lacked the uptake hydrogenase enzyme, while the other was its wild type (WT). Both strains were grown in a medium with high carbon and minimal nitrogen. The H_2 and PHB contents of the reactors were all measured at the end of the experiment. The cell concentration measurements show that the growth trends were similar in both strains. The maximum H_2 productivities of the YO3 (*hup*$^-$) strain and WT strain were found as 0.534 mmol/(L.h) and 0.323 mmol/(L.h), respectively. While the PHB amount of the YO3 (*hup*$^-$) strain was 11.7%, the PHB amount of the WT strain was 10.1%. More studies will be conducted to further optimize the H_2 and PHB production, and to understand the partition of resources towards H_2 and PHB.

Keywords: Hydrogen, Poly-β-hydroxybutyrate (PHB), *Rhodobacter Capsulatus*, Acetate

#189

PRODUCTION OF CYANODIESEL AS A PROMISING WAY TO CREATE A WASTE-FREE TECHNOLOGY FOR WASTEWATER TREATMENT AND CARBON DIOXIDE UTILIZATION

[1*] *Elena V. Zadneprovskaya,* [1*] *Ayshat M. Bozieva,* [1] *Anastasiya A. Krapivina,* [2] *Kenzhegul Bolatkhan,* [2] *Assem K. Sadvakasova,* [2] *Bolatkhan K. Zayadan,* [2] *Ardak B. Kakimova,* [2] *Fariza K. Sarsekeyeva,* [2] *Bekzhan D. Kossalbayev,* [3] *Saleh Alwasel,* [1,2,3] *Suleyman I. Allakhverdiev*
[1]Controlled Photobiosynthesis Laboratory, K.A. Timiryazev Institute of Plant Physiology, Russian Academy of Sciences, Botanicheskaya Street 35, Moscow, 127276, Russia
[2]Department of Biotechnology, Faculty of Biology and Biotechnology, Al-Farabi Kazakh National University, Al-Farabi Avenue 71, 050038, Almaty, Kazakhstan
[3]Zoology Department, College of Science, King Saud University, Riyadh, 12372, Saudi Arabia
*Corresponding authors e-mail: zadneprovskaya@ifr.moscow, ayshat2696@mail.ru

ABSTRACT

Forecasts of energy and freshwater shortages lead to the search for new technologies for environmental purification and the need to study the possibilities of using biological objects in the energy sector. The development of waste-free technologies makes it possible to overcome the shortage of resources, as well as to increase their efficiency. In the course of our work, we studied the influence of various concentrations of CO_2 and household wastewater on the growth of cyanobacteria in order to determine their capabilities in purification processes.

The obtained results allowed us to establish the optimal value of the concentration of carbon dioxide for the cultivation of cyanobacteria. For *Cyanobacterium* sp. IPPAS B-1200 and *Desertifilum* sp. IPPAS B-1220, this indicator was 10%, and for *Cyanobacterium aponinum* IPPAS B-1201 - 5%. It was found that the cultivation of *Cyanobacterium* sp. IPPAS B-1200 on wastewater from the reservoir reduces the concentration of organic pollutants and, accordingly, improves the physicochemical properties of water. It was shown that the most optimal ratio of wastewater to nutrient media for cyanobacteria cultivation were 25:75 and 50:50.

Keywords: Cyanobacteria, Cyanodiesel, Lipids

#198

STUDY OF CYANOBACTERIA CHARACTERISTICS IMPORTANT FOR BIOFUEL PRODUCTION

[1*] *Ayshat M. Bozieva,* [1] *Maria A. Sinetova,* [1] *Elena V. Kupriyanova,* [1] *Roman A. Voloshin,* [2] *Sergey K. Zharmukhamedov,* [1,2] *Suleyman I. Allakhverdiev*
[1] K.A. Timiryazev Institute of Plant Physiology, Russian Academy of Sciences, Botanicheskaya Street 35, Moscow 127276, Russia
[2] Institute of Basic Biological Problems, Russian Academy of Sciences, Pushchino, Moscow Region 142290, Russia
*Corresponding author e-mail: ayshat2696@mail.ru

ABSTRACT

The scarcity of fossil energy sources forces to an active search for alternative energy sources. The development of effective methods for obtaining various types of fuel from raw materials of biological origin and its use in conjunction with traditional fossil fuels will solve many problems in the energy sector. At present, all over the world, various technologies for using the biomass of phototrophic microorganisms for energy and raw material purposes are being developed and widely implemented, among which cyanobacteria and microalgae attract special attention as potential producers of so called "third generation" biofuel – biohydrogen.

The purpose of this study was to assess the characteristics important for potential biohydrogen producers, such as photosynthetic activity and growth rate of cyanobacterial strains.

Keywords: Cyanobacteria, Bioactivities, Biohydrogen, Photosynthesis

#211

HYDROGEN PRODUCTION AND UTILIZATION OF BREWERY SPENT GRAINS WASTE BY *ESCHERICHIA COLI*

[1,2,5]*Satenik Mirzoyan,* [3]*Toleugazykyzy Akerke,* [3]*Bekbayev Kairat,* [2,4]*Anait Vassilian,* [1,2,5]*Anna Poladyan,* [1,2,5*]*Karen Trchounian*
[1] Department of Biochemistry, Microbiology and Biotechnology, Faculty of Biology, Yerevan State University, 1 Alex Manoogian, 0025, Yerevan, Armenia
[2] Scientific-Research Institute of Biology Faculty of Biology, Yerevan State University, 1 Alex Manoogian, 0025, Yerevan, Armenia
[3] Department of Food Technology and Processing Products,
Technical Faculty, S. Seifullin Kazakh Agro Technical University, 62 Zhenis avenue, Z11F9K5, Nur-Sultan, Kazakhstan
[4] Department of Ecology and Nature Protection, Faculty of Biology, Yerevan State University, 1 Alex Manoogian, 0025, Yerevan, Armenia
[5] Microbial Biotechnologies and Biofuel Innovation Center, Yerevan State University, 1 Alex Manoogian, 0025, Yerevan, Armenia
*Corresponding author e-mail: k.trchounian@ysu.am

ABSTRACT

Molecular hydrogen (H_2) production by bacteria is considered as one of the ways to contribute to overall production of alternative and renewable energy sources. It is well known that bacteria such as *E. coli* perform mixed acid fermentation and produce H_2 as one of the end products. The most important challenge nowadays is to find suitable substrates which will be economically beneficial. It is suggested to use brewery spent grains as waste products with the mixture of glycerol and after appropriate treatment to produce H_2. It was shown that *E. coli* can ferment the treated BSG and produce efficiently H_2. Especially, the H_2 generation was optimized and it was prolonged till 24-48 h and with the application of multiple mutations it was possible to enhance cumulative H_2 production ~3 fold. Taken together it is suggested that by further optimizing waste treatment conditions and understanding the metabolic pathways of BSG utilization it could be possible to produce bio-H_2 very efficiently and develop new H_2 production technology based on wastes as a feedstock.

Keywords: Bio-H_2 Production, Bacteria, Brewery Waste, Optimized Waste Treatment and H_2 Generation, pH

#254

FOCUSING ON A NEW BIOHYDROGEN PRODUCTION STRATEGY USING *CHLAMYDOMONAS REINHARDTII* MUTANTS

*Çağla Yarkent[1], İzel Oral[1], Deniz Şenyay Öncel[2], Suphi S. Oncel[1]**
University of Ege, Faculty of Engineering, Department of Bioengineering, 35100, Bornova, İzmir, Turkiye
Dokuz Eylul University, Dpt. of Biomechanics, Balçova, İzmir, Turkiye
*Corresponding author e-mail: suphi.oncel@ege.edu.tr

ABSTRACT

Microalgae have been drawn great attention due to their biohydrogen production potentials. In this study, we investigated biohydrogen production potentials of *Chlamydomonas reinhardtii* strains as D1 protein mutant strain D240-41, PGRL1 single mutant PGRL1 mt (+), PGRL1 double mutant PGRL1x∆nd4 Véro. Biohydrogen productions were carried out according to HS-HS strategy. This new strategy is based on performing hydrogen production by completing two successive phases, aerobic and anaerobic. In the first phase, the cultures were cultivated in HS medium under aerobic condition, then in the second phase they were transferred to anaerobic photobioreactors containing fresh HS medium. As result, we observed that all strains were able to produce hydrogen during this new HS-HS strategy.

Keywords: Biohydrogen, *Chlamydomonas Reinhardtii*, *C. Reinhardtii* Mutants, Photobioreactor, HS

#261

BIOGAS AND BIOHYDROGEN PRODUCTION USING SPENT COFFEE GROUNDS

[1,2,3] Liana Vanyan, [4] Adam Cenian, [1,2] Karen Trchounian
[1]Department of Biochemistry, Microbiology and Biotechnology, Faculty of Biology, Yerevan State University, 1 Alex Manoogian Str., 0025 Yerevan, Armenia
[2] Scientific Research Institute of Biology, Faculty of Biology, Yerevan State University, 0025 Yerevan, Armenia
[3] Microbial Biotechnologies and Biofuel Innovation Center, Yerevan State University, 0025 Yerevan, Armenia
[4]Institute of Fluid Flow Machinery, Polish Academy of Sciences, Physical Aspects of Ecoenergy Department, Fiszera 14 Street, 80-231, Gdańsk, Poland
*Corresponding author e-mail: k.trchounian@ysu.am

ABSTRACT

Alternative usages for Spent Coffee Grounds considering them as a source for eco-friendly and renewable energy source generation with application of anaerobic digestion of treated and untreated wastes for biogas and biohydrogen generation were investigated. Acidic hydrolyses with diluted sulphuric acid was used for SCG treatment. Hydrogen production was absent when untreated SCG were used both with inoculum pH 5.5 and pH 7.5, meanwhile biogas yield was respectively 118±3.5 dm^3/kg V. S. and 238±7 dm^3/kg V. S. Efficient hydrogen production was observed when initially 4% (w/v) and 6%(w/v) SCG containing hydrolysates were used as a substrate. The latter was optimal when inoculum with pH 5.5 was used and thus hydrogen yield was 3.85±0.12 dm^3/kg V. S. or 2.9±m^3/t dry matter. Further optimization of pretreatment technologies and pH control may lead to increased and prolonged hydrogen production.

Keywords: Biohydrogen, Spent Coffee Grounds (SCG), Anaerobic Digestion, Dark Fermentation.

#264

OPTIMIZATION OF BIOHYDROGEN PRODUCTION YIELDS WITH LOCALLY ISOLATED THERMOPHILIC BACTERIA FROM HOT SPRINGS

[1]*İlayda Akaçin*,[1]*Şeymanur Ersoy*, [2]*Tuğba Keskin Gündoğdu*,[1]***Mine Güngörmüşler*
[1]Division of Bioengineering, Graduate School, Izmir University of Economics, Sakarya Caddesi No: 156, Izmir, 35330 Turkey
[2]Department of Environmental Protection Technologies, Izmir Democracy University, 35140, Izmir, Turkey
*Corresponding author e-mail: mine.gungormusler@ieu.edu.tr

ABSTRACT

Hydrogen, a carbon-free clean fuel and a strong alternative to conventional fossil energy sources, has many production strategies including biological routes, acknowledged as sustainable and environmentally friendly. The hydrogen yields acquired by those routes with either pure or mixed cultures are predominantly dependent on the environmental factors. Accordingly, in the literature, statistical experimental designs were proven to be useful to understand the effects of independent parameters including macro and micro nutrients, organic or inorganic substrates, pH and temperature. Within this scope, the aim of this study was to optimize the bio-H_2 yields using the Box-Behnken design (BBD) with 3 different independent parameters (temperature(°C), pH and inorganic substrate (CO volume (mL)) with a comparative approach using both mixed and pure thermophilic cultures isolated from Izmir hot springs. The maximum H_2 yields were reported as 0.13 mmol H_2/mmol CO for mixed cultures at pH 7, 60°C and 15 mL CO addition whereas the pure culture reached 2.5 fold higher yields by 0.46 mmol H_2/mmol CO. The results demonstrated the effectiveness of the utilization of the statistical design of experiments to improve the bioproduction yields via local thermophilic isolates.

Keywords: Biohydrogen, Box-Behnken Design, Water-Gas Shift Reaction

#346

INHIBITORY EFFECTS OF FREE ACETIC ACID ON DARK-FERMENTATIVE HYDROGEN PRODUCTION

[1] *Yanan Yin*, [1, 2]**Jianlong Wang*
[1] Laboratory of Environmental Technology, INET, Tsinghua University, Beijing 100084, P. R. China
[2] Beijing Key Laboratory of Radioactive Waste Treatment, INET, Tsinghua University, Beijing 100084, P. R. China
*Corresponding author e-mail: wangjl@mail.tsinghua.edu.cn

ABSTRACT

The aim of this work was to study the inhibitory of free acetic acid on dark fermentative hydrogen production by mixed cultures. Results showed that hydrogen production was affected by both initial pH and total acetic acid concentration, but no specific correlations were observed. While free acetic acid concentration was well correlated with cumulative hydrogen production and substrate degradation rate. Inhibition model analysis demonstrated that cumulative hydrogen production was more sensitive to the toxicity of free acetic acid with lower 50% inhibition concentration. Inhibition recovery experiments showed that the microbes in groups with free acetic acid concentration of lower than 0.05 g/L could recover to be active in hydrogen production, while microbes the rest groups were permanently inhibited.

Keywords: Biohydrogen, Dark Fermentation, Acetic Acid, Free Volatile Fatty Acids, Inhibition.

#358

VALORIZATION OF GREEN MARKET WASTE FOR BIOHYDROGEN PRODUCTION

[1] *İlknur Hacıoğlu,* [1,2*] *Serpil Özmıhçı,* [1,2]*İlgi Karapınar,* [3]*Meltem Küs,* [3]*Ali Keleş,* [3]*İlhami Kargül*
[1] Dokuz Eylul University, Natural and Applied Sciences, Biotechnology Department, 35390, İzmir, Turkey
[2] Dokuz Eylul University, Engineering Faculty, Environmental Engineering Department, 35390, İzmir, Turkey
[3] GKE Energy R&D Center, 48200, Muğla, Turkey
*Corresponding author e-mail: serpil.ozmihci@deu.edu.tr

ABSTRACT

Hydrogen as a clean environmental friendly fuel has the potential to meet energy demand of the world. High organic carbon wastes can be used for biohydrogen production reducing raw material cost. In the energy sector the utilization of green market wastes (GMW) offers certain advantages to produce high value-added products with low cost. An important factor affecting biohydrogen production is temperature. In this study, the GWM (a mixture of lettuce, parsley, spring onion and dill) was used for biohydrogen production by dark fermentation using pretreated anaerobic sludge. Hydrogen production potential at mesophilic conditions (37°C, initial pH 7.2) at different initial substrate concentrations varying between 1000-5000 g wb was utilized. After mesophilic experiments, 5000 g wb was conducted to thermophilic conditions to compare the effect of temperature.

The highest CHF (8.9 L) and the highest yield (0.012 mol H_2/ g TOC) was obtained with 5000 g wet weight in mesophilic conditions. Thermophilic conditions gave higher CHF (14.2 L) when compared with mesophilic one. Thermophilic conditions gave 1.6 times higher yield than mesophilic conditions; demonstrating suitability for organic substrates having high density.
Keywords: Biohydrogen Production, Green Waste, Thermophilic, Mesophilic, Dark Fermentation

#374

ASSESSMENT OF BIOHYDROGEN PRODUCTION ROUTES FROM ORGANIC SOLID WASTE: THE CASE OF CARTAGENA, COLOMBIA

[1]*Carel Lizarazo,* [1]*William Hurtado,* [1]*Oscar Venegas,* [1*]*Oscar Pupo-Roncallo,* [1]*Lesme Corredor*
[1]Universidad del Norte, Kilometer 5 Via Puerto Colombia, Barranquilla, Colombia
*Corresponding author e-mail: opupo@uninorte.edu.co

ABSTRACT

The growing demand for energy worldwide requires a transition towards clean and renewable energy sources in order to mitigate the negative effects of greenhouse gases. During the last decade, hydrogen has been included in multiple national energy roadmaps as a promising alternative to traditional fossil fuels due to its energy content and conversion efficiency. This study aims to assess different biohydrogen production routes from organic solid waste in order to select the best cost-effective alternative for the city of Cartagena, Colombia. Therefore, six different criteria were defined using the Analytical Hierarchy Process (AHP). Subsequently, these criteria were used in order to compare seven biohydrogen production routes. The results obtained in this study suggest that the production of hydrogen through the biogas steam reforming process could be an attractive technology compared to other methods.

Keywords: Biohydrogen, Biogas Steam Reforming, Anaerobic Digestion, Colombia, Analytical Hierarchy Process (AHP).

#410

ADAPTATION OF *CALDICELLULOSIRUPTOR BESCII* TO UNPRETREATED CATTLE MANURE: A NOVEL APPROACH FOR HYPERTHERMOPHILIC BIOHYDROGEN PRODUCTION

[1] *Berivan Tunca, Yasemin Dilsad Yilmazel
[1]Middle East Technical University, Department of Environmental Engineering, Ankara, Turkey
*Corresponding author e-mail: dilsad@metu.edu.tr

ABSTRACT

Animal manure is an abundant, renewable, and cost-effective resource that is rich in valuable organic matter. In this work, utilization of unpretreated cattle manure (UCM) at high loadings (15, 25 and 50 g VS/L) as the sole carbon source for biohydrogen production by hyperthermophilic *Caldicellulosiruptor bescii* was examined. To enhance biohydrogen production, *C. bescii* was adapted to lower concentrations of UCM, which showed a significant increase in biohydrogen production compared to non-adapted *C. bescii*. The highest H_2 yield achieved from adaptation operation using 15 g VS/L of UCM as 161.3 ± 1.6 mL H_2/g VS_{added}, followed by 25 g VS/L as 89.1 ± 2.6 mL H_2/g VS_{added}. The achieved yields are the highest dark fermentative H_2 yields reported in the literature when unpretreated animal manure has been used for dark fermentation. A striking enhancement has been achieved via laboratory culture adaptation of the cellulolytic hyperthermophilic bacterium. Biohydrogen production has been improved by 124% at 15g VS/L and by 142% at 25 g VS/L compared to non-adapted culture of *C. bescii*. Even though the impact of inhibition was lowered by adaptation, the yield was still low in comparison to other concentrations studied.

Keywords: Manure, Hyperthermophilic, Biohydrogen, Laboratory Culture Adaptation, *Caldicellulosiruptor Bescii*

#437

BIOELECTROCHEMICAL HYDROGEN PRODUCTION FROM DARK FERMENTATION EFFLUENTS IN HYPERTHERMOPHILIC MICROBIAL ELECTROLYSIS CELLS

*Aykut Kas, Berivan Tunca, Yasemin Dilsad Yilmazel**
Middle East Technical University (METU), Department of Environmental Engineering, Ankara, Turkey
*Corresponding author e-mail: dilsad@metu.edu.tr

ABSTRACT

Biohydrogen production at extremely thermophilic conditions (>70°C) has a high potential as it provides increased reaction rates, enhanced feedstock solubilization, and lower risk of contamination. Hyperthermophilic cellulolytic bacteria *Caldicellulosiruptor bescii* is capable of utilizing cattle manure as the sole carbon source and produce hydrogen with a superior yield in comparison to other dark fermentation (DF) processes. Yet, acetic acid produced as an end product of DF remain unused in the system. Hyperthermophilic microbial electrolysis cells (MECs) offer a great potential to further process soluble DF products by employment of electro-active microorganisms with no need for chilling. In this study, *C. bescii* was used to produce hydrogen from untreated cattle manure and DF effluent was rich in acetate, thus sufficient for feeding to electro-active hyperthermophiles. Therefore, we designed experiments to process DF effluent of *C. bescii* based bioprocess in hyperthermophilic (80 – 85 °C) MECs to evaluate the potential of sequential operation of DF and MECs at hyperthermophilic conditions for the first time in the literature. To this purpose, experiments were conducted in single chamber MECs with an applied voltage of 0.7 V and inoculated with recently proven electro-active archaea, namely, *Geoglobus acetivorans* and *Ferroglobus placidus*. Hydrogen production rate of the sequential operation was around 0.11 ± 0.02 m^3 H_2/m^3/day, to which MECs contributed significantly as 0.08 ± 0.01 m^3 H_2/m^3/day. This study is the first report of sequential application of DF and MECs at hyperthermophilic conditions and presents a proof-of-concept.

Keywords: Dark Fermentation, Hydrogen, Microbial Electrolysis Cells, Electrohydrogenesis, Hyperthermophilic

#1450

MODELING OF H_2 PRODUCTION FROM WASTEWATER USING MICROBIAL ELECTROLYSIS CELL (MEC) AND CONCURRENT COD REDUCTION APPLYING ARTIFICIAL NEURAL NETWORK (ANN)

[1*] *A. K. M. Khabirul Islam,* [2] Patrick *SM. Dunlop,* [1] *Neil J Hewitt,* [1]*Caterina Brandoni*
[1]Ulster University, Faculty of Computing Engineering and Built Environment Ulster, Belfast School of Architecture and the Built Environment, Newtownabbey, UK
[2] Ulster University, Faculty of Computing Engineering and Built Environment Ulster, School of Engineering, Newtownabbey, UK
*Corresponding author e-mail: islam-akmk@ulster.ac.uk

ABSTRACT

H_2 generation from wastewater in MEC is a revolutionary yet challenging technology because of the process's multiple variables. While laboratory experiments are fairly promising, MEC pilot efforts utilizing wastewater(WW) as substrate are unreliable and inefficient. ANN-based modeling is a robust and powerful modeling approach that can be used to forecast the optimal H_2 production rate for MEC employing WW before implanting any trial project to save money and time. In this paper, ANN modeling has been conducted considering six factors as input and two factors as target variables. 92 data points were extracted from relevant publications, and a feed-forward back propagation neural network with a topology of 6-10-2 was adapted. Correlation coefficients of 0.992, 0.985, and 0.986 were obtained for training, validation, and testing, respectively, indicating a very high degree of agreement between experimental and anticipated output. Other identical three-set input-output data set were taken from three published works and tested in ANN. The average correlation value was 0.999, demonstrating the model's efficacy in forecasting both H_2 production and bioremediation.

Keywords: ANN, MEC, H_2 Production, COD Reduction, Wastewater

#1529

BATCH DARK FERMENTATIVE BIOHYDROGEN PRODUCTION FROM FIG FRUIT: THE EFFECT OF C/N RATIO

[1]*Wasiu Abibu,* [2]*Musa Kaya,* [2]*Yağmur Karadas,* [1,2]*İlgi Karapınar*
[1] Dokuz Eylul University, Natural and Applied Sciences, Biotechnology Department, 35390, İzmir, Turkey
[2] Dokuz Eylul University, Engineering Faculty, Environmental Engineering Department, 35390, İzmir, Turkey
*Corresponding author e-mail: ilgi.karapinar@deu.edu.tr

ABSTRACT

In this study, mesophilic batch fermentation experiments were conducted to investigate the effects of varying C/N ratios on biohydrogen production. The fermentable sugar was obtained from microwave hydrolyzed waste Fig (*Ficus carica*) which is a Mediterranean fruit rich in sugar. The initial total sugar (TS) was kept constant at 40 g/L and nitrogen concentration was varied to adjust the C/N between 25 -150. A control experiment without external nitrogen addition was also conducted to evaluate if the nitrogen content of hydrolyzed fig sustains biohydrogen production. The highest cumulative hydrogen volume of CHV = 861 ml and volumetric production of 4.3 $L/L_{reactor}$ were obtained at C/N=50. The yield varied between 0.9 and 1.1 mol H_2/ mol TS $_{consumed}$ for C/N= 25-100. The highest production rates achieved were 11.5 ml/h and 57.5 ml/L h at C/N=50. Thus, the best ratio in terms of substrate conversion to hydrogen is C/N=50 which can be evaluated as the nitrogen-limited condition. The nitrogen content of the hydrolyzed waste fig is not sufficient for efficient biohydrogen production and external nitrogen addition is required to obtain a higher production rate.

Keywords: Fig, Biohydrogen, Microwave, Hydrolysis, Total Sugar Production

Track 4.

Hydrogen Production: Nuclear

#131

STUDY ON THE CATALYTIC PERFORMANCE OF SULFURIC ACID DECOMPOSITION IN IODINE-SULFUR CYCLE HYDROGEN PRODUCTION

[1]*Qunxiang Gao*, [1,2]*Ping Zhang*, [1,2,*]*Wei Peng*, [1,2]*Gang Zhao*

[1]Institute of Nuclear and New Energy Technology, Advanced Nuclear Energy Technology Cooperation Innovation Center, Key Laboratory of Advanced Nuclear Engineering and Safety, Ministry of Education, Tsinghua University, Beijing 100084, China;

[2]Tsinghua University-Zhang Jiagang Joint Institute for Hydrogen Energy and Lithium-Ion Battery Technology, Tsinghua University, Beijing 100084, China

*Corresponding author e-mail: pengwei@tsinghua.edu.cn

ABSTRACT

The present study uses surface reaction and porous media models to calculate the decomposition performance of bayonet heat exchangers with different catalyst sizes. The results show that the first step of sulfuric acid decomposition reaction is relatively thorough, and the second step of sulfuric acid decomposition reaction is more efficient in the first two-thirds of the catalytic zone. At the same time, the smaller the porosity or particle size of the catalytic zone, the higher the system pressure drop and decomposition rate. The maximum decomposition rate and pressure drop under the current design conditions are 79% and 193Pa, respectively.

Keywords: Sulfuric Acid Decomposition, Surface Reaction, Porosity, Particle Size

#164

BUILDING THE BUSINESS CASE FOR HYDROGEN PRODUCTION WITH OPERATING NUCLEAR POWER PLANTS

[1*] *Aliki van Heek*, [1] *Yuichiro Yuasa*, [1] *Brianna Lazerwitz*

[1]Planning and Economic Studies Section, International Atomic Energy Agency, Wagramer Str. 5, 1220 Vienna, Austria

*Corresponding author e-mail: A.vanHeek@iaea.org

ABSTRACT

Efforts to deploy hydrogen widely in the industrial, transportation and electric power sectors will support the creation of a decarbonized future. Nuclear power can provide 24/7 availability of both electricity and heat to support the efficient production of hydrogen through different processes. Hydrogen production from nuclear power can provide a strong opportunity for operating nuclear power plants to avoid curtailment and pair with renewable energy generation to create a decarbonized and flexible energy system. Regional and national nuances will indicate the best use for hydrogen in each country, and a combination of hydrogen applications in each sector will contribute to global decarbonization goals. The option of using currently operating nuclear power plants for hydrogen production, including when and how hydrogen production makes sense economically, is being explored at the International Atomic Energy Agency, by bringing together utilities with various hydrogen production projects. The study includes case studies of existing nuclear hydrogen demonstration projects to gauge project similarities and differences.

Keywords: Hydrogen, Nuclear, Electrolyser

#1484

A HYBRIDIZED SOLAR-NUCLEAR ENERGY SYSTEM FOR GENERATING MULTIPLE USEFUL OUTPUTS WITH HYDROGEN

[1*] *Mert Temiz*, [1] *Ibrahim Dincer*

[1]Clean Energy Research Laboratory (CERL), Faculty of Engineering and Applied Science, Ontario Tech. University,
2000 Simcoe Street North, Oshawa, Ontario L1H 7K4, Canada

*Corresponding author e-mail: Mert.Temiz@uoit.ca

ABSTRACT

A unique, solar and nuclear based hybrid system is developed to generate hydrogen, ammonia, heat, food, power and fresh water in an integrated and sustainable fashion. The integrated system is analyzed according to the first and second laws of thermodynamics, extensively, for five different cities in a time-dependent manner. The floating and bifacial PV options are considered and analyzed as two different options for the cities. In the average year in Istanbul, 2 × 250 MW_{th} high temperature gas cooled reactors with 120 MW_p PV plants in the integrated system met 738.7 GWh annual electrical load, generated 20828 tons of hydrogen in the floating PV option and 22360 tons of hydrogen in the bifacial PV option. The overall energy and exergy efficiencies are found to be 52.34% and 57.61% for the floating PV option 54.13% and 59.54% for the bifacial PV option in Istanbul.

Keywords: Floating Photovoltaic, Bifacial, Hydrogen Energy, Ammonia, Exergy

#1526

MULTIOBJECTIVE OPTIMIZATION OF A PWR NUCLEAR COGENERATION PLANT FOR HYDROGEN PRODUCTION

[1*] *Tayfun Tanbay,* [2] *Ahmet Durmayaz*
[1]Bursa Technical University, Faculty of Engineering and Natural Sciences, Department of Mechanical Engineering, Bursa, Türkiye
[2] Istanbul Technical University, Energy Institute, Maslak, Istanbul, Türkiye
*Corresponding author e-mail: tayfun.tanbay@btu.edu.tr

ABSTRACT

In this paper, the multiobjective optimization of a nuclear cogeneration plant for hydrogen production is carried out. The analysis focuses on the secondary cycle of a pressurized water reactor nuclear cogeneration plant providing process heat and electrical energy to a high-temperature steam electrolysis facility. The utopia point method is used to determine the values of heat/electricity energy ratio, hydrogen production capacity, live steam temperature and steam extraction node that yield a compromise optimum solution between thermal efficiency, thermal-to-hydrogen production efficiency, exergy efficiency and utilization factor. For a hydrogen production capacity of 7 kg/s, an energy ratio of 0.0561 results with the best overall performance, while an energy ratio of 0.10 gives the best performance for a capacity of 0.1 kg/s.

Keywords: Hydrogen Production, Nuclear, Multiobjective Optimization, PWR, High-Temperature Steam Electrolysis

#1592

NUCLEAR HYDROGEN PERSPECTIVES IN ROMANIA

[1*] *Ioan Iordache,* [2] *Mihai Varlam,* [2] *Elena Carcadea,* [2] *Mihaela Iordache*
[1] National Institute for Research, Development and Testing in Electrical Engineering – ICMET, Decebal Str., Craiova, Romania
[2] National Research and Development Institute for Cryogenics and Isotopic Technologies -ICSI, Uzinei Str., Rm. Vâlcea, Romania
*Corresponding author e-mail: iordache.ioan@icsi.ro

ABSTRACT

This work presents the latest advances of nuclear hydrogen perspectives in Romania. The topic is really new and nuclear hydrogen is considered a new perspective through its low carbon or zero carbon production. The role of nuclear hydrogen production in a low-carbon economy is analysed now by many scientist and many stakeholders, especially national or local authorities, consider that as a new perspective for nuclear energy sector.

Keywords: Romania, Nuclear Hydrogen

#1593

NUCLEAR HYDROGEN PROJECTS TO SUPPORT CLEAN ENERGY TRANSITION

[1*]*Alina Constantin*
[1]International Atomic Energy Agency, Vienna, Austria
*Corresponding author e-mail: a.constantin@iaea.org

ABSTRACT

Hydrogen is expected to be a game changer in the fight against climate change, being able to support the clean energy transition through a variety of roles: decarbonizing different hard-to-abate industrial sectors (such as steel, cement production) and transport (in long haul vehicles, ships and aviation), direct use as a fuel, chemical feedstock or in the form of synthetic fuels, and providing the ability to integrate with hybrid energy systems and renewables, enhancing energy storage and tapping full potential of renewable energy sources. As a consequence, significant increase in hydrogen production is foreseen by 2050, with all the generation coming from zero-carbon processes (electrolysis/thermochemical cycles using clean electricity and heat) or from a low carbon process using steam methane reforming with carbon capture and storage. Nuclear energy can be capitalized on both electricity and heat to provide a clean and reliable source of hydrogen through various processes. There are currently various demonstration projects undergoing in several countries to showcase use of nuclear energy to produce clean hydrogen, considering both the current reactor fleet and advanced reactors. This paper provides an overview of these projects.

Keywords: Nuclear Power; Hydrogen; Decarbonization; Clean Energy

#1628

NUCLEAR-SOLAR PV POWERED ELECTROLYTIC HYDROGEN PRODUCTION AT HIGH TEMPERATURE

[1*] *R. Boudries,* [2] *A. Khellaf*
[1]Hydrogen Division, Centre de Développement des Energies Renouvelables (CDER) BP 62 Bouzareah, Algiers, Algeria
[2] Centre de Développement des Energies Renouvelables (CDER) BP 62 Bouzareah, Algiers, Algeria
*Corresponding author e-mail: r_zaka@yahoo.fr

ABSTRACT

The present work is focused on the techno-economic investigation of electrolytic hydrogen production system powered by a hybrid nuclear-solar unit. The aim is to determine how well nuclear and solar technologies perform together. In the present study, the case of high temperature electrolysis is considered. A hybrid high temperature nuclear reactor-solar PV field is used to power a solid oxide electrolyzer for hydrogen production. The effects of the solar fraction, the solar insolation and the PV cell efficiency on the system techno-economic performance have been investigated. The effect of heat recovery on the hydrogen production cost has also been studied.

Keywords: Hydrogen Production, Hybrid System, High Temperature Reactor, Solar PV, Solid Oxide Electrolyzer

#1630

COMPARED ECONOMIC ASSESSMENT OF SELECTED THERMOCHEMICAL CYCLES UTILIZING NEXT-GEN NUCLEAR REACTORS USING IAEA'S HEEP

[1*] *Hasan Özcan,* [2] *Alperen Tozlu*
[1]Yıldırım Beyazıt University/Mechanical Engineering Department, Ankara, 06830, Turkey
[2] Bayburt University/Mechanical Engineering Department, Bayburt, 69000, Turkey
*Corresponding author e-mail: hozcan@ybu.edu.tr

ABSTRACT

In this study four hybrid thermochemical cycles are considered for an economic comparison using nuclear energy with the IAEA's HEEP software. The hydrogen production cost of cycles is evaluated, and the results are compared. For achieving a realistic result, it is necessary to determine the CAPEX costs of the cycles. The CAPEX costs of the cycles are estimated to be $ 200, 264, 462 and 210 million for HyS, CuCl, MgCl and CaBr cycles, respectively. The hydrogen production costs are found to be lower than that of 2.80 $/kg, 2.99 $/kg and 3.61$/kg in HyS, CuCl and MgCl cycles, respectively. On the other hand, the hydrogen production cost of CaBr is found in the range of 2.86-3.03 $/kg. Knowing that HyS cycle is abandoned due to complexity in the electrolysis technology, CuCl cycle is the most economically viable option that has been comprehensively studied among others.

Keywords: Hydrogen Production, Thermochemical Cycles, HEEP Software.

Track 5.

Hydrogen Separation and Purification

#34

NEW ASPECTS CONCERNING THE IMPROVING OF HYDROGEN ISOTOPES SEPARATION BY HYDROGEN-WATER ISOTOPIC EXCHANGE

[1*]*Gheorghe Ionita, Ciprian Bucur, Ionut Spiridon*
[1]National Research Institute for Cryogenics and Isotopic Technologies - ICSI Rm. Valcea, ICSI Nuclear Department, Uzinei Street; No. 4; PO Box 7, Raureni, 240050 - Rm Valcea, Romania
*Corresponding author e-mail: gheorghe.ionita@icsi.ro

ABSTRACT

The isotopic exchange between hydrogen and liquid water (LPCE) is one of the most efficient process for hydrogen isotopes separation in order to remove tritium from nuclear effluents, produced in fission and fusion reactors. In order to increase the efficiency of isotopic exchange process, the chemical exchange (promoted by hydrophobic catalyst) is usually associated with conventional distillation process (promoted by hydrophilic packing), both processes being promoted by using so called "mixed catalytic packing". A new catalytic support (modified organic copolymer) and two new procedures (A and B), based on chemical and thermal treatments of hydrophilic packing has been proposed and tested. The main characteristics of the catalyst and hydrophilic packing have been evaluated and discussed in deep correlation with hydrogen isotopes separation performances. The experimental results showed as the new catalytic support and the treatment based on solution B, at increased temperature are a promising idea and can be applied to manufacture a new improved mixed catalytic packing. This type of mixed catalytic packing is under testing to be proposed to equip the isotopic exchange columns of the future Tritium Removal Facility for heavy water detritiation.

Keywords: Hydrogen isotopes, Hydrophobic catalysts, Hydrogen-water isotopic exchange, Mixed catalytic packing

#50

SIMULATION MODELING OF HYDROGEN PERMEATION ACROSS PURE PALLADIUM MEMBRANES

[1*]*Mostafa El-Shafie*
[1]Gifu University, Environmental and Renewable Energy Systems Division, Graduate School of Engineering, 1-1 Yanagido, Gifu, 501-1193, Japan
*Corresponding author e-mail: mostafaelshafie81@gmail.com

ABSTRACT

Further advances in the hydrogen separation membranes field require investigating materials with high H_2 permeation and selectivity by predicting the performance from simulation modeling. In this study, a two-dimensional CFD simulation model is developed for investigating the hydrogen separation process across the pure palladium membrane type. The influences of feeding pressure, H_2 feeding flow rate, and membrane thickness on the hydrogen permeation process were investigated. Two Pd-membrane thicknesses of 15μm and 20μm were investigated to understand the hydrogen embrittlement and diffusion through pure Pd-membrane. The velocity, concentration, and diffusion mass transfer flux distribution were numerically achieved by the model. The results showed that the higher feeding pressure can promote the concentration and hydrogen flux distributions that lead to more separated hydrogen. The feeding pressure plays an important factor in membrane separation processes. The simulation analysis showed that the hydrogen velocity distribution increased with the feeding gas flow rate. Furthermore, the diffusion flux was enhanced with the permeation time and the feeding flow rate increased. It can be concluded that the hydrogen concentration and diffusion mass transfer flux through thick membranes was low compared with lower membrane thickness. However, high membrane cost has limited development that requires thin membranes because the best membrane separation materials are precious metals. It can be expected that the CFD simulation model will aid in the membrane separation design, selection, and development.

Keywords: Numerical simulation, Palladium membrane (Pd), Hydrogen separation, Hydrogen flux

#75

CARBON-BASED MEMBRANES FOR HYDROGEN PURIFICATION FROM STEAM METHANE REFORMING: INSIGHTS FROM MOLECULAR SIMULATIONS

[1]Daniel Bahamon, [1]Maryam Khaleel, [2]Eun Seon Cho, [1]Lourdes F. Vega*
[1] Research and Innovation Center on CO_2 and Hydrogen (RICH). Department of Chemical Engineering. Khalifa University of Science and Technology, PO Box 127788, Abu Dhabi, UAE.
[2] Korea Advanced Institute of Science and Technology (KAIST), Department of Chemical and Biomolecular Engineering. 291, Daehak-ro, Yuseong-gu, Daejeon, REPUBLIC OF KOREA
*Corresponding author e-mail: lourdes.vega@ku.ac.ae

ABSTRACT

This contribution is devoted to molecular simulations on carbonaceous materials, from building the model of the materials to their application for hydrogen purification. The transport of H_2/CH_4 and H_2/CO_2 mixtures through carbon-based membranes is evaluated under different thicknesses and surface functionalization. Equilibrium and Non-Equilibrium Molecular Dynamics were combined to predict diffusion coefficients, density profiles, gas permeabilities and permeation selectivities, for both single-component and binary mixtures. The thermal behavior of the gases and the effect of the initial gas pressure were also examined. In specific, it was found an increase in the permeation selectivity for H_2 and a decrease in the diffusion of CO_2 as the oxygen-functionalization increased in the membrane.

Keywords: Hydrogen separation, Syngas, Graphene oxide, Membrane, Molecular simulations

#140

CORROSION PHENOMENON IN DENSE MEMBRANE MADE OF PALLADIUM BASED ALLOY

[1,2]Hatem Alsyouri, [3]Farqad Al-Hadeethi, [3]Sohaib Dwairi*
[1]Department of Chemical Engineering, School of Engineering, The University of Jordan, Amman, Jordan
[2]Department of Chemical Engineering, College of Engineering and Technology, American University of the Middle East, Egaila, Kuwait
[3] Independent Researchers, Amman, Jordan
*Corresponding Author: farqadfms@yahoo.com

ABSTRACT

Hydrogen is considered the energy of the future. In order to achieve this goal several technological obstacles and gaps related to the ultra-purification of hydrogen must be solved and improved. One of the adopted means used to purify Hydrogen is related to the usage of dense membranes made of Pd based alloys (i.e. Pd/Cu) due to its perfect permeability and selectivity towards hydrogen. Therefore, the current work was focused on showing the negative impact generated due to corrosion of Pd, Cu and Pd/Cu in accelerated corrosive acidic media (0.25 M HCl) at various operating conditions [temperatures (30 and 50 °C) and speeds of agitation (0, 300, 600, and 900 RPM)] to simulate the actual corrosion reaction resulted from hydrogen gas in real applications. The results reveled that copper will dissolute in a greater way if combined with palladium in an alloy to fabricate dense membranes to purify hydrogen.

Keywords: Corrosion, Hydrogen purifiers, Pd, Cu

#161

H_2/CO_2 SEPARATION WITH NEW IONIC LIQUID-BASED MEMBRANES

[1]Adele Brunetti, [1]Francesco Galiano, [2]Raffaella Mancuso, [3]Lorenzo Guazzelli, [4]Michele Mauri, [3]Cinzia Chiappe, [4]Roberto Simonutti, [3]Christian S. Pomelli, [1]Giuseppe Barbieri,[1,2]Bartolo Gabriele, [1]Alberto Figoli
[1] Institute on Membrane Technology, National Research Council (CNR-ITM), via P. Bucci 17/C, Rende (CS), 87036, Italy
[2] Laboratory of Industrial and Synthetic Organic Chemistry (LISOC), Department of Chemistry and Chemical Technologies, University of Calabria, Via Pietro Bucci 12/C, 87036Arcavacata di Rende (CS) Italy
[3] Department of Pharmacy, University of Pisa, Via Bonanno 33, 56126, Pisa, Italy
[4] Department of Materials Science, University of Milano-Bicocca, 2012 Milan, Italy
*Corresponding author e-mail: a.brunetti@itm.cnr.it

ABSTRACT

In this work, we report the synthesis and application of novel polymeric membranes, based on polymerized ionic liquids (PILs), to be used for the separation of hydrogen from gas mixtures with CO_2. Dense membranes have been developed by using phosphonium-based PILs copolymerised within an original acrylate formulation that allowed to overcome some of the main limitations related to ionic liquid membranes. The membranes showed remarkable separation properties exceeding the Robeson upper bound for the CO_2/H_2 gas pair.

Keywords: Polymerizable ionic liquids, Ionic liquid membranes, CO_2 separation, Hydrogen

#170

GAS SEPARATION PROPERTIES OF MIXED MATRIX MEMBRANES PREPARED WITH GRAPHENE OXIDE

[1*] *Sevgi Çança,* [1] *Sennur Deniz*
[1] Yıldız Technical University, Faculty of Chemical and Metallurgical Engineering, Chemical Engineering Department, 34220, Esenler, Istanbul, Turkey
*Corresponding author e-mail: f2020058@std.yildiz.edu.tr; deniz@yildiz.edu.tr

ABSTRACT

Hydrogen is a potential alternative for fossil fuels. Membrane technology has been a prominent separation approach for H2 purification. The recently discovered new membranes based on GO and rGO show superior properties such as high hydrophilicity, good dispersion in water, nanopores and good mechanical behavior. The main objective of this project is to develop mixed matrix membrane with different polymeric bases of PEBA and PI with graphene oxide (GO) incorporation as inorganic filler. Gas permeability and selectivity of polymer membranes prepared by solution casting method were tested. Gas separation tests of the membranes were carried out at 35°C and 3 bar feed pressure. Gas permeability and selectivity results indicated that PEBA/rGO membrane with 0.3 wt% of GO has the highest H_2 and CO_2 permeability at 10.3247 and 54.8786, respectively, H_2/N_2 selectivity of 7.9828 and CO_2/CH_4 selectivity of 21.0590. PI/rGO membrane with 0.3 wt% of GO has the highest H_2 and CO_2 permeability at 7.3533 and 0.9026 barrer at 3 bar, respectively, H_2/N_2 selectivity of 50.2650 Barrer and H_2/CH_4 selectivity of 287.6653. Work continues with the addition of copper-based MOF structures.

Keywords: *Gas separation, Mixed matrix membranes, Poly(ether-b-amide), Polyimide, Graphene oxide,* Reduced graphene oxide

#184

H_2 SEPARATION FROM CO_2 AND CH_4 MIXTURES USING A SAPO-34 MEMBRANE

[1]*Pasquale Francesco Zito,* [1*]*Adele Brunetti,* [1]*Alessio Caravella,* [1]*Giuseppe Barbieri*
[1]Institute on Membrane Technology, National Research Council (ITM-CNR), via P. Bucci, Cubo 17C, 87036 Rende, Cosenza, Italy
*Corresponding author e-mail: a.brunetti@itm.cnr.it

ABSTRACT

The performance of a SAPO-34 membrane for separation of H_2 from CO_2 and CH_4 was investigated in this work. In particular, a mass transport model that takes into account the competition between surface and gas translation diffusion was proposed for describing the mixture permeation [1]. It was found that the presence of CO_2 and CH_4 drastically reduce the hydrogen permeation in mixture compared to its behavior as pure gas. In fact, although hydrogen presents a higher diffusivity than carbon dioxide and methane, the much stronger CO_2 and CH_4 adsorption is prevalent, exerting a hindering effect on H_2. In addition, permeation of CO_2 and CH_4 was improved by the presence of faster hydrogen. These two effects caused a significant difference in membrane behavior from single gas to mixture. In fact, CO_2/H_2 selectivity was increased, whereas H_2/CH_4 was decreased.

Keywords: Membrane selectivity, Gas separation, Surface diffusion

#236

MIXED MATRIX MEMBRANES FOR HYDROGEN RECOVERY FROM INDUSTRIAL WASTE STREAMS

[1] *Gonzalo Moral,* [1*] *Alfredo Ortiz, Daniel Gorri,* [1] *Inmaculada Ortiz*
[1]*Chemical and Biomolecular Engineering Department, University of Cantabria, Av. Los Castros 46, 39005, Santander, Spain*
*Corresponding author e-mail: ortizal@unican.es

ABSTRACT

The increase of the energy efficiency is one of the main challenges which is facing the manufacturing sector since the rising price of fossil fuels and political framework of the decarbonization roadmap. In this sense, the recovery of hydrogen from industrial waste streams is presented as a great niche of opportunities due to the wide range of applications of hydrogen as energy vector. Among hydrogen-containing off-gases, coke oven gas (COG), ammonia purge gas (APG) and methanol purge gas (MPG) stands out since the high hydrogen concentration (>50 vol.% H_2). Nevertheless, the recovery of hydrogen requires a purification system. In this study, the synthesis and characterization of mixed matrix membranes (MMMs) are analyzed as an alternative to improve the separation performance of pristine polymer membranes. ZIF-8 and ZIF-90 were selected as fillers with potential to improve H_2-selectivity and Matrimid® 5218 as high-performance polyimide. The permeability and selectivity of the membranes were evaluated by continuous permeation experiments with multicomponent gas mixtures whose composition correspond to the industrial waste streams. Furthermore, the influence of the temperature on transport parameters in gas permeation was studied.

Keywords: Hydrogen recovery, Mixed matrix membranes, Coke oven gas, Methanol purge gas, Ammonia purge gas

#246

PSEUDO-DYNAMIC MODELING AND OPTIMIZATION OF HEAVY PARAFFIN DEHYDROGENATION PROCESS FOR SELECTIVE OLEFIN AND HYDROGEN PRODUCTION USING MEMBRANE REACTORS

[1]M. Dehdashti, [2]*M. Binazadeh, [3]M. Farsi
[a] Department of Chemical Engineering, School of chemical and Petroleum Engineering, Shiraz University, Shiraz 71345, Iran
*Corresponding author e-mail: binazadeh@shirazu.ac.ir

ABSTRACT

Linear alkyl benzenes (LABs) are used in alkyl sulfonates production, which are utilized in biodegradable detergents and emulsifiers. Catalytic dehydrogenation of heavy paraffin molecules ($C_{10} - C_{14}$) is the most well-known path of LAB production. In this study, a radial flow Pd/Ag membrane reactor (RF-MR) is pseudo-dynamically modeled and its outputs are compared with an industrial conventional reactor to prove RF-MR efficacy in the enhancement of olefins and hydrogen yields. Steady-state and pseudo-dynamic RF-MR simulations. It is shown that olefin production increases in RF-MR compared to that of RF-TR mainly due to hydrogen permeation through the Pd/Ag membrane. Finally, the optimal RF-MR operating conditions were obtained *via* a multi-objective genetic algorithm optimization.

Keywords: Heavy paraffin dehydrogenation, Radial flow membrane reactor, Pseudo-dynamic model, Pd/Ag membrane, Genetic algorithm

#259

DEVELOPMENT AND INVESTIGATION OF A NOVEL ELECTROCHEMICAL HYDROGEN COMPRESSOR CELL DESIGN BASED ON HYDRAULIC CLAMPING

[1*]Ulrich W. Rost, [2]Lester Engelhardt, [2]Florian J. Wirkert, [2]Michael Brodmann
[1]ProPuls GmbH, Neidenburger Straße 10, D-45897 Gelsenkirchen, Germany
[2] Westfälische Hochschule University of Applied Sciences, Westfälisches Energieinstitut, Neidenburger Straße 43, D-45897 Gelsenkirchen, Germany
*Corresponding author e-mail: ulrich.rost@propuls.de

ABSTRACT

Due to low outlet pressure level of hydrogen production facilities, high-pressure hydrogen storage systems today still require an additional gas compression unit. However, typical mechanical compressors decrease the overall system efficiency, emit noise, and increase investment costs as well as operational expenditures due to regular maintenance. In this work a novel electrochemical hydrogen compressor based on hydraulic cell clamping is presented. In comparison to the state-of-the-art mechanical cell clamping, according to this design variant, a hydraulic medium whose pressure level is e.g., 15 bar above the hydrogen outlet pressure level, surrounds the single cells of a stack entirely and compresses the cells to ensure the contact of the active components. A laboratory device was realised with a single cell offering a 25 cm^2 active area that showed a pressure increase from 0 bar at the anode to 10 bar at the cathode. Due to homogeneous operation condition related to pressure, current density, and temperature distribution over the active cell area, the novel design seems promising for future devices, especially in large scale.

Keywords: Electrochemical hydrogen compressor, Stack design, Hydraulic clamping

#268

TOWARDS A BETTER SUSTAINABILITY OF ELECTROLESS PORE-PLATED MEMBRANES: LIFE CYCLE ASSESSMENTS ON FABRICATION STRATEGIES

[1*]*David Alique*, [2]*Pedro Leo*, [3]*David Martinez-Diaz*, [2]*Raúl Sanz*, [1]*José Antonio Calles*
[1] Department of Energy, chemical and Mechanical Engineering, Rey Juan Carlos University, c/ Tulipan s/n 28933 Móstoles, Spain
[2] Department of Chemical and Environmental Engineering, Rey Juan Carlos University, c/ Tulipan s/n 28933 Móstoles, Spain
[3] Department of Applied Mathematics, Material Science and Engineering and Electronic Technology, Rey Juan Carlos University,
c/ Tulipan s/n 28933 Móstoles, Spain
*Corresponding author e-mail: david.alique@urjc.es

ABSTRACT

Pd-based membranes attract great attention to be used as independent separators or combined with catalysts in a membrane reactor for H_2-production. The membrane fabrication was improved for years, reaching ultra-thin Pd-films with high permeability and selectivity. However, commercialization at industrial level is still scarce due to the limited knowledge about their economy, lifespan and environmental concerns. In this context, the current study expands the unique life cycle assessment focused on the preparation of Pd-based composite-membranes by Electroless Pore-Plating (ELP-PP) in literature. Based on this, the current research go into deep when the membrane incorporates Pd-CeO_2 as intermediate layer and the total length of the membrane is increased up to 100 cm. The associated environmental impacts were estimated through ReCiPe methodology by using Simapro 8.5. Climate change, human toxicity, acidification, freshwater ecotoxicity, metal depletion and fossil fuel resources depletion were the most relevant impacts generated during the membrane manufacturing, although they were reduced up to 50% respect to membranes without ceramic intermediate barriers. Moreover, CeO_2 doping reduces the number of ELP-PP recurrences, hence further improving the environmental sustainability. Finally, an additional reduction of the environmental impacts was also achieved by scaling-up the process for the preparation of longer membranes.

Keywords: Membrane fabrication, Palladium, Electroless plating, Life cycle assessment, Scale-up

#312

ELECTROCHEMICAL HYDROGEN SEPARATION FROM REFORMATE USING POLYBENZIMIDAZOLE/MOF COMPOSITE MEMBRANES

[1,2]*Gizem Nur Bulanık Durmuş*, [3]*Enis Oğuzhan Eren*, [1*]*Yılser Devrim*, [4]*C. Ozgur Colpan*, [5]*Necati Özkan*
[1]Atılım University, Department of Energy Systems Engineering, Incek Golbasi Ankara, 06830, Turkey
[2]Atılım University, Graduate School of Natural and Applied Sciences, Department of Mechanical Engineering, Incek Golbasi Ankara, 06830, Turkey
[3]Max Planck Institute of Colloids and Interfaces, Potsdam, 14476, Germany
[4]Department of Mechanical Engineering, Dokuz Eylul University, Buca, Izmir, Turkey
[5]Middle East Technical University, Polymer Science & Technology, Ankara, 06800, Turkey
*Corresponding author e-mail: yilser.devrim@atilim.edu.tr

ABSTRACT

This study introduces the experimental results of a high-temperature electrochemical hydrogen purification (ECHP) cell through poly 2.2-m-phenylene-5.5-bibenzimidazole/metal organic framework (PBI/MOF) composite membranes in the temperature range of 140°C-180°C. Synthesis of ZIF-8 and UiO-66 MOFs was conducted through a typical solvothermal method, and composite membranes containing 2.5 wt. %. MOF was fabricated. Experiments were conducted with pure hydrogen (H_2) and reformate gas mixtures containing H_2, carbon monoxide (CO), and carbon dioxide (CO_2). A gas chromatography device (GC) was used to analyze the gas composition at the exit of the ECHP cell. The final output H_2 purity was found to be >99.9 % for the $H_2/CO_2/CO$ mixed-phase and >99.7% for the H_2/CO mixed phase.

Keywords: Electrochemical hydrogen separation, Metal-organic framework, ZIF-8, UIO-66

#333

DEVELOPMENT OF BIMETALLIC ELECTROCATALYSTS FOR HIGH-TEMPERATURE ELECTROCHEMICAL HYDROGEN PURIFICATION

[1]*İlay Bilge Bal*, [1,2]*Gizem Nur Bulanık Durmuş*, [2*]*Yılser Devrim*
[1]Atılım University, Graduate School of Natural and Applied Sciences, Department of Mechanical Engineering, Ankara, Turkey
[2]Atılım University, Department of Energy Systems Engineering, Ankara, Turkey
*Corresponding author e-mail: **Error! Hyperlink reference not valid.**

ABSTRACT

In this study, PtRu/GNP, PtIr/GNP, and RuIr/GNP bimetallic catalysts were synthesized by microwave-assisted synthesis method, and their performances on the high-temperature electrochemical hydrogen purification (HT-ECHP) were compared. The structural and electrochemical characteristics of the bimetallic catalysts were examined by the TGA, XRD, XPS, and CV techniques. ECHP Tests were performed with reformate gas mixtures containing hydrogen (H_2), carbon monoxide (CO), and carbon dioxide (CO_2) at temperatures between 140-180°C. The gas at the exit of the ECHP cell was analyzed with the gas chromatography device (GC), and high H_2 purity was achieved.

Keywords: Electrochemical hydrogen purification, Bimetallic catalyst, Graphene nanoplatelet, High temperature

#426

DEVELOPMENT OF Pd-BASED DENSE METALLIC MEMBRANE WITH SULFUR RESISTANT MOF COATED FOR HYDROGEN SEPARATION

[1]*Sevgi Kalkan*, [2*]*Gamze Gümüşlü Gür*
[1] Istanbul Technical University, Chemical Engineering Department, Istanbul, Turkey
[2] Istanbul Technical University, Chemical Engineering Department, Istanbul, Turkey
*Corresponding author e-mail: gamgur@itu.edu.tr

ABSTRACT

Hydrogen plays a key role in both the chemical and energy industries. However, it is essential for H_2 to be in high purity in order to be used. In countries with large coal reserves, H_2 is separated from the syngas ($CO+H_2$) obtained from coal gasification. The separation process includes units that adjust the required operational temperature and pressure with high energy needs and costs. The use of Pd-based dense metallic membranes allows the production of ultra-high purity H_2 without significant changes in temperature and pressure. However, sulfur compounds in coal-derived syngas limit the use of these membranes. Sulfur sticks to Pd atoms disrupt the membrane structure and prevent the dissociation of hydrogen on the membrane surface. Therefore, developing a thin Pd film, coated on low-cost support with an additional layer that will protect this film from sulfide compounds will make an important contribution to the literature and improve the applications of these membranes. In this study, a new membrane structure was developed by coating a thin layer of Pd film on low-cost α-Al_2O_3 tablets and growing a secondary UiO-66 layer on Pd. The experimental data proved the effect of the UiO-66 layer in preventing the Pd layer from sulfur compounds.
Keywords: Dense metallic membranes, Pd, Metal-organic frameworks, Hydrogen

#1502

DEVELOPMENT OF HYDROGEN PURIFICATION MEMBRANE BASED ON Pd-Mn-Ag TERNARY SYSTEM

[1,2*]*Mehmet Mert Köse*, [2,3]*Fatih Piskin*, [1,2]*Tayfur Öztürk*
[1] Dept. of Metallurgical and Materials Engineering, Middle East Technical University, Ankara, TURKEY
[2] ENDAM, Center for Energy Storage Materials and Devices, Middle East Technical University, Ankara, TURKEY
[3] Dept. of Metallurgical and Materials Engineering, Muğla Sıtkı Koçman University, Muğla, TURKEY
*Corresponding author e-mail: mehmetmertkose@gmail.com

ABSTRACT

In this paper, we investigate Pd-Mn-Ag ternary system for potential alloys as separation membranes. For this purpose, thin film membranes of varying compositions were produced via magnetron sputtering. These were evaluated via four probe resistivity measurements up to temperature of 450°C. A reactivity index ρ_{H2}/ρ_{Ar} was used as a measure of the suitability of the thin film as separation membrane. Here ρ_{H2} and ρ_{Ar} are the resistivity of the film under hydrogen and argon respectively. The temperature at which this index was maximum was taken as potential operating temperature of the membrane. The preliminary results show that alloys with compositions confined to a triangle where Pd >=38 are candidates for possible hydrogen separation membrane
Keywords: Hydrogen separation, Dense metallic membranes, Palladium alloys

#1505

ENERGY ANALYSIS OF A MEMBRANE REACTOR-BASED HYDROGEN PRODUCTION SYSTEM

[1*]*Yagmur Nalbant Atak*, [2]*C. Ozgur Colpan*, [3]*Adolfo Iulianelli*
[1] Dokuz Eylul University, School of Natural and Applied Sciences, Mechanical Engineering Department, Buca, Izmir/Turkey
[2] Dokuz Eylul University, Faculty of Engineering, Mechanical Engineering Department, Buca, Izmir/Turkey
[3] Institute on Membrane Technology of the National Research Council of Italy (CNR-ITM), at University of Calabria, Rende, Italy
*Corresponding author e-mail: yagmurnalbant.yn@gmail.com

ABSTRACT

In the present time, hydrogen is generally produced from natural gas using the conventional reactors that have some disadvantages such as thermodynamic equilibrium equation, high temperature, and carbon deposition. To overcome these disadvantages, the interest in the membrane reactors that provides both hydrogen production and hydrogen separation in the same unit is increasing, therefore the produced hydrogen is permeated from the reaction side to the permeation side continuously, and thus this decreases the thermodynamic equilibrium limitation. In this study, a mathematical model of a membrane reactor was coupled with the models of the balance of plant components (compressor, boiler, burner, pump, blower, and two mixers), and a system-level energy analysis was conducted. Molar flow rates, temperatures, and pressures for all states in the system were found. In addition, the effects of reaction temperature on H_2 production, CO_2 production, H_2 yield, and system efficiency were investigated. When the membrane reactor operating temperature increases from 673 K to 773K, the H_2 production, collected CO_2, H_2 yield, and system efficiency are increased by 9.88%, 1.48%, 9.94%, and 9.86%, respectively.
Keywords: Membrane reactor, Hydrogen production, Energy analysis

#1559

PARAMETRIC INVESTIGATION ON THE PURIFICATION CHARACTERISTICS OF $La_{0.9}Ce_{0.1}Ni_5$ UNDER VARIOUS ABSORPTION/DESORPTION CONDITIONS

[1] *Alok Kumar*, [2*]*P Muthukumar*
[1]School of Energy Science and Engineering, Indian Institute of Technology Guwahati, Guwahati, Assam 781039, India
[2]Department of Mechanical Engineering, Indian Institute of Technology Guwahati, Guwahati, Assam 781039, India
*Corresponding author e-mail: pmkumar@iitg.ac.in

ABSTRACT

Metal hydride-hydrogen system can provide efficient solution for hydrogen separation from the impure gas mixtures. The present study reports the effect of various absorption/desorption conditions on the hydrogen separation and alloy poisoning characteristics of $La_{0.9}Ce_{0.1}Ni_5$. The experiments are being conducted by varying absorption pressure in the range of 5-20 bar, absorption temperature between 20-30°C and desorption temperature between 60-90°C. According to the experimental outcomes, absorption kinetics improves with increase in the absorption pressure and decrease in the absorption temperature. For 20 bar and 20°C, 12.8232 g of hydrogen get absorbed for 10% impure gas mixture. The desorption temperature played a significant effect on the bed poisoning characteristics of the reactor bed. Desorption kinetics improves with increase in the bed temperature, and is significant for 80-90°C. For lower range of desorption temperature (60-70°C), the bed poisoning was significant. Even for 10% impurity, the reaction kinetics of alloy decreases significantly after 4-5 purification cycle. However, for higher desorption temperature (90°C), the alloy regenerated itself and the bed poisoning is delayed. The system is capable of delivering 99.9995% pure hydrogen for an impurity range from 5-15% for gaseous impurities like CO_2, CH_4, N_2, Ar etc.

Keywords: Metal hydride, Hydrogen storage, Hydrogen purification, Alloy poisoning, Alloy regeneration.

#1566

INVESTIGATION OF LOW-TEMPERATURE POLYMER ELECTROLYTE MEMBRANE FOR ELECTROCHEMICAL HYDROGEN COMPRESSOR

[1,2*]*Anil Can Turkmen*, [3]*Ceyda Elif Meydan*, [3]*Kubranur Agtoprak*, [4]*Hilal Acidereli* [3]*Ramiz Gultekin Akay*, [3]*Murat Efgan Kibar*, [1]*Cenk Celik*
[1]Kocaeli University Faculty of Engineering, Department of Chemical Engineering, Kocaeli 41380, Turkey
[2]ACT Scientific Ltd., Budotek Teknopark, Istanbul, 41380, Turkey
[3]Kocaeli University Faculty of Engineering, Department of Mechanical Engineering, Kocaeli 41380, Turkey
[4]Dumlupınar University, Faculty of Arts & Sciences, Department of Chemistry, Kütahya, 43266, Turkey
*Corresponding author e-mail: anilcan.turkmen@hotmail.com

ABSTRACT

In recent years, one of the most important sources used as fuel for energy production is hydrogen. Especially, research in hydrogen technologies has gained importance with the increase in commercialization applications of fuel cells. When it comes to the development of hydrogen technologies, it is of great importance to carry out studies in the field of purification and storage of hydrogen as well as production methods. Considering the disadvantages of conventional compressors, which are widely used in the world, electrochemical hydrogen compressor technology that can pressurize hydrogen with an electrochemical method is the best alternative. In this study, the development of low-cost, long-life materials and compressor systems for the compression of hydrogen were investigated. In this study, Nafion 117 membrane and commercial Pt/C electrocatalyst were tested in the EHC system.

Keywords: Hydrogen, Polymer electrolyte membrane, Electrocatalyst, Pressurization, EHC, Compression

#1580

EVALUATION OF THE EFFECT OF TEMPERATURE, AIR EXPOSURE AND GAS MIXTURE ON Pd_{82}-Ag_{15}-Y_3 FOR HYDROGEN SEPARATION

[1]*Omid Jazani*, [1]*Moses Adejumo*, [1*]*Simona Liguori*
[1]Chemical and Biomolecular Engineering Dept, Clarkson University, Potsdam, NY, USA
*Corresponding author e-mail: sliguori@clarkson.edu

ABSTRACT

Hydrogen permeation and separation properties of a ternary Pd-alloy are evaluated at temperature and pressure range of 300 °C and 600 °C and 2 – 5 bar (abs), respectively. The membrane Pd_{82}-Ag_{15}-Y_3 is unsupported, prepared by cold rolling and it is characterized by ~ 35 μm of thickness. The membrane shows good thermal and chemical stability when exposed to air and at different temperature. In particular, its surface area increases by 2.5x from room temperature to 600 °C indicating a potential improvement of hydrogen permeation. The permeation characteristics of the membrane and the effects of the other gases on hydrogen permeation will be investigated by varying temperature and pressure evaluating the effects of dilution, depletion, concentration polarization, and competitive adsorption on the H_2 permeating flux.

Keywords: ternary alloy membrane, Pd-based, Hydrogen separation

#1583

OVERVIEW OF ELECTROCHEMICAL HYDROGEN PURIFIER PERFORMANCE DIAGNOSTICS

[1,2,3*]*Anamarija Stoilova Pavasovic*, [1,2]*Ivan Pivac*, [1,2]*Frano Barbir*
[1] Center of Excellence STIM, R. Boskovica 31, Split, Croatia
[2] University of Split, FESB, R. Boskovica 32, Split, Croatia
[3] University of Split, KTF, R. Boskovica 35, Split, Croatia
*Corresponding author e-mail: astoilov@fesb.hr

ABSTRACT

The energy world is moving beyond fossil fuels and should power our entire society with clean energy in the future. For hydrogen to become a widespread energy carrier that can provide an emissions-free transportation fuel, it must be produced from the clean energy sources. Therefore, clean hydrogen production and storage is currently undergoing extensive research. However, none of the present widely-use hydrogen production processes, besides electrolysis, are sufficiently pure to enable immediate use of hydrogen as an energy carrier in fuel cells or in storage. Therefore, purification of hydrogen is mandatory, especially on a large scale. This paper gives a brief literature overview of the current state-of-the-art electrochemical hydrogen purifiers (EHPs), with emphasis on their performance diagnostics, including current technology issues, challenges, and different approaches with suggestions for potential solutions and improvements in future.

Keywords: Electrochemical hydrogen purifier, Performance diagnostics, Polarization curve, Electrochemical impedance spectroscopy, Gas chromatography

#1612

PARAMETER OPTIMIZATION OF A PBI MEMBRANE-BASED HIGH TEMPERATURE-ELECTROCHEMICAL HYDROGEN COMPRESSOR FED WITH H_2 AND CO MIXTURE

[1*]*Cemil Kuzu*, [2]*C. Ozgur Colpan*, [3,4]*Gizem Nur Bulanık Durmuş*, [3]*Yilser Devrim*
[1] Dokuz Eylul University, Graduate School of Natural and Applied Sciences, Tinaztepe Campus, Izmir, 35397, Turkey
[2] Dokuz Eylul University, Faculty of Engineering, Mechanical Engineering Department, Tinaztepe Campus, Izmir, 35397, Turkey
[3]Atılım University, Graduate School of Natural and Applied Sciences, Department of Mechanical Engineering, Incek Golbasi Ankara, 06830, Turkey
[4] Atılım University, Department of Energy System Engineering, Ankara, 06836 Incek, Turkey
* Corresponding author e-mail: kuzucemil@gmail.com

ABSTRACT

In today's world, the increase in the amount of energy needed with the increase in the human population and the depletion of fossil fuels has pushed researchers to search for alternative fuels. Hydrogen is expected to take an important share among the alternative fuels in the future. However, it has some challenges in terms of its storage and pressurization. In this study, the effect of back diffusion on the performance of a PBI membrane-based electrochemical hydrogen compressor operating at 160°C. Pressure values are calculated and validated with experimental results; and the change of flux, voltage and cell efficiency with time are presented.

Keywords: Electrochemical hydrogen compressor, modeling, compression, back diffusion polarization curve, reformate gas, PBI membrane

#1635

SYNTHESIS AND CHARACTERIZATION OF A NOVEL NICKEL-RUTHENIUM BASED CATALYST FOR BIOGAS STEAM REFORMING TO GENERATE HYDROGEN IN CONVENTIONAL AND MEMBRANE REFORMERS

[1*]*Adolfo Iulianelli*, [2]*Cristina Italiano*, [1]*Adele Brunetti*, [2]*Antonio Vita*
[1] Institute on Membrane Technology of the Italian National Research Council, Via P. Bucci 17C, Rende (CS), 87036, Italy
[2] The Advanced Energy Technology Institute of the National Research Council of Italy (CNR-ITAE), Salita Santa Lucia Sopra Contesse 5, 98126, Messina (ME), Italy
*Corresponding author e-mail: a.iulianelli@itm.cnr.it

ABSTRACT

Nowadays, the application of the principles of Process Intensification Strategy is gradually leading to a revolution of the conventional H_2 energy production processes and, among a number of alternative technologies, membrane engineering is playing a crucial role in the substitution of traditional devices used in the process engineering with membrane-based units. According to the requests of the Circular Economy and in the framework of the so-called H_2 Economy, H_2 generation coming from derived of biomass as renewable sources may play an interesting role as a valid option to the fossil fuels exploitation. In this work, the production of blue H_2 via reforming reactions of a synthetic biogas mixture was performed in a Pd-Ag membrane reformer packed with a novel Ni-Ru/La-Y-ZrO_x catalyst at 673 K and between 150 and 250 kPa of reaction pressure. As best result, 99% of CH_4 conversion was reached at 673 K, 250 kPa and S/C = 2/1, recovering 40% of H_2 with a purity > 99.9999%, meanwhile collecting a CO_2 reach stream in the unpermeated stream, to be further captured.

Keywords: Hydrogen, biogas steam reforming, membrane reactor technology, Pd-based membranes

Track 6.

Hydrogen Storage

#28

LABVIEW MODELING AND SIMULATION OF A STAND ALONE PHOTOVOLTAIC/WIND SYSTEM WITH HYBRID STORAGE H_2-BATTERY

[1] Hakim Azoug, [2] Hocine Belmili*
1University of Science and Technology Houari-Boumédiène USTHB, Department of Electrical Engineering, Bab Ezzouar, Algeria
2Unité de Développement des Equipements Solaires, UDES, Centre de Développement des Energies Renouvelables, CDER, Tipaza, Algeria
*Corresponding author e-mail: hm.azoug@gmail.com

ABSTRACT

This paper investigates in the modeling and simulation under LabVIEW Software of stand-alone photovoltaic/wind power system using hybrid storage hydrogen and lead-acid battery. The proposed graphical programming environment has proven to be a versatile platform for the design, sizing, data acquisition, analysis and parameter identification of each compound of these systems, including PV generator, wind generator, storage systems, power converter, electrolyzer, fuel cell, gas compressor and tank for pressurized hydrogen storage. Combining solar and wind energy is a very important issue, but it depends on geographical position. The proposed system can be very useful for Engineers and experts who require a simple, fast and accurate PV/ wind storage simulator to design their systems.
Keywords: PV/WIND-H_2-Battery system, hybrid storage, hydrogen, fuel cell, lead-acid battery

#77

TECHNO-ECONOMIC REQUIREMENTS FOR UNDERGROUND RENEWABLE HYDROGEN STORAGE IN POROUS MEDIA

*Jan Michalski**
Ludwig-Bölkow-Systemtechnik GmbH (LBST), Daimlerstr. 15, 85521 Ottobrunn, Germany
*Corresponding author e-mail: jan.michalski@lbst.de

ABSTRACT

This paper provides first results from the FCH JU funded HyStorIES project (**Hy**drogen **Stor**age **I**n **E**uropean **S**ubsurface) addressing the main technical feasibility questions and assessing the techno-economical potential of underground large-scale storage of renewable hydrogen in porous media by 2050. Within the project Work Package 5 (WP5) conducts an in-depth techno-economic assessment of the future scenarios for a widespread deployment of underground renewable hydrogen storage in the EU across the period 2025-2050. In this context, it models and analyses optimal design and operation of different elements of the future energy system including renewable electricity supply, production of renewable hydrogen, associated gas compression and hydrogen pipeline networks to transfer hydrogen to/from the underground storage. The preliminary analysis of expected techno-economic requirements for underground renewable hydrogen storage reveals significant energy storage needs across Europe between 40 to 700 TWh_{H2} in the long-term. In particular, the six big economies with the largest energy demand in Europe including Germany, France, Italy, the UK, Spain and Poland would account for 75% of the overall storage capacities in Europe. Based on the long-term assumption of climate neutrality in Europe the underground renewable hydrogen storage would be operated on a seasonal basis with 1-9 full cycle equivalents regardless of hydrogen demand and storage capacity in all countries.

Keywords: Underground H_2 storage, aquifers, storage needs, energy system modelling

#90

FROM BATCH REACTOR TO CONTINUOUS FLOW MICROCHANNEL REACTOR FOR DEHYDROGENATION OF PERHYDRO-DIBENZYLTOLUENE: A PRELIMINARY STUDY

[1,2] *Ahsan Ali,* [1] *Ajith Krishnan R,* [1*] *Hee Joon Lee*
[1] School of Mechanical Engineering, Kookmin University, Seoul, Republic of Korea
[2] Department of Mechanical Engineering, Gachon University, Seongnam, Republic of Korea
*Corresponding author e-mail: joellee@kookmin.ac.kr

ABSTRACT

Hydrogen stored in liquid organic hydrogen carriers (LOHCs) like dibenzyltoluene makes it a simple and safe technology along with long term storage. In this study, a preliminary study regarding the dehydrogenation of perhydro-dibenzyltoluene with switching from a stirred batch reactor to a continuous flow microchannel reactor is presented. The performance of the reactors was investigated with a 2% Pt/Al_2O_3 catalyst. The hydrogen production percentage in the case of a continuous flow microchannel reactor was found higher (58% hydrogen production) when compared to that of a stirrer type reactor (only 12 % hydrogen production) in 12 hours of operation. Moreover, the effect of microchannel bottom plate temperature on the hydrogen production was also investigated. The hydrogen production was increased from 64.15% to 82.20% with the increase in bottom plate temperature from 260 to 320°C for 0.01 mL/min flow rate of H18-DBT and 20 hours experiment. With the increase in the operating time, the hydrogen production found to increase slowly. A maximum of 88% of hydrogen was generated for a 40 hours' operation, at a bottom wall temperature of 290°C. The results revealed that a continuous microchannel reactor can be an appropriate technology for the dehydrogenation of H18-DBT.

Keywords: Dehydrogenation, liquid organic hydrogen carrier, microchannel reactor, dibenzyltoluene

#119

DIGITAL DEVELOPMENT OF AN OPTIMIZED HEAT MANAGEMENT DESIGN FOR AN INTEGRATED SOLID-STATE H_2-STORAGE RESERVOIR

[1,2*] *Phillip S. Krause,* [1,2] *Jan Warfsmann,* [1,2] *Eike Wienken,* [1,2] *Julian Jepsen,* [1,2] *Thomas Klassen,* [1,2] *Julián Puszkiel*
[1] Institute of Materials Research, Helmholtz-Zentrum HEREON, Max-Planck-Straße 1, 21502 Geesthacht, Germany
[2] Faculty of Mechanical Engineering, Institute of Materials, Helmut Schmidt University, Holstenhofweg 85, 22043, Hamburg, Germany
*Corresponding author e-mail: phillip.krause@hereon.de

ABSTRACT

The main drawback of large-scale metal hydride storage systems is the low thermal conductivity of most metal hydrides and the corresponding difficulties for the heat management system. In this work, the optimization of the internal heat management of a hydrogen storage tank is investigated by finite element simulations. Different design parameters of internal fins are analyzed, such as number, thickness, and length of the fins. It is found that a specific configuration of fins results in a notable improvement of heat transfer and corresponding improvement in desorption kinetics.

Keywords: Hydrogen storage, room temperature metal hydride, heat transfer management, tank design, AB2-alloy

#120

MODELING AND PROCESS SIMULATION OF A METAL HYDRIDE TANK COUPLED WITH A PEM ELECTROLYZER

[1,2*] *Eike S. Wienken,* [1,2] *Phillip S. Krause,* [1,2] *Jan Warfsmann,* [1] *José Bellosta von Colbe,* [1,2] *Julian Jepsen,* [1,2] *Thomas Klassen,* [1,2] *Julián A. Puszkiel*

[1] Helmholtz-Zentrum Hereon, Institute of Hydrogen Technology, Max-Planck-Straße 1, 21502 Geesthacht, Germany

[2] Helmut Schmidt University, Faculty of Mechanical Engineering, Institute of Materials, Holstenhofweg 85, 22043, Hamburg, Germany

*Corresponding author e-mail: eike.wienken@hereon.de

ABSTRACT

To cope with the tight timeframe of the global transformation from fossil to renewable energy sources, efficient methods and tools such as process and system simulation are essential for rapid development, cost-efficient design and scale-up validation of new energy systems. This numerical analysis investigates the coupling of a stationary metal hydride (MH) hydrogen storage system with a low-temperature 10 kW proton exchange membrane (PEM) electrolyzer as a fast-responding and well-controllable hydrogen source. The heat management of the solid-state storage tank is improved through additional aluminum fins and an external cooling jacket. For modeling and process simulation, Aspen Custom Modeler® is used to study the mass and heat transfer phenomena in the hydrogen storage tank, as well as the interaction with the electrolyzer. The hydrogen tank is designed to store a total capacity of 700 g of H_2 using 62.5 kg commercial room temperature AB_2-alloy, Hydralloy C5®. The operating pressure varies from 5 to 38 bar H_2, while the coolant temperature varies from 20 to 60 °C depending on the exothermic absorption or endothermic desorption processes.

Keywords: Simulation, hydrogen storage, room temperature hydrides, PEM electrolyzer, emergency power supply

#122

HIGH H_2 UPTAKE ON Co(II)- AND Ni(II)- EXCHANGED ZSM-5 AND US-Y HAVING OPTIMAL HEAT OF ADSORPTION VALUES

[1] *Nurkan Sarohan,* [2] *M. Olus Ozbek,* [1] *Yasemin Kaya,* [1*] *Bahar Ipek*

[1]Middle East Technical University, Faculty of Engineering, Department of Chemical Engineering, 06800, Ankara, Turkey

[2] Gebze Technical University, Faculty of Engineering, Department of Chemical Engineering, 41400, Gebze, Kocaeli, Turkey

*Corresponding author e-mail: bipek@metu.edu.tr

ABSTRACT

Hydrogen adsorption capacity of Ni(II) and Co(II)- exchanged ZSM-5 and US-Y were investigated at 298 K and 10 bar. Mesopore added zeolites that have a total pore volume value reaching 0.5 cm^3/g, showed a gravimetric H_2 storage capacity of 0.14wt.% and a volumetric storage capacity of 4.2 g/L at 298 K and 10 bar. The calculated isosteric heat of H_2 adsorption values ranged from 16 and 32 kJ/mol with the highest values observed on Ni(II)-ZSM-5. Theoretical heat of H_2 adsorption values were also calculated using density functional theory utilizing both cluster and periodic models for Co(II)- or Ni(II)-exchanged ZSM-5. The theoretical heat of adsorption values was calculated between 11 and 38 kJ/mol, in consistence with the experimental values.

Keywords: Cobalt, nickel, zeolite, isosteric heat of adsorption, density functional theory

#126

HYDROGEN ABSORPTION/DESORPTION OF THE $(TiVNb)_{85}Cr_{15}$ MULTICOMPONENT ALLOY

[1*] *Bruno Hessel Silva,* [2] *Claudia Zlotea,* [1,4] *Walter José Botta,* [4] *Yannick Champion,* [1,4] *Guilherme Zepon*
[1]Federal University of São Carlos, Graduate Program in Materials Science and Engineering (PPGCEM/UFSCar), Rodovia Washington Luiz – km 235, São Carlos, São Paulo, Brasil
[2] Univ Paris Est Créteil, CNRS, ICMPE, UMR 7182, 2 Rue Henri Dunant, 94320, Thiais, France
[3] Univ Grenoble Alpes, CNRS, G-INP, SIMap, 38000 Grenoble, France
[4] Federal University of São Carlos, Department of Materials Engineering (DEMa/UFSCar), Rodovia Washington Luiz – km 235, São Carlos, São Paulo, Brasil
*Corresponding author e-mail: brunohesselpgb@gmail.com

ABSTRACT

Ti-V-Nb-Cr multicomponent alloys are promising materials for hydrogen storage. In this work, we investigated in detail the hydrogen absorption/desorption reactions of the $(TiVNb)_{85}Cr_{15}$ alloy. The alloy was produced via electric arc melting and characterized by X-ray diffraction (XRD), Scanning Electron Microscopy (SEM) and Energy Dispersive X-ray Spectroscopy (EDS) analyses. The alloy presented single-phase BCC structure and dendritic morphology with small segregation of Ti and Cr to the interdendritic regions. Samples of the alloy were hydrogenated at different H/M (number of hydrogen atoms per metal atoms) ratio. XRD and Thermo Desorption Spectroscopy (TDS) analyses showed multi-step processes of hydrogenation/dehydrogenation. XRD analyses suggest that the alloy initially absorbs hydrogen via solid solution and subsequently forms an intermediate BCC hydride up to low levels of H/M absorbed (0.83 H/M). Afterwards, the intermediate hydride also absorbs hydrogen via solid solution leading to the formation of a FCC hydride, which absorbs hydrogen up to 2 H/M. TDS results showed multi-step desorption reactions which were associated to the desorption of the FCC and BCC hydrides. Moreover, Pressure Composition Isotherms (PCI) measurements indicated the existence of two plateaus of absorption and desorption, which also were associated to the BCC and FCC hydrides.

Keywords: Hydrogen storage, multicomponent alloy, BCC alloy, metal hydrides

#133

EASY UP-SCALEABLE APPROACH TO IMPROVE THE PROPERTIES OF METAL-ALLOYS FOR HYDROGEN STORAGE

[1,2*] *Jan Warfsmann,* [1]*Maximilian Passing,* [1,2] *Phillip S. Krause,* [1,2] *Eike Wienken,* [1,2] *Julian Jepsen,* [1,2]*Thomas Klassen,* [1,2] *Julián Atilio Puszkiel*
[1]Helmholtz-Zentrum Hereon, Institute of Hydrogen Technology, Max-Planck-Straße 1, 21502 Geesthacht, Germany
[2] Helmut Schmidt Universität – University of the Federal Armed Forces Hamburg, Holstenhofweg 85, 22043 Hamburg, Germany
*Corresponding author e-mail: jan.warfsmann@hereon.de

ABSTRACT

Methods to increase the heat conductivity and reduce the expansion stress of metal alloys during hydrogen absorption are investigated. The applied approach focuses on strategies, which are time-efficient and can be up-scaled for larger batches of metal alloy. The properties of the commercial available room-temperature metal alloy HydralloyC5 ($Ti_{0.95}Zr_{0.05}Mn_{1.46}V_{0.45}Fe_{0.09}$) are successfully improved by applying wash-coating techniques. By adding 10 wt.% ENG (expanded natural graphite) or aluminum-powder onto the metal surface prior to hydrogen absorption, the heat conductivity of the samples is improved. Furthermore, the overall expansion stress of the metal alloy during hydrogen absorption is reduced by 20% by adding only small amounts of Aerosol as a glidant agent (0.2 wt.%) to the coating mixture.

Keywords: Hydrides, hydrogen storage, swelling, heat transfer, wash coating

#134

HYDROGEN - HEAT STORAGE SYSTEM BASED ON METAL HYDRIDE AND PHASE CHANGE MATERIAL

[1*]Jussara Barale, [2]Giovanni Capurso, [3]Thorbjorn Stühff, [4]Federico Nastro, [5]Bettina Neumann, [2]José Bellosta von Colbe, [1]Paola Rizzi, [4]Carlo Luetto, [3]Holger Stühff and [1]Marcello Baricco

[1] Department of Chemistry and NIS - INSTM, University of Turin, Via Pietro Giuria 7, 10125 Torino, Italy

[2] Institute of Hydrogen Technology, Helmholtz-Zentrum Hereon, Max-Plank-Straße 1, 21502 Geesthacht, Germany

[3] Stühff Maschinen- und Anlagenbau GmbH, Mercatorstraße 53, 21502 Geesthacht, Germany

[4] Tecnodelta S.r.l., Via Francesco Parigi 5H, 10034 Chivasso (To), Italy

[5] GKN Sinter Metals Engineering GmbH, Krebsöge 10, D-42477 Radevormwald, Germany

*Corresponding author e-mail: jussara.barale@unito.it

ABSTRACT

The goal of the HyCARE project is to store renewable energy using hydrogen as energy carrier by means of a metal hydride (MH), coupling a phase change material (PCM) for the heat management. The feasibility of the concept has been investigated thanks to the realization of a prototype including a MH-tank and a PCM module storing about 0.5 kg of H_2. The innovation of the use of PCM in the heat management of MH system is linked to the reduction of external heat intake, and during the tests the optimal conditions of hydrogen flow, thermal fluid flow, starting temperature have been evaluated, in order to minimize the external power contribution. It was highlighted that, in the optimal conditions, the PCM was able to collect and supply the heat generated/required by the MH storage system, with the external power source contributing only to compensate the heat losses.

Keywords: Hydrogen storage, heat storage, metal hydride, phase change material

#139

MODELING AND PARAMETERIZATION OF A PEM FUEL CELL STACK FOR A SYSTEM INTEGRATION INTO A METAL HYDRIDE BASED HYDROGEN STORAGE SYSTEM

[1,2*] Myriam Covarrubias Guarneros, [1,2] David Dreistadt, [1,2] José Bellosta von Colbe, [2] Giovanni Capurso, [3] Marion Siegers [1,2]Julian Jepsen, [1,2] Julián Puszkiel, [1,2] Thomas Klassen

[1] Faculty of Mechanical Engineering, Institute of Materials, Helmut Schmidt University, Holstenhofweg 85, 22043, Hamburg, Germany

[2] Institute of Materials Research, Helmholtz-Zentrum HEREON, Max-Planck-Straße 1, 21502 Geesthacht,Germany;

[3]Environmental Engineering Department, Faculty of Life Science, Hamburg University of Applied Science, Ulmenliet 20, 21033, Hamburg, Germany

*Corresponding author e-mail: covarrum@hsu-hh.de

ABSTRACT

Power systems using renewable energy sources have emerged as a sustainable solution for decarbonizing the energy sector. Implementing such systems requires integrating them with an efficient storage medium to improve their reliability and flexibility. This work explores the modeling and parameterization of a fuel cell system, with the purpose of coupling it with a metal hydride-based hydrogen storage reservoir. An electrical and thermal 0D simulation model for a 1.6 kW air-cooled proton exchange fuel cell stack is developed to investigate its performance, heat transfer and temperature development. The model validation and simulation are done by testing it with four different steady-state power demand scenarios. Experimental results show an efficient thermal coupling between the fuel cell stack and the metal-hydride system. Simulations and experimental results show an excellent agreement. The developed modeling approach is also appliccable to the design of different gas-to-power configurations and sizes, for the design of fuel cell–metal hydride storage systems.

Keywords: PEM fuel cell, 0D-modelling, Matlab-Simulink-Simscape, system integration, gas-to-power

#142

SIZE OPTIMIZATION OF A HYBRID WIND/PHOTOVOLTAIC/FUEL CELL GRID-CONNECTED SYSTEM WITH HYDROGEN STORAGE

[1] *Leila Abdolmaleki,* [1*] *Umberto Berardi*
[1] Department of Architectural Science, Ryerson University, 350 Victoria Street, Toronto, ON, M5B 2K3, Canada
*Corresponding author e-mail: uberardi@ryerson.ca

ABSTRACT

Sustainable resource and energy management are essential considerations in designing hybrid energy systems. Finding an optimal framework that combines the requirements for a reliable design and satisfaction of continuous operation at minimal costs in all operating conditions is essential to clients and investors. This study emphasizes the size optimization of grid-connected hybrid photovoltaic, wind, and hydrogen storage systems. In this regard, by adopting the Hybrid Optimization Model for Electric Renewable (HOMER) energy-balance methods, the optimal design architecture is established. Additionally, the system's technical and economic aspects were examined in this study. Analysis of hourly simulations was performed to decide the optimal size, cost, and performance of the hybrid system. The optimum design configuration consists of a 2 kW PV array, 1 wind turbine, 1.33 kW converter, 2 kW electrolyzer, 5 kg hydrogen tank, 2.5 kW fuel cell, and 100 kW grid. Levelized Cost of Energy (COE) and Net Present Cost (NPC) are 0.169 $/kWh and $ 25,879.11 respectively, for different renewable energy fraction (RF) values of 91.5%.

Keywords: Renewable energy, optimum sizing, solar energy, wind energy, hydrogen

#145

INVESTIGATION OF TEMPERATURE AND PRESSURE EFFECT ON THE HYDROGEN SORPTION KINETICS IN THE INTERFACE OF Mg/MgH_2 BY MOLECULAR DYNAMICS

[1,2] *Mehmet Fazıl Kapçı,* [1*] *Zhen Wu,* [2] *Burak Bal*
[1]Xi'an Jiatong University, School of Chemical Engineering and Technology, 710049, Xi'an, PR China
[2] Abdullah Gul University, Department of Mechanical Engineering, 38080, Kayseri, Turkey
*Corresponding author e-mail: wuz2015@mail.xjtu.edu.cn

ABSTRACT

Molecular dynamics simulations were performed in order to analyze the hydrogen sorption kinetics between α-MgH_2 and hcp Mg structures under different temperatures and pressures. Results showed that hydrogen desorption from magnesium hydride and absorption by hcp magnesium increase at the higher temperatures. During the hydrogen desorption from magnesium hydride and absorption into hcp magnesium, crystallographic orientation change in the magnesium atoms was observed. At 400°C, the pressure was found to have a negative impact during the hydrogen desorption from magnesium hydride due to the prevention of recrystallization.

Keywords: Magnesium hydride, Hcp magnesium, molecular dynamics, hydrogen sorption kinetics

#149

EFFECTS OF INITIAL AND BOUNDARY CONDITIONS ON HYDROGEN REFUELING PERFORMANCES

[1,2] *Hao Luo,* [2] *Richard Chahine,* [2] *Pierre Bénard,* [1,2*] *Jinsheng Xiao*
[1] Wuhan University of Technology, School of Automotive Engineering, Hubei 430070, China
[2] Université du Québec à Trois-Rivières, Hydrogen Research Institute, QC G8Z 4M3, Canada
*Corresponding author e-mail: Jinsheng.Xiao@uqtr.ca

ABSTRACT

In order to ensure the safety of all tank systems under all conditions, the initial and boundary conditions of the refueling systems are usually set very conservative and lead to the waste of refueling time and energy consumption. In this paper, we analyzed the thermodynamics of hydrogen storage tanks and established the model of hydrogen refueling by Simulink. Based on the parameter research method, a three-dimensional graph combined with a two-dimensional graph and a Design-Export graph are used for the analysis. The results show that in the pressure range set in this paper, compared with the initial temperature and inlet temperature, the initial pressure significantly affects the refueling time and SOC (state of charge). The precooling temperature need not always be kept very low and should be adjusted according to the actual situation, which is significant for saving energy.

Keywords: Hydrogen storage, hydrogen refueling, initial condition, boundary condition, refueling performance

#155

MODELING THE KINETIC BEHAVIOR OF THE Li-RHC SYSTEM FOR HYDROGEN STORAGE UNDER DESORPTION CONDITIONS

[1,2*] *André Neves,* [1,2] *Julián Puszkiel,* [2] *José Maria Bellosta von Colbe,* [1,2] *Thomas Klassen,* [1,2] *Julian Jepsen*
[1]Helmut Schmidt University (HSU), University of the Federal Armed Forces, Department for Mechanical Engineering, Holstenhofweg 85, 22043, Hamburg, Germany
[2] Helmholtz-Zentrum Hereon, Institute for Hydrogen Technology, Design for Mobility, Max-Planck-Straße 1, 21502, Geesthacht, Germany
*Corresponding author e-mail: andre.neves@hereon.de

ABSTRACT

In the current work, we present an investigation about modeling the lithium reactive hydride composite (Li-RHC) under desorption conditions. Such modeling is fundamental to enable finite element simulations (FEM) to design optimized hydrogen storage systems. In order to obtain the kinetic data for the study, the dynamic behavior of ball-milled Li-RHC powder is characterized in a Sievert apparatus. Different combinations of pressure and temperature are assessed and the reaction mechanisms of both MgH_2 and $LiBH_4$ are individually identified. The MgH_2 decomposition follows a JMAEK with n = 1 reaction mechanism, while the Prout-Tompkins (PT) model describes the reaction mechanism of $LiBH_4$ very well. However, the PT model involves a new parameter, t_0, associated with the vertical translation of the fitted curve. In order to make the equation applicable for FEM simulations, a novel method is here developed to represent t_0 as a function of the system's parameters, namely, temperature and pressure. This study provides new capabilities of using the PT model to predict the behavior of the desorption of $LiBH_4$ within a wide range of temperature and pressure conditions.

Keywords: Hydrogen Storage, kinetic modeling, reactive hydride composite, desorption, borohydrides

#171

HYDROGEN PRODUCTION FROM THE CATALYTIC DEHYDROGENATION OF HYDRAZINE BORANE OVER Pd-Ni-B CATALYST

[1] *Merve Rabia Gürlük,* [1*] *Göksel Özkan*
[1]Gazi University, Faculty of Engineering, Department of Chemical Engineering, Maltepe, Ankara, Turkey
*Corresponding author e-mail: gozkan@gazi.edu.tr

ABSTRACT

This study aimed to investigate the hydrogen generation from the hydrazine borane. Efficient and reversible hydrogen release can be achieved from the boron-based materials such as M_xBH_4 (M: Li, Na, Ca, Mg), B-N-H (amine boranes) through catalytic and non-catalytic dehydrogenation. Particularly, hydrazine borane ($N_2H_4BH_3$) has been taken into account as a chemical hydrogen storage material due to its high hydrogen content (15.4%). Hydrogen production was carried out by catalytic dehydrogenation of as-synthesized hydrazine borane. Therefore, palladium-nickel (Pd-Ni) bimetallic catalyst supported on Ni-B-O (boride and oxide mixtures) was successfully prepared by co-precipitation method, and its catalytic properties and performance were assessed (SEM, XPS and XRD analyses) for catalytic dehydrogenation. The results showed that 3.58 moles of (H_2+N_2) gas were produced in the presence of Pd-Ni-B catalyst by the hydrolysis of hydrazine borane.

Keywords: Hydrogen, hydrazine borane, catalytic dehydrogenation

#181

EFFICIENT HYDROLYTIC DEHYDROGENATION OF ETHYLENE DIAMINE BISBORANE OVER Pd-Ni-Zr-B CATALYST IN THE ETHYLENE DIAMINE MEDIA

[1*] *Hatice Begüm Murathan,* [2] *Gülay Özkan,* [3] *Göksel Özkan*
[1, 3] Gazi University, Department of Chemical Engineering, Ankara, Turkey
[2] Ankara University, Department of Chemical Engineering, Ankara, Turkey
*Corresponding author e-mail: begummurathan@gazi.edu.tr, gozkan@eng.ankara.edu.tr, gozkan@gazi.edu.tr

ABSTRACT

This study focuses on the catalytic dehydrogenation of ethylene diamine bisborane (EDABB). For this goal, Pd-Ni-Zr-B catalyst was prepared in two steps by using co-precipitation method with $NaBH_4$ and impregnation method. The catalyst was characterized with XRD, XPS, SEM-EDX and multi-point BET analysis. The effect of temperature (90 °C-120 °C) was investigated on dehydrogenation of EDABB. The hydrogen production yields significantly increased at the temperature increases and also the reaction time reduced as well. Highest yield of equivalent hydrogen has reached 5.94 moles at 120 °C. Reusability test of the catalyst was also carried out and average HGR result was obtained.

Keywords: Catalytic dehydrogenation, ethylene diamine bisborane, ethan 1, 2-diamine borane

#192

DEVELOPMENT OF NOVEL POLYMERIC MATERIAL GRADES AND EXPERIMENTAL METHODS TO BE USED IN HIGH-PRESSURE H_2 GAS ATMOSPHERES

[1*] *Winoj Balasooriya,* [1] *Clara Clute,* [2] *Karabi Halder,* [2] *Géraldine Theiler,* [1] *Andreas Hausberger,* [3] *Gerald Pinter*
[1] Polymer Competence Center Leoben GmbH, Roseggerstrasse 12, 8700, Leoben, Austria
[2] Bundesanstalt für Materialforschung und -prüfung (BAM), 12203, Berlin, Germany
[3] Chair of Materials Science and Testing of Polymers, Montanuniversität Leoben, Otto Glöckel-Strasse 2, 8700, Leoben, Austria
*Corresponding author e-mail: Winoj.balasooriya@pccl.at

ABSTRACT

Polymeric grades play a vital role with their unique properties in many components realizing the "Hydrogen Economy". The elastomeric grades in sealing applications are exposed to high-pressure hydrogen (H_2) gas and a wide range of temperatures, therefore, the development of novel materials is an ongoing process in order to fulfill the future requirements. This study focuses on the development of novel elastomeric grades, introducing novel filler strategies to improve the transport and mechanical properties, and subsequently minimizing possible degradation/damage. The proposed grades were initially tested for identifying the fulfillment of required properties, the resistance to rapid gas decompression (RGD), and deviations in high-pressure H_2 conditions. The used filler modification methods provided promising results on 2D filler functionalization and hydrogen exposure tests revealed dissolution of gas into the material and subsequent possible alterations of properties.

Keywords: Hydrogen gas storage, sealing, elastomers, filler modification, rapid gas decompression

#196

DIFFERENT WAYS TO STORE MASSIVE QUANTITIES OF HYDROGEN

[1*] *Louis F. Londe,* [1] *Arnaud Réveillère*
[1]Geostock SAS, 2 rue des Martinets, 92569 Rueil-Malmaison Cedex, France
*Corresponding author e-mail: louis.londe@geostock.fr

ABSTRACT

Hydrogen can be stored in underground caverns or geological structures in various ways.
The easiest way to store hydrogen is in salt caverns. These are created by injecting water into a well down to a salt geological layer, with the extraction of salt-saturated brine. This type of storage is suitable for storing hydrogen at extremely high pressures. The second way to store large quantities of hydrogen is to inject pure hydrogen or a hydrogen-methane mix into porous rock. The hydrogen content may vary from a few per cent to 100 per cent. Hydrogen can also be stored underground by converting it into a liquid carrier, such as ammonia, which can then be stored in a Lined Rock Cavern. A liner is often required to prevent contact between ammonia and water. Lastly, hydrogen can be stored underground by injecting it into a Lined Rock Cavern. This may take the form of compressed storage (gaseous hydrogen) or cryogenic storage (liquid hydrogen. A liner is required owing to extremely high pressures or extremely low temperatures. The present article exposes state of the art of all these techniques of hydrogen underground storage, outlines technical gaps and identifies main ongoing or required technology developments needed to bridge them.

Keywords: Underground, storage, salt, cavern, rock

#203

EVALUATION OF THE BIMETALLIC Pt-Ni AND Pt-Co CATALYSTS ON THE LOHC DEHYDROGENATION

[1] *K. Alconada,*[1*] *V.L. Barrio*
[1]School of Engineering (University of the Basque Country UPV/EHU), Plaza Ingeniero Torres Quevedo 1, 48013 Bilbao (Spain)
*Corresponding author e-mail: laura.barrio@ehu.eus

ABSTRACT

Liquid organic hydrogen carrier systems (LOHC) are presented as an alternative for energy storage and transportation. Platinum group metals (PGM) have proven to be efficient in LOHC hydrogenation/dehydrogenation reactions for hydrogen storage cycles. However, their cost and the high Pt/LOHC ratio are their major drawbacks. In this work, the performance of low-PGM and/or PGM-free catalysts on LOHC dehydrogenation is studied. Bimetallic systems are good candidates to replace or to decrease the PGM content increasing also the dehydrogenation yield.

Keywords: Hydrogen storage, liquid-organic hydrogen carrier (LOHC), dehydrogenation, bimetallic catalyst.

#221

HIGH SURFACE AREA ZEOLITIC IMIDAZOLATE FRAMEWORKS FOR HYDROGEN STORAGE AT ROOM TEMPERATURE

[1,2]Syedvali Pinjari, [2]Tapan Bera, [2]Rajesh M Badhe, [1]Erik Kjeang*
[1]Fuel cell research laboratory, Simon Fraser University, 250-13450 102 Avenue, Surrey, BC V3T0A3, Canada
[2] Alternative Energy – 1, Indian Oil R&D Centre, Sector-13, Faridabad, Haryana 121002, India
*Corresponding author e-mail: ekjeang@sfu.ca

ABSTRACT

Cost-effective hydrogen storage at commercial scale is a limiting factor for the propagation of hydrogen energy. Physisorption enhanced hydrogen storage at low to moderate pressure may offer a possible solution. In this paper, we report the synthesis of zeolitic imidazolate frameworks (ZIF-8) and hybrid material of ZIF-8 and carboxylate functionalized carbon nanotubes (ZIF/*f*CNT) for hydrogen storage applications at room temperature and moderate pressures. Both materials were further characterized by various physicochemical characterization tools to investigate the morphology, crystallinity, thermal stability, and textural properties. ZIF-8 exhibits the highest specific surface area of 2023.6 m^2/g whereas 1576.9 m^2/g was obtained for the hybrid material. Both samples showed rhombic dodecahedron morphology with three-dimensional framework structures. Thermogravimetric analysis revealed that the hybrid material possesses higher thermal stability, of securing 53 wt. % of the structure, than pure ZIF-8 due to the addition of *f*CNT. The carboxylate functionalized carbon nanotubes stored 0.15 wt. % of hydrogen at room temperature and pressure up to 50 bar. The process was reversible at this temperature, indicating a physisorption based storage mechanism. The results of hydrogen storage measurements of ZIF-8 and ZIF/*f*CNT will also be presented and discussed.

Keywords: Zeolitic imidazolate frameworks, hybrid material, hydrogen storage

#234

ELASTIC BRITTLE BEHAVIOR OF AN IRON – TITANIUM ALLOY DEDICATED TO HYDROGEN STORAGE

[1,2] Ludovic Bebon, [1,2] Anne Maynadier, [1]Yves Gaillard, [1,2] David Chapelle
[1] Université Bourgogne Franche-Comté, Femto-ST Institute UMR 6174, Department of Applied Mechanics,
[2] Fuell Cell LAB - FCLAB/UAR2200, 90000 Belfort, France
24 rue de l'Epitaphe, 25000 Besançon, France
*Corresponding author e-mail: ludovic.bebon@univ-fcomte.fr

ABSTRACT

Hydrogen solid state storage technology uses absorption and desorption of di-hydrogen gas at low pressure in metal alloys. In the tank the powder swells, shrinks and decrepitates leading to stress over the wall. The present study first deals with the mechanical characterization by three different methods at different scales, of a storage TiFe alloy. Compression tests of macroscopic samples, ultrasonic elastic characterization, and microscopic scale nano indentation give respectively: 50, 153 and 24 1~305 GPa. This discrepancy is directly linked to the scale and microstructural heterogeneities. An optimization process is proposed to identify a set of numerical parameters able to simulate with DEM the elastic brittle behaviour of our hydride under compression. These data are a first step to model the decrepitating phenomenon and to help design of solid storage tank of hydrogen.

Keywords: Hydrogen solid state storage, discrete element modeling, multiscale mechanical characterization

#245

GASEOUS AND SOLID-STATE HYBRID HYDROGEN STORAGE

[1,2] Haizhen Liu, [2] Li Xu*
[1] Guangxi University, School of Physical Science and Technology, No. 100, Daxue Road, Nanning, P. R. China
[2] Global Energy Interconnection Research Institute Co., Ltd., State Key Laboratory of Advanced Power Transmission Technology, No. 18, Binhe Road, Beijing, P. R. China
*Corresponding author e-mail: liuhz@gxu.edu.cn

ABSTRACT

In the present work, a gaseous and solid-state (G-S) hybrid hydrogen storage system with a low working pressure below 10 MPa for a 10 kW hydrogen energy storage experiment platform is developed and validated. A Ti–Mn hydrogen storage alloy with an effective capacity of 1.7 wt% was developed for the G-S hybrid hydrogen storage system. The G-S hybrid hydrogen storage tank has a high volumetric hydrogen storage density of 40.07 kg H_2 m^{-3} and stores hydrogen under pressure below 5 MPa. It can readily release enough hydrogen at a temperature of as low as −15 °C, without heat resource. This work provides a method on how to design a G-S hydrogen storage system based on practical needs and demonstrates that the G-S hybrid hydrogen storage is a promising method for stationary hydrogen storage application.

Keywords: Hydrogen storage, hybrid hydrogen storage, Ti–Mn alloy, cold booting

#247

MATHEMATICAL MODELLING OF ELECTROCHEMICAL HYDROGEN COMPRESSOR: TEMPERATURE INFLUENCE SIMULATION ANALYSIS

[1] Doria Marciuš, [1] Dinko Brezak, [1*] Ankica Kovač*
[1]University of Zagreb, Faculty of Mechanical Engineering and Naval Architecture, Department of Energy, Power and Environmental Engineering, Zagreb, Croatia
* Corresponding author e-mail: doria.marcius@fsb.hr, ankica.kovac@fsb.hr

ABSTRACT

High-pressure hydrogen storage systems are indispensable for the widespread implementation of hydrogen technology, which is why there is a requirement for an efficient compressor. The most used method of hydrogen compression is via mechanical compressors, but lately, electrochemical hydrogen compressors (EHCs) are increasingly getting more attention due to their many advantages. However, in published articles, there is a limited number of mathematical models due to the intricate nature of the EHC operating mechanism. In this paper, a mathematical model of EHC made in MATLAB/Simulink Software is described through simple equations based on the fundamental physics laws and electrochemical relations, considering occurring overvoltages, including hydrogen back-diffusion. The results obtained as time functions are analysed for various operating temperatures to give more detailed insight on temperature influence on different parameters which affect EHC performance. The simulation indicates temperature effect on multiple inner processes, necessitating optimisation of parameters to balance adverse temperature impact according to required EHC features.

Keywords: Electrochemical hydrogen compressor, proton exchange membrane, MATLAB/Simulink, temperature

#263

EXPERIMENTAL PROOF OF CONCEPT OF A NOVEL HIGH DENSITY, LOW PRESSURE HYDROGEN STORAGE SYSTEM UTILIZING THERMOCHEMICAL HEAT STORAGE

[1] Michael Lutz, [1] Marc Linder, [1] Inga Bürger*
[1] Institute of Engineering Thermodynamics, (DLR), Pfaffenwaldring 38-40, D-70569 Stuttgart, Germany
*Corresponding author e-mail: inga.buerger@dlr.de

ABSTRACT

In the next decades the global energy system will shift towards renewable energy. Hydrogen technologies have the potential to play a major role in the future´s energy grid. With hydrogen becoming more and more important, safe and efficient hydrogen storage systems are required. Metal hydrides are able to chemically store hydrogen free of loss, at low pressures and potentially high storage densities. However, hydrides with exceptionally high storage densities, such as magnesium hydride, require high operation temperatures above 250°C. Therefore, heat management is challenging, since heat at that temperature level has to be supplied and removed for hydrogen desorption and absorption, respectively. In this work, the experimental proof of concept of a novel hydrogen storage system using magnesium hydride and the thermochemical heat storage system $Mg(OH)_2$ / MgO is presented. Thereby, the heat of absorption is stored in the same reactor and – with the supply of water vapor - it is available for the hydrogen desorption again. Potentially, storage densities of 20.8 $g_{H2}\ L^{-1}$ can be stored at a hydrogen pressure of 9 bar. A water vapor pressure of 9.75 bar is sufficient to reach 300°C in the MgO compartment, which is sufficiently high to drive the H_2 desorption.

Keywords: Hydrogen storage, thermochemical heat storage, magnesium hydride, magnesium hydroxide

#269

CONTRIBUTION TO MODELING HYDROGEN PERMEATION AND BARRIER LAYER OPTIMIZATION IN BLOW MOLDED PLASTIC LINERS FOR AN ON-BOARD COMPRESSED HYDROGEN TANKS

Zohir Benrabah, Anna Bardetti, Florin Ilinca, Sylvain Bournival*
National Research Council Canada – Automotive and Surface Transportation
75 de Mortagne Blvd., Boucherville, QC J4B 6Y4, Canada
*Corresponding author e-mail: zohir.benrabah@cnrc-nrc.gc.ca

ABSTRACT

Blow Molded Plastic Liners (BMPL) for on-board type IV Compressed Gaseous Hydrogen (CGH2) storage tanks consist of a high-molecular-weight polymer wall that serves as a permeation layer for hydrogen gas. This paper presents the latest numerical model integrated in the BlowView software for predicting the hydrogen permeation in a BMPL. The prediction model is based on Fick's solution-diffusion laws, with pressure and temperature dependent transport properties, for steady/unsteady state permeation regimes through a polymeric wall. An overview of key simulation results for an industrial BMPL for a CGH2 tank, as well as the adopted methodology addressing the challenge to maximize the enclosed volume, while optimizing the wall thickness for light weighting and permeability performance, are also presented.

Keywords: type IV hydrogen tank, hydrogen permeation, plastic liner, simulation, fuel cell electrical vehicle (FCEV).

#271

A MULTICRITERIA ANALYSIS DECISION FOR PRIORIZATION OF LIQUID ORGANIC HYDROGEN CARRIERS

[1] Monica Almansa-Ortegon, [1] Juan Carlos Osorio, [1] Diego F. Manotas-Duque*
[1]Universidad del Valle, Facultad de Ingeniería, Escuela de Ingeniería Industrial, Calle 13 No 100-00, Cali, Colombia
*Corresponding author e-mail: diego.manotas@correounivalle.edu.co

ABSTRACT

The use of Liquid Organic Hydrogen Carriers (LOHC) is widely studied as a promising material for long-term hydrogen transport and storage, these materials have different techno-economic characteristics that directly influence the operating conditions and cost of the hydrogenation and dehydrogenation process. The selection Three LOHC pairs were selected and prioritized through TOPSIS multicriteria methodology and CRITIC weighting, through the ten technical criteria.

Keywords: LOHC priorization, multicriteria decision, CRITIC methodology, hydrogen storage, TOPSIS.

#278

NUMERICAL THREE-DIMENSIONAL MODELING AND SIMULATIONS OF ELECTROCHEMICAL HYDROGEN COMPRESSOR BASED ON PROTON-EXCHANGE MEMBRANE

[*] Jaeseung Lee, [1] Soobin Yoon, [1] Seonggu Heo, [1] Afroz Alam, [1] Jaeyoo Choi, [1] Kisung Lim, [1] Hyunchul Ju*
[1] Inha Univ., Department of Mechanical Engineering, 100 Inha-ro, Michuhjol-gu, Incheon 22212, Republic of Korea
*Corresponding author e-mail: hcju@inha.ac.kr

ABSTRACT

A 3-D single-phase model of electrochemical hydrogen compressor (EHC) based on proton-exchange membrane was developed on computational fluid dynamics (CFD) basis considering electrochemical reaction and mass transport in a single cell. In particular, this model accounts for the hydrogen transport behavior inside the microstructure with a microscale catalyst layer (CL) model. After coupling the micro-scale model with EHC, multi-scale simulations are carried out under a range of current density up to 1.2 A/cm^2 and validated with experimental data. It is found that the cell showed high performance in the high-pressure condition as the ohmic resistance is decreased. In addition, there is no significant difference according to porosity change.

Keywords: Electrochemical hydrogen compressor, Numerical model, PEMFC, Three-dimensional simulation, High pressure

#279

SYNTHESIS AND STABILIZATION OF ENERGY FUEL MATERIAL ALUMINUM HYDRIDE: A REVIEW

[1] *Youhai Liu*, [2]*Yang Zhang*, [1*] *Fusheng Yang*,[2] [*]*Fengqi Zhao* [1] *Zhen Wu*, [1] *Zaoxiao Zhang*
[1]Xi'An Jiaotong University, School of chemical Engineering and Technology, Xi'An, Shaanxi, China
[2] Xi'An Model Chemistry Research Institute, Xi'An, Shaanxi, China
[1]*Corresponding author e-mail: yang.fs@mail.xjtu.edu.cn, zhaofqi@163.com

ABSTRACT

Aluminum hydride(AlH_3) has a high gravimetric hydrogen energy density of more than 10.0 wt.% and volumetric density (148 kgH_2/m^3). The material has drawn much attention because of its high hydrogen storage capacity and rapid dehydrogenation at low temperatures, and has been used in various areas, including catalysts, fuel cell, reducing agents and rocket fuel additive. AlH_3 can largely promote the specific impulse of propellants when used as energetic additive in solid propellant. In this article, we focus on the research development in the field of synthesis and stabilization of AlH_3 in recent decades. Particularly, the stability of AlH_3 is critical for its application in solid propellants. The most widely used strategies are also introduced and compared, based on which some suggestions for possible future research directions are provided.

Keywords: Aluminum hydride, energy material, stability, solid propellant

#282

NUMERICAL SIMULATION AND PARAMETRIC ANALYSIS OF THE WALL STRAIN DISTRIBUTION OF VERTICALLY PLACED METAL HYDRIDE BASED HYDROGEN STORAGE CONTAINER

[1] *Shuaijie Cao*, [2]*Xuwen Yin*, [1*] *Fusheng Yang*,[3] *Lijun Jiang*, [3] *Yuanfang Wu*, [1] *Zhen Wu*, [1] *Zaoxiao Zhang*
[1] Xi'an Jiaotong University, School of Chemical Engineering and Technology, Xi'an, Shaanxi, P. R. China
[2] Xinjiang University, School of Mechanical Engineering, Urumqi, Xinjiang Uygur Autonomous Regions, P.R. China
[3] General Research Institute for Nonferrous Metals (GRINM) Co. LTD, Beijing, P.R. China
*Corresponding author e-mail: yang.fs@mail.xjtu.edu.cn

ABSTRACT

Pulverization, settling and agglomeration, and the consequent densification may occur for metal hydride particles during the charge-discharge cycles, which will affect the wall strain of their container for hydrogen storage. In order to study the effects of different factors on the wall strain of metal hydride hydrogen storage vessel, a reaction-thermal-mechanical coupling model for $LaNi_5$ alloy was modified with regard to some relevant parameters, by which sensitivity analysis was conducted. Finally, the strain distribution along the height of reactor filling Mg_2Ni was predicted by the model and compared with experimental results reported in literature.

Keywords: Metal hydride, volume expansion, wall strain, parametric analysis

#290

STUDIES ON HYDROGEN STORAGE PERFORMANCE OF CATALYZED MgH_2

[1*]*Satish Kumar Verma*[*], [1]*Mohammad Abu Shaz*, [1]*Thakur Prasad Yadav*
[1] Hydrogen Energy Centre, Department of Physics, Banaras Hindu University, Varanasi-221005, India.
*Corresponding author email: satish16kumar@gmail.com

ABSTRACT

MgH_2 is the widely investigated and one of the most prominent solid state hydrogen storage materials because of its high hydrogen storage capacity, low cost, and enormous elemental reserves in the earth crust and seawater. However, the high desorption temperature, sluggish kinetics and high thermal stability hinder its further onboard application. In present investigation, we have reported the enhanced kinetics and thermodynamics for MgH_2 catalyzed through different prominent catalysts/additives like graphene (Gr), VS_2, TiH_2@Gr, Ti@Gr, TiO_2@Gr, and high entropy alloy (HEA). Amongst these catalysts TiH_2@Gr is most suitable catalyst for empowering the kinetics and thermodynamics of MgH_2. The temperature programmed study reflects that MgH_2-TiH_2@Gr has lowest onset desorption temperature *i.e.* ~231°C with a storage capacity ~6.55 wt% which is ~190°C lower than the desorption temperature of pristine MgH_2. The better catalytic behavior of MgH_2-HEA on TiH_2@Gr also persists during de/re-hydrogenation kinetics of MgH_2. Thus MgH_2 catalyzed by HEA absorbs ~5.9 wt% of hydrogen at 300°C under 15 atm pressures in 1.5 min. A remarkable result coming out of the present investigation is concerning cyclability (reversibility) of MgH_2-HEA, up to 25 cycles.
Keywords: Hydrogen storage, magnesium hydride, graphene templated Ti-based catalyst, 2-d materials, reversibility.

#300

PERMEABILITY OF A DEFORMABLE METAL HYDRIDE BED DURING HYDROGEN ABSORPTION

[1,2*] *Dmitry Dunikov*, ,[1,2] *Dmitry Blinov*

[1]Joint Institute for High Temperatures of the Russian Academy of Sciences, Laboratory for Hydrogen Energy Technologies, 125412 Izhorskaya st. 13 bld. 2, Moscow, Russia

[2] National Research University "Moscow Power Engineering Institute", 111250 Krasnokazarmennaya 14, Moscow, Russia

*Corresponding author e-mail: ddo@mail.ru

ABSTRACT

Permeability of a metal hydride bed during hydrogen absorption is experimentally investigated by filtration of a H_2(10%)/CH_4 mixture through the bed (1 kg $LaNi_{4.8}Mn_{0.3}Fe_{0.1}$). Deformation of the bed due to swelling of the particles at absorption causes significant changes of the bed permeability, it decreases from 0.16 μm^2 at the start of the absorption to 0.031 μm^2 at C = 1.12%wt. The effect can be contributed to decrease of the bed porosity at absorption.

Keywords: Metal hydride, AB_5, permeability, deformable bed

#301

APPLICATION OF MISCHMETAL BASED LOW PRESSURE METAL HYDRIDES FOR SOLAR ENERGY STORAGE

[*1] *K. Sarath Babu*, [1] *E. Anil Kumar*

[1] Department of Mechanical Engineering, Indian Institute of Technology Tirupati, 517506, Tirupati, India

*Corresponding author e-mail: me18d001@iittp.ac.in

ABSTRACT

Efficient utilization of solar energy reduces the carbon footprints in the atmosphere. The intermittent nature of solar energy requires efficient energy storage systems. Solar energy available at low temperature (<120°C) find application in many domestic devices. In the present study, mischmetal based metal hydrides are selected to store solar energy as these hydrides are operated at low temperature and low pressures. Pressure concentration isotherms (PCIs) of mischmetal based hydrides namely, $MmNi_{4.2}Al_{0.8}$, $MmNi_4Al$ and $MmNi_{3.9}Co_{0.5}Al_{0.6}$ are measured. The thermodynamic properties such as enthalpy and entropy are evaluated from van't Hoff plot. The suitability of these materials for developing an absorption thermal energy storage (ATES) system to store solar thermal energy is studied. The ATES system is thermodynamically analysed to evaluate the performance parameters such as COP and energy storage density (ESD).

Keywords: Solar energy, Energy storage, Mischmetal, Metal hydrides

#303

STUDY OF THE EFFECT OF Zr_3Fe ADDITION ON HYDROGEN STORAGE BEHAVIOR OF Ti_2CrV ALLOYS

[1,2*] *Daniela Bellon Monsalve*, [1] *Jacques Huot*, [2] *Alejandro David Martínez Amariz*

[1] Hydrogen Research Institute, Université Du Québec à Trois-Rivières, QC, G9A 5H7, Canada

[2] Universidad de Santander, Facultad de Ingenierías y Tecnologías, Instituto de Investigación Xerira, Bucaramanga, Colombia

*Corresponding author e-mail: daniela.bellon@irh.ca

ABSTRACT

The aim of this study was to improve the first hydrogenation behavior of Ti_2CrV alloy, with the Zr_3Fe addition. The Ti_2CrV + X% Zr_3Fe (X= 0, 2, 4, 6, 8, and 10) system were studied. The compositions were synthesized by arc-melting. The powder was characterized by scanning electron microscopy and x-ray diffraction. In the as-cast samples, microstructure reveals a single bcc structure for Ti_2CrV, and the presence of a Zr-rich area for the samples with Zr_3Fe addition. The hydride fcc phase for 8% and 10% addition of Zr_3Fe was confirmed by x-ray diffraction. We found that when 8% and 10% of Zr_3Fe is added to the alloy, the first hydrogenation is improved not only in terms of hydrogen storage capacity but also kinetics. The sample with 10% of Zr_3Fe absorbs its maximum capacity of 3.8 wt.% in approximately 10 minutes at room temperature without any heat treatment.

Keywords: Hydrogen storage, TiCrV system, bcc alloy

#317

HYSTORIES PROJECT: TECHNICAL DEVELOPMENTS AND DEPLOYMENT OUTLOOKS FOR PURE HYDROGEN STORAGE IN DEPLETED FIELDS AND AQUIFERS

[1] Arnaud Réveillère, [2]Jan Michalski, [3]Bernd Loder, [4]Ceri Vincent, [5]Martin Wagner, [6]Jesús Simón, [7]Katarzyna Luboń*

[1]Geostock, 2, rue des Martinets 92500 Rueil-Malmaison, France
[2]Ludwig-Boelkow-Systemtechnik GmbH (LBST), Daimlerstr. 15, Ottobrunn 85521, Germany
[3]Montanuniversitaet Leoben, Franz Josef Strasse 18, Leoben 8700, Austria
[4]Co2geonet, 3 Av. Claude Guillemin, Orleans, France
[5]MicroPro GmbH, Magdeburger Str. 26b, Gommern 39245, Germany
[6]Foundation for the Development of New Hydrogen Technologies in Aragon (FHa), Parque Tecnológico Walqa
[7]MEERI PAS, Ul. Jozefa Wybickiego 7a, Krakow 31 261, Poland
*Corresponding author e-mail: arnaud.reveillere@geostock.fr

ABSTRACT

While storing pure hydrogen in salt caverns has been practiced since the 70s in Europe, pure hydrogen storage has not yet been carried out anywhere in depleted fields or aquifers. The Hystories project [1] is delivering technical developments applicable to a vast range of future aquifer or depleted field storage sites, and is providing insights into underground hydrogen storage for decision makers in government and industry. It has started in January, 2021, is gathering 24 European Companies, Universities or Research Institutes (as Partners or Third Parties), is supported by an advisory board composed of 13 large European companies and will have half of its results delivered by the time of the conference. Some results will be presented in detail during this WHEC. The present paper will complement them by giving an overall view on the technical gaps and improvements, and on the techno-economic insights for hydrogen subsurface storage.

Keywords: Underground, storage, aquifer, depleted field

#332

THE EFFECT OF FIBER BANDWIDTH ON STRESS DISTRIBUTION AND LAYER THICKNESS CHANGE AT THE DOME PART OF HYDROGEN STORAGE VESSEL

[1,2] İbrahim Yilmaz, [1,2] Ebubekir Pinar, [2] Osman Vedat Akgün*

[1] Uludag University, Engineering Faculty, Mechanical Engineering Department, 16059, Bursa, Turkey
[2] B Plas A.Ş., R&D Center, 16369, Bursa, Turkey,
*Corresponding author e-mail: ibrahimyylmz@gmail.com

ABSTRACT

In this study, dome thickness distribution and burst pressure determination were made for a type IV high-pressure hydrogen storage vessel. The netting theory and cubic spline function (CSF) method were used to design the cylindrical sections lay-up and accurately predict the dome thickness. The rowing numbers and bundle width were determined by considering burst pressure and fiber consumption, and finite element analysis models were created. In finite element analysis, these models were evaluated using Puck failure criteria to accurately predict the damage in composite layers.

Keywords: Type IV hydrogen vessel, filament winding, dome thickness

#345

EXPERIMENTAL STUDIES OF WELL INTEGRITY ISSUES RELATED TO CEMENT DURING UNDERGROUND HYDROGEN STORAGE

[1*] *Esteban R. Ugarte,* [1]*Daniel Tetteh,* [1]*Saeed Salehi*
[1]The University of Oklahoma, 660 Parrington Oval, Norman, OK, US
*Corresponding author e-mail: esteban.r.ugarte-1@ou.edu

ABSTRACT

Underground Hydrogen Storage (UHS) in the subsurface is an alternative to overcome limitations associated with renewable energy sources. The excess energy produced from a fluctuating production can be converted to hydrogen and stored in porous media. Hydrogen is injected and produced from geological formations via wells. There are a number of concerns regarding the interactions of hydrogen with the different well components such as cement. This experimental study aims to investigate the interaction between hydrogen and cement Class H by comparing the results obtained. The methodology consists of studying physical and chemical properties and their interactions with fluid through multiple experiments. Samples exposed to hydrogen exhibited a greater compressive strength in both short and long terms. In terms of casing-cement bond strength, no change was observed. Porosity analyzed using neuron magnetic resonance exhibited minimal difference while permeability measured using a permeameter showed a considerable difference in samples aged in a hydrogenated environment. Finally, based on the scanning electron microscopy aided by Fourier transform infrared spectroscopy, a model has been propped to explain and compare the difference between the samples aged in water and in a hydrogenated water environment.

Keywords: Underground hydrogen storage, alternative energy sources, petroleum wells-drilling/production/construction, well integrity

#347

EFFECTS OF HYDROGEN-METHANE GAS BLEND ON WELLBORE INTEGRITY IN UNDERGROUND HYDROGEN STORAGE: AN EXPERIMENTAL INVESTIGATION OF ELASTOMER PERFORMANCE

[1*] *Daniel Tetteh,* [2] *Esteban Ugarte,* [3] *Saeed Salehi,*
[1]University of Oklahoma, Mewbourne College of Earth and Energy, MPGE, 100 Boyd St, Norman, United States of America
*Corresponding author e-mail: Daniel.A.Tetteh-1@ou.edu

ABSTRACT

Although depleted natural gas reservoirs are the most economical option for large-scale underground hydrogen storage, minimal knowledge exists on the effects of interactions between the downhole gases and materials, given the novelty of the process. In this study, three selected API grade elastomers; Ethylene propylene diene monomer (EPDM), Fluoroelastomer (FKM/Viton), and Nitrile Butadiene Rubber (NBR), were aged in an autoclave pressurized with different gas mixtures (i.e., hydrogen, methane, and carbon dioxide) to investigate their interactions. Aging parameters were varied to determine their influence on elastomer performance, and this was measured via hardness, volumetric swelling, compressive strain-stress, and Scanning Electron Microscopy (SEM) tests. Preliminary test results showed less than 3% reduction in hardness of all samples when aged in a 100% Hydrogen environment at 22°C and 3Mpa. However, aging samples in a hydrogen-methane gas blend environment at similar conditions caused more significant hydrogen damage. Samples experienced up to a 5% reduction in hardness, and Viton was the most affected. CO_2 was the most corrosive of all three gases and caused between 2% and 9% reduction in hardness of samples. Hydrogen and hydrogen-methane blend damage on elastomers due to elastomer chain rupture are more severe at higher temperatures.

Keywords: Hydrogen, autoclave, elastomers, well integrity, underground storage.

#355

STUDY ON HYDROGEN STORAGE PERFORMANCE OF C14 TYPE $Ti_{0.24}V_{0.17}Zr_{0.17}Co_{0.17}Fe_{0.8}Mn_{0.17}$ HIGH ENTROPY ALLOY

[1*] *Abhishek Kumar*[a*], [2] *Nilay Krishna Mukhopadhyay*, [1] *Thakur Prasad Yadav*
[1] Hydrogen Energy Centre, Department of Physics, Banaras Hindu University, Varanasi-221005, India.
[2] Department of Metallurgical Engineering, Indian Institute of Technology Banaras Hindu University, Varanasi, India
*Corresponding author email: abhishek.physics.bhu@gmail.com

ABSTRACT

Multi-component High Entropy Alloys (HEAs) have been an exciting research area in theoretical and experimental studies in recent years, and have become an emerging class of advanced materials leading to a new field due to their superior mechanical and functional properties over traditional alloys based on a single principal element. Multi-component HEAs contain five or more principal elements, each at a concentration ranging from 5 to 35 atomic percent. In this study, we synthesized a single phase of C14 type Complex Concentrated Laves Phase intermetallic in a new hexanary $Ti_{0.24}$-$V_{0.17}$-$Zr_{0.17}$-$Co_{0.17}$-$Fe_{0.8}$-$Mn_{0.17}$ HEA for Hydrogen Storage Material research. Radio-Frequency (RF) induction melting in an argon atmosphere was used for the preparation of this alloy. Then X-ray diffraction (XRD) was done for the structural characterization of the alloy system. The XRD analysis shows that the alloy is a C14 type hexagonal laves phase with no evidence of an amorphous or other metastable phases in the current processing conditions. The hydrogen storage performance was measured using a fully computerized PCI apparatus in the study. A scanning electron microscope (SEM) was used to examine the surface morphology and elemental composition analysis of this HEA.

Keywords: Multi-component high entropy alloys, C14 laves phase, hydrogen energy, hydrogen storage

#361

THERMODYNAMIC ANALYSIS OF A METAL HYDRIDE BASED HYDROGEN COMPRESSOR USING $La_{1-x}Ce_xNi_5$ HYDRIDES

[1*] *Dinesh Dashbabu*, [2] *E. Anil Kumar*
[1,2] Indian Institute of Technology, Tirupati, Tirupati, India
*Corresponding author e-mail: me19d503@iittp.ac.in

ABSTRACT

The theoretical performance of a metal hydride based hydrogen compressor is studied using the materials $La_{1-x}Ce_xNi_5$ (where x=0,0.1,0.2), and the effect of cerium substitution for La in $LaNi_5$ on its performance is discussed. Using these hydrides hydrogen can be compressed from 20 to 142 bar using thermal energy at 140°C. A maximum isentropic efficiency of 0.23 and a pressure ratio of 7.1 can be achieved.

Keywords: Metal hydride compressor, pressure concentration isotherm, cerium substitution

#364

THE EFFECT OF DIFFERENT ORGANIC ACIDS ON THE HYDROLYSIS OF MAGNESIUM HYDRIDE

[1*] *Moegamat Wafeeq Davids*, [1] *Tshepo Kgokane Sekgobela*, [1] *Mykhaylo Lototskyy*,
[1] University of the Western Cape, South African Institute for Advanced Materials Chemistry (SAIAMC), Bellville, South Africa
*Corresponding author e-mail: mwdavids@uwc.ac.za

ABSTRACT

The influence of organic acids such as acetic acid, citric acid and oxalic acid and their concentration in aqueous solutions on the hydrolysis of magnesium hydride (MgH_2) has been investigated. The hydrolysis of MgH_2 was performed in a hydrogen generation reactor operated in a batch mode where the temperature and H_2 flow rate were logged. Different organic acid concentration of 1, 2, and 3 wt. % was used to study the effect on the hydrolysis of MgH_2. The hydrogen generation results indicate that the addition of organic acids to the aqueous solution increases the rate of H_2 generation as it limits the formation of the $Mg(OH)_2$ passivation layer. The increase in the concentration of the organic acid solutions leads to the increase in the rate and generation of H_2 via hydrolysis of MgH_2. The organic acid with the fastest hydrogen generation rate is oxalic acid, acetic acid and then citric acid. The pH before and after hydrolysis was recorded and showed that the addition of organic acids suppresses the formation of $Mg(OH)_2$ passivation layer causing the aqueous solution to be more acidic which leads to less OH^- being formed during hydrolysis in the solution.

Keywords: Hydrolysis, hydrogen generation, MgH_2, organic acids

#369

DEVELOPMENT AND IMPLEMENTATION OF METAL HYDRIDE MATERIALS AND TECHNOLOGIES IN SOUTH AFRICA

[1] Mykhaylo Lototskyy*, [1] Moegamat Wafeeq Davids, [1] Vladimir Linkov, [1] Sivakumar Pasupathi*
University of the Western Cape, South African Institute for Advanced Materials Chemistry, HySA Systems Centre of Competence, Robert Sobukwe Road, Private Bag X17, Bellville 7535, South Africa
*Corresponding author e-mail: mlototskyy@uwc.ac.za

ABSTRACT

Metal hydrides (MH) offer promising solutions in several niche applications related to hydrogen storage – the most challenging problem which hinders implementation of efficient and environment-friendly hydrogen energy technologies. Additional motivation for the development and implementation of the MH materials and technologies in South Africa is in the necessity to beneficiate vast mineral resources of the country which include all the components used as raw materials for the manufacturing of main kinds of practically important MH alloys, particularly, AB_2- and AB_5-type ones. This presentation overviews research, development and innovation (RDI) activities in South Africa in the field of MH materials and related technologies. Since the first decade of 2000s, these activities are mostly carried out by the South African Institute for Advanced Materials Chemistry (SAIAMC) at the University of the Western Cape (UWC). The MH-related activities are one of the key technologies developed within Hydrogen South Africa (HySA) RDI Strategy in hydrogen and fuel cell technologies (2008–2023) coordinated by the Department of Science and Innovation (DSI). This key technology is implemented by HySA Systems Centre of Competence hosted by SAIAMC / UWC.

Keywords: Metal hydrides, South Africa, hydrogen storage, hydrogen separation and purification, hydrogen compression

#376

EFFECT OF STARTING RAW MATERIAL IN MECHANICAL ALLOYING OF TiFe HYDROGEN STORAGE ALLOY

[1] Kanta Tsuchikawa, [2*]Saule Zholdayakova, [3*]Haru-Hisa Uchida,*
[1]Graduate School of Human Environment, [2]Graduate School of Science and Technology,
[3]Department of Human Development, Tokai University,
4-1-1 Kitakaname, Hiratsuka, Kanagawa, Japan
*Corresponding author e-mail: kanta.t.0611@gmail.com

ABSTRACT

With its relatively high hydrogen storage capacity (1.8 wt%), TiFe hydrogen storage alloy is expected to be a low-cost material compared to other storage alloys. However, TiFe requires an initial activation process under high temperature and pressure. In order to improve the initial activation properties, the mechanical alloying (MA) process has been proposed to give a disordered surface structure; the MA process can obtain alloys with less energy than the solidification process and is considered to be environmentally and economically suitable.

In this study, we have investigated how the difference between metallic Ti and Ti hydride (TiH_2), the starting material of the MA process, affects the alloy formation. Ti hydride is obtained during the refining process of metallic Ti and is easily pulverized. We also added a small amount of a third element, such as Mn, to TiFe to study its effect on alloying and absorption properties. The obtained sample powder was observed by scanning electron microscopy (SEM) and the structure of the sample was identified by powder X-ray diffractometer (XRD).

Keywords: Hydrogen storage alloy, crystallization, storage capacity

#378

INTRODUCTION OF SPERA HYDROGEN SYSTEM™ FOR MASSIVE HYDROGEN STORAGE AND TRANSPORTATION

[1] Yoshimi Okada, [2] Kenichi Imagawa, [3] Hironori Kawai, [3] Tomoyuki Mikuriya [2] Fuyuki Yagi, [4] Naohiro Kaji*
[1]Chiyoda Croporation, Technology Development Department and Hydrogen Business Department, 4-6-2 Minatomirai Nishi-ku, 2208765 Yokohama, Japan
[2]Chiyoda Croporation, R&D Center, Technology Development Department, 3-13 Moriya-cho Kanagawa-ku, 2208765 Yokohama, Japan
[3]Chiyoda Croporation, Technology Development Department, 4-6-2 Minatomirai Nishi-ku, 2208765 Yokohama, Japan
[3]Chiyoda Croporation, Hydrogen Business Department, 4-6-2 Minatomirai Nishi-ku, 2208765 Yokohama, Japan
*Corresponding author e-mail: https://www.chiyodacorp.com/en/contact/index.php

ABSTRACT

Hydrogen energy carrier system is indispensable for decarbonisation through the expansion of renewable energy. The organic chemical hydride method for storing and transporting hydrogen under normal temperature and pressure conditions in the liquid state by incorporating hydrogen atoms into the molecular structure of liquid organic hydrogen carrier (LOHC) is safe and low risk method. Chiyoda started the development of a system employing the method since 2002, named the system "SPERA Hydrogen™" and system completed the international demonstration of massive hydrogen supply chain from Brunei Darussalam to Japan in 2020. It is the only system that has completed the international demonstration of the entire process and has moved to the commercialization stage. It is considered that the system is the most inexpensive except ammonia direct combustion with boiler at present and also has a high potential for cost reduction towards the future compared to other methods.

Keywords: Hydrogen, storage, transportation, SPERA hydrogen

#390

PERFORMANCE OF BENZYLTOLUENE AS PURE HYDROCARBON LIQUID ORGANIC HYDROGEN CARRIER (LOHC) IN STORAGE CYCLES

[1] Timo Ruede, [1]Patrick Preuster, [1]Moritz Wolf, [1]Peter Wasserscheid*
[1] FZ Jülich, Helmholtz-Institute Erlangen-Nuernberg for Renewable Energy (IEK 11), Egerlandstr. 3, Erlangen, Germany
*Corresponding author e-mail: t.ruede@fz-juelich.de

ABSTRACT

This study presents benzyltoluene/perhydro benzyltoluene (H0-BT/H12-BT) as favourable liquid organic hydrogen carrier (LOHC) system for potential technical applications. LOHCs can enable safe and efficient hydrogen logistics using the existent fuel infrastructure. Compared with the well-established LOHC systems toluene/methylcyclohexane and dibenzyltoluene/perhydro dibenzyltoluene (H0-DBT/H18-DBT), the H0-BT/H12-BT system combines a similarly high volumetric storage density and excellent robustness in hydrogenation/dehydrogenation cycles with low viscosity for easy handling in colder operation conditions. Herein, we report repeated hydrogenation and dehydrogenation cycles of technical grade LOHCs in semi continuous operation at 290 °C with a commercial platinum on alumina catalyst (Pt/Al_2O_3). Reaction rates for both, hydrogen uptake and release, are generally found to be higher for H0-BT/H12-BT when compared to the DBT-based LOHC system at identical reaction conditions. By-product formation is low during cycling of the H0-BT/H12-BT system and only small amounts of the dehydrocyclisation products, such as methylfluorene species, are formed that can themselves act as hydrogen carrier.

Keywords: Chemical hydrogen storage, benzyltoluene, repeated storage cycles, reaction rate, by-product formation

#399

PERFORMANCE ANALYSIS OF A SOLAR TOWER POWER PLANT INTEGRATED WITH HYDROGEN ENERGY STORAGE SYSTEM

[1] *Mohammad Hashem Mirbagheri,* [1*] *Ehsan Baniasadi,* [2]*Hadi Genceli*

[1] University of Isfahan, Department of Mechanical Engineering, Faculty of Engineering, Hezar Jerib Ave., Isfahan, Iran

[2]Yildiz Technical University, Faculty of Mechanical Engineering, Mechanical Engineering Department, Besiktas, Istanbul, 34349, Turkey

*Corresponding author e-mail: e.baniasadi@eng.ui.ac.ir

ABSTRACT

In this paper, an exergy-economic model is developed to analyze the performance of a direct steam solar tower - steam turbine - organic Rankine cycle (ORC) power plant under different working conditions. The solar power plant is connected to a power grid, and it is integrated with a hydrogen storage system. The hydrogen storage system is composed of an electrolyser, fuel cell, steam turbine and organic Rankine cycle. When solar energy is not available, electrical power is generated by the fuel cell, steam turbine and ORC using the hydrogen produced by the electrolyzer. The analyses are made for the maximum solar irradiation that is available in the city of YAZD in Iran. The effects of the current density and operating temperature on the performance of the solid oxide electrolyzer cell (SOEC) and solid oxide fuel cell (SOFC) are investigated. The effect of solar irradiation on the energy and exergy efficiencies of the cycle is investigated. The results indicate that increase of the solar irradiation leads to an increase of the energy and exergy efficiencies of the cycle. The solar tower has the highest exergy destruction and capital investment cost.

Keywords: Direct steam solar power tower, Solid oxide electrolyzer cell, solid oxide fuel cell, Organic Rankine cycle

#413

3D COFs FOR PHOTOCATALYTIC N_2 FIXATION: A COMPUTATIONAL STUDY

[1*] *Amro M. O. Mohamed,* [1] *Yusuf Bicer*

[1] Division of Sustainable Development, College of Science and Engineering, Hamad Bin Khalifa University, Qatar Foundation, Doha, Qatar

*Corresponding author e-mail: ammohamed@hbku.edu.qa

ABSTRACT

As a result of permanent porosity, tunability, and structural stability, covalent-organic frameworks (COFs) have been introduced in various environmental-related applications. COFs have been studied for various gas separation-related applications, primarily CO_2 capture from natural gas and flue gas. The performance of COFs towards gas separation can be investigated by computational techniques, including density functional theory (DFT) and molecular simulations based on force fields. In this work, several atomistic and molecular simulations techniques are used to identify COFs for the nitrogen conversion to ammonia photocatalytically. The experimental database is screened for desired conduction, valence band, and bandgap. A total of six structures are selected from the 3D structures. COF-300 has been shown to have desirable electronic properties (bandgap approximately 3.5 eV) and the highest N_2 adsorption among the six COFs. The simulations are performed using GCMC simulations to determine the nitrogen capacity of the COFs. Structures with one of the desired valence or conduction bands with desirable bandgaps are coupled in a COF/COF junction that potentially enhances charge separation and reduces charge carrier recombination rates. The study reports a 40 COF/COF heterojunction for the required application. Such high throughput screening typically involves databases (experimental based) and results in an essential structure-function relationship that accelerates materials discovery in several energy applications.

Keywords: Photofixation of nitrogen, green ammonia, COFs, computational screening

#416

COMPATIBILITY OF POLYMERS AND COMPOSITES WITH HYDROGEN IN TRANSPORT AND STORAGE EQUIPMENT

[1] Xavier Lefebvre,[1] Marie-Hélène Klopffer, [1] Camilo Castro Lopez*
[1] IFP Energies Nouvelles, Applied Physical Chemistry and Mechanics Division,
1&4 avenue de Bois-Préau, 92852 Rueil-Malmaison Cedex, France
*Corresponding author e-mail: xavier.lefebvre@ifpen.fr

ABSTRACT

With the growing place taken by hydrogen, some questions still remain about its delivery, transport and storage. In these domains, one of the key challenges to compete is the great permeability of hydrogen through polymer and composite infrastructures (pipes, connecting parts, pressure vessels, ...) compared to other gases such as methane for instance. In this context, the compatibility of hydrogen with polymeric components must be carefully qualified regarding permeation properties, blistering and collapse resistance. Long-time behaviour may be assessed with specific modelling. Beyond qualification aspects, this approach can be useful to support standards elaboration.

Keywords: Polymer, composite, permeation, blistering, hydrogen

#419

THEORETICAL APPROACH OF LIGHT METAL FUNCTIONALIZED SILIGENE FOR HYDROGEN STORAGE

[1] Brandom J. Cid, [1] Ángel R. Montoya, [2] Margarita C. Crisóstomo, [3] Luis A. Pérez, [1] Álvaro Miranda*
[1] Instituto Politécnico Nacional, ESIME Culhuacán, Av. Santa Ana 1000, 04440 Ciudad de México, México
[2] Instituto Politécnico Nacional, CECYT 8 Narciso Bassols, Av. de las Granjas 628, 02519, Ciudad de México, México
[3] Instituto de Física, Universidad Nacional Autónoma de México, C.P. 04510, Ciudad de México, México
*Corresponding author e-mail: amirandad@ipn.mx

ABSTRACT

In this work, the hydrogen storage capacity of alkali atoms (AM)-decorated siligene monolayer (SiGe-ML) was studied using a first principles approach based on density functional theory. The siligene monolayer was modelled by removing a surface of the direction from a perfect crystalline siligene crystal, and then an AM atom was placed on its surface, whereupon multiple H_2 molecules were placed in the vicinity of the AM, the atoms used were Li, Na, and K. The results indicate that the most favorable position for the AM to adsorb is on the hollow site of the SiGe-ML with the highest binding energy of 2.84, 3.16 and 3.55 eV for Li, Na and K, respectively. Voronoi population analysis revealed that all the metal decoration donated a fraction of their electronic charges to SiGe-ML. Pristine SiGe-ML does not have high storage capacity for H_2, since it can adsorb only one hydrogen molecule per site. The numerical results of the adsorption energies of H_2 molecules on the AM atoms are in the range physisorption. The Na and K-decorated SiGe-ML have the highest storage capacity, being able to bind up to six H_2 molecules, whereas Li-decorated siligene adsorbed three H_2 molecules. Formation energies show that all the studied cases of H_2 molecules adsorbed on AM atom-decorated SiGe-ML are energetically favorable, indicating that decorated SiGe-ML could have potential as an efficient hydrogen molecular storage media under ambient conditions.

Keywords: 2D materials, DFT, siligene, hydrogen storage, alkali metals.

#427

CATALYTIC PROPERTIES OF B-DOPED G-C_3N_4 ON METHANOLYSIS OF $NaBH_4$ TO PRODUCE H_2

[1]*Sahin Demirci,* [1,2,3,4]*Nurettin Sahiner**

[1]Canakkale Onsekiz Mart University, Faculty of Science and Arts, Department of Chemistry, Terzioglu Campus, Canakkale, 17100, Turkey.

[2] Canakkale Onsekiz Mart University, Nanoscience and Technology Research and Application Center (NANORAC), Terzioglu Campus, 17100 Canakkale, Turkey.

[3] Department of Chemical and Biomolecular Engineering, University of South Florida, Tampa, FL, 33620, USA.

[4] Department of Ophthalmology, Morsani College of Medicine, University of South Florida, 12901 Bruce B. Downs Blvd, MDC21, Tampa, FL 33612, USA.

*Corresponding author e-mail: sahiner71@gmail.com

ABSTRACT

Here, the synthesis of heteroatom doped graphitic-carbon nitride (g-C_3N_4) as a catalyst for hydrogen (H_2) production from sodium borohydride ($NaBH_4$) was reported. The synthesis process was carried out by direct condensation of nitrogen-containing organic precursors in the presence of boric acid as the heteroatom "B" sources. Melamine, dicyanamide, and urea were used as nitrogen-containing organic precursors. To prepare B-doped g-C_3N_4 species, various mole fractions of Boric acid: Melamine has been formulated such as 100:0, 75:25, 50:50, 25:75, and 0:100. Moreover, the B-doped g-C_3N_4 from the Boric acid: Dicyanamide/Urea was also prepared at the mole ratio of 50:50. The prepared B-doped g-C_3N_4 species were used as catalysts in the methanolysis reaction of $NaBH_4$ to produce H_2. The effect of hetero atom ratio in g-C_3N_4, g-C_3N_4 precursor, melamine, dicyanamide or urea, amount of catalyst, acid treatment, and the temperature was investigated for their catalytic performances. The important activation parameters, activation energy (Ea), enthalpy (ΔH), and entropy (ΔS) were calculated for B-doped g-C3N4 species prepared from melamine, dicyanamide, and urea.

Keywords: Carbon nitride, boric acid, heteroatom-doped C_3N_4, catalyst, methanolysis of $NaBH_4$, H_2 production

#441

NUMERICAL AND EXPERIMENTAL EVIDENCE OF DEFECTS CREATION IN EPDM AFTER HYDROGEN DECOMPRESSION

[1*]*Quentin Gardavaud,* [1]*Maximiliano Melnichuk,* [1]*Frédéric Thiébaud,* [1]*Dominique Perreux*

[1]Univ. Bourgogne Franche-Comté, FEMTO-ST Institute, UMR CNRS 6174, Department of Applied Mechanics, 24 rue de l'épitaphe, 25000 Besançon, FRANCE

*Corresponding author e-mail: quentin.gardavaud@femto-st.fr

ABSTRACT

Elastomers are main components in hydrogen systems. It was reported that these materials could be damaged when submitted to hydrogen high-pressure, especially in case of fast depressurisation. In order to predict this phenomenon, we define a prediction model, and assess it by depressurised elastomer samples.

Keywords: Type IV tanks, EPDM, cavitation, fast depressurization, tomography.

#1445

HYDROGEN STORAGE ON ALKALI METAL DECORATED GeC TWO-DIMENSIONAL: A FIRST PRINCIPLES STUDY

[1,2] *Lucia G. Arellano,* [3] *Francisco De Santiago,* [1] *Fernando A. Serrano,* [2] *Jun Nakamura,* [1*] *Miguel Cruz-Irisson*
[1]Instituto Politécnico Nacional, ESIME Culhuacán, Av. Santa Ana 1000, 04430 Ciudad de México, México
[2] Department of Engineering Science, The University of Electro-Communications (UEC Tokyo), 1-5-1 Chofugaoka,
Chofu, Tokyo 182-8585, Japan
[3] Instituto de Física, Universidad Nacional Autónoma de México, C.P. 04510, Ciudad de México, México
*Corresponding author e-mail: irisson.ipn@gmail.com

ABSTRACT

In recent years bidimensional (2D) nanostructures have been theorized to be optimal for hydrogen storage, owning to their large surface and low density. It has been proposed that a germanium carbide 2D monolayer may be more flexible than graphene, retaining some of its interesting properties. In this work, based on density functional theory calculations, the capacities of alkali metal atoms-decorated germanium carbide (GeC) as hydrogen storage media were investigated. The monolayers were modeled by removing an atomically thin layer of the [111] direction of an otherwise perfect GeC crystal, subsequently alkali metal atoms were placed in its surface whereupon H_2 molecules were placed in their vicinity. Results show that the calculated Li and Na binding energy of the GeC monolayer is lower than their corresponding bulk cohesive energy, which may suggest that clusterization happens, while in K this is avoided. By adsorbing Li atoms on both sides of GeC monolayer, the hydrogen capacity can reach as high as 5.02 wt%, and the average binding energy of H_2 molecules falls within the range of 0.35–0.14 eV, which is favourable for developing high-capacity hydrogen storage at room temperature. These numerical results may provide a potential alternative to design new hydrogen storage materials based on monolayered GeC.

Keywords: Hydrogen storage, Alkali, Germanium carbide

#1446

EFFECTIVE HYDROLYSIS OF ALKALINE SODIUM BOROHYDRIDE: CoB-TRITON CATALYST

[1*] *Cenk Kaya,* [2] *Jülide Hazal Türkcan,* [3] *Hüseyin Elçiçek,* [2] *Oğuz Kaan Özdemir,* [4] *Görkem Kökkülünk,* [4] *Kaan Ünlügençoğlu*
[1*]Istanbul Technical University, Marine Engineering, Istanbul, Turkey
[2]Yildiz Technical University, Metallurgical and Materials Engineering, Istanbul, Turkey
[3]Maritime Higher Vocational School, Sakarya University of Applied Sciences, Sakarya, Turkey
[4]Yildiz Technical University, Marine Engineering, Istanbul, Turkey
*Corresponding author e-mail: cenkkaya@itu.edu.tr

ABSTRACT

Chemical hydrides show promise in solving the storage challenge, which is one of the important problems in the widespread use of hydrogen. An important issue that needs to be developed regarding chemical hydride storage is the high speed of hydrogen release. For this reason, this study focuses on hydrogen release rates of alkaline sodium borohydride with different prepared catalysts. Different amounts of surfactant as Triton X-100 including CoB catalysts have been prepared and hydrogen release rates (HGR) have been compared. Results indicate that Triton addition has different effects, but optimum ratio improves catalyst performance. 150 µl Triton addition (CoB-T150) raises HGR from 12.61 $L_{H2}{*}g^{-1}{}_{cat}{*}min^{-1}$ to 17.69 $L_{H2}{*}g^{-1}{}_{cat}{*}min^{-1}$, as 40.2% increase compared to pure CoB catalyst. As a result, surfactants offer alternative to enhance catalyst performance and need further research.

Keywords: CoB catalyst, $NaBH_4$ hydrolysis, surfactant, Triton X-100, hydrogen storage

#1453

ANALYSIS OF THE FIRST STEP OF HYDROGEN RELEASE OF AMMONIA BORANE FOR PCA WITH DIFFERENT HEATING RATES

[1,2*] *Roberto Hinojosa-Nava,* [2] *E.V. Mejía-Uriarte,* [2] *R.Y. Sato-Berrú*
[1]Instituto de Ciencias Aplicadas y Tecnología, [2] Facultad de Ciencias,
Universidad Nacional Autónoma de México,
[2]Circuito Exterior S/N, Ciudad Universitaria, 04510, México City, México
*Corresponding author e-mail: hinro36@ciencias.unam.mx

ABSTRACT

Ammonia borane is a material with high hydrogen content, so it receives a lot of attention. Its handling and operating conditions are of great importance for technological applications. For this reason, in this work a study was carried out using high resolution Raman spectroscopy on the behavior of ammonium borane with four different heating ramps, in the first step of hydrogen release. With the data obtained, a principal component analysis (PCA) was made, in which the stability of AB in the release process can be noted. Stability is important in the release process, as it can be related to the formation of by-products.

Keywords: Ammonia borane, Raman spectroscopy, principal analysis component, heating rates

#1459

NUMERICAL SIMULATION ON PRESSURE REDUCTION PHENOMENON WITH LARGE-SCALE LIQUEFIED HYDROGEN TANK

[1*] *Kazuma Tani,* [1] *Takehiro Himeno,* [1] *Toshinori Watanabe,* [2] *Hiroaki Kobayashi,*
[3] *Shuntaro Unno,* [3] *Shoji Kamiya,* [3] *Yasumasa Nakashima,* [3] *Osamu Muragishi,* [3] *Katsuhiro Kanbe*
[1]The University of Tokyo, Department of Astronautics and Aeronautics, 7-3-1 Hongo, Bunkyo-ku, Tokyo, 113-8654, Japan
[2] Japan Aerospace Exploration Agency (JAXA), Institute of Space and Astronautical Science, 3-1-1 Yoshinodai, Chuo-ku, Sagamihara City, Kanagawa Prefecture, 252-5210, Japan
[3] Kawasaki Heavy Industries, Ltd., 1-1, Kawasaki-cho, Akashi City, 673-8666, Japan
*Corresponding author e-mail: tani@aero.t.u-tokyo.ac.jp

ABSTRACT

Kawasaki Heavy Industries, Ltd. has established the Hydrogen Energy Supply Chain (HESC) which aims to introduce a large amount of liquid hydrogen (LH_2) to Japan. LH_2 will be produced from brown coal in Australia and then shipped to Japan with LH_2 Carrier. After a long transportation, LH_2 inside the tanks of the Carrier will be pressurized and saturated by heat leakage from outside. Therefore, reducing the pressure to 1 atmosphere will be required for the safe tank operation. However, decreasing pressure will cause flashing, which will cause an excess of the venting capacity or liquid leakage because of an increase of vent mass. Hence, the purpose of this research is to reveal the pressure reduction rate and liquid behaviour through experimental and numerical approaches. Pressure reduction experiments were conducted by using 30 m^3 tank whose around 80% volume was filled with saturated LH_2. The experiments showed that the pressure undershoot occurred at the beginning, and then the pressure decreased based on the Clausius-Clapeyron equation. From numerical analysis by VOF based in-house CFD code, it was found that the pressure undershoot was caused by the boiling delay, and the tank pressure followed the saturation pressure after the liquid fully stirred.

Keywords: HESC, liquid hydrogen, large-scale liquid hydrogen tank, flashing, pressure undershoot

#1460

MACHINE LEARNING AS A TOOL FOR INTERPRETING VARIABLES IN HYDROGEN SORPTION DATA

[1] *Muhammad Irfan Maulana Kusdhany,* [1*] *Stephen Matthew Lyth*
[1] Department of Automotive Science, Kyushu University, 744 Motooka Nishi-ku, 8190374, Fukuoka, Japan
*Corresponding author e-mail: lyth@i2cner.kyushu-u.ac.jp

ABSTRACT

To realize the hydrogen economy, it is important to develop methods of storing hydrogen that are cost-effective, safe, and compact. One method of storing hydrogen which shows a lot of potential is through physisorption on high surface area carbon. However, the scientific literature offers conflicting information on which properties of the carbons are important to hydrogen storage and to what extent. This is chiefly because each experimental study on carbon materials only analyzes results on an incredibly small subset of carbon materials. To remedy this, we conducted an integrative data analysis wherein we collected experimental data from many studies in the literature to construct a large dataset. We then used this dataset to develop a machine learning model which can predict the hydrogen adsorption isotherm at 77K based on the porosity and chemical composition of the carbon. By analyzing this model using a post-hoc explanation method called Shapley Additive Explanations, we can analyze the structure-property relationships clearly.

Keywords: Hydrogen storage, porous carbon, machine learning

#1463

INFLUENCE OF HYDROGEN ON FLEXIBLE PIPE SERVICE

[1*] *Christelle Gabet,* [2] *Svein Kjenner*
[1] TechnipFMC, Flexible Technology, Rue Jean Huré, 76480 Le Trait, France
[2] TechnipFMC, EMS Project Engineering, Kirkegårdsveien 45, 3616 Kongsberg, Norway
*Corresponding author e-mail: christelle.gabet@technipfmc.com

ABSTRACT

Renewables in the offshore space are integrated with technologies to deliver at-scale solutions for offshore green hydrogen production and sustainable renewable energy. The system consists of offshore wind turbines and offshore hydrogen technologies for the production, storage and transportation of energy in the form of pressurized green hydrogen. It can also be used to produce, store and deliver hydrogen to consumers at sea or exported in a pipeline to shore.

Within this context, subsea pipelines are needed to transport gaseous hydrogen. Nevertheless, hydrogen is well known for its ability to cause steel embrittlement and is also a non-usual gas within standard offshore Oil & Gas sector. For these reasons, caution has to be taken and tests to be conducted before being able to propose transportation solutions.

Flexible pipes represent an effective solution for conveying gaseous hydrogen subsea from fixed or floating turbines or systems, in particular under dynamic conditions. Their intrinsic low allowable minimum bending radius, and tolerance to accommodate large relative motions, make it a perfect choice for floating offshore systems in shallow water areas targeted for deployment of offshore wind turbines with hydrogen technologies. Furthermore, the efficient installation time and cost enable to envisage an extended use for the offshore green hydrogen transportation systems. Finally, by construction, flexible pipes have their high strength steel wires in between two polymer sheathes, in a less severe, so called annulus, environment. Thus, with this kind of solution, such high strength steels submitted to lowered hydrogen pressures compared to bore, might be used without any embrittlement risk.

This paper presents experimental data (slow strain rate tensile tests and toughness tests) to demonstrate the poor influence of hydrogen on carbon steel wires, used for flexible pipes, service life in annulus conditions. Also included are results dealing with steel connection parts, which are lower strength steel but directly in contact with the carried hydrogen gas. Last part will be dedicated to polymer behaviours in contact with this unusual gas for Oil & Gas industry, namely, Rapid Gas Decompression (RGD) and ageing tests.

Those results enable to establish the flexible pipe solution as a reliable solution for hydrogen transportation, tolerating furthermore advantageously elevated hydrogen pressure (up to few hundreds bar). On this basis, a complementary qualification program is ongoing to generate the full set of experimental data allowing the safe engineering of flexible pipe solution for offshore wind farms. This work is likely one of the first to be discussing about the influence of hydrogen on materials used in flexible pipes for subsea transportation.

Keywords: Flexible pipes, subsea hydrogen transportation, hydrogen embrittlement, carbon steel wires and connectors, polymer RGD and ageing

#1465

CFD-ASSISTED HYDRODYNAMIC CHARACTERIZATION OF A CENTRIFUGAL LIQUID ORGANIC HYDROGEN CARRIER DEHYDROGENATION UNIT

[1] *Laurens Van Hoecke*, [2*] *Patrice Perreault*

[1] University of Antwerp, Faculty of Sciences, Department of Bioscience Engineering, Sustainable Energy Air and Water Technology (DuEL), Groenenborgerlaan 171 – 2020 Antwerpen, Antwerp, Belgium

[2] University of Antwerp, Faculty of Sciences/Blue App, Department of Bioscience Engineering, Instituut voor Milieu & Duurzame Ontwikkeling (IMDO), Groenenborgerlaan 171 – 2020 Antwerpen, Antwerp, Belgium

*Corresponding author e-mail: Patrice.Perreault@uantwerpen.be

ABSTRACT

Hydrogen release units from Liquid Organic Hydrogen Carriers suffer from two main drawback: high energy demand at high temperature, and inefficient H_2 release due to the viscosity of both the hydrogen gas produced and the liquid carrier. In this work, we present the CFD-assisted design of a centrifugal dehydrogenation reactor for the H_2 release from perhydro-dibenzyl toluene. Our proposed technology allows to negligibly affect the required residence required for the slow dehydrogenation of perhydro dibenzyl toluene, while allowing an extensive degassing of the LOHC by a combination of applied shear stress and radial pressure drop in the reactor. Reactive simulations are underway, in addition to experimental validation of the degassing rates.

Keywords: Liquid Organic hydrogen carriers (LOHC), reactor design, centrifugal fields

#1466

METAL HYDRIDE COMPOSITE MATERIALS FOR THERMO-CHEMICAL HYDROGEN COMPRESSION

[1] *Marius Lau*, [1,2] *Oliver Ehrensberger*, [1] *Felix Heubner*

[1] Fraunhofer Institute for Manufacturing Technology and Advanced Materials IFAM, Branch Lab Dresden, Winterbergstraße 28, 01277 Dresden, Germany;

[2] Mut Advanced Heating GmbH, Fritz-Winkler-Straße 1 - 2, 07749 Jena, Germany

*Corresponding author e-mail: marius.lau@ifam-dd.fraunhofer.de, felix.heubner@ifam-dd.fraunhofer.de, ehrensberger@mut-jena.de

ABSTRACT

Low temperature waste heat (e.g. 100°C) can be utilized for hydrogen compression with hydride forming materials. In order to increase productivity and to decrease cycle time of a metal hydride-based hydrogen compressor, it is necessary to face heat transport limitations and to accelerate the overall rate of reaction. The compression cycle time can be significantly decreased by using metal hydride composite materials (MHC) with increased thermal conductivity. In this contribution, the use of composite materials is compared with conventional metal hydride (MH) materials with low thermal conductivity. A dual stage hydrogen compressor was built in laboratory scale and demonstrated with MH and innovative MHC. MHC increase the productivity of a MH compressor by up to 500%.

Keywords: Hydrogen compression, metal hydride, metal hydride composite, thermo-chemical compression

#1488

REACTION PROCESS OF AMMONIA PRODUCTION FROM IRON NITRIDE AND CARBONATED WATER

[*1] *Hiromi Eba*, [1] *Tian Liu*, [1] *Keiichi Fukami*

[1] Faculty and Graduate School of Science and Engineering, Tokyo City University, Tamazutsumi 1-28-1, Setagaya, Tokyo, Japan

*Corresponding author e-mail: heba@tcu.ac.jp

ABSTRACT

The interstitial compounds, Fe_3N and Fe_4N, reacted with water to generate NH_3 and H_2. The reaction proceeded under normal temperature and pressure when carbon dioxide was added to the reaction system. The product ratio, NH_3/H_2, was larger than the value calculated from the reaction formula when iron nitride had reacted completely. The NH_3 formation proceeded easily because the activation energy calculated from the Arrhenius plot of temperature vs. reaction rate was lower for NH_3 formation than for H_2. As the reaction progressed, the lattice constant of iron nitride decreased, suggesting that N diffused between the lattices and moved to the surface to produce ammonia. Fe_3N, which has a crystal structure in which N readily diffuses between lattices, had a higher ammonia production rate than Fe_4N. Adding carbonate to the system accelerated the reaction. The elementary reaction involving carbonic acid was the rate-determining step: the reduction of H^+ in carbonic acid by reacting with Fe or removing Fe^{2+} from the reaction system by forming a soluble Fe^{2+} carbonate complex was the slowest reaction step.

Keywords: Ammonia production, carbon dioxide, carbonic acid, iron and steel, iron nitride

#1491

EFFECT OF IRON PARTICLE SHAPE AND ALLOY COMPOSITION ON HYDROGEN PRODUCTION EFFICIENCY IN THE WATER-IRON REACTION

[1]*Hayao Yagi*, [1*]*Hiromi Eba*
[1] Faculty and Graduate School of Science and Engineering, Tokyo City University, Tamazutsumi 1-28-1, Setagaya, Tokyo, Japan
*Corresponding author e-mail: heba@tcu.ac.jp

ABSTRACT

The relationship between the properties and reactivity of iron particles was investigated to develop a hydrogen production process from scrap iron using carbonated water. To evaluate the effect of alloy composition, Ni was selected from the range of alloy elements commonly present in steel that constitute scrap iron. A Ni salt was added to pure iron powder, stirred in an organic solvent, and dried. Subsequently, the redox reaction using the iron powder for hydrogen generation from water was analyzed. The final amount of hydrogen produced increased, which suggested that Ni may have penetrated the iron crystals. The hydrogen production efficiencies of pure iron powder and alloyed steel powders from the manufacturer were also compared. Ni partially alloyed steel powder (SIGMALOY2010) generated more hydrogen than pure iron powder of the same particle size. Moreover, a clear correlation between the particle size and hydrogen production was observed for SIGMALOY2010; the smaller the particle size, the higher the hydrogen production, which suggested that the reaction rate corresponds to the specific surface area. However, for other alloyed steel, no clear correlation exists with particle size. It was found that shape, porosity, and specific surface area also need to be analyzed and discussed.

Keywords: Hydrogen generation, carbon dioxide, iron and steel, scrap iron, Ni alloyed steel

#1506

MODELING OF A HYDROGEN STORAGE SYSTEM BASED ON METAL HYDRIDE AND PHASE CHANGE MATERIAL

[1*]*Walter H. Wiersma*, *Canan Acar*
[1] University of Twente, Drienerlolaan 5, Enschede, Netherlands
*Corresponding author e-mail: walter-wiersma@live.nl

ABSTRACT

This study analyzes the viability of a metal hydride–phase change material (MH-PCM) onboard storage system. Additionally, the effect of natural convection and thermal enhancements on the absorption time and gravimetric capacity are studied. To this study's knowledge, no studies have been performed on MH-PCM configurations while including natural convection. No significant attempts to include thermal enhancements were neither found in the literature. The results show that natural convection plays a significant role during the melting of PCM and absorption of hydrogen by the MH. The addition of natural convection causes a reduction of 68.9% in absorption time. Introducing thermal enhancements to the MH-PCM tank, the absorption is reduced by 92.4% while seeing a decrease of the gravimetric capacity of 30.42% compared to the case not including thermal enhancements. Performance indicators are gathered by having a defined car and the currently defined storage subjected to different driving cycles. From comparing these performance indicators with the targets set by the Department of Energy, it is concluded that an MH-PCM onboard storage system is not viable. The cause is contributed to the PCM mass required to store the released heat during absorption.

Keywords: Hydrogen storage, metal hydride, phase change material, heat transfer, thermal management

#1508

BORON-HYDROGEN MATERIALS TOWARDS DECARBONISATION

[1*]Sonnur Kurtuluş, [2]*Bilge Coşkuner Filiz*, [3]*Hülya Civelek Yörüklü*, [4]*Korkut Açıkalın*, [1]*Halit Eren Figen*, [5]*Umit Bilge Demirci*, [1]*Aysel Kantürk Figen*

[1] Department of Chemical Engineering, Yildiz Technical University, İstanbul, Turkey
[2] Department of Metallurgy and Materials Engineering, Yildiz Technical University, İstanbul, Turkey
[3] Department of Environmental Engineering, Yildiz Technical University, İstanbul, Turkey
[4] Department of Energy Systems Engineering, Yalova University, Yalova, Turkey
[5]Institut Europeen des Membranes, IEM – UMR 5635, Univ Montpellier, ENSCM, CNRS, Montpellier, France
*Corresponding author e-mail: kurtulussonnur@gmail.com

ABSTRACT

Boron-hydrogen (B-H) materials are used as hydrogen and heat sources, due to their reducing potential. It has been shown again with the COVID-19 pandemic that greenhouse gas activities are anthropogenic in origin. In particular, the conversion of carbon dioxide (CO_2) into valuable chemicals has an important place in the fight against the climate crisis. The conversion of anthropogenic CO_2 into valuable chemicals has important implications for a habitable world. In many studies in the literature, boron hydrides have been used to produce, hydrogen and convert carbon dioxide into valuable chemicals. Formic acid and methanol obtained by hydrogenation can be seen as the clean energy movement of the future with its value in hydrogen storage. The type of valuable chemicals that will be formed by the hydrogenation of CO_2 is directly related to the method to be followed. The type of catalyst used, or how much hydrogen molecule interacts with CO_2, determines the valuable chemical that will form. Disturbances in the thermodynamics of the hydrogenation of CO_2 have been tried to be eliminated by various types of catalysts and necessary condition optimizations. Many catalysts and methods developed for the hydrogenation of CO_2 were examined. This study discusses the use of B-H materials via catalytic conversion of CO_2 into valuable chemicals in terms of critical factors such as reaction conditions, selection of catalyst, and solvent.

Keywords: Hydrogenation, decarbonization, borane-hydrogen materials, carbon dioxide reduction

#1518

INFLUENCE OF DIFFERENT ADDITIVES IN THE HYDROLYSIS OF SODIUM BOROHYDRIDE

[1]*Lucía Gómez-Coma*, [2]*Diogo Silva*, [1*]*Alfredo Ortiz*, [2]*Alexandra M.F.R. Pinto*, [1]*Inmaculada Ortiz*

[1]Department of Chemical and Biomolecular Engineering. Universidad de Cantabria,
Av. Los Castros 46, 39005 Santander, Spain
[2]Transport Phenomena Research Center, Chemical Engineering Department, Faculty of Engineering, University of Porto Rua Dr. Roberto Frías s/n, 4200-465 Porto, Portugal
*Corresponding author e-mail: ortizal@unican.es

ABSTRACT

Achieving net-zero emissions in the atmosphere is one of the most critical challenges faced by society. Thus, the research efforts should be intended to develop and implement new green sources to substitute the traditional fossil fuels avoiding carbon dioxide emissions. Among others, hydrogen energy is positioned as promising renewable energy but still requires overcoming the disadvantages of storage. In this context, ensuring a safe process employing reasonable volumes and pressures is one of the hotspots which are needed to address. Sodium borohydrides with significant advantages such as low vapor pressure, stability, or high hydrogen storage capacity have been largely studied in the last years. Catalysts and the different operating conditions are well known in this field. This work intends to demonstrate the benefits of the employment of additives to improve process control in terms of yield. Specifically, sodium carboxymethyl cellulose additive in 1 wt %, provides performance of 85 %, concluding that although further efforts are required, this approach could improve the hydrolysis of borohydrides for hydrogen storage.

Keywords: hydrogen storage, sodium borohydrides, additives, hydrogen generation rate.

#1520

SYNTHESIS AND CHARACTERIZATION OF MIL-53(CR) METAL-ORGANIC FRAMEWORK FOR REMARKABLE HYDROGEN STORAGE

[1]*Abrar Hussain*, [1*]*Kuen-Song Lin**, [1] *Mu-Ting Tu*, [1] *You-Sheng Lin*, [1] *Yun Ko*, [1] *Yung-Chen Hsieh*
[1] Department of Chemical Engineering & Materials Science, Yuan Ze University, Taoyuan City, Taiwan
*Corresponding author e-mail: kslin@saturn.yzu.edu.tw

ABSTRACT

Metal-organic frameworks (MOFs) are deemed to be the most promising candidate for hydrogen storage material in this study. MIL-53(Cr) MOFs were synthesized from $Cr(NO_3)_3 \cdot 9H_2O$ combined with the terephthalic acid organic linker. Cleaning the MOFs crystals with various solvents at various warm temperatures was found to be effective and approved for increasing the specific surface area and porosity of MIL-53 (Cr) MOFs. The XRD patterns represented that MIL-53(Cr) MOFs had well crystalline structures. Nitrogen adsorption isotherms show that Mil-53(Cr) has approximately Type-I isotherm with the highest BET specific surface area of 1946 m^2g^{-1} after being treated with hot methanol. Hydrogen adsorption study shows that this material can store 0.45 wt.% of H_2 measured at 303 K and 32 bar. The pre-edge XANES spectra confirm the existence of Cr(III) in the crystalline framework of MIL-53(Cr) and the sharp feature at 6007 eV in XANES spectra represents the dipole-allowed electron transition from 1s to $4p_{xy}$. In addition, EXAFS spectra indicate that MIL-53(Cr) metal-organic frameworks structure has the Cr-O bond distance of 1.96 Å with a coordination number of 5.4.

Keywords: Metal-Organic frameworks, MIL-53(Cr), porous material, hydrogen storage, XANES/EXAFS.

#1528

SYNTHESIS OF CALCIUM BOROHYDRIDE WITH BORON-FLORIDE EXCHANGE AT HIGH PRESSURES

[1*] *Gökhan Gizer*, [1] *Fahim Karimi*, [1] *Claudio Pistidda*, [1] *Juliàn A. Puszkiel*
[1] Helmholtz-Zentrum Hereon, Institute of Hydrogen Technology, Max-Plank-Str. 1, 21502 Geesthacht, Germany
*Corresponding author e-mail: goekhan.gizer@hereon.de

ABSTRACT

In the present work, $Ca(BH_4)_2$ is synthesized by ball milling MgB_2 with CaF_2 and thereafter applying H_2 pressures of 1000 bar and temperatures of 350°C. Formation of α, β and γ-$Ca(BH_4)_2$ phases are confirmed, using in-situ synchrotron powder X-ray diffraction (SR-PXD). Volumetric measurements with a Sieverts' apparatus and mass spectrometry results indicate that 3.5 wt.% of H_2 can be stored reversibly. During hydrogenation, boron-fluoride exchange between MgB_2 and CaF_2 occurs. As a result, $Ca(BH_4)_2$ and MgF_2 are formed. During dehydrogenation, starting materials MgB_2 and CaF_2 are formed back, together with the H_2 release. Applying high pressures of H_2 can be helpful to investigate hydrogen storage systems that were reported to be partially reversible previously in the literature.

Keywords: High pressure, hydrogen storage, complex hydrides

#1532

STRUCTURAL EVOLUTION OF A Mg-C COMPOSITE OVER 1000 H_2 STORAGE CYCLES

[1,2] *Robert Carson*, [1*] *Brian Ellis*, [2] *Suraj Persaud*
[1] Canadian Nuclear Laboratories, Hydrogen Technologies Branch, 286 Plant Rd., Chalk River, Ontario, Canada
[2] Queen's University, Dept. of Mechanical and Materials Engineering, 130 Stuart St., Kingston, Ontario, Canada
*Corresponding author e-mail: brian.ellis@cnl.ca

ABSTRACT

With its high capacity (7.6 wt%), magnesium is a promising material for high temperature hydrogen storage applications [1]. To date, few studies have systematically tracked the morphological evolution of a material over a large number of hydrogen (de)sorption cycles. A Mg-C composite was prepared and exposed to 1000 hydrogen (de)sorption cycles. The experiment was interrupted at several points during cycling to retrieve a small aliquot of powder in order to characterize the crystallographic and morphological changes that were taking place in the material. The material demonstrated good capacity retention until about 700 cycles had been completed, at which point the kinetics of hydrogen (de)sorption began to slow. This could be explained by grain growth and particle densification observed in the material on extended cycling.

Keywords: Magnesium, magnesium hydride, hydrogen storage, long-term cycling, structural evolution

#1533

DEVELOPMENT OF THE NEC/12H-NEC LOHC SYSTEM AT CANADIAN NUCLEAR LABORATORIES

[1*] *Lorne Stolberg,* [1] *Blessing Ibeh,* [1] *Hongqiang Li,* [1] *Donald Ryland,* [1] *Sam Suppiah*
[1] Canadian Nuclear Laboratories, 286 Plant Road, Chalk River, Ontario, Canada
*Corresponding author e-mail: lorne.stolberg@cnl.ca

ABSTRACT

Because of the evolving hydrogen economy, there is a growing interest in the development and commercialization of suitable hydrogen storage technologies like liquid organic hydrogen carriers (LOHCs). N-ethylcarbazole/dodecahydro –N-ethylcarbazole (NEC/12H-NEC) LOHC application, although not currently commercialized, requires relatively low temperatures for the dehydrogenation step when compared to other systems that have been commercialized. What is reported in this study are results from ongoing efforts to develop and scale-up the NEC/12H-NEC LOHC system at Canadian Nuclear Laboratories. Preliminary dehydrogenation results using an in-house catalyst show the achievement of a target hydrogen release rate of 1.4×10^{-5} m^3/s, clearing the way for further scale-up.

Keywords: Liquid organic hydrogen carrier, catalysis, dehydrogenation, N-ethylcarbazole, hydrogenation

#1539

EVALUATION OF BASIC PHYSICAL PROPERTIES OF AMMONIA BORANE STORED IN LIQUID AMMONIA

[1*] *Fangqin Guo*,* [2] *Yufeng Wang,* [2]*Tomoyuki Ichikawa,* [3]*Hiroki Miyaoka,* [4]*Yoshihiro Shimizu,* [4]*Shuji Takamine,* [4]*Tessui Nakagawa,* [1]*Takayuki Ichikawa.*
[1]Graduate School of Advanced Science and Engineering, Hiroshima University, 1-3-1 Kagamiyama, Higashi-Hiroshima 739-8530, Japan
[2] Hydrolabo Inc., 3-10-31, Kagamiyama, Higashi-Hiroshima, 739-0046, Japan
[3] Natural Science Centre for Basic Research & Development, Hiroshima University, 1-3-1 Kagamiyama, Higashi-Hiroshima 739-8530, Japan
[4] Faculty of Science, University of the Ryukyus, 1 Senbaru, Nishihara-cho, Okinawa 903-0213, Japan
*Corresponding author e-mail: fang-qin-guo@hiroshima-u.ac.jp

ABSTRACT

Ammonia borane (AB: NH_3BH_3), as a potential hydrogen storage material, has been considered to be stored in different mediums for long-distance and safe transportation for practical usage. Three possible ways to store ammonia borane were parallelly considered: in the solid-state, liquid state of AB-NH_3 (NH_3 adducts or solution), and aqueous solution of AB. Among them, the liquid AB-NH_3 method shows promising advantages over other methods, in further, the basic properties of the AB-NH_3 system were studied in detail, such as absorption amount/pressure, temperature dependency of the density of the AB-NH_3 liquid, viscosity change when solved in liquid NH_3, and the thermal stability (shelf-life). The thermodynamical parameters of the reaction between AB and NH_3 were estimated and the enthalpy and entropy values were calculated to be -19.87 kJ/mol and 67.76 J/mol·K respectively. In this way, the above basic properties were clarified.

Keywords: Ammonia borane, liquid ammonia, viscosity, thermodynamics, storage density.

#1540

PLAIN COILED TUBE HEAT EXCHANGER FOR METAL HYDRIDE REACTORS

[1*] *K. Venkata Krishna,* [1] *Vivek Pandey,* [1] *M. P. Maiya*
[1] *Department of Mechanical Engineering, IIT Madras, Chennai-60036, Tamil Nadu, India*
**Corresponding author: me19d022@smail.iitm.ac.in*

ABSTRACT

This article proposes a plain coiled tube heat exchanger (PCTH) to enhance the heat transfer from the metal hydride-based hydrogen storage device. The PCTH design offers better absorption and heat transfer performance than the basic spiral tube design with constant tube and metal hydride volume. The PCTH and spiral tube designs take 520 and 746 s to absorb 90% storage capacity, respectively. The current design is further optimized by varying the no. of plain coils and tube diameter. The $LaNi_5$ alloy with 2 kg mass is selected for acquiring the optimum configuration of the proposed heat exchanger.

#1547

INTRODUCTION OF SPERA HYDROGEN SYSTEM™ FOR MASSIVE HYDROGEN STORAGE AND TRANSPORTATION

[1*] *Yoshimi Okada,* [2] *Kenichi Imagawa,* [3] *Hironori Kawai,* [3] *Tomoyuki Mikuriya* [2] *Fuyuki Yagi,* [4] *Naohiro Kaji*
[1]Chiyoda Corporation, Technology Development Department and Hydrogen Business Department, 4-6-2 Minatomirai Nishi-ku, 2208765 Yokohama, Japan
[2]Chiyoda Corporation, R&D Center, Technology Development Department, 3-13 Moriya-cho Kanagawa-ku, 2208765 Yokohama, Japan
[3]Chiyoda Corporation, Technology Development Department, 4-6-2 Minatomirai Nishi-ku, 2208765 Yokohama, Japan
[4]Chiyoda Corporation, Hydrogen Business Department, 4-6-2 Minatomirai Nishi-ku, 2208765 Yokohama, Japan
*Corresponding author e-mail: https://www.chiyodacorp.com/en/contact/index.php

ABSTRACT

Hydrogen energy carrier system is indispensable for decarbonisation through the expansion of renewable energy. The organic chemical hydride method for storing and transporting hydrogen under normal temperature and pressure conditions in the liquid state by incorporating hydrogen atoms into the molecular structure of liquid organic hydrogen carrier (LOHC) is safe and low risk method. Chiyoda started the development of a system employing the method since 2002, named the system "SPERA Hydrogen™" and system completed the international demonstration of massive hydrogen supply chain from Brunei Darussalam to Japan in 2020. It is the only system that has completed the international demonstration of the entire process and has moved to the commercialization stage. It is considered that the system is the most inexpensive except ammonia direct combustion with boiler at present and also has a high potential for cost reduction towards the future compared to other methods.

Keywords: Hydrogen, storage, transportation, SPERA hydrogen

#1557

A SIMPLE DYNAMIC MODEL FOR PREDICTING THE ABSORPTION AND DESORPTION BEHAVIOUR OF METAL HYDRIDE SYSTEMS

[1]*Abhishek Parida,* [2]*Sunku Prasad Jenne,* [3]**Muthukumar Palanisamy*
Department of Mechanical Engineering, Indian Institute of Technology Guwahati, Assam, India-781039
*Corresponding author e-mail: pmkumar@iitg.ac.in; pmkumariitg@gmail.com

ABSTRACT

In this study, a dynamic model is developed for predicting the absorption and desorption characteristics of the MH systems. The accuracy of the developed dynamic model is compared with the actual model. Further, the effect of reactor size on the overall performances of the system is studied. The dynamic model predicted the average bed temperature during absorption with a maximum deviation of 3.0% for the considered operating conditions compared to the actual model. At the same time, a maximum deviation of 2.06% was observed during desorption. The dynamic model exactly predicted the reaction completion time during absorption and desorption processes. The dynamic model is 306 times faster than the actual model reported in the literature, which saves computational time and cost with appreciable accuracy. The dynamic model can also be used to compute coupled systems like heat pumps, energy storage systems, compressors, and heating and cooling systems, which will be presented in our future work.

Keywords: Metal hydride, dynamic model, absorption; desorption; $LaNi_5$

#1565
NUMERICAL OPTIMIZATION OF MULTISTAGE MAGNETIC REFRIGERATION SYSTEM IN THE TEMPERATURE RANGE OF LIQUID HYDROGEN

[1,2] *Wenshuai Zheng,* [1,2*] *Jun Shen* [1,2,3*] *Zhenxing Li,* [1,2,3] *Ke Li,* [1,2] *Wei Dai,* [3] *Peng Hai,* [1,2] *Hongmei Huang,*
[1] Key Laboratory of Cryogenics, Technical Institute of Physics and Chemistry, Chinese Academy of Sciences, Beijing, China
[2] University of Chinese Academy of Sciences, Beijing, China
[3] Ganjiang Innovation Academy, Chinese Academy of Sciences, Ganzhou, Jiangxi, China
*Corresponding author e-mail: jshen@mail.ipc.ac.cn, zxli@mail.ipc.ac.cn

ABSTRACT

Based on a multi-stage regenerator design of magnetic refrigeration hydrogen liquefaction device, a two-dimensional transient numerical magnetic refrigeration model in the temperature range of liquid hydrogen was constructed. Some various factors on the cooling performance of the high temperature active magnetic regenerator (60 K - 80 K) were focused on, including operating frequency, fluid flow time ratio and filling mass of the magnetocaloric material. The simulation results showed that, as the operating frequency increases from 0.25 Hz to 4.00 Hz, the active magnetic regenerator can obtain is larger cooling power. Especially, under the condition of higher frequency and lower utilization factor, the larger cooling power and COP could be obtained. For fluid flow time ratio, the cooling power and efficiency increases with the increase of fluid flow time ratio from 40% to 80%. There is an increasing trend of corresponding utilization factor of the maximum cooling power, as the fluid flow time ratio increase. For the filling mass, the maximum cooling power has a linear relationship with the filling mass of the magnetocaloric material.

Keywords: Hydrogen liquefaction, multistage magnetic refrigeration, active magnetic regenerator, numerical simulation

#1575
DYNAMIC STUDY OF HYDROGEN ABSORPTION IN METAL HYDRIDE-BASED STORAGE SYSTEMS

[1,2] *Fawzi A.M. Elhamshri,* [2*] *Muhammet Kayfeci*
[1]Elmergib University-Department of Chemical Engineering, Algarhbolli, Libya
[2*] Karabuk University-Department of Energy Systems Engineering, 78050, Karabuk, Turkey
*Corresponding author e-mail: mkayfeci@karabuk.edu.tr

ABSTRACT

In this study, a performance analysis of metal hydride-based hydrogen storage during absorption process is presented. A 3-D mathematical model is developed in order to describing the reaction kinetic of the H_2 absorption by different metal hydride beds ($LaNi_{4.75}Al_{0.25}$ and $LaNi_5$). A novel simulation approach is proposed and performed for a cylindrical MHR configuration equipped with finned heat pipe. The simulating study is made by solving simultaneously the energy, mass-momentum, and kinetic differential equations of conservation by using COMSOL 5.2a multi-physics software. The reaction kinetic of H_2 is analyzed depending on some reactor design parameters such as; having heat pipe and fins at the reactor, metal hydride particle size, hydrogen inlet pressure, inlet radius of the reactor, coolant temperature, general convective heat transfer coefficient and wall thickness of the reactor. In general, the numerical simulations are in good agreement with the experimental data for $LaNi_5$ which have been previously published by the authors. Some parameters like the temperature inside the reactor, the kinetic of hydrogen reaction, the time durations, and the variations of the equilibrium pressure of the system were optimized. The obtained results show that the $LaNi_5$ material has the maximum amount of hydrogen storage capacity, while the $LaNi_{4.75}Al_{0.25}$ provides the fastest charging time in the cost of reduced charging capacity. Each of the metal hydride materials shows different hydriding results per their own thermo-physical properties. The maximum heat energy is released, and the maximum inner temperature is achieved when $LaNi_5$ material is used. The maximum temperature value which is achieved inside the reactor is at the maximum level for $LaNi_5$ material in general, whereas the minimum temperature value is for $LaNi_{4.75}Al_{0.25}$ material. For the given operating conditions, the time reaching the equilibrium by the cooling fluid temperature is the longest for $LaNi_5$ material, and the maximum amount of hydrogen mass to be stored is achieved for the $LaNi_5$ material, whereas the minimum values are achieved for $LaNi_{4.75}Al_{0.25}$ material. The time absorbing the hydrogen is the longest for $LaNi_5$ material and is the shortest for $LaNi_{4.75}Al_{0.25}$ material in general.

Keywords: Metal hydride, hydrogen storage, absorption, dynamic study, kinetics reaction, heat pipe and fins.

#1602

COMPARATIVE STUDY ON ACTIVE AND PASSIVE THERMAL MANAGEMENT OPTIONS OF A METAL HYDRIDE HYDROGEN STORAGE TANK

[1] Tacettin Dişli, [1] Sera Ayten Çetinkaya, [2] Mehmet Akif Ezan, [2] C. Özgür Çolpan*
[1] The Graduate School of Natural and Applied Sciences, Dokuz Eylul University, Izmir, Turkey
[2] Department of Mechanical Engineering, Faculty of Engineering, Dokuz Eylul University, Izmir, Turkey
*Corresponding author e-mail: dislitacettin@gmail.com

ABSTRACT

With the increase in the importance of hydrogen energy, studies on storage for the use of hydrogen have also increased. Although metal hydride tanks have a higher hydrogen storage capacity in terms of volume, they are more inefficient in terms of weight and thermal management than other storage systems. The bonding of hydrogen to the metal in MH tanks is exothermic during the absorption event, while the separation of hydrogen from the metal is endothermic during the desorption event. By incorporating phase change material (PCM) around the metal hydride tank, a 2D mathematical model will be developed in this work. In terms of thermal management, this model will be investigated both actively and passively.

Keywords: Metal-hydride hydrogen storage, PCM, hydrogen energy, hydrogen storage

#1603

OPTIMIZATION OF DESIGN PARAMETERS FOR A PHASE CHANGE MATERIAL INTEGRATED METAL HYDRIDE HYDROGEN STORAGE TANK

[1] Sera Ayten Çetinkaya, [1] Tacettin Dişli, [2] Mehmet Akif Ezan, [2] C. Özgür Çolpan*
[1] The Graduate School of Natural and Applied Sciences, Dokuz Eylul University, Izmir, Turkey
[2] Department of Mechanical Engineering, Faculty of Engineering, Dokuz Eylul University, Izmir, Turkey
*Corresponding author e-mail: seraaytencetinkaya96@gmail.com

ABSTRACT

Nowadays, with the development of technology and the increase in energy demand, hydrogen has become one of the important energy carriers. Hydrogen must be stored before it can be used in hydrogen-based applications. Among the various storage options such as compressed, liquid, cryo-compressed, metal-hydride or carbon nanotubes, hydrogen storage in metal hydride (MH) tanks can store more hydrogen in volume than other ways. However, in order to realize the charging and discharging of hydrogen in MH tanks, thermal management must be done well. For thermal management in MH tanks, many applications such as phase change material (PCM), heat exchangers, or fins can be used. In this study, a 1D mathematical model of a metal hydride tank and PCM will be developed. Properties such as the PCM thickness required for the PCM to reach the temperature required during the temperature change in the tank will be optimized according to the material during the absorption and desorption events in the metal hydride tank.

Keywords: Metal-hydride hydrogen storage, PCM, hydrogen energy, chemical hydrogen storage

#1614

INVESTIGATION OF INFRASTRUCTURE STUDY AND OPERATION PLANNING OF UNDERGROUND HYDROGEN STORAGE AREA

[1]Hatice Karakilcik*
[1]Faculty of Engineering, Department of Geology Engineering, Cukurova University, 01250, Adana, Turkey
*Corresponding author e-mail: hkilcik@cu.edu.tr

ABSTRACT

In this study, infrastructure works and operation planning of underground hydrogen storage areas was examined. Important points to be considered in the feasibility study were determined in the creation of salt caverns to build in salt domes, which are an important underground storage area. As well as producing hydrogen with clean energy sources such as wind and sun, it is also very important to store it economically in very large volumes. It has been seen that infrastructure works and operational planning are of great importance for the hydrogen storage areas created in salt domes to be technically, economically and financially efficient and sustainable. It was determined that hydrogen could be stored efficiently and economically in well-planned salt caverns at low pressure and on a very large scale. For this purpose, it is found that the storage cost, which is one of the most important problems in front of the hydrogen economy in the future, can be reduced. At the same time, it is seen that very important effects on the development of hydrogen economy and technologies. As a result, it has been seen that operational planning plays a key role in the use of salt caverns for long-term safe and healthy hydrogen storage.

Keywords: Underground hydrogen storage, salt dome, salt cavern, hydrogen economy

#1619

INVESTIGATION OF HYDROGEN KINETICS OF COPPER PELLETS WITH ENG ADDITIVES

[1,2*] *Gamze Atalmis,* [1,2] *Nebi Yelegen,* [3] *Mehmet Demiralp,* [1,2]*Yuksel Kaplan*
[1] Nigde Omer Halisdemir University, Mechanical Engineering Department, 51245, Nigde, Turkey
[2] Nigde Omer Halisdemir University Prof. Dr. T. Nejat Veziroglu Clean Energy Research Center, 51245, Nigde, Turkey
[3] Nigde Omer Halisdemir University, Nigde Vocational School of Technical Sciences, 51200, Nigde, Turkey
*Corresponding author e-mail: gamzee_umudum@hotmail.com

ABSTRACT

In this study, the hydrogen storage capabilities and thermal conductivity of the materials will be improved by applying both expanded natural graphite (ENG) addition and copper plating methods to the $LaNi_5$ alloy. The optimized $LaNi_5$-Cu alloy will be selected, ENG will be added at 1%, 5%, 10% and 20% ENG to this alloy and its application together with copper will be optimized. The obtained materials were characterized by XRD, SEM, BET and their thermal conductivity coefficients were measured with the Hot Disk Thermal Constants Analyzer device. In addition, the effect of storage materials with improved thermal conductivity on the hydrogen charging/discharging process in the metal hydride reactor will be experimentally investigated at the determined pressure.

Keywords: Hydrogen storage, expanded natural graphite (ENG), metal hydrides, thermal conductivity

Track 7.

Fuel Cells: PEMFC

#16

COMPACT FUEL CELL SYSTEM WITH DIESEL REFORMING

[1] Remzi Can Samsun,[1] Matthias Prawitz, [1] Andreas Tschauder, [1] Jan Meißner, [1] Joachim Pasel, [1] Ralf Peters*
[1] Forschungszentrum Jülich, Institute of Electrochemical Process Engineering (IEK-14), 52425, Jülich, Germany
*Corresponding author e-mail: r.c.samsun@fz-juelich.de

ABSTRACT

A compact auxiliary power unit in the 7.5 kW_e class was developed. The system is composed of two high-temperature PEFC stacks operated on reformate produced by a diesel fuel processor and the corresponding balance of plant components. In order to maximize the power density, each fuel processor component is designed as a multifunctional reactor. The stacks and the fuel processor are combined using manifolds applying additive manufacturing technology. Using the developed reactors, manifolds, as well as the selected fuel cell stacks and the balance of plant components, a compact system was designed and manufactured with a volume of 187.5 l. Preparatory experiments with the fuel processor focused on the validation of the system concept, aiming to maximize the fuel conversion while keeping the CO level in the fuel processor outlet below 1% for the ideal operation of the high-temperature PEFC. With various diesel and kerosene fuels, it was possible to identify the best operating parameters with each fuel at a very high fuel conversion of > 99.95% at full load of the fuel processor. In each experiment, the CO concentration remained stable and below the target value mentioned above.

Keywords: Autothermal Reforming, Fuel Cell System, Fuel Processor, HT-PEFC, Jet Fuel

#20

ON THE ORIGIN OF FUEL-CELL CATALYST-LAYER LOCAL RESISTANCES

*A. Chowdhury, S. A. Berlinger J. Petrovick, A. Kusoglu, C. J. Radke and A. Z. Weber**
Lawrence Berkeley National Laboratory, Energy Technologies Area, 1 Cyclotron Rd, Berkeley, CA 94720, USA
*Corresponding author e-mail: azweber@lbl.gov

ABSTRACT

To achieve high mass activity at low platinum loading, the local transport resistance endemic to polymer-electrolyte fuel cells must be ameliorated. This transport resistance is intimately linked to interactions between and within the proton-conducting polymer (ionomer) and the metal electrocatalyst in the porous catalyst layers. In this talk, the origin and impact of this resistance will be discussed. Specifically, both *in-situ* measurements using limiting current and *ex-situ* ones using a novel microelectrode setup and other techniques will discussed. Such studies provide a holistic view of the resistance components including interfacial effects and transport phenomena. Finally, discussion on the origin of these resistances during catalyst-layer formation and ink processing will be detailed. Throughout, theory will compliment the experimental studies, and various mitigation pathways to decrease the local resistance will be suggested.

Keywords: Fuel Cell, Resistance, Transport Phenomena, Ionomer, Microelectrode

#27

THERMAL MANAGEMENT OF EDGE-COOLED 1 kW PORTABLE PROTON EXCHANGE MEMBRANE FUEL CELL STACK

[1*] *Ivan Tolj,* [1] *Željko Penga,* [1] *Frano Barbir*
[1] *Faculty of Electrical Engineering, Mechanical Engineering and Naval Architecture*
University of Split, R. Boskovica 32, 21000 Split, Croatia
*Corresponding author e-mail: itolj@fesb.hr

ABSTRACT

In order to study thermal management influence on the performance of 1kW edge-cooled proton exchange membrane fuel cell stack without external humidification comprehensive numerical analyses are conducted. Two numerical approaches are considered and compared for a prescribed load profile: (i) lumped model and novel (ii) real-time transient computational fluid dynamics model incorporating realistic modeling of forced air convection on the edge-cooling of the stack. The developed computational fluid dynamics model is used to study the influence of (i) bipolar plate materials (ii) operating delta pressure along the flow field and (iii) different cooling fin configurations on the water and heat balance inside the stack. The results indicate that (i) maximal and average temperatures of the stack are almost linearly correlated to the thermal conductivity of bipolar plate materials and maximal temperatures can be significantly higher (ii) the operating delta pressure can be manipulated to increase the performance of the stack and (iii) the cooling fin redesign has major influence on the overall temperature uniformity across the stack. Additionally, the heat transfer between the stack and metal hydride tank is studied.

Keywords: PEM fuel cell, Portable stack, Water and heat management

#30

ELECTROSPUN HYBRID ELECTRODES WITH LOW PLATINUM LOADING FOR PEM FUEL CELLS

[1*] *Begüm Yarar Kaplan,* [2] *Bilal Sayyed Said Iskandarani,*[2] *Naeimeh Rajabalizadeh Mojarrad* [1] *Alp Yürüm,* [1,2] *Selmiye Alkan Gürsel*
[1] Sabancı University, Faculty of Natural Science and Engineering, 34956, Istanbul, Turkey
[2] Sabancı University Nanotechnology Research and Application Center (SUNUM), 34956, Istanbul, Turkey
*Corresponding author e-mail: begumyarar@sabanciuniv.edu

ABSTRACT

In the present study, sulfonated silica (S-SiO_2) nanoparticles (NPs) which are cheap and stable at low humidity are synthesized and employed in electrode structure of PEM fuel cell. Here, electrospinning is utilized to prepare hybrid fiber PEM fuel cell electrodes containing commercial Pt/C catalyst and S-SiO_2 NPs with poly(vinylidene fluoride) (PVDF) and poly(vinylidene fluoride-*co*-trifluoroethylene) (PVDF-TrFE) binders (carrier polymers). The morphology of electrospun electrodes have been investigated by scanning electron microscopy (SEM) to determine optimum electrospinning conditions to achieve a uniform Pt/C and S-SiO_2 NPs distribution on carrier polymer and fiber thickness. Consequently, catalyst distribution along the nanofibers have also been investigated by transmission electron microscopy (TEM). Moreover, sprayed electrodes are prepared and morphology of electrospun and sprayed electrodes are compared. After obtaining fiber-based hybrid and sprayed electrodes, membrane electrode assemblies (MEA) are prepared and fuel cell tests are performed with using H_2/air at different humidity. In-situ cyclic voltammetry (CV) and impedance analysis have also been performed. These novel electrospun hybrid electrodes possess not only superior PEM fuel cell performance compared to sprayed electrodes but also better performance at low humidity.

Keywords: Electrospinning, Catalyst layer, Electrode, Sulfonated silica, PEM fuel cells

#41

REFINERY HYDROGEN AS FUEL FOR LOW-TEMPERATURE POLYMER ELECTROLYTE MEMBRANE FUEL CELLS

S. Meenakshi, Sachin Chugh, Alok Sharma, G.S. Kapur, S. S. V. Ramakumar
Research & Development Centre, IndianOil Corporation Ltd., Sec-13, Faridabad Haryana-121007, India
*Corresponding author e-mail: chughs@indianoil.in

ABSTRACT
The hydrogen produced from the Oil refineries by steam reforming of natural gas/ naphtha may act as a potent energy carrier for operating fuel cells but it needs purification of key impurities like CO, CO_2 and CH_4. While it is widely reported that CO_2 and CH_4 do not impact the performance/durability of low-temperature polymer electrolyte fuel cell (PEMFC), the presence of CO is a major deterrent to its performance. Hence, for using refinery hydrogen directly in fuel cells, there is a need to develop novel catalyst that has a highly oxidative surface for desorbing CO molecule. Thus in this study, a single cell PEMFC assembly of 25 cm^2 active area containing anode (Pt/C, Pt-Ru/C) and Pt/C cathode catalyst is optimized for determining the operating parameters with neat hydrogen at 70°C. Physical characteristics of the novel catalyst are analyzed through XRD, TEM, SEM & XPS and the performance tests are performed by doping the contaminants (CO, CO_2, CH_4) to simulate refinery hydrogen composition. The performance evaluation of PEM fuel cell based on various electro-catalyst recipes operating on neat hydrogen and refinery hydrogen are discussed in this work.
Keywords: Refinery hydrogen, PEMFC, Contamination, Pt-Ru/C catalyst

#44

SYNTHESIS AND INVESTIGATION OF THE Pt-DECORATED POLYPYROLLE NANOTUBES IN PEM FUEL CELLS

[1]Yevheniia Lobko, [1]Yaroslava Novakova, [1]Yurii Yakovlev, [2]Dušan Kopecký, [3]Maryna Vorokhta, [1]Alina M. Darabut, [1]Lucinda Blanco Redondo, [1]Vladimir Matolin, [1]Iva Matolinova*
[1]Charles University, Faculty of Mathematics and Physics, Department of Surface and Plasma Science, V Holešovičkách 747/2, 180 00 Praha 8, Prague, Czech Republic
[2]University of Chemistry and Technology, Technická 5, 166 28 Praha 6, Prague, Czech Republic
[3]Czech Academy of Sciences, Institute of Rock Structure and Mechanics, Department of Geochemistry, V Holešovičkách 41, 180 00 Praha 8, Czech Republic
*e-mail: yevheniia.lobko@mff.cuni.cz

ABSTRACT
The catalysts for fuel cells, based on the platinum-decorated polypyrrolle nanotubes were synthesized. The structure, element contents, electrochemical surface areas of the catalysts' nanoparticles were investigated using TEM, EDX, XPS, RDE analysis. Using obtained catalysts, the catalyst-coated membranes were prepared by ultrasonic spraying techniques. The performance, electrochemical surface areas, high frequency resistance and durability of the CCMs were tested in proton exchange fuel cells.
Keywords: Fuel Cells, Polypyrrolle Nanotubes, Platinum Nanoparticles, Performance, Durability.

#45

PREPARATION OF ELECTROCONDUCTIVE THERMALLY EXPANDED GRAPHITE FOR PEM FUEL CELLS' COMPOSITE BIPOLAR PLATES

[1] Alina Madalina Darabut, [1] Yevheniia Lobko, [1]Yurii Yakovlev, [1]Miquel Gamon Rodriguez, [1]Kateřina Veltruska,[1] Peter Kuš, [1]Jaroslava Nováková,[2]Maryna Vorokhta, [3]Vladimír Kopecký, [3]Marek Procházka, [4]Milan Dopita, [1]Iva Matolínová, [1]Vladimír Matolín*
[1]Charles University, Faculty of Mathematics and Physics, Department of Surface and Plasma Science, V Holešovičkách 747/2, 180 00 Prague 8, Prague, Czech Republic
[2] Czech Academy of Sciences, Institute of Rock Structure and Mechanics, Department of Geochemistry, V Holešovičkách 41, 180 00 Prague8, Czech Republic
[3]Charles University, Faculty of Mathematics and Physics, Institute of Physics, Division of Biomolecular Physics, Ke Karlovu 5, 12116 Prague 2, Czech Republic
[4]Charles University, Faculty of Mathematics and Physics, Department of Condensed Matter Physics, Ke Karlovu 5, 12116 Prague 2, Czech Republic
*Corresponding author e-mail: alinadarabut@gmail.com

ABSTRACT
The thermally expanded graphites (TEGs) as fillers for PEM bipolar plates were obtained. The influence of the air and nitrogen atmosphere, as well as the different temperatures on the structure and properties of TEGs were investigated. The morphology, porous structure, chemical composition of the TEGs were analysed using SEM, XRD, BET, EDX, and XPS. It was shown that the obtained TEGs have three times higher electrical conductivity, comparable with commercial graphites. The obtained TEG is used as filler in the preparation of the polymer composites bipolar plates with electrical conductivity reaching DOE targets.
Keywords: Thermally Expanded Graphite, Carbon Fillers, Polymer Composites, Bipolar Plates, PEM Fuel Cells

#54

MASS TRANSFER ANALYSIS OF MICROPOROUS LAYERS FOR POLYMER ELECTROLYTE FUEL CELLS USING PORE NETWORK MODEL

[1] Hironori Nakajima, [2] Shintaro Iwasaki, [1] Tatsumi Kitahara*
[1] Department of Mechanical Engineering, Faculty of Engineering, Kyushu University, 744 Motooka, Nishi-ku, Fukuoka, Japan
[2] Department of Hydrogen Energy Systems, Graduate School of Engineering, Kyushu University, 744 Motooka, Nishi-ku, Fukuoka, Japan
*Corresponding author e-mail: nakajima@mech.kyushu-u.ac.jp

ABSTRACT
Liquid water accumulated in the catalyst layer and gas diffusion layer (GDL) of a polymer electrolyte fuel cell (PEFC, PEMFC) results in performance deterioration due to inhibition of transport of the reactant oxygen in the cathode (Flooding). To enhance the drainage in the GDL, the application of a microporous layer (MPL) is effective to the catalyst layer side of the GDL substrate. To elucidate the effects of two-phase flow on the oxygen transport in an MPL for its optimized designs, we model three-dimensional porous structures of in-house MPLs with pore network model (PNM) for convective air permeation and oxygen diffusion. Pore diameter distribution derived by a focused ion beam scanning electron microscope is employed in the PNM. Air permeation measurements combined with oxygen diffusion measurements with changing liquid saturation by using gas chromatography validate the model.
Keywords: Polymer electrolyte fuel cell, Gas diffusion layer, Microporous layer, Pore network model, Pore diameter distribution

#65

DYNAMIC MODELING OF A RESIDENTIAL INTEGRATED PEMFC-BASED MICRO-CHP SYSTEM

[1] Rafik ElKhatib, [2] Hasna Louahlia*
[1]Caen university, LUSAC, 120 rue de l'exode, 5000, Saint Lo, France
[2] Caen university, LUSAC, 120 rue de l'exode, 5000, Saint Lo, France
*Corresponding author e-mail: rafik.elkhatib@unicaen.fr

ABSTRACT
Cogeneration is the parallel high-efficiency generation of thermal and electrical energy from a single main energy source. It allows the recuperation of lost heat during the generation of power, resulting in 20 to 30% more efficient than independent generation. Recently, among many candidates in micro-cogeneration systems, the PEMFC (proton-exchange membrane fuel cell) represents a promising technology, allowing the use of hydrogen (H_2) as a fuel source in the building and outperforming by its higher flexibility and low investment cost. In this article, the behavior of a micro-cogeneration system based on a PEFMC for a 120 m^2 inhabited house is studied. This system is used to meet the thermal (DHW and heating) and electrical needs of a family of 3 people which its annual electrical and thermal energy demands are 2607 kWh and 12705 kWh respectively. The system component are a PEMFC cell, a hydrogen boiler, a hydrogen supply circuit, an air supply circuit, water management system and a heat management and recovery system. The findings indicate that this technology is very promising. The total efficiency of the system exceeds 75% in most of the time and the effective coverage rate of annual thermal and electrical needs is achieved.
Keywords: Micro-cogeneration, Fuel cells, Hydrogen

#79

DESIGN AND INVESTIGATION OF A VARIABLE-NOZZLE EJECTOR FOR A 120 kW PEMFC STACK

[1] Yikang Lu, [2] Xuhui Wang, [3] Sichuan Xu*
School of Automotive Studies, Tongji University, 201804, Shanghai, China
*Corresponding author e-mail: scxutj@163.com

ABSTRACT
Ejector is an ideal recirculation device which entrains anode exhaust from PEMFC stack via the entraining effect of supersonic low-pressure jet. Ejectors have advantages of tiny size, light weight, simple structure and no parasitic power consumption but achieves bad performance in off-design conditions, especially when stack load is relatively low. A variable-nozzle ejector applied for 120 kW stack is designed based on a 1-D ejector model. The results show that through shrinking throat ejector's entraining performance can be improved effectively. When stack load is higher than 60kW, the performance with maximum throat can meet the requirements. With load decreasing to 8.9 kW, the throat diameter should be gradually reduced to 0.4mm and the demand of primary pressure is raised to 1181 kPa accordingly.
Keywords: PEMFC Ejector, Variable-nozzle, Entrainment Ratio

#91

GIANTLEAP PROJECT: DEVELOPMENT OF A FUEL CELL RANGE EXTENDER FOR A BATTERY ELECTRIC BUS

[1*] *Frano Barbir,* [2] *Nadia Yousfi Steiner,* [3] *Federico Zenith*
[1]University of Split, Faculty of Electrical Engineering, Mechanical Engineering and Naval Architecture, Split, Croatia
[2] University of Franche-Comté, FEMTO-ST Institute, Belfort, France
[3] SINTEF Mathematics and Cybernetics, Trondheim, Norway
*Corresponding author e-mail: fbarbir@fesb.hr

ABSTRACT
Project Giantleap developed a fuel cell range extender for a battery electric bus. Several enhanced control functionalities were implemented to observe the state of health and to reduce the fuel cell stack degradation. The operation of the stack was remarkable. It showed very low degradation level in different operating conditions including some transient operations failures in coolant circuit. The range extender system was built in a trailer attached to a battery electric bus and successfully tested and demonstrated.
Keywords: Fuel cell, Range extender, Diagnostics and Prognostics, Control Unit

#96

MULTI-OBJECTIVE OPTIMIZATION OF A TURBINE IMPELLER FOR FUEL CELL VEHICLES

[1] *Haoyu Mao,* [2] *Yuemeng Zhang,* [3*] *Sichuan Xu*
[1] School of Automotive Studies, Tongji University, 201804, Shanghai, China
[2] School of Automotive Studies, Tongji University, 201804, Shanghai, China
[3] School of Automotive Studies, Tongji University, 201804, Shanghai, China
*Corresponding author e-mail: scxutj@163.com

ABSTRACT

Turbines can effectively recover 25-40% of the power consumed by centrifugal compressors, which significantly improve the efficiency of the proton exchange membrane fuel cell system. In this paper, a turbine impeller for an 80kW fuel cell stack is optimal designed. A multi-objective optimization method for turbine impellers is presented via integrating uniform design, back-propagation neural network and multi-island genetic algorithm. The numerical results indicate a considerable improvement to total-static expansion ratio and isentropic efficiency of the turbine impeller by 4.2% and 6.8% at the design point, respectively. It is shown that reducing impeller outlet diameter ratio can improve the efficiency. A lower impeller inlet width and a higher outlet diameter ratio are beneficial to increase the expansion ratio.

Keywords: Turbine, Fuel Cell Vehicle, Uniform Design, Back-propagation Neural Network, Multi-island Genetic Algorithm

#103

SYNTHESIS AND CHARACTERIZATION OF MWCNT-SUPPORTED PBI MEMBRANES FOR HT-PEM FUEL CELLS

[1,2*] *Mehmet Turan Görüryılmaz,* [3]*Sibel Özenler,* [4]*Bihter Zeytuncu,* [1]*Nilgün Karatepe*
[1]Department of Energy Science and Technology, Energy Institute, Istanbul Technical University, Istanbul, Turkey
[2] Department of Energy Science and Technologies, Turkish-German University, Istanbul, Turkey
[3] Department of Material Science and Technologies, Turkish-German University, Istanbul, Turkey
[4] MEM-TEK Prof. Dr. Dincer Topacık National Research Center on Membrane Technologies, Istanbul Technical University, Istanbul, Turkey
*Corresponding author e-mail: mtgoruryilmaz@gmail.com

ABSTRACT

Polybenzimidazole (PBI) membranes are highly sought after for HT-PEMFCs due to their thermal stability, mechanical strength and protonic conductivity. In this study, PBI polymer and the membranes were synthesized for HT-PEMFC applications. Then, the polymer was characterized by using NMR and TG analyses. All the characteristic peaks were observed in the NMR results and PBI polymer decompose around 550 °C. After the synthesis, pristine and multi-walled carbon nanotube (MWCNT) supported membranes were prepared, doped with phosphoric acid and characterized by using TGA, FT-IR, XRD, SEM and EIS tests. The characteristic bonds of the polymer for both undoped and doped membranes were seen in FT-IR results. XRD results showed the semi-crystalline structure of the polymer. SEM results enabled to observe the homogeneous dispersion of the MWCNTs within the membrane. Finally, EIS tests were carried out in anhydrous conditions. The conductivities were obtained for pristine PBI membrane as 0.0518 S/cm, 0.0667 S/cm and 0.0895 S/cm, respectively. For the 0.5wt% PBI/MWCNT membrane, they were calculated as 0.0401 S/cm, 0.0586 S/cm and 0.0613 S/cm for 120 °C, 140 °C and 160 °C, respectively. For the 1wt% PBI/MWCNT membrane, slightly higher conductivities were obtained as 0.0429 S/cm, 0.0621 S/cm and 0.0655 S/cm for the temperatures 120 °C, 140 °C and 160 °C, respectively.

Keywords: PBI, MWCNT, PEM, fuel cell, membrane.

#110

DEVELOPMENT AND TESTING OF A PROTON EXCHANGE MEMBRANE FUEL CELL STACK ENVISIONING UNMANNED AERIAL VEHICLE APPLICATIONS

Diogo F.M. Santos, Rui B. Ferreira, D.S. Falcão, A.M.F.R. Pinto***
Transport Phenomena Research Center (CEFT), Chemical Engineering Department (DEQ), Faculty of Engineering of University of Porto (FEUP), Rua Dr. Roberto Frias, 4200-465 Porto, Portugal
*Corresponding author; E-mail address: rferreira@fe.up.pt
**Corresponding author; E-mail address: apinto@fe.up.pt

ABSTRACT

In this work, a 20 W 3-cell proton exchange membrane (PEM) fuel cell stack is developed and studied. This is an initial prototype for the future development of a 200 W stack to be used in an unmanned aerial vehicle (UAV). For this specific application, several considerations need to be made, such as size, weight and operation mode of the stack. The influence of several operating parameters on the stack performance is evaluated. The fans speed (air supply and temperature regulation) and the short-circuit (water production) are the most influential parameters due to their effect on the humidification state of the stack. H_2 purge and pressure do not significantly impact the performance. The purge, however, could be a more important factor in a larger stack.

Keywords: Proton Exchange Membrane, Fuel Cell Stack, Unmanned Aerial Vehicles

#123

1D CALCULATION MODEL OF PROTON EXCHANGE MEMBRANE FUEL CELL ENERGY CHARACTERISTICS

[1] Aleksander V. Geliev, [1] Anton N. Varyukhin, [1] Victor S. Zakharchenko, [1] Ivan O. Kiselev
[1] Central Institute of Aviation Motors, 2, Aviamotornaya Street, Moscow 111116, Russia
*Corresponding author e-mail: avgeliev@ciam.ru

ABSTRACT

A semi-empirical 1-D calculation model of current-voltage characteristics of a proton-exchange membrane fuel cell (PEMFC) is presented. The model allows calculating the electrical and thermal powers generated by the PEMFC, as well as its efficiency. The model is developed to be used in automatic control system of power unit based on PEMFC with a relevant information. The main parameters of the model are the fuel cell consumption of hydrogen and air, hydrogen pressure at the anode, oxygen partial pressure at the cathode, temperature of the interface between the reacting agents, air and hydrogen dew points, and geometric characteristics of the membrane electrode assembly (MEA).

Keywords: Fuel Cell, PEMFC, Calculation Model, Hydrogen

#124

EXPERIMENTAL DYNAMIC LOAD CYCLING AND CURRENT DENSITY MEASUREMENTS OF A PARALLEL SERPENTINE PEMFC DESIGN

[1] Baltasar Toharias, [1] Christian Suárez, [1,2] Alfredo Iranzo, [3] Artem Chesalkin, [1] Javier Pino, [1] Felipe Rosa*
[1] Thermal Engineering Group, Energy Engineering Department, School of Engineering, University of Seville, Spain
[2] AICIA, Andalusian Association for Research & Industrial Cooperation, Seville, Spain
[3] ENET Centre – Research Centre of Energy Units for Utilization of Non Traditional Energy Sources, VSB Technical University of Ostrava, Czech Republic
*Corresponding author e-mail: btoharias@us.es

ABSTRACT

In the present work, the behaviour of a parallel serpentine bipolar plate of a proton exchange membrane fuel cell (PEMFC) working under dynamic load cycling (FC-DLC) was experimentally studied. Current density and temperature distribution along the cell active area was examined at different stages for the dynamic load of the urban cycle representative of fuel cell electric vehicle applications. Experimental results showed uniform temperature distribution in the active area of the fuel cell at both low and high intensities, with temperature differences below 2 °C. This homogeneity in temperature distribution supported the suitability of the proposed parallel serpentine design concept.

Keywords: Fuel Cell, Bipolar Plate, Dynamic Load Cycle, Current Density Measurement

#143

OPTIMIZING FUEL CELL MEMBRANES THROUGH THICKNESS AND CATION DOPING

Xiaoyan Luo[1], Adlai Katzenberg[1], A.R. Crothers[1], Victoria Ehlinger[1], A.Z. Weber[1], R.L. Borup[2], and A.Kusoglu[1,]*
[1] Lawrence Berkeley National Laboratory, Energy Technologies Area, 1 Cyclotron Rd, Berkeley, CA 94720, USA
[2] Los Alamos National Laboratory, Los Alamos, New Mexico 87545, USA
*Corresponding author e-mail: akusoglu@lbl.gov

ABSTRACT

Efforts towards improving performance and durability of polymer-electrolyte fuel cells (PEFCs) require an understanding and expansion of the design space for proton-exchange membranes (PEMs) in the presence of additives used to enhance their stability. One such additive utilized in PEMs is Cerium, due to its ability to act as radical scavenger to improve membrane stability. While showing promise in durability improvement, doping a multivalent cation such as Cerium into a proton-form PEM ionomer alters it structure and transport properties, the implications of which for membrane and cell performance remain relatively unexplored. In addition to the doping strategies employed for optimizing durability, membrane thickness is another factor for optimizing cost and performance. Thus, it is of interest to understand and quantify the extent to which membrane properties are dependent on these distinct factors that can be used as design parameters. This talk presents a summary of key aspects of doping and thickness effects in a membrane based on a comprehensive experimental study on PEM properties, including water uptake, conductivity and nanostructure characterization, which are then implemented into multi-physics fuel-cell models to demonstrate the expanded design space for PEMs that account for the materials and environmental parameters affecting both performance and durability.

Keywords: Fuel Cell, Ionomers, Cerium, Thickness, Durability

#147

MODELING OF AN ASSISTED COLD START OF A PEMFC COUPLED WITH A METAL HYDRIDE REACTOR

Tom Gießgen, Thomas Jahnke*
German Aerospace Center (DLR), Institute of Engineering Thermodynamics,
Pfaffenwaldring 38-40, D-70569 Stuttgart, Germany
* Tom.Giessgen@dlr.de

ABSTRACT

One challenge for the automotive application of polymer electrolyte fuel cells (PEMFC) is the start-up at sub-zero temperatures due to the freezing of water inside the cell. The temperature has to rise above 0 °C before the ice completely blocks the cathode pores and inhibits the oxygen reduction and species transportation. A promising solution to quickly increase the temperature of the fuel cell in a sub-zero environment is a metal hydride reactor. This thermochemical heater can exothermally absorb hydrogen and heat up the heat transfer fluid of a PEMFC stack.

This work presents a transient 2D numerical model of a single fuel cell thermally coupled to a metal hydride reactor via the heat transfer fluid. Both components are validated with experimental data. The simulation of the coupled system yields the necessary preheating time up to 0 °C to avoid any ice formation and potential damages due to ice in the cathode. Another cold start strategy is the potentiostatic start-up after a shorter preheating time, i.e. ice may be formed but a quicker cold start is possible. The criterion for a successful start in this work is an average temperature of 20 °C in the cathode catalyst layer, because the cold start can fail due to the blockage of the pores in the catalyst layer with ice but also with liquid water. For temperatures from - 5 °C to - 30 °C and cell voltages from 0.9 V to 0.1 V the preheating duration is varied to determine the optimum cold start procedure.

Keywords: PEMFC, Simulation, Cold start, Metal hydride, Preheating

#163

COMBINED NUMERICAL AND EXPERIMENTAL ANALYSIS OF LIQUID WATER DISTRIBUTION INSIDE PEMFCs

[1] Željko Penga, [1] Ivan Tolj, [1]Petar Bosnić, [1]Jure Penga, [1]Jakov Šimunović, [1]Gojmir Radica [1]Frano Barbir*
[1]Faculty of Electrical Engineering, Mechanical Engineering and Naval Architecture, University of Split, Croatia
*Corresponding author e-mail: zpenga@fesb.hr

ABSTRACT

The main objectives for the design of modern PEM fuel cells are to ensure minimize costs and size and ensure operation at elevated power densities with minimized accumulation of water inside the flow fields. Currently, number of authors are dedicated to increasing the flow field complexity, resulting in higher performance but also elevated manufacturing costs. By minimizing the complexity of the flow field and avoiding complex 3D structures, the main candidate still remains the serpentine flow field due to favorable characteristics of low pressure drop and good water removal. Due to discrepancies found in literature, in this work, the focus is on investigation of the liquid water accumulation inside the flow field of PEM fuel cell using up-to-date numerical model and full-scale single cell geometry with active area of 25 cm^2, experimentally and numerically using computational fluid dynamics modeling. The initial simulation model is calibrated using experimental data and later modified according to literature recommendations, outlining the influence of designs on water accumulation, resulting in significant performance improvement using simple geometry. The future goal of the research is upscaling the developed geometry for 50 cm^2 active area and comparing the numerical results with experimentally obtained locally resolved current density distribution.

Keywords: PEM Fuel Cells, Computational Fluid Dynamics, Experimental, Flow Fields

#190

TOPOLOGY OPTIMIZATION OF RADIAL FLOW FIELD IN CIRCULAR PEM FUEL CELLS

[1] Fereshteh Razmara, [1] Luís Fernando Nogueira de Sá, [1] Jéssica Alves Nogueira, [1] Thiago Lopes, [1] Julio Romano Meneghini, [1] Emílio Carlos Nelli Silva*
[1] Research Centre for Greenhouse Gas Innovation, University of Sao Paulo, Escola Politecnica, Av. Prof Mello Moraes 2231, Sao Paulo, SP 05508030, Brazil
*Corresponding author e-mail: f.razmara@usp.br

ABSTRACT

This research applies the topology optimization method to propose an optimum radial flow field in polymer electrolyte membrane fuel cells with circular endplates. The cathode flow field is investigated in two dimensions, with the reactant gas modelled as a single-phase isothermal flow at steady-state. The gradient-based topology optimization approach is used, where the objective function is set to maximize the amount of power generated. The flow field evolves freely within the circular domain, and the resulting geometry is compared to a square endplate fuel cell with a single serpentine flow field. The results show that the optimized radial flow field significantly outperforms the serpentine flow field in power generation. Furthermore, the optimized radial flow field presents a lower pressure loss than the traditional serpentine flow field.

Keywords: PEM Fuel Cell, Topology Optimization, Radial Flow Field, Circular Endplate

#222

INVESTIGATION ON AIRFLOW PERFORMANCE OF OPEN CATHODE PROTON EXCHANGE MEMBRANE FUEL CELL

[1,2] Ebubekir Pinar, [1] Gürsel Şefkat*
[1]Uludag University, Engineering Faculty, Mechanical Engineering Department, 16059, Bursa, Turkey
[2] B Plas A.Ş., R&D Center, 16369, Bursa, Turkey
*Corresponding author e-mail: ebubekirpinar@gmail.com

ABSTRACT

Fuel-cell systems have been considered as an alternative power source to replace internal combustion engines in future vehicles to reach zero emission transportation target. A trustworthy and straightforward fuel cell system is needed to adopt a fuel cell-based power unit successfully. Open cathode fuel cell offers a simple configuration where the ambient air is used directly to provide cooling and serve as an oxidant. Therefore, an open cathode fuel cell system eliminates the requirement for a complex air supply subsystem, minimizing accessory load and reducing the overall cost of the system. The main challenge with the open cathode design is the strong dependence of the stack performance on the ambient conditions. Numerous studies considering the performance of open cathode fuel-cell and various factors affecting them have been reported. This paper presents the investigation of the effects of the environmental parameters on open cathode fuel-cell.

Keywords: Open Cathode PEM Fuel Cell, Airflow Management, Forced Convection.

#230

EFFECT OF PLATINUM PARTICLE GRADIENT DISTRIBUTION IN LOW PLATINUM LOADING CATHODE CATALYST LAYER ON MEA PERFORMANCE

* *Rui Lin, Shengchu Liu*
Tongji University, School of Automotive Studies, 4800 Caoan Road, Shanghai, China
*Corresponding author e-mail: ruilin@tongji.edu.cn

ABSTRACT

The durability and performance of membrane electrode assembly (MEA) compose the bottleneck of fuel cells industrialization. In this paper, the effects of gradient distribution of Pt particles in the catalyst layer of MEA are studied. Polarization curves are carried out to evaluate the performance of MEAs with different Pt gradient dispersion under different relative humidity. It is found that when the Pt content of the catalyst layer remains unchanged, and the Pt particles are distributed near the membrane, the MEA has better performance because of the smaller oxygen transport resistance.

Keywords: Proton Exchange Membrane Fuel Cells, Pt Dispersion, MEA, Catalyst Layer

#262

SURFACE TOPOGRAPHY EVALUATION DURING LONG-RUN MICRO-STAMPING OF BPPs AND ITS EFFECT ON CORROSION AND CONTACT RESISTANCE CHARACTERISTICS

[1*] *Mevlüt Fatih Peker,* [2] *Hasan Gedikli,* [2,*] *Ömer Necati Cora,* [3] *Muammer Koç*
[1] İSTAÇ, İstanbul Environment Management Industry and Trade Company, 34379, Şişli, İstanbul, Turkiye
[2] Karadeniz Technical University, School of Engineering, Department of Mechanical Engineering, Trabzon, Turkiye
[3] Hamad bin Khalifa University, College of Science and Engineering, Sustainable Development Division, Doha, Qatar
*Corresponding author e-mail: oncora@ktu.edu.tr

ABSTRACT

Long-run stamping of bipolar plates affects die life, and bipolar plate geometric accuracy, formability and surface quality characteristics. These characteristics, in turn, would affect the corrosion and contact resistance of BPPs, consequently the fuel cell performance. The aim of this study was to investigate the reasons and consequences of the interactions during the mass manufacturing of micro-stamped sheets, and establish correlations between surface interactions vs. corrosion and contact resistance of BPPs. In experimental part of this study, 10,000 SS316L sheet blanks with 51μm in thickness were micro-stamped under 175-225 kN stamping force levels with a constant stamping speed of 1mm/s. Surface inspections, corrosion and contact resistance tests were carried out on the BPPs, periodically. On the other hand, 3-D finite element model of micro-stamping process was established to determine the coefficient of friction at the contact interface of micro-stamping dies and BPPs, von-Mises equivalent stress, plastic strain and final sheet thickness distributions. The results revealed that the roughness values for die pairs and BPPs followed similar trends during 10,000 micro-stampings. The corrosion resistance variation as a consequence of long-run manufacturing was found to be statistically insignificant, and the relation between surface roughness and corrosion resistance was found to be indirect.

Keywords: Bipolar Plates, Stamping, Surface Topography, Contact Resistance, Corrosion Resistance

#276

HIGHLY EFFICIENT LOW METAL LOADING NANOSTRUCTURED ELECTROCATALYSTS

[1] *A. M. Valenzuela-Muñiz*, [2] *H. Valenzuela-Ramos*, [1] *M. E. Zi-Chi*, [3] *M. Miki-Yoshida*, [1*] *Y. Verde-Gomez*
[1]Tecnológico Nacional de México/IT de Cancún, Av. Kabah Km 3, Cancún, Q. Roo, México, 77500
[2] Tecnológico Nacional de México/IT de Chihuahua, Av. Tecnológico # 2909, Chihuahua, Chih. México, 31310
[3] Centro de Investigación en Materiales Avanzados S. C., Av. Miguel de Cervantes # 120, Chihuahua, Chih. México, 31136
*Corresponding author e-mail: jose.vg@cancun.tecnm.mx

ABSTRACT

In order to increase the utilization of PEM fuel cells, it is very important to develop alternatives that allow wider commercialization. It is well known that one of the most expensive components of the mentioned technology are the electrocatalysts [1] since they are based on scarce metals, such as Platinum. Diverse approaches have been taken to overpass this problem; different research works propose the combination of metals to achieve the required activity. Also, a variety of supporting materials have been studied to increase stability. However, a clear alternative there is still not available. This research work proposes to design and development of PEM fuel cell electrocatalysts with adequate activity and stability, but also optimizing the platinum loading. Multiwalled Carbon Nanotubes were obtained using a modified chemical vapor deposition method and used as support of Platinum particles deposited via a colloidal procedure. Low loadings were achieved. The obtained materials were physical and chemically analyzed with scanning and transmission electron microscopies. Also, an electrochemical evaluation towards the PEM fuel cell reactions was performed using cyclic and linear voltammetry, the proposed system exhibited higher current density per mg of Pt compared to a commercial material.

Keywords: PEM Fuel Cell, Nanostructured Electrocatalyst, Low Pt Loading, Carbon Nanotubes Support

#277

MULTI-OBJECTIVE OPTIMIZATION OF PEM FUEL CELL COMPONENTS BASED ON RESPONSE SURFACE METHODOLOGY

[1] *Masoomeh Ghasemi*, [1] *Jaeyoo Choi*, [1] *Jaeseung Lee*, [1] *Kisung Lim*, [1*] *Hyunchul Ju*
[1]Department of Mechanical Engineering, Inha University 100 Inha-ro Michuhol-Gu, Incheon 22212, Republic of Korea
*Corresponding author e-mail: hcju@inha.ac.kr

ABSTRACT

Nowadays energy crisis is assumed as one of the important issues in developing and developed countries according to increasing urbanization and industrialization. Plus, the application of green and renewable energy can be used instead of fossil fuel-based energy resources for different usages. In this study, Proton Exchange Membrane Fuel Cell (PEMFC) as a novel green technology for energy harvesting is optimized by integrated Central Composite Design-Response Surface Methodology (CCD-RSM). However, all simulation process of PEMFC is operated in the Computational Fluid Dynamics (CFD) which is done based on the combination of conventional programming and ANSYS-FLUENT environment. Through this research, for the first time, two responses containing voltage and pressure drop are optimized simultaneous as per Gas Diffusion Layer (GDL) thickness, channel depth, channel width, and land width. The outcomes of this study demonstrate that the quadratic model covers the cure-fitting process with high efficiency (More than 0.9% R^2). Likewise, based on the mentioned computations, through Analysis of Variance (ANOVA) assessment, for voltage and pressure drop, the most important roles are related to land width (P-Value < 0.0001) and channel depth (P-Value < 0.0001), correspondingly.

Keywords: PEMFC, Optimization, CCD-RSM Model, Multi-objective Model, Component Design.

#297

EFFECT OF CHITOSAN ON THE CORROSION INHIBITION FOR ALUMINIUM ALLOY IN H_2SO_4 MEDIUM

[1,3] *I Gusti Ayu Arwati,* [1]**Edy Herianto Majlan,* [1]*Loh Kee Shyuan,* [1]*Khuzaimah Ariffin ,* [1]*Teuku Husaini,*[2] *Sagir Alva,* [2] *Wahyu Muhammad,* [3]*Nabilah Afiqah Mohd Radzuan*

[1] Fuel Cell Institute, National University of Malaysia, 43600 UKM Bangi, Selangor Darul Ehsan, Malaysia
[2] Engineering Faculty, Mercu Buana University,11650, Indonesia
[3]Centre for Materials Engineering and Smart Manufacturing, Faculty of Engineering and Built Environment, Universiti Kebangsaan Malaysia, 43600 Bangi, Selangor, Malaysia.
* *Corresponding author: edyhm71@gmail.com*

ABSTRACT

Aluminum Alloy (AA 5052) is an inexpensive and lightweight metal that has been used in a variety of applications including as a bipolar plate in Proton Exchange Membrane Fuel Cells (PEMFC). The alloy has good electrical conductivity and low corrosion, corrosion rate will increase during PEMFC operation with increasing temperature. Inorganic dyes such as chromate are commonly used to reduce metal corrosion, unfortunately, they are toxic and have a negative impact on the environment. To solve this problem, chitosan as an organic solvent is green, cheap, nontoxic and environmentally friendly. Thickening electrophoresis (EPD) technique was used to coat the surface of AA 5052 with chitosan. To measure the level of corrosion rate using electrochemical and weight los methods (in 0.5 M H_2SO_4 solution). Levels of AA 5052, with and without chitosan, were 0.1702 mgcm^{-2} h^{-1} and 0.0552 mgcm^{-2} h^{-1}, respectively. Based on the polarization test, chitosan inhibitors can decrease the corrosion rate and will increase with increasing temperature.

Keywords: PEMFC, Inhibitor Chitosan, EPD, Corrosion rate

#305

DESIGN, INTEGRATION AND VALIDATION OF A TESTING SETUP FOR PEMFC STACK CHARACTERISATION AT HEAVY DUTY AND MARITIME LOAD PROFILES

* *Piotr Bujlo, Øystein Ulleberg*
Institute of Energy Technology (IFE), Department of Hydrogen Technology, 18 Instituttveien, 2007 Kjeller, Norway
*Corresponding author e-mail: piotr.bujlo@ife.no

ABSTRACT

This study presents the design, integration, and validation of a PEMFC stack testing setup, which was realized at the Hynor Laboratory – IFE. The design of the testing setup, which includes an anode/cathode loop and a cooling, power conditioning, and control system, is described in detail. The setup is used for fuel cell stack testing (up to 20 kW power) using a system-like configuration, fuel cell system testing (up to 135 kW power) and the characterisation of its components, and fuel cell system operation using a hybrid configuration with Li-ion battery modules (up to 100 kW power). The integrated fuel cell testing setup is planned to be used for research investigations related to the utilisation of fuel cell technology in heavy duty and maritime applications.

Keywords: fuel cell stack, testing setup, PEM fuel cell

#316

MODELING OF A FUEL CELL FORKLIFT FOR MATERIAL HANDLING IN OIL REFINERIES

Kapil Sonkar, Sachin Chugh, Tarun Jindal, Amit Katiyar, Alok Sharma, G.S Kapur, S. S. V. Ramakumar
Research & Development Centre, IndianOil Corporation Ltd., Sec-13, Faridabad Haryana-121007, India
*Corresponding author e-mail: chughs@indianoil.in

ABSTRACT

Oil refineries are one of the biggest producers and captive consumers of hydrogen where material handling is an important spoke in the refinery operations. The electric forklifts which are quite common in refineries suffer from demerits pertaining to their charge cycle, weight-to-power ratio and inventory management. Hydrogen based fuel cells are gaining traction as a potential alternative due to their efficient and clean power generation. The present paper aims to develop and recommend an optimized power management strategy for addressing material handling activities in a typical refinery. The simulation model considering a parallel hybrid electric forklift with a Proton Exchange Membrane fuel cell as the prime mover is conceptualized and validated with stack level testing. Based on the refinery specific duty cycle characterized by different operating speed and forklift loads, the study involves development of model involving multiple control strategies for sizing fuel cell stack and battery capacity by considering durability, state-of-charge (SOC) of battery and fuel consumption as constraint functions for optimization. From the analysis, it is observed that the fuel cell forklifts have approximately 45.55% higher energy efficiency as compared to their battery electric counterparts.

Keywords: Hydrogen, PEM Fuel Cell Forklift, Li-ion Battery Forklift, Energy Efficiency, MATLAB

#320

EXPERIMENTAL STUDY OF MODIFIED POLYBENZIMIDAZOLE/ PHOSPHONATED POLYVINYL ALCOHOL BLEND MEMBRANE FOR FUEL CELL OPERATIONS

[1] Aygun Cali, [2] Alpay Sahin, [3] İrfan Ar*
[1]Gazi University, Graduate School of Natural and Applied Sciences, Chemical Engineering Department, Eti Mah., Maltepe/Çankaya, Ankara, Turkey
*Corresponding author e-mail: ayguncali@yahoo.com

ABSTRACT

Polybenzimidazole (PBI) is a high-temperature polymer that is used for many purposes in polymer technology since its high hydrophilic nature and mechanic stability. Polyvinyl alcohol (PVA) has advantages, such as its easily modifiable structure and high ionic conductivity features. Polybenzimidazole and polyvinyl alcohol polymers were used as blend membrane structures with different percentage ratios such as 90:10, 70:30, 50:50 for proton exchange membrane fuel cell (PEMFC) applications. Firstly, PBI was synthesized by the solution polycondensation method which means that polyphosphoric acid was applied as both condensation agent (catalyst) and monomer solvent. The H-Nuclear Magnetic Resonance (H-NMR) was applied to identify the structural formation of the polymer. PVA and synthesized PBI polymers were dissolved in different solvents separately and both polymers were mixed by sol-gel method to prepare the blend membrane. The blend membrane was treated with phosphoric acid which was used as a phosphonation agent. The PBI/Phosphonated-PVA (PPVA) blend membrane was examined for evaluating the suitability for proton exchange membrane fuel cell (PEMFC) operations. The characterization tests, i. e; water uptake capacity, FT-IR Analysis, Ion-exchange capacity, Thermal Gravimetric Analysis measurements were applied to the synthesized blend membrane. The synthesized PBI membrane has 2.12 meq gr^{-1} Ionic exchange capacity (IEC) while PBI/PPVA-90:10 blend membrane has 4.15 meq gr^{-1} IEC value.
Keywords: Polybenzimidazole (PBI) Polymer, PBI/PVA Blend Membrane, Polyvinyl Alcohol, PEMFC

#321

INTELLIGENT MONITORING OF HYDROGEN/VANADIUM REDOX FLOW BATTERY

[1] Chi-Yuan Lee, [2] Chia-Hung Chen, [3] Chin-Lung Hsieh, [1] Yu-Chun Chen, [1] Siao-Yu Chen*
[1] Department of Mechanical Engineering, Yuan Ze Fuel Cell Center, Yuan Ze University, Taoyuan, Taiwan
[2] HOMYTECH Global CO., LTD, Taoyuan, Taiwan
[3] Institute of Nuclear Energy Research, Taoyuan, Taiwan
*Corresponding author e-mail: cylee@saturn.yzu.edu.tw

ABSTRACT
This work attempts to innovatively develop a hydrogen/vanadium redox flow battery stack and improve the previous vanadium redox battery encountered by our team when the electrolyte leaks easily and the strong acid corrosion environment may cause the vanadium redox battery and the micro sensor to age or fail. Utilize MEMS to innovatively develop hydrogen concentration and conductivity micro sensors, and integrate the flexible five-in-one (voltage, current, temperature, flow and pressure) micro sensors developed by our team. Corrosion-resistant, thinner and miniaturized flexible seven-in-one micro sensor embedded in the hydrogen/vanadium redox flow battery for real-time microsensing and diagnosis.
Keywords: Hydrogen/Vanadium Redox Flow Battery, Flexible Seven-in-One Micro Sensor, Real-Time Microsensing and Diagnosis

#322

DEVELOPMENT OF MONITORING TOOL FOR HIGH VOLTAGE PROTON EXCHANGE MEMBRANE WATER ELECTROLYZE

[1] Chi-Yuan Lee, [2] Chia-Hung Chen, [1] Shan-Yu Chen, [1] Zhi-Yu Huang*
[1] Department of Mechanical Engineering, Yuan Ze Fuel Cell Center, Yuan Ze University, Taoyuan, Taiwan
[2] HOMYTECH Global CO., LTD, Taoyuan, Taiwan
*Corresponding author e-mail: cylee@saturn.yzu.edu.tw

ABSTRACT
Proton exchange membrane water electrolyzer (PEMWE) requires high operating voltage for hydrogen production, so it is easy to accelerate the decomposition of hydrogen molecules, and it is easy to cause PEMWE to age or fail. This research uses micro-electro-mechanical systems (MEMS) technology to innovatively develop the micro oxygen sensor inside PEMWE so as to know the oxygen production rate in real time. This information is one of the important information on PEMWE aging. The flexible six-in-one (voltage, current, temperature, humidity, flow and pressure) micro sensor developed by our team has been integrated into a flexible seven-in-one micro sensor. It embedded in the high voltage PEMWE to monitor oxygen, voltage, current, temperature, humidity, flow and pressure. And we observe whether the high voltage PEMWE is aging or damaged so as to prolong its service life.
Keywords: MEMS, Flexible seven-in-one micro sensor, High voltage proton exchange membrane water electrolyzer

#339

PLATINUM-BASED HONEYCOMB-LIKE NANOCOMPOSITES DIRECTED BY SELF-ASSEMBLY FOR OXYGEN REDUCTION REACTION IN FUEL CELLS

[1]Zhida Wang, [1,2]Yi Yang, [1]Hongyi Tan, [1]Zhuoxin Lu, [1,2]Changfeng Yan*
[1] Guangzhou Institute of Energy Conversion, Chinese Academy of Sciences, 2ST Nengyuan, Tianhe District, Guangzhou, China
[2] University of Chinese Academy of Sciences, Beijing, China, 100039
*Corresponding author e-mail: wangzd@ms.giec.ac.cn

ABSTRACT

Pt-based nanocomposites with well-organized pores are desirable for the electrocatalysts in fuel cells. Herein, we show for the first time an in-situ strategy of developing N-doped ordered honeycomb (N-OHC) nanopattern anchored with well-dispersed Pt moieties by using the self-assembly of block copolymer (BCP). The Pt ~2.5 nm ultrafine nanoparticles (NPs) were hierarchically located on the inner walls and the outer surfaces of the N-OHC mesopores (Pt/N-OHC), forming well-dispersed Pt-N active sites and showing efficient catalytic activity towards oxygen reduction reaction (ORR). By changing the film thickness of the pristine Pt/BCP template, double-layered Pt/N-OHC could be designed and the ORR activity could be correspondingly improved. The electron transfer from Pt to N gave rise to the formation of Pt-N covalent bonds, which resulted in a lower d band center and a weaker O adsorption energy and endowed the Pt/N-OHCs with enhanced ORR activity.

Keywords: Ordered nanostructure, Self-assembly, Fuel cell, ORR, DFT

#341

COMPARATIVE STUDY ON THE EFFECT OF SELECTED DISPERSION TECHNOLOGIES FOR FUEL CELL INK PREPARATION ON THE OVERALL PEMFC PROCESS CHAIN

[1*] *Amin S. Amin,* [1] *Fatih Özcan,* [1,2]*Doris Segets*
[1] *Particle Science and Technology (IVG-PST)*
[2] *Centre for Nanointegration Duisburg-Essen (CENIDE)*
University of Duisburg-Essen, Duisburg (UDE), Germany
*Corresponding author e-mail: amin.amin@uni-due.de

ABSTRACT
In this paper, we report on the influence of different dispersion technologies on fuel cell performance. We present the complete process chain from dispersing the dry powder components in a liquid phase to final performance testing on the electrode level in order to identify process-structure-property relations. For comparing different dispersion technologies, we use both an ultrasound-based batch-type method and a continuously operable wet impact milling device that can be operated at elevated hydrostatic pressures of up to 245 MPa. We use analytical centrifugation to analyse the sedimentation behaviour of concentrated inks and the surfaces of the electrode layers are characterised by means of Atomic Force Microscopy (AFM). The results of the ink characterisation were visualised in self-developed transmittograms in the working group. In addition, we spray the inks and prepare electrodes for a final evaluation in a fuel cell. We found that ink dispersion by wet impact millling ends up in more stable formulations than when dispersion by ultrasound is applied. This is also reflected in the performance of the fuel cells, i.e., the electrodes made from inks generated by wet impact milling did perform better with regard to polarization curves than those made from inks generated by ultrasonic Sonotrode.
Keywords: PEMFC, Ink Preparation, Wet Impact Milling, Sonication, Transmittograms

#353

OPTIMUM SERPENTINE FLOW FIELD FOR PEM FUEL CELLS ACCORDING TO CRITICAL PARAMETERS

[1] *Mehran Ghasemian,* [2*] *Mazaher Rahimi-Esbo,* [3] *Seyed Majid Rahgoshay,* [3] *Kamran Dadashi*
[1] Faculty of Mechanical Engineering, Babol Noshirvani University of Technology, Babol, Iran.
[2*] Northern Research Center for Science & Technology, Malek Ashtar University of Technology, Iran.
[3] Researcher, Northern Research Center for Science & Technology, Malek Ashtar University of Technology, Iran.
*Corresponding author e-mail address: mrahimi@mut.ac.ir

ABSTRACT
Polymer Electrolyte Membrane (PEM) fuel cell is widely used as a new source of energy that is clean and environmentally friendly. Among different flow field channel designs used in PEM fuel cells, serpentine channels are the most common because of their high performance. In this manner, many studies focused on improving serpentine channel designs and diminishing the disadvantages such as high pressure drop. In this study, firstly, a numerical validation is performed with an experimental study to ensure the accuracy of the solution. Then, it is tried to find the optimum serpentine channel design by comparing inspired and novel serpentine designs. Two novel serpentine designs are proposed for the first time in the present study which is inspired by reviewing the literature, and three other serpentine designs are directly used from the literature. Five channel designs are compared by analyzing the resulting I-V curve, generated water, and performance evaluation criteria. Two evaluation criteria are used to ensure the superiority of the optimum serpentine design. The results revealed that the new proposed designs show better performances than the base serpentine channels. Also, the selected efficient designs indicated good performances, with the waved serpentine design showing the best performance due to the variable channel depth structure.
Keywords: PEM Fuel Cell, Water Management, Gas Flow Field, Evaluation Criteria.

#357

OPTIMIZATION AND FABRICATION OF COMPOSITE GRAPHITE PLATES FOR PEMFC APPLICATIONS

Mojtaba Ghadimi, Mohammad Momenifar, Mohammad Mahdi Barzegari, Kamal Mohammadi*
Northern research center for science and technology, Malek Ashtar University of technology, Iran
*Corresponding author e-mail: momenifar@mut.ac.ir

ABSTRACT
In this paper, manufacturing of the composite polymer/graphite plates using hot compression moulding method for PEM fuel cell application was investigated. The physical, mechanical & electrical properties of manufactured composite plates are investigated by applying water absorption, density calculation, flexural strength and contact resistance tests. In order to optimize the properties of the manufactured plates Minitab software was applied to design experiments. Thirteen experiments are fabricated and the mentioned tests are applied for each manufactured sample to optimize the baking parameter such as pressure of the press and the time of baking.
Keywords: Composite Bipolar Plate, Compression Moulding, PEM Fuel Cell

#360

HYDROGEN CROSSOVER DIAGNOSIS IN A PEMFC USING GALVANOSTATIC METHOD

* Mohammad Gholami, Majid Sedighi, Mohammad Rezaei Firozjaei, Vahid Kord Firozjaei
Northern Research Center for Science & Technology, Malek Ashtar University of Technology, Iran
*Corresponding author e-mail: gholami9697@mut.ac.ir

ABSTRACT
Determining the Hydrogen crossover of a single cell by conventional voltammetry methods can lead to accurate results. But analyses of the large stack with them are impractical. The galvanostatic method is a fast way for investigating the state of health of a large stack. Like CV method, the galvanostatic method allows measuring ECSA in addition to hydrogen crossover. In this work, we measure hydrogen crossover of a single cell by galvanostatic method and compare the result with CV. There is a reasonable agreement between hydrogen crossover values determined using the galvanostatic method and CV.
Keywords: Hydrogen Crossover, Fuel Cells, Galvanostatic Method

#371

INFLUENCE OF OPERATING PARAMETERS ON THE COLD START OF POLYMER ELECTROLYTE FUEL CELL SYSTEMS FOR TRANSPORTATION AND AEROSPACE APPLICATIONS

[1*] Gema Montaner Ríos, [2] Johannes Schirmer
[1] German Aerospace Center (DLR), Institute of Engineering Thermodynamics, Hein-Saß-Weg 22, 21129, Hamburg, Germany
[2] German Aerospace Center (DLR), Institute of Engineering Thermodynamics, Pfaffenwaldring 38-40, 70569, Stuttgart, Germany
*Corresponding author e-mail: Gema.MontanerRios@dlr.de

ABSTRACT
Understanding the influence of operating parameters on the cold start of polymer electrolyte fuel cell (PEFC) is essential for the development of improved cold start strategies for transportation and aerospace applications. The effects of different operating parameters on the cold start performance at temperatures down to -30°C have been investigated using a 4-kW PEFC system. The results showed that the start-up temperature, coolant volume flow rate, cell voltage, cathode excess ratio and gas, make a significant impact on the cold start time and performance. The PEFC system was able to self start-up at -30°C, though it led to a standard slow cold start performance with three stages. The results indicate that lowering the start-up cell voltage and operating with oxygen enhance the cold start since more current and heat are generated, thus reducing ice formation. In addition, increasing the cathode excess ratio assists to overcome flooding issues once ice melts.
Keywords: Cold Start, Ice Formation, Operating Parameters, Polymer Electrolyte Fuel Cell (PEFC)

#372

INVESTIGATIONS ON THE MICRO-SCALE SURFACE INTERACTIONS AND TRIBOLOGICAL SIZE EFFECT IN MICRO-STAMPING OF SS316L SHEETS

[1*] Mevlüt Fatih Peker, [2] Hasan Gedikli, [2,*] Ömer Necati Cora, [3] Muammer Koç
[1] İSTAÇ, İstanbul Environment Management Industry and Trade Company, 34379, Şişli, İstanbul, Turkiye
[2] Karadeniz Technical University, School of Engineering, Department of Mechanical Engineering, Trabzon, Turkiye
[3] Hamad bin Khalifa University, College of Science and Engineering, Sustainable Development Division, Qatar
*Corresponding author e-mail: oncora@ktu.edu.tr

ABSTRACT
Micro-stamping is a convenient sheet-metal forming technology providing small tolerances, surface accuracy, low-cost and fast production of thin metallic sheets. Compared to macro-forming operations, tribological changes in micro-forming processes are harshened. Tribological size effect should be considered for a better understanding of surface interaction on micro-scale. The objective of this study is to establish numerical and experimental models for micro-stamping of stainless steel blanks regarding the tribological size effect and determine the effects of feature size of the dies and stamping force onto friction, von-Mises stress, plastic strain, part thickness changes. Numerical models of micro-stamping process for the dies with 3 distinct channel sizes (250 μm, 750 μm and 2500 μm) were established in FEA package Ls-Dyna. Several coefficients of friction values were imposed and runs were performed. Micro-stamping were also conducted to verify the established FE models. It was noted that the dies with different channel sizes showed different magnitudes and distributions of von-Mises stress and plastic strain. In addition, different friction coefficients were encountered for the micro-stamping dies with 250 μm, 750 μm and 2500 μm channel sizes. The lower channel size the higher coefficient of friction was observed as a result of tribological size effect.
Keywords: Bipolar Plates, Stamping, Surface Topography, Contact Resistance, Corrosion Resistance

#375

EFFECT OF HUMIDIFICATION TEMPERATURE AND HYDROGEN FLOW RATE ON THE PERFORMANCE OF A PEMFC USING Pt/C AND CoFe/N-C CATALYST IN THE MEA

[1,2] Dedi Rohendi, [2] Dwi Hawa Yulianti, [1] Juwita, [1,2] Nirwan Syarif, [1,2] Addy Rachmat, [3]Afriyanti Sumboja, [2] Nyimas Febrika S.,[2] Icha Amelia*

[1] Universitas Sriwijaya, Faculty of Mathematic and Natural Sciences, Department of Chemistry, Jl. Palembang-Prabumulih Km 32, Indralaya, Ogan Ilir, Indonesia

[2] Univesitas Sriwijaya, Center of Research Excellent in Fuel Cell and Hydrogen, Jl. Srijaya Negara, Palembang, Indonesia

[3] Institut Teknologi Bandung, Faculty of Mechanical and Aerospace Engineering, Materials Science and Engineering Research Group, Jl. Ganesha 10, Bandung, Indonesia

*Corresponding author e-mail: rohendi19@unsri.ac.id

ABSTRACT

The effect of humidification temperature and hydrogen flow rate on the performance of the Proton Exchange Membrane Fuel Cell (PEMFC) using Pt/C and CoFe/N-C catalysts influenced the performance of Membrane Electrode Assembly (MEA). In this report, two types of MEA using Nafion-212 membrane are prepared and tested. The anode and cathode of the first MEA are coated with a Pt/C and CoFe/N-C catalyst, respectively, while the second MEA uses Pt/C catalyst on both electrodes. The electrodes with Pt/C and CoFe/N-C catalyst are characterized using Cyclic Voltammetry (CV) and Electrochemical Impedance Spectroscopy (EIS) to obtain Electrochemical Surface Area (ECSA) and electrical conductivity of the electrode, respectively. The Pt/C electrode exhibits higher ECSA (60.88 cm^2/g) than the CoFe/N-C electrode (4.83 cm^2/g). Similarly, the Pt/C electrode also possesses higher conductivity (7.2 x 10^{-3} S/cm) than the CoFe/N-C electrode (4.4 x 10^{-3} S/cm). Consequently, the OCV (Open Circuit Voltage) of the second MEA with Pt/C catalyst on both electrodes shows a higher value (0.890 V) than the OCV of the first MEA (0.790 V). Furthermore, humidifier temperature is found to be optimum at 80 °C, achieving a power density as high as 10.14 mW/cm^2 and 3.43 mW/cm^2 for the second and the first MEA, respectively. In addition to humidification temperature, MEA performance is also influenced by the hydrogen flow rate as a fuel supply to the PEMFC. The optimum hydrogen flow rate of the first MEA is at 400 mL/min, achieving a power density of 4.93 mW/cm^2. On the other hand, the second MEA requires a lower hydrogen flow rate (200 mL/min) to achieve a maximum power density of 10.14 mW/cm^2.

Keywords: PEMFC, Pt/C, CoFe/N-C, Humidification Temperature, Hydrogen Flowrate.

#385

SYNTHESIS AND CHARACTERIZATION OF CATIONIC MEMBRANES WITH POLY(INDENE) SULPHONATED POLYELECTROLYTE FOR FUEL CELL APPLICATION

[1] Hannah Corrêa de M. M. Thomaz,[1] João Víctor M.R. de Souza, [1] Alexandre Furtado Ferreira, [1] Fábio José Bento Brum*

[1]Universidade Federal Fluminense, Avenida dos Trabalhadores, 420, Vila Santa Cecília, 27255-125 Volta Redonda, RJ, Brazil.

*Corresponding author e-mail: hannah_correa@id.uff.br

ABSTRACT

In this work, results of the synthesis and characterization of cationic hydrocarbon membranes with application in fuel cells will be presented. Semi-interpenetrating membranes based on PVA with sulfonated aromatic electrolyte polymer were prepared. In the polarization tests in a fuel cell prototype, the membrane with the best result obtained the value of open circuit potential and power equal to $0.8\,V$ and $7.5x10^{-2}\,W$, respectively, very close values when compared to Nafion®, an industrial membrane that reaches $0.8\,V$ and $9.0x10^{-2}\,W$, respectively, thus proving the applicability of the synthesized membrane in fuel cells.

Keywords: Electrolyte Polymers, Fuel Cells, Membranes, Polarization Curve

#386

USE OF TWO-PHASE COOLING FOR THE FUEL CELL SYSTEM

[1] *Thanyarak Bogdanske,* [2] *Andreas Sklarow,* [3*] *Johannes Gulden*
[1] University of Applied Sciences Stralsund (HOST), Fak. Mech. Eng., Zur Schwedenschanze 15, 18435 Stralsund, Germany
[2] University of Applied Sciences Stralsund (HOST), IRES, Zur Schwedenschanze 15, 18435 Stralsund, Germany
[3] University of Applied Sciences Stralsund (HOST), Fak. Elec. Eng. & IRES, Zur Schwedenschanze 15, 18435 Stralsund, Germany
*Corresponding author e-mail: Johannes.gulden@hochschule-stralsund.de

ABSTRACT

Hydrogen mobility is becoming increasingly important and is seen as an alternative to electric and conventional mobility. As a student project the ThaiGer-H2-Racing Team at the University of Applied Sciences Stralsund has been working on hydrogen propulsion since 2007 and is building ultra-light prototype vehicles with fuel cells. Within the fuel cell system cooling is a crucial problem to be solved for future applications. We report on an experiment with a two-phase cooling system, which was developed for the fuel cell stack. An engineered liquid Novec 7000 from 3M was used as the cooling medium. The cooling medium evaporates in the fuel cell stack at about 45 °C and thus transports the heat to the outside. The cooling circuit is driven by the evaporation of the cooling medium and thermosiphon effect and therefore does not require an additional cooling pump. Since the cooling circuit is operated at a slight overpressure, the membranes in the stack are more uniformly compressed by the metallic bipolar plates, which might increase the performance of the stack. The two-phase cooling system was successfully tested in the new vehicle on a track. By saving the cooling pump and reducing the consumption, the overall efficiency of the fuel cell system was significantly improved.

Keywords: Two-phase cooling, Thermosiphon, Cooling System, Fuel Cell, 3M Novec

#395

STUDYING PROTON CONDUCTIVITY OF SULFONATED/FLUORINATED PROTON EXCHANGE MEMBRANES BY ARTIFICIAL NEURAL NETWORKING

[1*] *Maryam Mohammadi,* [2] *Narges Mohammadi,* [3] *Shahram Mehdipour-Ataei*
[1, 3] Iran Polymer and Petrochemical Institute, Faculty of Polymer Science, Department of Polyurethane and Advanced Materials, P.O. Box 14965/115, Tehran, Iran
[2] Universidad de Seville, Department of Mechanical Engineering and Materials, P.O. Box 159163-4311, Seville, Spain
*Corresponding author e-mail: ma.mohammadi@ippi.ac.ir

ABSTRACT

Proton conductivity of proton exchange membranes is the determining factor of performance and efficiency for the related energy conversion, harvesting, and storage systems. The presence of both sulfonated and fluorinated groups in the structure of polymer is proposed to achieve improved conductivity and stability, simultaneously. Applying theoretical assessment techniques will be also useful to design a high performance membrane. To this end, proton conductivity of membrane samples based on sulfonated/fluorinated polysulfones are studied using artificial neural network (ANN). Fluorinated regions are put in the composition of sulfonated polymers via three strategies including synthesis of sulfonated/partially fluorinated polymers, blending sulfonated and fluorinated polymers, and composite membranes of electrospun fluorinated mat impregnated with a sulfonated matrix. Sulfonation degree (WR_S), content of fluorinated groups (WR_F), and the trend of membrane cost are studied as determining factors of conductivity. According to ANN, there is a direct relationship between WR_S with proton conductivity. Regarding WR_F, the optimal value must be allocated to achieve suitable conductivity. Membrane cost including WR_S, WR_F, and diol structure has the highest impact on proton conductivity.

Keywords: Artificial neural network, Proton conductivity, Proton exchange membrane, sulfonated/fluorinated poly(aryl ether)

#405

TWO-DIMENSIONAL SIMULATION OF COLD START PROCESS FOR PEMFC STACK WITH VARIOUS CURRENT LOADING MODES

*Jing Liu, * Tong Zhang*
School of Automotive Studies, Tongji University, Shanghai 201804, China
*Corresponding author e-mail: tzhang@tongji.edu.cn

ABSTRACT

Rapid cold start of proton exchange membrane fuel cell (PEMFC) stack is imperative for the widespread commercialization of fuel cell vehicles. In the present work, a two-dimensional transient cold start model of a PEMFC stack with coolant recirculation is developed to explore a fast start-up strategy and the corresponding required operating conditions. Five current loading modes are evaluated for the stack performance from – 20 °C, including three constant current loading modes and two current ramping loading modes. It is found that a linear current ramping strategy with a larger initial current density can generate more heat and facilitate rapid cold start without excessive voltage undershoot. Meanwhile, the cell voltage variation of the 20 cells during the cold start process is recorded and two end side cells show smaller output voltage due to lower cell temperature than that of the middle cells. In order to maintain cell voltage consistency, external heating or insulation is necessary for PEMFC stack cold start stably and successfully.

Keywords: PEMFC Stack, Cold Start, Current Loading Strategy

#418

AIR SUPPLY MODULE FOR PRESSURIZING FUEL CELLS IN AIRBORNE APPLICATIONS

[1] Daniel Frank, [1] Jonas Schröter, [1] Christiane Bauer, [1] Caroline Willich*
[1]Ulm University, Institute for Energy Conversion and Storage, Albert-Einstein-Allee 47, 89081 Ulm, Germany
*Corresponding author e-mail: caroline.willich@uni-ulm.de

ABSTRACT

In order to obtain high power and efficiency while operating PEM fuel cells in airborne applications, pressurizing the inlet air is a prerequisite. An air supply module and its control strategy was developed in order to provide air at optimal conditions for different ambient conditions (low pressure, temperature and humidity) and varying power demand. The system was successfully tested statically and dynamically and afterwards connected to a fuel cell system.

Keywords: PEM Fuel Cell, Air supply, Aviation

#423

THE OPTIMISATION OF GRAPHENE-BASED MICROPOROUS LAYERS FOR POLYMER ELECTROLYTE FUEL CELLS

F.C. Lee [a], M.S. Ismail [a, b**], D.B. Ingham [a], K.J. Hughes [a], L. Ma [a], A. El-Kharouf [e], M. Pourkashanian[a,b].*
[a] Energy 2050, Department of Mechanical Engineering, Faculty of Engineering, University of Sheffield, Sheffield S3 7RD, United Kingdom.
[b] Translational Energy Research Centre, University of Sheffield, Sheffield S3 7RD, United Kingdom
[e] Centre for Fuel Cell and Hydrogen Research, University of Birmingham, B15 2TT, United Kingdom
* Corresponding author: fclee1@sheffield.ac.uk

ABSTRACT

The viability of graphene-based microporous layers for polymer electrolyte fuel cells is critically assessed through detailed characterisation of the morphology, microstructure, and transport properties. Microporous layer composition was optimised by the fabrication of several hybrid MPLs produced from various ratios of graphene to Vulcan carbon black. Single cell tests were performed at various operating conditions: between 25 % and 100% relative humidity, and at 80°C, in order to give a detailed understanding of the MEA performance over a range of conditions.

Keywords: Polymer Electrolyte Fuel Cells; Graphene; Gas Diffusion Layers; Hydrogen

#440

CONTROLLING AND COMPARISON OF PEM FUEL CELL BASED DC-DC CASCADE BOOST CONVERTER WITH CLASSIC CONTROL METHODS

[1] Sude Kart ,[2]İlhan Kocaarslan , [3]Naci Genç, [4]Hasan Üzmuş*
[1]Karabük University, Electrical and energy, TOBB vocational school of technical sciences, Karabük, Turkey
[2]Istanbul Technical University, Electrical and Electronics, Ayazağa, İstanbul,Turkey
[3] Yalova University, Electrical and Electronics Engineering Department, Yalova, Turkey
[4] Van Yuzuncu Yil University, Electrical and Electronics Engineering Department, Van, Turkey
*Corresponding author e-mail: sudekart@karabuk.edu.tr

ABSTRACT

Efforts to obtain clean and efficient energy have gained momentum in recent years against the increasing energy demand in the world. The main clean energy sources are biomass, geothermal, hydrogen, solar and wind energies. Among them, hydrogen energy has gained importance in recent years and fuel cells can be used in a wide range of applications, including transportation, material handling and stationary, portable, and emergency backup power.

One of the disadvantages of clean energy sources used today is that the electrical voltage produced in the system remains at low levels. In this study, a cascade boost DC-DC converter was used to increase the output voltage of the PEM fuel cell, which is one of the clean energy sources. The biggest advantage of cascade boost DC-DC converter is that it can increase the output voltage without increasing the duty cycle much. Control of the system is important for optimum efficiency. For this reason, in order to operate the system at maximum efficiency, an extremum seeking (ES) controller, which is one of the Maximum Power Point Tracking (MPPT) algorithms was applied to the system first. However, the ES controller has a disadvantage which is ripples in the output voltage of the system due to oscillations around the maximum power point. Therefore, different controllers (PI, PD and PID) have been added to the ES controller serially to reduce ripples in the system's output power. The results were compared and the best result among these controllers was achieved in series connection with PI controller.

Keywords: PEM Fuel Cell, Cascade Boost Converter, PI, PD, PID.

#1454

A STUDY ON CORROSION DURABILITY IMPROVEMENT OF CrAl COATED METAL BIPOLAR PLATE FOR PEMFC BY 3D LASER CLADDING METHOD

[1] Ha Eun Kang, [1] Ji Hyeok Choi, [1] Hyeong Woo Min, [2*] Dong Joo Kim, [1*] Young Soo Yoon*
[1]Department of Materials Science and Engineering, Gachon University, 1342 Seongnam-daero, Seongnam, Republic of Korea
[2] Department of Mechanical Engineering, Auburn University, Auburn, AL 36849, Unitied states
*Corresponding author e-mail: benedicto@gachon.ac.kr

ABSTRACT

In the field of metallic bipolar plates for PEMFCs, since coating technology can achieve improved resistance and surface properties without changing the base material, numerous studies have been conducted. The cost of the vacuum coating process and corrosion resistance and electrical conductivity of the coating materials are still under discussion. In order to improve the corrosion resistance of metallic bipolar plates, we select materials and technologies that are in the spotlight at ATF and conduct convergence research. The 3D laser cladding method was applied to the base material as metallic bipolar plate and the CrAl binary alloy was coated to evaluate its performance.

Keywords: PEMFC, Bipolar Plates, Corrosion, 3D Laser Cladding, Coatings

#1455

INVESTIGATION OF WASTE HEAT RECOVERY FROM PROTON EXCHANGE MEMBRANE FUEL CELL USING ORGANIC RANKINE CYCLE WITH ZEOTROPIC

[1] Tahir Abdul Hussain Ratlamwala, [1] Muhammad Furqan Siddiqui, [1]Syed Muhammad Ali, [1]Muhammad Muneeb Vohra, [1]Abdul Sami, [1]Khurram Kamal*
[1]National University of Sciences and Technology, Islamabad, Pakistan
*Corresponding author e-mail: tahir.ratlamwala@pnec.nust.edu.pk

ABSTRACT

In view of the rapid depletion of fossil fuel sources and growing concerns on adverse environmental effects; including ozone depletion, global warming, sea-level rise and air-quality degradation. In last decade, there has been great endeavors to search for viable alternate energy resources. Fuel cells have shown great potential for energy production application because of their short start up time, low temperature operation and most importantly very little environmental cost of use. The present paper discusses the viability of using Organic Rankine Cycle (ORC) for waste heat recovery from Proton Exchange Membrane Fuel Cells (PEMFCs) is investigated. PEMFC and ORC system is modelled in Matlab® Simulink®. Thermodynamic property data of the working fluid is imported though Cool-Prop Python library. As the working fluid, suitability of multiple zeotropic mixtures is assessed. Finally, first law and second law thermodynamic analysis of the system is carried out. The developed ORC waste heat recovery system increased the overall power output of the system by 5.46 percent.

Keywords: PEMFC, Zeotropic, Matlab

#1457

NUMERICAL INVESTIGATION ON THE EFFECTS OF INHOMOGENEOUS GAS DIFFUSION LAYER AND IMPACT OF INTERFACIAL CONTACT RESISTANCE ON PERFORMANCE OF POLYMER ELECTROLYTE FUEL CELLS

[1] Umesh Shinde, [1] Pranav Padavu, [1] Poornesh Kumar Koorata*
[1] Electrochemical Energy System Design Lab, Department of Mechanical Engineering,
National Institute of Technology Karnataka, Surathkal, Mangalore – 575 025, India
*Corresponding author e-mail: kpkoorata@nitk.edu.in

ABSTRACT

A three-dimensional single-channel is modeled numerically to simulate homogeneous and inhomogeneous gas diffusion layer (GDL). The effect of interfacial contact resistance (ICR) between flow field ribs and GDL is also studied. The present study involves GDL being considered as a single component (homogeneous) in one case while in another case, GDL being considered with varying porosities to depict the inhomogeneity. The inhomogeneity in GDL is assumed to occur due to localized deformation induced due to non-uniform contact pressure. The study reveals increased availability of reactants at higher current loads in the case where ICR is assumed negligible. This study explains how the presence and absence of ICR impact reaction concentrations, water concentration, current density and polarization curve of polymer electrolyte fuel cells. It is observed in polarization curve that the presence of ICR has effect both in ohmic and mass transport region. This work involves considering 4 cases viz: homogeneous GDL, inhomogeneous GDL, homogeneous GDL with ICR and inhomogeneous GDL with ICR.

Keywords: PEM Fuel Cell, Gas Diffusion Layer, Interfacial Contact Resistance, Porosity, Cell Performance.

#1461

PERFORMANCE EVOLUTION OF PEM FUEL CELLS WITH STRAIGHT AND WAVY PARALLEL FLOW CHANNELS OF VARIOUS WAVELENGTHS USING CFD SIMULATION

[1] Rashed Kaiser, [1] Gyu-Mok Jeon, [1] Jong-Chun Park*
[1] Pusan National University, Dept. of naval architecture and ocean engineering, Busan, South Korea
*Corresponding author e-mail: jcpark@pnu.edu

ABSTRACT

Polymer electrolyte membrane fuel cell (PEMFC) is one of the emerging fuel sources which have the potential to replace the conventional fossil fuels continuously endangering the earths climate system. The purpose of this paper is to evaluate the performance and the reliability of PEMFCs with straight channel in comparison to three wavy channels in the basis of polarization curve, pressure drop and velocity on cathode channel. The higher pressure drop of wavy channels facilitates the water removal and improve the cell efficiency. Eventually the wavy channel with short wavelengths showed the best performance.

Keywords: Fuel Cell, Flow Channel, Wavelength, Pressure Drop, Water Accumulation.

#1464

SUPERHYDROPHOBIC FLUORINATED CARBON FOR IMPROVED MICROPOROUS LAYERS IN POLYMER ELECTROLYTE FUEL CELLS

[1*] *Enes M. Can,* [2,3] *Kazunari Sasaki,* [1,3,] **Stephen M. Lyth*
[1]Department of Automotive Science, Kyushu University, Fukuoka, Japan
[2] Next-Generation Fuel Cell Research Center (NEXT-FC), Kyushu University, Fukuoka, Japan
[3] International Research Center for Hydrogen Energy, Kyushu University, Fukuoka, Japan
* *Stephen M. Lyth*: lyth@i2cner.kyushu-u.ac.jp

ABSTRACT

Flooding is one of the major issues in polymer electrolyte fuel cells (PEFCs), especially under high current density operation. Therefore, gas diffusion layers (GDLs) coated with hydrophobic microporous layers (MPLs) are usually employed to decrease water saturation at the cathode side of the cell. In this study, fluorinated carbon powders are synthesized to create superhydrophobic microporous layers to facilitate water management and prevent flooding. Fluorinated carbons are synthesized by a solvothermal method and characterized by various technics techniques. Then, either fluorinated carbon or commercially available carbon black are formed into a slurry and screen printed onto a commercial GDL to form MPLs. These MPLs are then characterized by water contact angle measurements, air permeability tests, and oxygen transport resistance measurement. Furthermore, their performance in a PEFC is evaluated using I-V measurements in a PEFC under various conditions. The results indicate that fluorinated carbon based MPLs are superhydrophobic, leading to lower oxygen transport resistance and significantly higher fuel cell efficiency compared to conventional carbon black.

Keywords: PEFC, Microporous Layer, Fluorinated Carbon Powder, Superhydrophobicity

#1471

HIGHLY DISPERSED PtCo NANOPARTICLES ON SELF-ASSEMBLED HIERARCHICALLY ORDERED MESOPOROUS CARBON SUPPORT FOR POLYMER ELECTROLYTE MEMBRANE FUEL CELLS

[1,2] *Yi Yang,* [1*] *Zhida Wang,* [1]*Lisha Shen,* [1,2*] *Changfeng Yan*
[1] Hydrogen Production and Utilization Group, Guangzhou Institute of Energy Conversion, Chinese Academy of Sciences, Guangzhou, China, 510640.
[2] University of Chinese Academy of Sciences, Beijing, China, 100039.
*Corresponding author e-mail: wangzd@ms.giec.ac.cn; yancf@ms.giec.ac.cn

ABSTRACT

PtCo nanoparticles (NPs) on hierarchically ordered mesoporous carbon (PtCo/OMC) are synthesized for polymer electrolyte membrane fuel cells (PEMFCs) aiming to improve the catalytic performance of the Pt-based catalyst towards oxygen reduction reaction (ORR). Specifically, a triblock copolymer PEO-PPO-PEO is employed as the structure agent to prepare the OMC through a solvent evaporation induced self-assembly (EISA) method, followed by annealing in the nitrogen atmosphere. The block copolymer-derived carbon shows a large surface area (495.65 $m^2 \cdot g^{-1}$), uniform mesoporous structure and a high degree of graphitization. PtCo nanoparticles (NPs) are fabricated with an average diameter of 3.3 nm by H_2 reduction and galvanic replacement in an acid solution, and then are uniform dispersed onto the OMC via wet impregnation. The unique mesoporous structure of the OMC enhances the uniformly distribution and thermal stability of the PtCo NPs. The PtCo/OMC catalyst exhibits excellent activity and stability in the cyclic voltammetry (CV) and single cell test. In the electrochemical tests, PtCo/OMC shows a large electrochemically active surface area (ECSA) of 88.56 $m^2 \cdot g^{-1}$, and a ECSA retention of 77.5 % after 5000 CV cycles. The PtCo/OMC has excellent physical properties and shows enhanced catalytic performance, which endows it with great potential in future PEMFC applications.

Keywords: PtCo Nanoparticles, Block Copolymer Self-Assembly, Ordered Mesoporous Carbon, Oxygen Reduction Reaction, Polymer Electrolyte Membrane Fuel Cells.

#1489

INVESTIGATING THE WATER FLOODING EFFECTS ON THE PERFORMANCE OF LOW-TEMPERATURE PROTON EXCHANGE MEMBRANE FUEL CELLS

[1] *Akshaykumar N. Desai,* [2] *Surajeet Mohanty,* [1*] *Venkatasailanathan Ramadesigan,*
[1] *Suneet Singh,* [2] *Shaneeth M.*
[1] Department of Energy Science and Engineering, Indian Institute of Technology Bombay, Mumbai, 400076, India
[2] Fuel cell development division, Vikram Sarabhai Space Centre, ISRO, Thiruvananthapuram, 695022, India
*Corresponding author e-mail: venkatr@iitb.ac.in

ABSTRACT

Liquid water flooding in low-temperature proton exchange membrane fuel cells (LT-PEMFCs) is one of the key issues, significantly reducing its performance. This study investigates the impact of water flooding on the reactant transport across the porous domain, active surface area of the catalyst layer (CL), and membrane water content. The main objective of this work is to estimate the LT-PEMFC performance in the mass transport region using a 3-D, multiphase, non-isothermal, physics-based model. The model is validated using the data obtained from experiments performed on a 32 cm^2 area LT-PEMFC with the hybrid flow configuration. The results show that the multiphase model with a root mean square current density error of 39 mA/cm^2 is in good agreement with the experimental results compared to the single-phase model with an RMS current density error of 60 mA/cm^2. The substantial drop in O_2 mass fraction from 0.95 at the flow channels to 0.14 at the CL at 0.4 V cell potential indicates a reduction in reactant transport due to the liquid water. On the other hand, water generation helps to improve water content inside the membrane, which increases the membrane's ionic conductivity from 1.5 to 5.3 S/m with a decrease in cell potential.

Keywords: Low-Temperature Proton Exchange Membrane Fuel Cell, 3-D Physics-Based Model, Multiphase Flow, COMSOL Multiphysics

#1493

MICROWAVE-ASSISTED SYNTHESIS OF POROUS CARBON FROM PEANUT SHELLS

[1]*Hilal Doğan,* [1]*Tuğba Meşeli,* [1*]*Gamze Genç,* [1]*Gülşah Elden*
[1]Erciyes University, Engineering Faculty, Department of Energy Systems Engineering, 38039 Kayseri, Turkey
*Corresponding author e-mail: gamzegenc@erciyes.edu.tr

ABSTRACT

Porous carbon materials have been more attractive and promising ones since their outstanding properties such as high surface area, accessible active sites, mass transport, diffusion. This study aims to synthesize bio-carbon based catalysts via the microwave method and KOH activation agent. By the reason of the abundant of Peanut shells in Turkey besides being an important agricultural by-product, they were used as a carbon source in this study. The obtained carbon was analyzed by Brunauer - Emmett - Teller (BET), X-ray diffraction (XRD), Raman spectroscopy.

Keywords: Porous Carbon, Electrocatalyst, Biomass, Peanut Shell.

#1494

FACILE SYNTHESIS FOR POROUS CARBON FROM BIOMASS SUGARCANE BAGASSE

[1] *Tuğba Meşeli,* [1] *Hilal Doğan,* [1*] *Gülşah Elden* [1] *Gamze Genç*
[1]Erciyes University, Engineering Faculty, Department of Energy Systems Engineering, 38039 Kayseri, Turkey
Corresponding author e-mail: gulsah@erciyes.edu.tr

ABSTRACT

This study presents the synthesis of porous carbon from the sugarcane bagasse precursor. Carbon material obtained from sugarcane bagasse was synthesized by two different methods. In the first method, Sugarcane was carbonized without pretreatment and then impregnated with KOH. In the second method, It was activated with KOH. The surface areas of the prepared carbon materials were determined by Brunauer Emmet-Teller and the vibrational modes of the material properties were examined by Raman Spectrum analysis. The specific surface area of porous carbons was found at 646.96 m^2/g and 566.96 m^2/g, respectively.

Keywords: Biomass, Sugarcane Bagasse, Porous Carbon

#1498

EVALUATION OF ETHANOL MICROFLUIDIC DEVICE AT LOW ELECTROCATALYSIS LOADING

*A. Martínez-Lázaro[1], J. Ledesma-García[1], L.G. Arriaga[2] and A. Arenillas[3]**

[1]División de Investigación y Posgrado, Facultad de Ingeniería, Universidad Autónoma de Querétaro, 76010, Querétaro, México.

[2]Centro de Investigación y Desarrollo Tecnológico en Electroquímica, 76703, Santiago de Querétaro, México.

[3]Instituto de Ciencia y Tecnología del Carbono, INCAR-CSIC. Francisco Pintado Fe, 26. 33011 Oviedo, Spain.

*Corresponding author e-mail: aapuente@incar.csic.es

ABSTRACT

Microfluidic fuel cells (MFCs) have received a great deal of attention in the last two decades for their high utility and versatility in portable electronics devices. Microfluidic-fuel cell technology used a liquid electrolyte, which show a great advantage compared to cells that include conventional polymer membranes (physical barrier). To date, different MFC configurations have been designed, in which ethanol have been used as fuel, however the implementation of high electrocatalysts materials is still the key for improvement performance of real devices applications.

The present work shows high performance in a MFC with ethanol as fuel, the excellent performance is due to use Pd-M (M= Co) based aerogels anode electrode, within the configuration of a microfluidic cell system. The use of hybrid aerogels allows the use of low catalyst masses of just 0.1 mg/cm^2 to generate current densities close to 400 mA cm^{-2}.

Keywords: Unsupported Aerogel, Microwave Heating, Microfluidic Fuel Cell, Nanotechnology, Electrocatalyst.

#1507

GRAPHITE BASED-POLYMER COMPOSITE BIPOLAR PLATES FOR PEM FUEL CELLS

*Miquel Gamón Rodríguez, * Alina Madalina Darabut, Yevheniia Lobko, Yurii Yakovlev, Iva Matolínová, Vladimír Matolín*

Charles University, Faculty of Mathematics and Physics, Department of Surface and Plasma Science, V Holešovičkách 747/2,

180 00 Prague 8, Prague, Czech Republic

*Corresponding author e-mail: alinadarabut@gmail.com

ABSTRACT

The polymer composite bipolar plates based on commercially available and self-prepared graphite and epoxy resin were obtained. The electrical conductivity, gas permeability, and other characteristics of materials were measured. The percolation behavior of the composites was analyzed. The own-designed bipolar plates were prepared using compression molding technique. The in-situ tests in fuel cells' stations were performed.

Keywords: Bipolar Plates, Polymer Composites, Thermally Expanded Graphite, Electroconductive Fillers, PEM Fuel Cells

#1510

HIGHLY POROUS PT-CEO$_2$-C THIN FILM CATALYST PREPARED BY MAGNETRON CO-SPUTTERING FOR PROTON EXCHANGE MEMBRANE FUEL CELLS

Xianxian Xie, Yurii Yakovlev, Peter Kúš, Jaroslava Nováková, Kateřina Veltruská, Yevheniia Lobko, Vladimír Matolín, Ivan Khalakhan, Iva Matolínová**

Charles University, Faculty of Mathematics and Physics, Department of Surface and Plasma Science, V Holešovičkách 2, 18000 Prague, Czech Republic

*Corresponding author e-mail:khalakhan@gmail.com

ABSTRACT

The Pt-CeO$_2$-C thin film catalyst was prepared by magnetron co-sputtering in Ar+O$_2$ atmosphere. The electrochemical surface area (ECSA) of thin film catalysts was tested in half-cell rotating disk electrode (RDE) system and showed 2.5 times higher than that for pure platinum. When Pt-CeO$_2$-C deposited directly on polymer-electrolyte membrane, creates a porous structure. The Pt-CeO$_2$-C catalyst coated membrane (CCM) was further measured in single-cell and exhibited only 21% power density loss during the accelerated stress test (AST).

Keywords: Thin Film, Catalyst, Porous Structure, Fuel Cell

#1521

MATERIALS BASED ON Pt-Ru-Ir, MADE BY THERMAL PYROLYSIS TO BE USED IN URFC

[1*] *A.M. Fernández,* [2] *A. Altamirano-Gutiérrez*
[1]Instituto de Energías Renovables. Universidad Autónoma de México. Privada Xochicalco s/n, 62580 Temixco, Morelos, México,
[2]Centro Universitario de Tonalá, Universidad de Guadalajara, Av. Nuevo Periférico No. 555 Ejido San José Tatepozco, C.P. 45425, Tonalá, Jalisco, México,
*Corresponding author e-mail: afm@ier.unam.mx

ABSTRAC

Regenerative fuel cells have two bifunctional electrodes: the oxygen electrode and the hydrogen electrode. Water oxidation and oxygen reduction reactions took at the oxygen electrode, the latter being the slowest. For this reason, it is necessary to use electrocatalytic materials with suitable kinetic characteristics to carry out these reactions. The different electrocatalytic materials used range from metal oxides to alloys. According to previous reports, $Pt_xRu_yIr_z$ type alloys have electrocatalytic characteristics as bifunctional oxygen electrodes. The main objective of this work is to demonstrate that $Pt_xRu_yIr_z$ alloys, prepared by the thermal pyrolysis technique, are used for the construction of bifunctional electrodes. Structural, morphological, atomic composition and electrochemical characterization studies for the samples had reported.

Keywords: Bifunctional, Fuel Cells, Electrocatalytic Materials

#1530

EXPERIMENTAL VALIDATION OF A 2-D MULTI-LAYER MODEL FOR FUEL CELL DIAGNOSIS USING MAGNETO-TOMOGRAPHY

[1*] *Antony Plait,* [1] *Frédéric Dubas*
[1]FEMTO-ST Institute, FCLAB, Univ. Bourgogne Franche-Comté, CNRS, 90000, Belfort, France
*Corresponding author e-mail: antony.plait@gmail.com

ABSTRACT

This paper focuses on the fuel cell (FC) diagnosis by using the magneto-tomography, which involves mapping the magnetic field produced by any electric device. Since the magnetic field and the current density are directly related, this study could describe the (ab)normal operation of a FC. For this purpose, a two-dimensional (2-D) multi-layer model based on the Maxwell-Fourier methods is developed. In order to validate the model developed for the FC diagnosis, an experimental bench was set up to emulate the FC operating mode. The purely analytical model is validated since the average difference between analytical results and experimental measurements is about 7%.

Keywords: Fuel Cell, Magnetic Field, Magneto-Tomography, Experimental Validation, Diagnostic.

#1551

NUMERICAL ANALYSIS OF LIQUID WATER PERMEATION PROCESS THROUGH THE DEFORMED GAS DIFFUSION LAYER OF PEM FUEL CELL

[1*] *Yingxu Liu,* [1] *Yinming Du,* [1] *Maximilian Wick,* [1] *Stefan Pischinger*
[1]Chair of Thermodynamics of Mobile Energy Conversion Systems,
RWTH Aachen University, Forckenbeckstrasse 4, Aachen, Germany
*Corresponding author e-mail: liu@tme.rwth-aachen.de

ABSTRACT

This research studies the impact of the gas diffusion layer (GDL) deformation on liquid water diffusion. A GDL model of a solid microstructure with randomly dispersed fibers is built parametrically. The Finite Element Method (FEM) is used to simulate the fiber deformation and porosity change at the rib's border area under different stresses. Finally, the deformed GDL's liquid water diffusion and dispersion are examined with the help of the Lattice Boltzmann Method. According to the findings of this study, the assembly pressure and radius of the rib corner has a crucial role in the liquid water penetration process.
Keywords: PEM Fuel Cell, Liquid Water, Gas Diffusion Layer, Lattice Boltzmann Method, Rib Corner

#1558

THE IMPACT OF AMBIENT TEMPERATURE ON HIGH-TEMPERATURE PEM FUEL CELL

[1] *Phil-Jacques Alphonse,* [1] *Mert Taş,* [1,2*] *Gülşah Elden*
[1] Erciyes University, Engineering Faculty, Energy Systems Engineering Department, 38039, Kayseri, Turkey
[2] Erciyes University, Energy Conversions Research and Application Center, 38039, Kayseri, Turkey
*Corresponding author e-mail: gulsah@erciyes.edu.tr

ABSTRACT

The temperature management and temperature distribution in the fuel cell are important issues in terms of improving reaction kinetics. To examine the impacts of the different ambient temperatures on the heat transfer occurring inside a high-temperature PEM fuel cell, two dimensional and steady-state model is developed by using COMSOL 5.5 Multiphysics. While the operating temperature is kept constant at 150°C, the different ambient temperatures (10°C, 20°C, 30°C and 40°C) are applied to the model. The obtained results show that the fuel cell performance is improved with lower ambient temperatures. Moreover, the highest cell temperature is found in the $T_{ambient}$ = 40°C case, which is around 425 K.
Keywords: HTPEM Fuel Cell, Modeling, Temperature Distribution, Reaction Kinetics

#1567

MODELING OF H_2/BR_2 REDOX FLOW BATTERY IN FUEL CELL MODE

[1,2*]*Anil Can Turkmen,* [1]*Kursat Can Ata,* [1]*Cenk Celik*
[1]Kocaeli University Faculty of Engineering, Department of Mechanical Engineering, Kocaeli 41380, Turkey
[2]ACT Scientific Ltd., Budotek Teknopark, Istanbul, 34776, Turkey
*Corresponding author e-mail: anilcan.turkmen@hotmail.com

ABSTRACT

A single-channel H_2/Br_2 redox flow battery is modeled in this study. Within the scope of the modeling, the use of the redox flow battery only in the discharge mode has been studied. In this context, Nafion 115 was used as the membrane and SGL 34BC was used as the diffusion layer. The highest power density obtained in this context was reached at 0.8 V, and this value was obtained as 0.62 W/cm^2.

Keywords: Hydrogen, Bromide, Redox Flow Battery

#1569

DEVELOPMENT OF HYDROGEN RANGE EXTENDER FOR A SPECIALIZED MULTIPURPOSE VEHICLE

[1*] *Ing. Lukáš Polák, Ph.D.* [1] *Ing. Aleš Doucek, Ph.D.,* [1] *Ing. Stanislav Kříž*
[1]ÚJV Řež, a.s., Department of Hydrogen Technologies and Innovations in Energetics, Hlavní 130, 250 68 Husinec-Řež, Czech Rep.
*Corresponding author e-mail: lukas.polak@ujv.cz

ABSTRACT

The scope of the project is a research and development of a hydrogen range extender by implementing a hydrogen fuel cell, high pressure cylinders and other supporting components in a commercial battery-based multipurpose vehicle. In the final phase, the long term real-operation testing of the prototype vehicle will be carried out. The documentation for a small serial production will be prepared after a final optimisation of the whole electric power train system.

Keywords: Hydrogen, Fuel Cell, Multipurpose Vehicle, Range Extender

#1570

TRANSIENT CHARACTERISTICS OF IN-PLANE WATER TRANSPORT IN THE GAS DIFFUSION LAYER OF PEM FUEL CELLS

[1] *Sung Yong Jung*, [2*] *Mehdi Mortazavi*

[1]Department of Mechanical Engineering, Chosun University, 309 Pilmun-Daero, Dong-gu, Gwangju, 61452 Republic of Korea

[2] Department of Mechanical Engineering, Western New Englan University, Springfield, Massachusetts, 01119 USA

*Corresponding author e-mail: mehdi.mortazavi@wne.edu

ABSTRACT

Understanding about water transport in gas diffusion layer (GDL) is important for the water management of proton exchange membrane fuel cells (PEMFC). In this study, the in-plane water transport in a commercial GDL was visualized to investigate the transient characteristics using an optical imaging system providing a high spatial resolution. Previously proposed non-dimensional scaling model and specific interfacial area were obtained from measured wetted area, perimeter, and percolation pressure. In addition, the wetted area with time is graphically presented by spatiotemporal maps. It is newly found that the transition of flow characteristics including flow pattern and transport mechanism occurs. Results indicate that at higher compressions, the transition occurs earlier under lower saturation, and water invades along a more complex path through pores that are altered by compression.

Keywords: In-Plane Water Transport, Proton Exchange Membrane Fuel Cells, Gas Diffusion Layer

#1571

AQUEOUS AMMONIA DROPLET EVAPORATION FROM GAS-DIFFUSION LAYER SURFACES

[1*] *Anthony Santamaria**, [1] *Mehdi Mortazavi*

[1]Western New England University, Department of Mechanical Engineering, 1215 Wilbraham Road, Springfield, MA, United States

*Corresponding author e-mail: asantamaria@ucdavis.edu

ABSTRACT

Recent interest in ammonia as a carbon-free energy vector, including its electrochemical synthesis and its use in low temperature direct ammonia fuel cells (DAFC), motivates the need to understand fundamental wetting and mass transport behavior between the liquid phase and electrode surfaces. This work measures evaporation rates of aqueous ammonia from the surface of carbon gas-diffusion layers (GDL) which are commonly used in the membrane-electrode assemblies (MEA) of these technologies. Ammonia solution droplets of 0%, 10%, and 20% concentration NH_3 by weight were micropipetted onto GDL surfaces. An environmental chamber mounted to the goniometer was used to maintain temperatures of 60 °C and 100 °C. NH_3 concentration and temperature effects on wetting behavior and evaporation rates were probed using a digital scale and automated goniometer. Higher NH_3 concentrations lead to higher initial evaporation rates; as the ammonia concentration falls the rates decrease toward the rate of water. Higher temperatures increased the evaporation rates for all cases and at 100 °C slow nucleate boiling was observed at the GDL/droplet interface. During evaporation, droplet contact widths remained constant while height and static contact angles decreased as wetting was dominated by pinning effects to the GDL fibers.

Keywords: Hydrogen Storage, Multicomponent Droplet Evaporation, Gas-diffusion layer, Direct Ammonia Fuel cell, Electrochemical Ammonia Synthesis

#1579

GDL DEGRADATION EFFECT ON FLOWS INSIDE FLOW CHANNEL ON POLYMER ELECTROLYTE MEMBRANE FUEL CELL

[1] *Jong Woon Moon,* [1] *Seong Keun kim,* [1*] *Sung Yong Jung*
[1]Chosun University, Department of Mechanical Engineering, 309 PILMUN-DAERO, DONG-GU, GWANGJU 61452, Rep. of KOREA
*Corresponding author e-mail: syjung@chosun.ac.kr

ABSTRACT

Performance reduction of polymer electrolyte membrane fuel cell caused by the degradation of gas diffusion layer (GDL) is hydrodynamically analyzed by comparing visualized two-phase flows in flow channels. GDL was chemically degraded using hydrogen peroxide, and the degree of GDL degradation was controlled by changing soaking time. The I-V curves for fresh and aged GDLs were compared using a commercial single cell, and the behavior of water in the cathode flow channel was visualized using a specially designed single cell having a transparent window. Two-phase flow characteristics were quantitatively compared after applying image processing technique to captured images. As a result of the experiment, it was confirmed that the hydrophobicity of GDL decreases as it degrades, absorbing the water generated inside, and reducing the efficiency by blocking the supply of reactants.

Keywords: Proton Exchange Membrane Fuel Cell, Gas Diffusion Layer Degradation, Flow Visualization, Reduced Hydrophobicity, Mass Transport Loss

#1582

NON-TRADITIONAL MACHINING METHODS FOR METALLIC BIPOLAR PLATE MATERIALS

Orhan Çakır
Yildiz Technical University, Faculty of Mechanical Engineering, Department of Mechanical Engineering, Istanbul, Turkey
*Corresponding author e-mail: orhanc@yildiz.edu.tr

ABSTRACT

Bipolar plates are important part of fuel cell and their manufacturability is extremely influential when the cost is considered. Various manufacturing methods can be used for shaping metallic bipolar plate materials, but it is significant to find optimum manufacturing technique to minimize the cost and increase efficiency [1,2].

Various manufacturing methods are candidates to be used in metallic bipolar plate materials. The geometrical integrity will be a factor to be gained by using optimum manufacturing method. One of the possible manufacturing processes can be non-traditional machining methods. These methods are commonly employed for machining complex geometries in case of difficult-to machine materials such as stainless steel, nickel alloys etc [3-6].

In this study, brief information regarding metallic bipolar materials and general knowledge about non-traditional machining processes will be provided. Than feasible non-traditional machining methods in production of metallic bipolar materials will be discussed in detail through particular research studies.

***Keywords**:* Metallic Bipolar Plate, Non-Traditional Machining Processes, Cost Effectiveness

#1585

A SCALABLE ANALYTICAL MODEL FOR RAPID MULTIPHYSICAL ANALYSIS AND STRUCTURAL OPTIMIZATION OF PEM FUEL CELLS

[1*] *Markus Kohrn,* [1] *Yingxu Liu,* [1] *Maximilian Wick,* [1] *Stefan Pischinger*
[1]Chair of Thermodynamics of Mobile Energy Conversion Systems,
RWTH Aachen University, Forckenbeckstrasse 4, Aachen, Germany
*Corresponding author e-mail: kohrn@tme.rwth-aachen.de

ABSTRACT

To further improve the overall marketability of fuel cell vehicles, improves are necessary in particular on the durability of the employed proton exchange membrane fuel cells. A key factor in durability is the distribution of mechanical stresses within the cells, which can be reduced by optimization of the bipolar plate rib structure. However, this optimization should not be performed without taking into account further physical quantities such as porosity and electric resistivity, as these have a direct impact on the cell performance. Therefore, this study presents a multiphysical simulation model based on a new analytical approach, which, in addition to the stress and strain distribution can also compute a variety of relevant physical quantities. The model's capability is demonstrated on an exemplary fuel cell layout. Compared to FEM models, the computation time can be reduced by a factor of up to 1000. Thus, extensive simulation studies with multi-criterial optimization can be implemented with reasonable computational effort.

Keywords: PEM Fuel Cell, Analytical Model, Gas Diffusion Layer, Mechanical Stresses, Physical Properties

#1590

STUDY OF CATALYST LOADING AND GDL POROSITY GRADIENT VARIATION EFFECT TO PEMFCs PERFORMANCE THROUGH RECURRENT NEURAL NETWORK (RNN) DATA-DRIVEN ASSISTED MODELLING

Hanhui Lei
Northumbria University, UK
*Corresponding author e-mail: hanhui.lei@northumbria.ac.uk

ABSTRACT

The required electrochemical activities and mass transport rates of polymer electrolyte membrane fuel cell (PEMFCs) is different owing to the inhomogeneous distributions of reactants and products within the membrane electrode assemblies (MEAs). The graded distributions of Pt loading in the catalyst layer (CL) and porosity of gas diffusion layer (GDL) along the in-plane and through-plane directions significantly affect the spatial distributions of electrochemical reaction and mass transport rates, thus influence the cell performance, i.e., the limiting current density. Herein, we developed a two-dimensional (2D), multi-physics, two-phase flow model to investigate the gradients of linear change of two design parameters, i.e., platinum loading and GDL porosity at the cathode. Both the profiles of platinum loading and GDL porosity obey an elliptic function, leading to the linear variations of these two design parameters along the in-plane and through-plane directions (see Fig. 1a and 1b). Six parameters were selected, and their interaction was numerically studied by the recurrent neural network (RNN) model, including the 1). platinum loading at the CL-GDL interface at the cathode inlet, 2). platinum loading gradient along the in-plane direction (from inlet to outlet), 3). Platinum loading gradient along the through-plane direction (from CL-GDL interface to PEM-CL interface), 4). GDL porosity at the CL-GDL interface at the cathode inlet, 5). GDL porosity gradient along the in-plane direction (from inlet to outlet), and 6). GDL porosity gradient along the through-plane direction (from CL-GDL interface to GDL-channel interface). The combination of these parameters will generate 5000 permutations at the accuracy of 0.1. To reduce the computational time and resources of solving the mechanistic model, a data-driven surrogate model is developed based on RNN algorithm, which is used to assist the identification of the relationship between the chosen parameters and the objective function (current density at 0.1V).

#1591

SULFONATED SILICA/NAFION® BASED COMPOSITE ELECTROSPUN MEMBRANES FOR PEM FUEL CELLS

[1] Naeimeh Rajabalizadeh, [1] Ahmet Can Kırlıoğlu [1,2] Selmiye Alkan Gürsel and [2]Begüm Yarar Kaplan*
[1] Sabancı University, Faculty of Natural Science and Engineering, 34956, Istanbul, Turkey
[2] Sabancı University Nanotechnology Research and Application Center(SUNUM), 34956, Istanbul, Turkey
*Corresponding author e-mail: nrajabaliazdeh@sabanciuniv.edu

ABSTRACT

In this study, dual electrospinning were employed to fabricate proton conducting membranes comporising sulfonated silica, Nafion® and PVDF or P(VDF-TrFE) as the carrier polymers. Firstly, dual electrospinning was carried out to obtain dual fiber-based mats and converted into compact membranes via hot-pressing. After obtaining compact membranes, effect of various amounts of Nafion and type of carrier polymers were investigated. FTIR, ionic conductivity, ion exchange capacity (IEC), water uptake measurements and mechanical test were conducted for these membranes. Finally Membrane-electrode-assemblies (MEAs) were prepared via composite electrospun membranes and sprayed electrodes and fuel cell performance tests were performed. The fuel cell test showed that presence of sulfonated silica in the composite membranes improved the performance at lower humidity conditions. The P(VDF-TrFE)-Nafion®/S-SiO_2 membranes with 60/30 wt% Nafion®/S-SiO_2 composition showed the best ionic conductivity and fuel cell performance.

Keywords: Dual Electrospinning, Sulfonated Silica, Sol-Gel, Membranes, PEM Fuel Cells

#1596

PREPARATION OF KAOLIN AND BENTONITE ADDED NAFION COMPOSITE MEMBRANES

[1] Fahriye Dönmez, [2] Nezihe Ayas*
[1]Eskişehir Technical University, Engineering Faculty, Department of Chemical Engineering, Eskişehir, Turkey
*Corresponding author e-mail: nazcan@eskisehir.edu.tr

ABSTRACT

Clay (kaolin, bentonite) doped Nafion composite membranes are considered as an alternative material for proton exchange membrane fuel cell (PEMFC). In this study, 10% clay (wt./wt.) doped Nafion membranes were prepared by solution casting method and characterized by water uptake capacity, ion exchange capacity (IEC), X-Ray diffractometry (XRD) and Fourier transform infrared spectrometry (FT-IR). The results showed that kaolin and bentonite doped Nafion membranes can be evaluated for PEM fuel cells.

Keywords: Nafion, Kaolin, Bentonite, Membrane, Fuel Cell

#1617

MODELING OXYGEN TRANSPORT IN CARBON SUPPORT MICROSTRUCTURE OF PROTON EXCHANGE MEMBRANE FUEL CELL ELECTRODES USING PORE NETWORKS

[1,2,3*] *Alper Can Ince,* [3,4]*Mustafa Fazil Serincan,* [3]*Hasnain Hafiz,* [5]*Edward F. Holby,* [6]*J. S. Spendelow,* [1,2]*U. Pasaogullari,* [3]*Wilton J. M. Kort-Kamp*

[1] Center for Clean Energy Engineering, University of Connecticut, Storrs, CT, USA
[2] Department of Mechanical Engineering, University of Connecticut, Storrs, CT, USA
[3] Theoretical Division, Los Alamos National Laboratory, MS B262, Los Alamos, NM, USA
[4]Gebze Technical University, Faculty of Engineering, Mechanical Engineering Department, Gebze, Kocaeli, Turkey
[5] Sigma Division, Los Alamos National Laboratory, Los Alamos, NM, USA
[6] Materials Physics and Applications Division, MS D429, Los Alamos National Laboratory, Los Alamos, NM, USA
*Corresponding author e-mail: alper_can.ince@uconn.edu

ABSTRACT

The structural morphology of high surface area carbon (HSC) on which both the platinum catalyst and ionomer are dispersed is very complex and critical for understanding the transport of oxygen (O_2). This study aims to develop a model to simulate O_2 transport in the cathode catalyst layer of proton exchange membrane fuel cells fabricated using HSCs. A stochastic two-dimensional multiscale domain, including micro and mesopores, and connecting throats is constructed. Steady state coupled transport and electrochemical reaction models are then implemented into using transport properties estimated using in-house atomistic level calculations. This study provides a multi-scale approach by relating the pore-scale approach with the atomistic level model, allowing to represent a large modeling domain at higher detail. Oxygen concentration in HSC surfaces is predicted for dry and flooded cases. Results show an effective diffusivity of $8.752 \cdot 10^{-8}$ m^2/s and $4.851 \cdot 10^{-8}$ m^2/s for the flooded case and non-flooded case, respectively. Oxygen concentration drops significantly when micropores are flooded, consequently Pt utilization decreases.

Keywords: Pore-scale modeling, PEMFC, catalyst layer, transport phenomena, multiscale modeling, high surface carbon area

#1623

OPTIMIZATION OF CHARACTERIZATION ROUTINES FOR CARBON BLACKS USED IN ENERGY RELATED APPLICATIONS

[1*] *Fatih Özcan,* [1] *Amin S. Amin,* [1,2] *Doris Segets*

[1] Particle Science and Technology (IVG-PST), University of Duisburg-Essen (UDE), Duisburg, Germany
[2] Centre for Nanointegration Duisburg-Essen (CENIDE), Duisburg, Germany
*Corresponding author e-mail: fatih.oezcan@uni-due.de

ABSTRACT

Here, we report on characterization routines for carbon blacks both in terms of their intrinsic properties resulting from their synthesis history and process-related quality parameters. We establish characterization methods based on analytical centrifugation which work fast, reliable and at low cost and were developed in-house. We apply them to analyze CB particle properties (particle size distribution, morphology, surface properties) and link them with ink properties. First results indicate that small deviations in feed quality can be determined by our stability trajectories. By the same methods, we found out that mixing parameters in the course of ink preparation greatly influence stability parameters which are important in the subsequent process chain of electrode production.

Keywords: Carbon Black, PEMFC, Stability Trajectories, Analytical Centrifugation, Hansen Solubility Parameters

#1634

AERODYNAMIC AND PEM FUEL CELL SYSTEM OPTIMIZATION FOR A DESIGNED UNMANNED AIR VEHICLE

[1*] Ahmet Şumnu, [2] Raif Kenanoğlu
[1]İskenderun Technical University, Faculty of Aeronautics and Astronautics, Department of Aerospace Engineering, İskenderun, Hatay, Turkey
[2]İskenderun Technical University, Faculty of Engineering and Natural Science, Department of Mechanical Engineering, İskenderun, Hatay, Turkey
*Corresponding author e-mail: ahmet.sumnu@iste.edu.tr

ABSTRACT

Today the energy crisis is almost reached top level on the world. The effect of global warming and environmental pollution has decreased the interest in fossil fuels and increased the interest in the use of alternative energy sources. This situation increases the use of alternative energy in air vehicles as in land vehicles. Developing technology has increased the use of unmanned air vehicles (UAVs), but has also accelerated energy and battery consumption, which causes more environmental pollution. Supporting the batteries with hydrogen energy for minimum use both increases the range of the aircraft by charging the battery, and provides instant high power by feeding the engine with the battery during instant high power consumption. In this study, optimum energy consumption strategies of hydrogen fuel cell with battery were conducted. In addition, energy efficiency was taken into account during the design.

Increase of the energy saving can be achieved by optimizing the geometry of any air vehicle. In this study, aerodynamic shape optimization of wing of designed unmanned air vehicle (UAV) has been performed to increase aerodynamic performance. For this purpose, Computational Fluid Dynamic (CFD) solution has been carried out to determine performance of designed UAV for the baseline wing geometry using ANSYS Fluent. Lift to drag ratio is the most important parameter to determine aerodynamic performance. Therefore, the objective of optimization problem is selected as maximization of lift to drag coefficients ratio. The constraints of wing geometry parameters are determined according to size of the fuel sticks. The optimization method is determined as Genetic algorithm (GA) since it gives good results for the complex problems. After optimization study is carried out, CFD analysis has been repeated for optimized wing geometry to verify and validate the results of study. The results are compared with each other and it is concluded that optimized wing has shown superior performance for AUV. These applied methods in this study can be used to increase performance and saving energy for the most of air vehicles.

Keywords: Hydrogen, Fuel Cell, UAVs, Optimization, Design

Track 8.

Fuel Cells: SOFC and other types

#7

DEVELOPMENT OF HIGHLY DURABLE AND DENSE GDC BUFFER LAYER FOR ANODE-SUPPORTED PLANAR SOFC

Amjad Hussain[1,2], Muhammad Zubair Khan[1], Rak-Hyun Song[1,2], Dong Woo Joh, Jong-Eun Hong[1], Seung-Bok Lee[1,2], Tak-Hyoung Lim[1,2]*
[1]Fuel Cell Research Center, Korea Institute of Energy Research, Korea
[2]Department of Advanced Energy and System Engineering, University of Science and Technology (UST), Korea
Corresponding author e-mail*: rhsong@kier.re.kr

ABSTRACT

Solid oxide fuel cells (SOFCs) are highly efficient, low emission and fuel flexible (H_2, CH_4, and CO) future energy device that can also operate in reverse as co-electrolysis cell, converting the CO_2 and H_2O into useful fuel (H_2). However, among numerous sources of electrochemical degradation, the inter-diffusion between electrolyte and cathode has been identified as pre-dominant factor in long run operation, facile method for manufacturing GDC buffer layer should be accomplished for long-term stability and cost effectiveness. Herein, established a highly reliable durable buffer layer that exclusively suppresses the detrimental elemental diffusion at high temperature. This buffer layer is manufactured via tape casting film approach, in which both electrolyte and buffer layer films are laminated by warm iso-static press (WIP) to control the interfacial and bulk properties. The simple approach for electrolyte and buffer layer enables to manufacture a desired thin film structure. Subsequently, the formation of harming insulating phases and decomposition of cathode are effectually prevented, resulting in a remarkably enhancement in electrochemical performance and long-term stability. The scalability and feasibility of mass production are confirmed via the fabrication of large area cells.

Keywords: Solid oxide fuel cell, Thin film SOFC, WIP (Warm iso-static pressing), Buffer layer, Interfacial

#107

NUMERICAL INVESTIGATION OF NI MIGRATION IN SOC FUEL ELECTRODE USING PHASE FIELD MODEL AND LATTICE BOLTZMANN MODEL

[1,2] Yang Wang, [2] Siyuan Zhao, [2] Zengjia Guo, [1] Qing Du, [1] Kui Jiao, [1,3] Bingfeng Zu, [2**] Meng Ni*
[1]State Key Laboratory of Engines, Tianjin University,
135 Yaguan Road, Tianjin, China
[2] Department of Building and Real Estate, Research Institute for Sustainable Urban Development (RISUD) & Research Institute for Smart Energy (RISE), Hong Kong Polytechnic University, Hung Hom, Kowloon, Hong Kong, China
[3] Internal Combustion Engine Research Institute, Tianjin University, 92 Weijin Road, Tianjin, China
*Corresponding author e-mail: zbf@tju.edu.cn (B. Zu)
**Corresponding author e-mail: meng.ni@polyu.edu.hk (M. Ni)

ABSTRACT

The long-term stability of Solid Oxide Cells (SOCs) is seen as one of the key obstacles hindering commercialization. The effects of morphological changes in fuel electrodes account for a large part of the cell performance degradation during long-term operation. The morphological changes refer to the migration processes of the Ni phase in Ni-based composite electrode at high operating temperature (600-1000 ℃). The initial smaller Ni particles will agglomerate to reduce the surface energy and form larger particles, and this is the Ni coarsening process which will occur in both fuel cell and electrolysis mode. The Ni coarsening will reduce the density of three-phase boundaries (TPBs) and increase the cell overpotential. Another Ni migration process may be quite destructive, which refers to the redistribution of the Ni phase from one location to another. The redistribution of the Ni phase usually occurs in the electrolysis mode. A series of experimental studies have revealed that the Ni phase will migrate away from the most active functional layer close to the dense electrolyte, which greatly aggravates the performance degradation process. In this study, we conduct a numerical investigation on the Ni migration process in SOCs using an integrated model. First, a phase field model is established to track the morphology evolution of Ni-based electrodes. After experimental validation, the phase field model provides a good characterization of the Ni migration process. Then a lattice Boltzmann model is used to evaluate the electrochemical performance of the fuel electrode at different operating times. The results show that severe Ni depletion can cause an increase of the total overpotential by 0.081 V at high operating current density. Besides, the effects of initial microstructure and operating conditions are also investigated.

Keywords: Solid Oxide Cells, Ni migration, Numerical simulation, Phase field model, Lattice Boltzmann method

#173

EFFICIENT REGENERATIVE HYDROGEN/VANADIUM FUEL CELL USING TRICHOME-LIKE ELECTRODES FOR ENHANCED VANADIUM ELECTROLYTE UTILIZATION AND ITS SYSTEM INTEGRATION

[1*] *Barun K. Chakrabarti,* [2] *Yashar S. Hajimolana,* [3] *Mengzheng Ouygang,* [4] *J. Rubio-Garcia,* [2] *Abhishek K. Singh,* [3] *Yuhua Xia,* [1] *Nigel P. Brandon,* [5] *Vladimir Yufit*

[1] WMG, Warwick, Electrochemical Engineering Group, Energy Innovation Centre, University of Warwick, Coventry CV4 7AL, United Kingdom; RFC Power Ltd., London SW7 2PG, United Kingdom

[2] Department of Thermal and Fluid Engineering, University of Twente, Enschede 7500 AE, The Netherlands

[3] Department of Earth Science and Engineering, Imperial College London, London SW7 2AZ, United Kingdom

[4] SweetGen Limited, London SW7 2PG, United Kingdom

[5] Addionics Ltd., London W12 0BZ, United Kingdom

*Corresponding author e-mail: Barun.Chakrabarti@warwick.ac.uk

ABSTRACT

In this work we explore an in-house made carbon metal fabric (CMF) electrodes for enhanced performances in regenerative hydrogen/vanadium fuel (or flow) cells. CMF is manufactured via a sophisticated electrospinning method followed by carbonization that leads to the development of carbon nanotubes and trichome-like structures with iron nanoparticles that improve the vanadium electrolyte utilization in the RHVFC significantly. The long-term storage costs of the RHVFC are reduced when CMF is used as electrodes, and this leads to a successful systems integration for water desalination and/or solar energy storage plants.

Keywords: Hydrogen, Regenerative fuel cell, Electrospinning, Levelized cost, System integration

#215

ELECTROLYTE IN-SITU REPLENISHMENT TO EXTEND MCFC LIFETIME

[1,2]*Kab In Kim,* [1,3]*Jae Kwan Bae,* [1]*Audasso Emilio,* [1]*Seung Wan Choi,* [1,2]*Hyun Woo Kim,* [1]*Hyun S. Park,* [1]*Seong-Cheol Jang,* [2]*Yong Soo Cho, and* [1,*]*Sung Pil Yoon*

[1]Center for Hydrogen-Fuel Cell Research, Korea Institute of Science and Technology, 02792, Seoul, Republic of Korea

[2] Department of Chemical Engineering, Yonsei University, 03722, Seoul, Republic of Korea

[3] Department of Material Science and Engineering, Yonsei University, 03722, Seoul, Republic of Korea

*Corresponding author e-mail: spyoon@kist.re.kr

ABSTRACT

Molten carbonate fuel cell suffers from limited operation time due to excessive electrolyte losses. In this study, the authors investigate two in-situ techniques to replenish the electrolyte during cell operations: atmospheric pressure chemical vapor deposition (AP-CVD) and atmospheric pressure electrochemical vapor deposition (AP-EVD). These methods consist in directly injecting one or more precursors as vapor to turn them into the required electrolyte by reaction with either CO_2 and O_2 gases or CO_3^{2-} ions. For a cell operating with a $(LiNa)_2CO_3$ electrolyte, LiI and NaI are selected through thermodynamic calculations as they possess high vapor pressure and a considerably high conversion to carbonate at the operating conditions. These precursors are tested in different cells set up with insufficient electrolyte by applying the aforementioned techniques to study the recovery of the performance and the reduction of N_2 cathode to anode cross-over. Using both techniques the authors are able to recover the cell performance of more than 100 mV at a working current density of 150 mA cm^{-2} while also reducing the N_2 cross-over to values lower than 1%. In this way the authors demonstrate that is possible to enhance the molten carbonate fuel cells operation by maintaining stable performance.

Keywords: Molten carbonate fuel cell, Atmospheric pressure electrochemical vapor deposition, Atmospheric pressure chemical vapor deposition, Long-term operations.

#273

COMBINATORIAL DEVELOPMENT OF LSF/RP-LSF/ScSZ COMPOSITE CATHODE FOR INTERMEDIATE TEMPERATURE SOLID OXIDE FUEL CELLS

[1*] *Fahrettin Kılıç*, [1,2] *Tayfur Öztürk*
[1]Middle East Technical University, Metallurgical and Materials Engineering, Ankara, Turkey
[2] ENDAM, Center for Energy Storage Materials and Devices, Middle East Technical University, Ankara, Turkey
*Corresponding author e-mail: fahrettinkkilic@gmail.com

ABSTRACT

This study focuses on the synthesis, characterization, and processing of LSF based composite cathode for solid oxide fuel cells. The cathode comprises three oxides; LSF, rp-LSF and ScSZ which are synthesized by co-sputtering using combinatorial approach. The electrolyte was Scandia doped Zirconia (ScSZ), as it has attractive ionic conductivity at lower temperatures. Having chosen the electrolyte ScSZ as electrolyte. After detailed analysis regarding conductivity and thermal expansion for each oxide, the compositions selected were $La_{0.8}Sr_{0.2}FeO_{3-\delta}$, $LaSr_3Fe_3O_{10-\delta}$, and $Sc_{0.15}Zr_{0.85}O_{2-\delta}$ LSF, rp-LSF, ScSZ respectively. A total of 21 composite cathodes were deposited on electrolytes, each with a different composition. The performance of cathodes was characterized via EIS measurements on symmetric cells. A temperature ranges from 600 ^{0}C up to 800 ^{0}C was covered at 50 ^{0}C interval. LSF-rpLSF-ScSZ ternary diagram was mapped in terms of area specific resistance (ASR). The ASR values at 600 ^{0}C varied from 2.159 to 34.68 ohm.cm^2. At 800 ^{0}C the values were significantly better which ranged from 0.1649 to 0.85 ohm.cm^2.

Keywords: SOFC cathodes, Electrochemical impedance spectroscopy, Magnetron sputtering

#294

IDENTIFICATION OF OXYGEN ION CONDUCTIVITY OF TWO LAYERS YTTRIA STABILIZED ZIRCONIA MATRIX IMPREGNATED BY LITHIUM/POTASSIUM ELECTROLYTE FOR MOLTEN CARBONATE FUEL CELLS

[1*] *Jaroslaw Milewski*
[1]Warsaw University of Technology, Faculty of Power and Aeronautical Engineering, Institute of Heat Engineering, 21/25 Nowowiejska street, Warsaw, Poland
*Corresponding author e-mail: Jaroslaw.milewski@pw.edu.pl

ABSTRACT

It is proposed that dual conductive electrolytes have the potential to improve the performance of Molten Carbonate Fuel Cells by using oxygen ion conductors as matrix material, creating what is termed composite electrolyte. This paper presents the results of testing of a composite electrolyte layer based on Yttria Stabilized Zirconia and Lithium/Potassium carbonates for its electrochemical performance as a matrix for MCFC. The voltage–current density curves were collected for a range of temperatures: 500–800°C. Without very accurate measurements it is not easy to determine the additional electric charge provided by oxygen ions ($O^=$). We tried to build a mathematical model which takes into account both conductivities and, based on the model, estimated the ratio of electric charge provided by oxygen ions and carbonate ions.

Keywords: MCFC, Composite electrolyte, Dual conducting, YSZ, Li/K

#313

ECONOMIC OPTIMIZATION OF A HYBRID FUEL CELL-GAS TURBINE SYSTEM FOR POWER AND HEATING PRODUCTION

Leyla Khani[1], *Gülden G. Akkurt*[2], *Mousa Mohammadpourfard*[1*]
[1]Faculty of Chemical and Petroleum Engineering, University of Tabriz, Tabriz, Iran
[2]Department of Energy Systems Engineering, Izmir Institute of Technology, Izmir, Turkey
*Corresponding author e-mail: mohammadpour@tabrizu.ac.ir

ABSTRACT

Due to the importance of waste heat recovery from thermodynamic systems and its economical benefits, a hybrid solid oxide fuel cell-gas turbine system for heat and power cogeneration is considered and optimized from the exergoeconomic viewpoint. Each equipment of the system is simulated as a steady-state control volume using mass, energy, exergy, and exergoeconomic balance equations. Also, electrochemical equations are applied for the solid oxide fuel cell. The obtained set of equations is solved in Engineering Equations Solver (EES) software. Then, the system is economically optimized by implementing the genetic algorithm. The obtained results show that for the optimal operating condition, the unit cost of fuel cell power, gas turbine power, and pressurized hot water is calculated as 28.25, 29.34, and 71.25 $/GJ, respectively. Also, increasing the operating temperature of the fuel cell reduces the optimum amount of total cost of products. The highest exergoeconomic factor belongs to the water pump, while its lowest value occurs in the combustion chamber. Moreover, the system exergy is destructed mostly in the fuel cell, steam generator, and combustion chamber, respectively.

Keywords: Fuel cell, Gas turbine, Exergoeconomic analysis, Optimization

#325

OPTIMIZATION OF LOW-GRADE CGO TRANSPORT PROPERTIES FOR SOFC APPLICATIONS

Eduarda.Gomes[1], Devaraj Ramasamy[1], António A.L. Ferreira[1], João C.C. Abrantes[1,2,]*
[1]proMetheus, Instituto Politécnico de Viana do Castelo, 4900-347 Viana do Castelo, Portugal
[2] CICECO, Aveiro Institute of Materials, Universidade de Aveiro, 3810-193 Aveiro, Portugal
*Corresponding author e-mail: jabrantes@estg.ipvc.pt

ABSTRACT

Grain boundaries are frequently responsible for a poor performance of gadolinium-doped ceria-based electrolytes, due to a low ionic conductivity, orders of magnitude smaller than the bulk conductivity. Silica, the dominant impurity in many low-grade ceramics, namely, in ceria-based materials, has a detrimental effect on grain boundaries conductivity. Several previous works had explored the silica-scavenging effect. In the present work, we exploit an alternative approach using the addition of 5% (w/w) of Y_2O_3, as silica scavenging agent, and sintering by hot pressing at low temperature to minimize bulk dissolution of yttrium in the CGO lattice. Gadolinium-doped ceria-based powders were co-fired with additions of 1% (w/w) of silica, and silica and yttrium oxide to test the silica scavenging role of yttrium. The samples were prepared by hot press at low temperature (1000ºC) and were characterized by impedance spectroscopy as a function of temperature in air, in order to de-convolute different microstructural contributions to the overall electrical behaviour. Combined information obtained from structural, microstructural, and electrical characterization allowed one to study the impact of new phases on the resulting ceria-based solid electrolytes.

Keywords: Ceria, Yttria, Scavenge effect, Heterogeneities, Hot press.

#326

ELECTRICAL CONDUCTIVITY OF Y-DOPED CGO BASED MATERIALS SINTERED BY HOT PRESS

[1]Devaraj Ramasamy, [1]Eduarda Gomes, [1]António A.L. Ferreira, [1,2]João C.C. Abrantes*
[1]proMetheus, Instituto Politécnico de Viana do Castelo, 4900-347 Viana do Castelo, Portugal
[2]CICECO Aveiro Institute of Materials, Universidade de Aveiro, 3810-193I Aveiro, Portugal
*Corresponding author e-mail: jabrantes@estg.ipvc.pt

ABSTRACT

Commercial ceria–gadolinia powders were used to prepare dense CGO (5 mol% Gd) samples, by hot press method at relatively low temperature (1000°C). To study the effect of post-sintering, further the as-sintered bodies were subjected into different thermal treatments 1100ºC-1400ºC. The sintered samples were characterized by impedance spectroscopy as a function of temperature in air, in order to identify each microstructural contribution to the overall electrical behaviour. Scanning electron microscopy shows that the increase in the temperature of thermal treatment leads to grain growth. Electrical properties were studied with different oxygen partial pressures and ion blocking methods. Y_2O_3 (5 wt%) additions were used to seek the grain boundaries heterogeneities effects in CGO material, prepared by hot press and subjected into post sintering thermal treatments. Electrical conductivities of CGO samples were analysed with and without Y_2O_3 additions.

Keywords: SOFC, Hot press, CGO, Electrical conductivity, Heterogeneities.

#327

OPTIMIZATION OF LOW-GRADE TETRAGONAL ZIRCONIA BY PRASEODYMIUM OXIDE ADDITIONS

[1] António A.L. Ferreira, [1] Devaraj Ramasamy, [1] Eduarda Gomes, [1,2] João C.C. Abrantes*
[1] proMetheus, Instituto Politécnico de Viana do Castelo, 4900-347 Viana do Castelo, Portugal
[2] CICECO, Aveiro Institute of Materials, University of Aveiro, 3810-193 Aveiro, Portugal
*Corresponding author e-mail: jabrantes@estg.ipvc.pt

ABSTRACT

Zirconia-based materials are still the state of art electrolyte for high temperature electrochemical systems, and for non-electrochemical applications. Their purity is known to affect performance, thus requiring high-grade expensive precursors and additional concerns about contamination during high temperature processing and/or during long term applications at intermediate temperatures, as found for contamination by silica. Thus, the purpose of this work was to demonstrate the scavenging ability of praseodymium oxide to minimize or suppress the impact of contamination by silica.

In the present work, one used TZP precursor powders from Tosoh and Innovnano. Starting materials of both powders contained significant fractions of monoclinic phase, coexisting with tetragonal zirconia, and yielded highly dense samples after sintering at 1450°C/2h. Praseodymium oxide and/or silicon oxide additions did not affect significantly the sintering behaviour. Additions of Pr and Si yielded co-existing tetragonal and cubic phases, as revealed by XRD and Rietveld refinements, with an impact on lattice parameters of the cubic phase. The electrical characterization showed the expected severe decrease in conductivity after the addition of silicon oxide addition and showed that this negative impact is at least partially reverted by additions of praseodymium oxide.

Keywords: Solid electrolyte, Yttria-stabilized zirconia, Praseodymium oxide, Scavenging, Silica impurity

#366

ACCELERATED STRESS TESTING OF SOLID OXIDE FUEL CELLS VIA EX-SITU CHEMICAL REDOX CYCLING OF Ni-CGO FUEL ELECTRODES

[1] *Massimiliano Della Pietra,* [1*,2] *Andrea Monforti Ferrario,* [1] *Davide Pumiglia,* [1] *Livia Della Seta* [1] *Stephen McPhail*
[1] ENEA, Laboratory of Energy Storage, Batteries and Hydrogen Production & Use, Department of Energy Technologies and Renewable Sources (TERIN-PSU-ABI), C.R. Casaccia, Via Anguillarese 301, 00123 Rome, Italy
[2] Department of Industrial Engineering and Mathematical Sciences (DIISM), Università Politecnica delle Marche, Via Brecce Bianche 12, 60131 Ancona, Italy
*Corresponding author e-mail: andrea.monfortiferrario@enea.it

ABSTRACT

Although Solid Oxide Fuel Cells (SOFC) are key for the energy transition, current lifetimes represent a critical barrier for deployment and a full understanding of the degradation mechanisms is yet to be reached. In this work an innovative testing approach has been implemented to evaluate an Accelerated Stress Test (AST) via chemical redox cycling as stressor for electrolyte supported SOFC Ni-CGO fuel electrodes. The fuel electrodes were aged with an *ex-situ* approach by exposing half-cells to alternating redox cycles (up to 12 cycles). Successively, fresh oxygen electrodes were screen-printed and the resulting full-cells with pre-aged anodes were electrochemically tested (comparing IV curves and EIS spectra with a virgin full-cell) and characterized with SEM post-test imaging. Preliminary results show that chemical redox cycling seems a viable AST pathway, showing a coherent performance degradation (both in terms of voltage and impedance) with increasing number of cycles. The accelerated degradation ascribed to the anode processes (both charge and mass transfer) by the impedance analyses is confirmed by SEM observations which show Ni particle agglomeration within the fuel electrode. However, full-cell stability with high number of redox cycles might represent a limiting factor in terms of AST replicability and testing performance, since recurrent cathode detachment is observed.

Keywords: Solid oxide fuel cells, Accelerated stress tests, Redox chemical cycling, Electrochemical testing, SEM

#1452

THEORETICAL AND EXPERIMENTAL ANALYSES OF ETHANOL-FUELED SOFC MICRO-COGENERATOR

[1*] *Alberto Coralli,* [1] *Selma Aparecida Venâncio,* [1] *Paulo Emílio Valadão de Miranda*
[1]Laboratório de Hidrogênio, PEMM-PET/Coppe, Universidade Federal do Rio de Janeiro, Rua Moniz Aragão 207,
Cidade Universitária, Ilha do Fundão, 21941-594, Rio de Janeiro (RJ), Brazil
*Corresponding author e-mail: alberto.coralli@coppe.ufrj.br

ABSTRACT

In Brazil, bioethanol is produced from sugarcane on a large scale and with high process efficiency. Characterized by simple logistics, low toxicity and small environmental impact, it represents a convenient fuel for Solid Oxide Fuel Cells (SOFCs). This perspective motivated the present research that aimed at developing theoretical and experimental analyses of ethanol-fueled SOFC micro-cogenerator. It included a stack designed for hydrogen and bearing conventional materials, running on ethanol under internal reforming regime, and a Balance of Plant (BoP) specifically designed to allow direct ethanol supply, avoiding carbon deposition on the BoP tubing. To validate the project and the components, the stand-alone system was tested with hydrogen and an ethanol/water mixture, demonstrating the capability of conveniently producing electricity and heat under such conditions. After determining the BoP efficiency, possible actions to improve it were identified and the projected efficiency that can be reached applying them was calculated, resulting close to pre-established targets. In addition, electrochemical performance results obtained with proprietary developed nickel-free anodes were promising for the direct utilization of anhydrous ethanol in an SOFC.

Keywords: Solid oxide fuel cells, Balance of plant, Micro-cogeneration, Direct utilization of ethanol, nickel-free multifunctional SOFC.

#1467

A HIGHLY STABLE COBALT SPINEL-GDC NANOCOMPOSITE CATHODE FOR INTERMEDIATE-TEMPERATURE SOLID OXIDE FUEL CELLS

[1] *Saeed Ur Rehman, Muhammad Haseeb Hassan,[1] Hye-Sung Kim,[1,2] Rak-Hyun Song,[1,2] Tak-Hyoung Lim,[1] Jong-Eun Hong,[1,2] Seok-Joo Park,[1,2]* Seung-Bok Lee*
[1] High Temperature Energy Conversion Laboratory, Korea Institute of Energy Research, 152 Gajeong-ro, Yuseong-gu, Daejeon 34129, Republic of Korea
[2] Department of Advanced Energy and System Engineering, University of Science and Technology, 217 Gajeong-ro, Yuseong-gu, Daejeon 34113, Republic of Korea
*Corresponding author e-mail: sblee@kier.re.kr

ABSTRACT

Cobalt spinel oxide (Co_3O_4) and gadolinium-doped ceria (GDC) nanocomposite were prepared via sol-gel processing and were studied as cathode material for intermediate-temperature solid oxide fuel cells (SOFCs). XRD analysis confirmed separate precipitation of Co_3O_4 and GDC phases during the calcination process thus, producing a nanocomposite. Various nanocomposite compositions were tested for their electrical property where a nanocomposite having a Co to GDC mole ratio of 1 (CGC1) showed the highest electrical conductivity. Electrochemical impedance spectroscopy and DC polarization measurements were conducted to study the performance of SOFC consisting of CGC1 cathode. The SOFC showed an initial maximum power density of 484 mW cm^{-2} at 800 °C however, the cell performance gradually increased, and a maximum power density of 1380 mW cm^{-2} was observed after a 168 h operation.

Keywords: Solid oxide fuel cell, Cathode, Nanocomposite, Cobalt, Spinel.

#1497

WASTE CANE MOLASSES BASED-COMMERCIAL FUEL CELL THAT CAN PLAY A SIGNIFICANT ROLE IN THE TECHNOLOGY OF THE NEW MILLENNIUM

Kaman Singh
Department of Chemistry, School of Physical and Decision Science
Babasaheb Bhimrao Ambedkar University (A Central University) Lucknow-226 025, U.P. India

ABSTRACT

A fuel cell is a device that generates electricity through an electrochemical redox reaction, not combustion. Electricity, heat, and water are produced in a fuel cell employing hydrogen and oxygen. Moreover, fuel cell technology is the future of the energy sector and energy crises can be solved using this sustainable technology. Hydrogen-oxygen fuel cells create water and hydrogen as raw materials that could be made from prolonged water supplies (an abundant source) in the long run. Water is a sustainable renewable resource, unlike fossil fuels like petrol or diesel. Moreover, the efficiency of the fuel cells is much more (>75%) than fossil fuel power stations or costly chemical batteries. Graphite is a costly material, however, porous graphite used as anode and cathode has been prepared to employ a method of making substitute carbon electrodes for a battery by heating molasses and carbonaceous matter under pressure. Thus, further reduces the total cost of production of electricity and it seems an exhaustible material for electrical power generation. According to a report, molasses seems to be a case of mixed (ionic-electronic) conductors. However, the moist state electrochemistry of molasses may be expected to open new potentialities in fuel cell technology. Here, the possibility of using moist molasses in an electrochemical power source has been studied.

Keywords: *Moist molasses (substitute for carbon electrodes) Fuel Cell, Commercial production of electrical power, Sustainable source of energy*

#1499

EFFECT OF A REDUCTION OF THE CATALYST LOADING ON THE PERFORMANCE OF A MINI PASSIVE DIRECT METHANOL FUEL CELL

[1,2] *C.S. Moreira,* [1,2] *A.M.F.R. Pinto,* [1,2]* *V.B. Oliveira*
[1]CEFT - Transport Phenomena Research Center, Faculty of Engineering, University of Porto, Rua Dr. Roberto Frias, 4200-465 Porto, Portugal
[2]ALiCE - Associate Laboratory in Chemical Engineering, Faculty of Engineering, University of Porto, Rua Dr. Roberto Frias, 4200-465 Porto, Portugal
*Corresponding author e-mail: vaniaso@fe.up.pt

ABSTRACT

Passive direct methanol fuel cells (pDMFCs) appear as a promising alternative for power portable electronic devices, since they use a liquid fuel, which is easy to handle, storage and distribute and have a quick refuelling, high efficiency and low environmental impacts. However, some issues need to be solved before the introduction of this technology in the market, such as methanol and water crossover through the membrane, low lifetime and high costs. In this way, the present work studies the effect of reducing the catalyst loadings, on both anode and cathode sides, on the performance of a mini passive DMFC towards a reduction of these systems costs. Moreover, the different phenomena that affect the cell performance were identified based on the polarization measurements and quantified using the electrochemical impedance spectroscopy (EIS) technique. The main goal of this study was to reduce the costs of these systems without a significant lost on their performance and analyse in detail the different losses that negatively affect the cells under the light of the EIS technique. Therefore, it was proposed an innovative equivalent electric circuit (EEC) that reproduces with accuracy the system under study.

Keywords: Passive direct methanol fuel cell, Catalyst loading, Power output, Electrochemical impedance spectroscopy, Equivalent electric circuit

#1501

DEVELOPMENT OF LSF-LSM COMPOSITE CATHODES FOR IT-SOFC

[1,2*] *Ramin Babazadeh Dizaj,* [1,2] *Fahrettin Kılıc,* [1,2] *Tayfur Öztürk*
[1] Dept. of Metallurgical and Materials Engineering, Middle East Technical University, Dumlupınar Blv., Ankara, Turkey
[2] ENDAM, Center for Energy Storage Materials and Devices, Middle East Technical University, Ankara, Turkey
*Corresponding author e-mail: ramin.dizaj@metu.edu.tr

ABSTRACT

Following a pioneering study on (La,Sr)CoO_3- (La,Sr)$_2CoO_4$ amorphous cathodes which was synthesized via sputter deposition, a similar work was carried out for (La,Sr)FeO_x – (La,Sr)MnO_3 composite cathodes to see if the cathode can be used in amorphous form with acceptable ORR. First a thorough search was made in LSM/LSF/ScSZ ternary system to identify most favorable compositions. Unfortunately, even in most favorable cathode composition, an acceptable ASR value of 0.15 ohm cm^2 was obtained at temperature not lower than 800 °C where the cathode, was already crystalline. This study however showed that a thorough investigation is needed in LSM-LSF binary system where a more favorable results may be obtained. Accordingly, a set of 6 cathodes were sputter deposited in combinatorial geometry using LSM and LSF sputter targets where the cathode make-up varied over a wide range. Electrochemical performance of the cathodes were measured using symmetric cell. The tests were performed starting from 450 °C at 50 °C interval and stopped when ASR <=0.15 ohm *cm^2. Cathodes which were amorphous in the deposited state were monitored so as to determine the temperature of crystallization. The aim is to identify compositions where the cathode is still amorphous with an acceptable ASR values. The role of ScSZ addition in improving the stability of amorphous cathode was also investigated.

Keywords: SOFC, Cathode, LSM, LSF, Magnetron sputtering.

#1503

A NEW CLASS OF AMOURPHOUS/NANOCRYSTALLINE (La,Sr)CoO_3 BASED CATHODES FOR IT-SOFCS

[1,2]Dogancan Sari, [1,2]Ziya Çağrı Torunoğlu,[1,2]Bengisu Yaşar[1,2] Yunus Eren Kalay [1,2]Tayfur Öztürk*
[1]ENDAM, Center for Energy Materials and Storage Devices,METU, Ankara Turkey
[2]Department of Metallurgical and Materials Engineering, METU, Ankara,Turkey
* Corresponding author e-mail: ozturk@metu.edu.tr

ABSTRACT

In this study, we report results of an investigation carried out on (La,Sr)CoO_3- (La,Sr)$_2CoO_4$ dual phase oxides as cathode for IT- SOFCs. Cathodes were produced via sputter deposition where the volume fraction varied over a wide range from 0.10 <(La,Sr)$_2CoO_4$ < 0.90 and screened electrochemically using symmetric cells. The study showed that the compositions with volume fractions in the range 0.40 < (La,Sr)$_2CoO_4$ < 0.60 were particularly significant in yielding cathodes of improved performance. Refocusing the combinatorial screening to this range yielded (La,Sr)CoO_3- (La,Sr)$_2CoO_4$=0.45:0.55 as the most favorable composition. Taking ASR=0.15 Ω · cm2 as a useful benchmark, the study showed that cathodes in this range may be used at temperatures as low as 575 °C. It was further shown that composite cathodes have amorphous structures in co-sputtered conditions and could remain so when used at reduced temperatures. At temperatures close to 700 °C the amorphous cathode turns into nanocrystalline two phase structure with grains not more than 10 nm in size. Moreover, this refined cathodes were extremely stable and resistant to Sr segregation. The results imply a new class of LSC based amorphous/nanocrystalline cathodes for IT-SOFCs.

Keywords: IT- SOFCs, ORR catalysts, Amorphous cathodes, (La,Sr)CoO_3- (La,Sr)$_2CoO_4$ dual phase oxides

#1511

EFFECT PARTIAL SUBSTITUTION OF LANTHANUM ON THE THERMAL PROPERTIES OF $La_{0.7-X}Ln_XCa_{0.3}MnO_3$ (Ln = Pr or Sm) PEROVSKITES

Jessica Ramírez-Hernández[1], Aidé M. Torres-Huerta[2], Silvia B. Brachetti-Sibaja[1], Miguel A. Domínguez-Crespo[2], Diana Palma-Ramírez[3], Wencel de la Cruz[4], Francisco Gutiérrez-Galicia[2].
[1]Tecnológico Nacional de México, IT de Ciudad Madero, D.E.P.I., Cd. Madero, Tamps., C.P. 89440, México.
[2]Instituto Politécnico Nacional, UPII-Hidalgo, San Agustín Tlaxiaca, Hidalgo, C.P. 42162, México.
[3]Instituto Politécnico Nacional, CMPL, Cd. de México, C.P. 07340, México.
[4]UNAM, Centro de Nanociencias y Nanotecnología, Ensenada, B.C, C.P. 22860, México.
* Corresponding author e-mail: atorresh@ipn.mx

ABSTRACT

$La_{0.7-x}Ln_xCa_{0.3}MnO_3$ (Ln = Pr or Sm) perovskites synthesized by Pechini method with different stoichiometries (x = 0.1, 0.3, 0.5 and 0.6) were analyzed in order to evaluate the effect of cationic substitution and final composition on thermal properties; specific heat, thermal conductivity and thermal diffusivity at different temperatures are specifically reported. The results are discussed in terms of the potential use as a cathode material to be applied in solid oxide fuel cells (SOFCs) applications at intermediate temperatures (600 to 800 °C). The results showed that thermal conductivity decreases as Pr doping increases; but a different trend is observed with samarium: first, a decrease is observed from x = 0.1 to x = 0.3, and then, from x = 0.3 to x = 0.6, an increase is determined. Also, thermal diffusivity presents a marked behavior when Sm-based perovskites display a high cation substitution (x = 0.6). Thermal expansion coefficient studies are in progress.

Keywords: ABO_3 perovskites, Thermal conductivity, Solid oxide fuel cells

#1564

INVESTIGATION OF PALLADIUM COATED NICKEL FOAM ANODE ELECTRODE APPLICATION FOR DIRECT ETHANOL FUEL CELLS

[1] Cansu Kılıç, [2]Kürşat Can Ata, [2]Anıl Can Türkmen, [1]Sibel Demirel, [2]Cenk Çelik*
[1]Chemistry Dept., Kocaeli University, Umuttepe Campus, İzmit/Kocaeli
[2]Mechanical Eng. Dept., Kocaeli University, Umuttepe Campus, İzmit/Kocaeli
*Corresponding author e-mail: kursatcanata@gmail.com

ABSTRACT
Direct ethanol fuel cell (DEFC) is a subcategory of proton exchange membrane fuel cell (PEMFC). Ethanol as a fuel for DEFC is easier to obtain, store and transport than hydrogen. Additionally, ethanol has advantages over methanol due to lower toxicity, easier usability, and renewability. Therefore, DEFC is more suitable for mobile and portable power supplies if the disadvantages such as low efficiency and high total operating costs are resolved in the future. In this study, the use of Pd coatings on nickel foam in DEFC was investigated. SEM and EDS analyzes were performed for the characterization of the foam coatings. Also, the effect of Pd coatings made on nickel foam on the efficiency will be investigated by using highly-sulfonated SPEEK membranes in DEFC, the anode electrode for DEFC will be developed and its performance parameters will be examined in detail.
Keywords: Direct ethanol fuel cell, Electrocoating, Metal foam, SPEEK membrane, Hydrogen energy

#1572

DEVELOPMENT OF NOVEL MEMBRANE STRUCTURES VIA RADIATION INDUCED GRAFTING AND ELECTROSPINNING TECHNIQUE FOR ANION EXCHANGE MEMBRANE FUEL CELLS

[1] Ahmet Can Kırlıoğlu, [1] Naeımeh Rajabalizadeh, [1,2] Selmiye Alkan Gürsel and [2]Begüm Yarar Kaplan*
[1]Sabancı University, Faculty of Natural Science and Engineering, 34956, Istanbul, Turkey
[2] Sabancı University Nanotechnology Research and Application Center (SUNUM), 34956, Istanbul, Turkey
*Corresponding author e-mail: kirlioglu@sabanciuniv.edu

ABSTRACT
Development and commercialization of fuel cells, as an alternative to fossil fueled engines, are at its highest importance and urgency due to global climate change crisis. Proton Exchange Membrane Fuel Cells (PEMFC) made a huge technological leap with the breakthrough of development of Nafion® membranes however its high catalysts and membrane costs hinders further developments. Anion Exchange Membranes Fuel Cells (AEMFC) doesn't require expansive Pt group catalysts to be efficient which can solve the cost problem, but it is still needed to develop a cheap, durable membrane with high anion conductivity and ion exchange capacity. Membranes with radiation-induced grafted polymers can provide good ion exchange capacity and conductivity while weakens the mechanical robustness. Therefore, we used dual electrospinning technique to fine tune mechanical properties without sacrificing the functionality. We have prepared anion conducting membranes for AEM fuel cells by a dual-electrospinning technique using inert poly(vinylidene fluoride) (PVDF) powders and radiation induced grafted PVDF with vinyl benzyl chloride (VBC) with various compositions. The dual fiber-based mats are hot-pressed, aminated and ion exchanged in this order. We have investigated and optimized the grafting levels, mechanical properties and morphologies of the duel electrospun membranes.
Keywords: Electrospinning, Radiation induced grafting, Anion exchange membrane, Fuel cells

#1581

DEVELOPMENT OF BROMINE RESISTANT ANODE CATALYST FOR HYDROGEN OXIDATİON AND REDUCTION REACTIONS IN HYDROGEN BROMINE FLOW BATTERIES

[1] Burcu Kirtoklu, [2] Berker Fiçicilar*
Ondokuz Mayıs University, Faculty of Engineering, Chemical Engineering, Turkey, Samsun
*Corresponding author e-mail: *burcukirtoklu@gmail.com

ABSTRACT
Hydrogen-bromine flow cell system is considered a highly advantageous electrical energy storage system due to its high energy capacity, high charge-discharge efficiency, and low cost. The hydrogen oxidation reaction (HOR) that takes place on the anode side of the hydrogen-bromine flow cell is generally catalyzed by high-activity (platinum) catalysts. The bromine reduction reaction (BRR) on the cathode side can be catalyzed with platinum-based high-performance catalysts to obtain high power density, while it can also be directly catalyzed by carbon structures. Bromine ions passing from the cathode to the anode side via the ion-permeable membrane poison the anode catalyst, causing a decrease in anode kinetics and thus battery performance. A new anode catalyst resistant to the bromine environment needs to be developed to eliminate this crossover problem, which significantly reduces the catalyst performance and lowers the hydrogen oxidation reaction (HOR) kinetics. This project, it is aimed to improve the kinetics of the hydrogen oxidation reaction by developing bromine resistant anode electrocatalysts with high catalytic activity.
Keywords: Bromine tolerant electrocatalyst, Hydrogen bromine flow batteries

#1609

A NEW METHOD FOR MANUFACTURING ANODE SUPPORTED SOLID OXIDE FUEL CELLS WITH AFL

[1*] *Osman Yağız Akduman,* [2] *Mehmet Sinan Uyanık,* [1,3] *Elif Kabakcı,* [2] *Ali Murat Soydan*
[1] *Gebze Technical University, Engineering Faculty, Department of Material Science and Engineering, Gebze, Kocaeli, Turkey*
[2] *Gebze Technical University, Institute of Energy Technologies, Gebze, Kocaeli, Turkey*
[3] *Canakkale 18 Mart University, Engineering Faculty, Department of Material Science and Engineering, Gebze, Kocaeli, Turkey*
*Corresponding author e-mail: oakduman@gtu.edu.tr

ABSTRACT

In this study, a new method to manufacture anode supported SOFCs (solid oxide fuel cells) with AFL (anode functional layer) is proposed. To manufacture the anode supports, anode mixture with polyethylene glycol (PEG) is prepared and anode mixture is fed into a twin screw extruder and extruded in the shape of tubes. PEG in the anode tubes is selectively removed to by water debinding and sweat debinding methods and AFL layer is obtained with different microstructure and porosity. SEM (Scanning electron microscope) images of the manufactured SOFCs show AFL layers with the thickness of approximately 7 µm, which is akin to the values given in the literature. Electrolyte and cathode layers are added to the anode tubes using dip coating. Effects of AFL on performance of the manufactured cells are tested.

Keywords: Solid oxide fuel cells, Anode functional layer, Anode supported SOFCs

#1621

EXPERIMENTAL AND EXERGY ANALYSES OF INTERNAL REFORMING SOLID OXIDE FUEL CELL FED WITH REFORMATE GAS

[1,2*] *Anil Erdogan,* [2] *Federico Capotondo,* [2] *Anke Hagen,* [3] *C. Ozgur Colpan*
[1]The Graduate School of Natural and Applied Sciences, Dokuz Eylul University, Buca, Izmir, Turkey
[2]Department of Energy Conversion and Storage, Technical University of Denmark (DTU), DK-2800 Kgs., Lyngby, Denmark
[3]Faculty of Engineering, Department of Mechanical Engineering, Dokuz Eylul University, Buca, Izmir, Turkey
*Corresponding author e-mail: anerdo@dtu.dk, anilerdogan1992@hotmail.com

ABSTRACT

In this study, a thermodynamic and mathematical model for an internal reforming and anode-recirculated SOFC fed with reformate gas is developed. Experimental testing of SOFC fed with reformate gas is also performed in order to validate the model. A parametric analysis is conducted to study the effect of the SOFC operating temperature, current density, and steam-to-carbon ratio (S/C) on the the exergy destruction of the SOFC. In addition, XRD and EIS analyses results for SOFC obtained from the experimental studies are presented.

Keywords: Experimental test, Mathematical modeling, SOFC, Anode recirculation, Reformate gas

Track 9.

Integrated Hydrogen Energy Systems

#9

DEVELOPMENT OF INNOVATIVE HYDROGEN COMBUSTION SYSTEMS FOR INDUSTRIAL GAS TURBINES

[1*] *Nurettin Tekin,* [2] *Atsushi Horikawa,* [3] *Mitsugu Ashikaga,* [4] *Harald Funke*
[1]Project Manager, Kawasaki Gas Turbine Europe, Nehringerstr. 15, 61352 Bad Homburg, Germany
[2] Researcher, Kawasaki Heavy Industries, LTD. Technical Institute Akashi, 673-8666 Japan
[3] Project Manager, Kawasaki Heavy Industries, LTD. Technical Institute Akashi, 673-8666 Japan
[4] Professor for Gas Turbines and Aircraft Engines, Aachen University of Applied Sciences, Hohenstaufenallee 6, 52064 Aachen
*Corresponding author e-mail: n.tekin@kge-gmbh.com

ABSTRACT

Combined with the use of renewable energy sources for its production, hydrogen represents a possible alternative gas turbine fuel within future low emission power generation.
Kawasaki Heavy Industries, LTD. (KHI) has research and development projects for future hydrogen societies; production of hydrogen gas, refinement and liquefaction for transportation and storage, and utilization with gas turbines / gas engines for the generation of electricity.
Due to the large difference in the physical properties of hydrogen compared to other fuels such as natural gas (NG), well established gas turbine combustion systems cannot be directly applied for Dry-Low-Emission (DLE) hydrogen combustion. Thus, the development of DLE hydrogen combustion technologies is an essential and challenging task for the future of hydrogen fueled gas turbines.
The DLE Micro-Mix combustion principle (MMX) for hydrogen fuel has been in development for many years to significantly reduce NOx emissions. This combustion principle is based on cross-flow mixing of air and gaseous hydrogen which reacts in multiple miniaturized flames. The major advantages of this combustion principle are the inherent safety against flashback (stable flame) and the low NOx-emissions due to a very short residence time of the reactants in the flame region of the micro-flames.
Keywords: Hydrogen gas turbine, Micro-mix combustion, Dry low mission (DLE), Carbon free

#18

REACTOR EVALUATION FOR ALTERNATIVE FUEL SYNTHESIS OF METHANOL AND DIMETHYL ETHER (DME) FROM CO_2 AND RENEWABLE HYDROGEN

Stefan Weiske[1], Nils Beltermann[1], Rafael Becka[1], Remzi Can Samsun[1], Ralf Peters[1], Detlef Stolten[2,3]*
[1]Forschungszentrum Jülich GmbH, Electrochemical Process Engineering (IEK-14), 52425 Jülich, Germany
[2] RWTH Aachen, Chair for Fuel Cells, 52072 Aachen, Germany
[3]Forschungszentrum Jülich GmbH, Techno-economic Systems Analysis (IEK-3), 52425 Jülich, Germany
*Corresponding author e-mail: s.weiske@fz-juelich.de

ABSTRACT

In this contribution different reactor types are evaluated in the context of the synthesis of alternative fuels like methanol and dimethyl ether (DME) from carbon dioxide and renewable hydrogen produced via water electrolysis. The evaluation is based on a theoretical approach, which combines computational fluid dynamics (CFD) simulations of the synthesis reactors with ANSYS Fluent® and process analyses with ASPEN PLUS®. Multiple optimization strategies were applied to the synthesis reactors to increase the productivity. A membrane reactor setup could show a maximal increase of 181 % in space time yield for the direct synthesis of DME form CO_2. By this result the significance of tailor-made reactors and processes for fuel synthesis from CO_2 and renewable hydrogen are highlighted.
Keywords: Power-to-fuel, Hydrogenation, Methanol, Dimethyl ether (DME), Reactor engineering

#33

OPTIMAL TRACKING OF GRID OPERATED LOAD DEMAND WITH HYDROGEN BASED STORAGE SYSTEM USING MODEL BASED PREDICTIVE CONTROL

[1] Muhammad Bakr Abdelghany, [1]Muhammad Sheshzad, [1]Valerio Mariani, [2]Davide Liuzza, [1]Luigi Glielmo*
[1] University of Sannio, Department of Engineering, Piazza Roma, 82100, Benevento, Italy
[2] ENEA Fusion and Nuclear Safety Department, Via Enrico Fermi 45, 00044 Frascati (Rome), Italy
*Corresponding author e-mail: bmuhammad@unisannio.it

ABSTRACT
It has become imperative for the power and energy engineers to look out for the renewable energy sources such as sun, wind, geothermal, ocean and biomass as sustainable, cost-effective and environment friendly alternatives for conventional sources. However, since they are inherently unreliable, during the last decades the scientific community addressed research efforts to their integration with the main grid by means of properly designed energy storage systems (ESSs). However, due to the complexity of the involved systems in terms of number of inputs, number of outputs, number of decision variables, constraints and costs this topic is still open. In particular, advanced control strategies for the management of ESSs in order to take into account all the reported aspects need to be designed.
In this paper we present a model predictive controller (MPC) which operates a hydrogen-based ESS (HESS) within a wind farm fence. The controller is derived in order to minimize the operating and economical costs of the HESS and the difference between the available power and that required by the grid operator through a suitable reference, while satisfying physical constraints and considering the dynamics of the system. In order to capture both continuous/discrete dynamics and transitions among different operating modes, the plant is modelled as a mixed logic dynamic system. The study has been developed within the EU-FCH 2 JU funded project HAEOLUS aiming at building and integrating advanced control strategies for a ESS within a wind farm. Numerical simulations show the feasibility and the effectiveness of the proposed approach.
Keywords: Hydrogen-based energy storage systems, Energy management, Model predictive control.

#35

DYNAMICS OF AMMONIA AUTOIGNITION; THE EFFECTS OF H_2O_2 ADDITION

[1]Dimitris M. Manias, [2]Dimitris G. Patsatzis, [1,3,]Dimitrios C. Kyritsis and [1,3]Dimitris A. Goussis*
[1] Department of Mechanical Engineering, Khalifa University of Science and Technology, Abu Dhabi, UAE
[2]School of Chemical Engineering, National Technical University of Athens, 15773, Athens, Greece
[3] Research and Innovation Center on CO_2 and H_2 (RICH), Khalifa University of Science and Technology, 127788, Abu Dhabi, UAE
*Corresponding author e-mail: dimitrios.kyritsis@ku.ac.ae

ABSTRACT
The dynamics of homogeneous autoignition of ammonia/air mixtures at constant volume is analyzed with the Computational Singular Perturbation algorithm. The reactions contributing the most to the explosive mode, that characterises the ignition process, are identified. It is shown that the thermal runaway occupies the largest part of the very long ignition delay, thus resulting in very slow ignition. It is also shown that H_2O_2 is one of the species that relates the most to the explosive mode. When added in the starting mixture, the ignition delay reduces considerably. The changes in ignition delay, final temperature and final NO due to the presence of H_2O_2 in the initial mixture are discussed.
Keywords: Autoignition, Ammonia, Additives, Ignition delay control, NO_x

#37

COKE OVEN GAS AS POTENTIAL FUEL FOR STATIONARY SI ENGINES

Rafael Ortiz-Imedio, [*] Alfredo Ortiz, Daniel Gorri, Inmaculada Ortiz
Chemical and Biomolecular Engineering Department, University of Cantabria, Av. Los Castros 46, 39005, Santander, Spain
*Corresponding author e-mail: ortizal@unican.es

ABSTRACT
Internal combustion engines (ICE) can be fuelled with hydrogen rich waste streams coming from industry providing good performance and low emissions. Coke oven gas (COG), a by-product of coke manufacture, has a high volumetric percentage of H_2 and CH_4 and can be used as auxiliary support for electric generation. Computational fluid dynamics (CFD) simulation tool has been used to assess the combustion and performance of COG compared to pure H_2 and pure CH_4. Simulations were validated with experiments in a Volkswagen Polo 1.4 L port-fuel injection spark ignition (SI) engine varying engine speed from 2000 to 5000 rpm at wide open throttle (WOT), optimum spark advance for maximum brake torque (MBT) and air-fuel ratios (λ) between 1 and 2. Comparison is made through power, heat release, pressure and temperature combustion variables. Results show that COG combines benefits of both pure fuels, widening the operation range, with good performance and low wall heat transfer at intermediate λ values. Furthermore, the energy content of an industrial waste stream can be harnessed for the industrial plants where is produced.
Keywords: Coke oven gas, Hydrogen, Internal combustion engine, Computational fluid dynamics (CFD), Methane

#46

GREEN HYDROGEN PRODUCTION FROM GEOTHERMAL POWER PLANTS: KIZILDERE (DENIZLI-TURKEY) GEOTHERMAL POWER PLANT CASE STUDY

[1] *Raziye Şengün*[1],[2]*Füsun S. Tut Haklıdır*[2]
[1]Zorlu Energy Company, Sarayköy Denizli-Turkey
[2] İstanbul Bilgi University, Santral Campus Istanbul-Turkey
*Corresponding author e-mail: raziye.sengun@zorlu.com

ABSTRACT

The widespread use of especially solar, wind, geothermal and biomass investments for electricity generation coincides with the Paris Climate Agreement and the European Green Deal Act decarbonization targets and is supported by the whole world now. Green hydrogen can produce from renewable energy sources; it has been attracting attention recently because it is more environmentally friendly and in line with decarbonization targets. Geothermal power plants have the highest capacity factor among renewable energy plants and they are systems that can produce electricity all day long without interruption.

In this study, a perspective towards green hydrogen production from geothermal power plants is discussed with the Kızıldere geothermal power plant (GPP) in Denizli, Turkey.This concept study is proposed for hydrogen production by Proton Exhange Membrane (PEM) type fuel cell at multi-flash geothermal power plants.

Keywords: Green hydrogen, hydrogen production, PEM, geothermal energy, Kızıldere GPP

#47

THERMAL BALANCE IN FUEL CELL VEHICLES WITH LIQUID HYDROGEN UTILISATION

[1]*Anatoliy Unitsky,* [2] *Ilya Kavalcuk,* [3] *Irina Skitsunova,* [4] *Vera Yanchuk,* [4] *Sergey Artyushevskiy,*
[1] CEO, Unitsky String Technologies Co., Minsk, Belarus
[2] Head of Epectricap Engineering Department, Alasala University, Dammam, Saudi Arabia
[3] Department of thermal power technologies, JSC "Belgorkhimprom, Minsk, Belarus
[4] Advanced R&D Department, Unitsky String Technologies Co., Minsk, Belarus
*Corresponding author e-mail: s.artyushevskiy@unitsky.com

ABSTRACT

Hydrogen storage and its efficiency is one of the key challenges, which has been developed in line with the popularity of the fuel cell systems. However, fuel cells operation is linked with intensive heat release, which should be utilised by the cooling system to prevent membrane damage. With on-board cooling system, the overall efficiency of the vehicle decreases further. This paper provides design of a novel system to utilise heat of the fuel cells, drivetrain elements and ventilation system to vaporize liquid hydrogen and reach higher efficiency of the system with cooling system capacity decrease.

Keywords: Fuel cells, Liquid hydrogen, Thermal balance

#64

OPTIMIZATION OF ENERGY MANAGEMENT STRATEGY FOR FUEL CELL-RANGE EXTENDED ELECTRIC VEHICLE

[1*] *Yan Sun,* [1] *Changgao Xia*
[1] School of Automotive and Traffic Engineering, Jiangsu university, Zhenjiang, 212013, China
*Corresponding author e-mail: 1360118360@qq.com

ABSTRACT

For the fuel cell-range extended electric vehicle (FC-REEV), the fuel cell system can work at a fixed output power point and have a good durability. However, the differences in output power and start-stop threshold can lead to a significant difference in energy loss and degradation of power sources. Based on the thermostat control strategy (TCS), the economy of vehicle is considered in the evaluation function. Furtherly, the artificial bee colony (ABC) optimization algorithm is used to increase driving range, in order to improve the durability of fuel cell, a penalty factor is added in the performance index function, and a novel optimized ABC-TCS (OABC-TCS) is proposed. Different strategies are tested under FTP-72 and WLTC drive cycle respectively, result shows that compared with TCS, the optimized driving range proportion of OABC-TCS is about 10.59% and 10.3%.

Keywords: Fuel cell vehicle, Range extend, Artificial bee colony algorithm, Thermostat control strategy

#69

DESIGN OF A NEW HYDROGEN DRIVEN INTEGRATED POWERING SYSTEM FOR FERRY APPLICATIONS

*Ali Erdogan Karaca, Ibrahim Dincer
Clean Energy Research Laboratory (CERL), Faculty of Engineering and Applied Science, Ontario Tech. University, 2000 Simcoe Street North, Oshawa, Ontario L1H 7K4, Canada
* Corresponding author's email: ali.karaca@ontariotechu.net

ABSTRACT

In the current study, a new hydrogen energy-based integrated powering system is designed and analysed for ferry applications. The system comprises photovoltaic (PV) solar cells and Darrieus type wind turbines mounted on the ferry's body to harness renewable energy and produce the required hydrogen on-board. A proton exchange membrane (PEM) electrolyzer, a PEM fuel cell, a thermal seawater desalination unit and a heat pump are some other major sub-components of the integrated system. The system offers green hydrogen, fresh water, heating, cooling and electricity as useful outputs. In the scope of the study, the system is evaluated energetically and exergetically. Impact of the primary design and operational parameters, e.g. solar irradiance and wind speed, on the system performance are investigated by conducting parametric studies. The system is capable of producing the required hydrogen on-board while operating with energy and exergy efficiencies of 26.75% and 18.20%, respectively.

Keywords: Sustainability, Solar energy, Wind energy, Hydrogen, Hydrogen vehicle, Thermodynamic analysis.

#89

THE ULTRA-EFFICIENT FC-ICE HYBRID CYCLE WITH THERMOCHEMICAL RECOVERY OF THE WASTE HEAT - FINITE-TIME AND FINITE-SPEED THERMODYNAMICS ANALYSIS

[1] David Diskin, [2]* Leonid Tartakovsky
[1,2]Technion – Israel Institute of Technology, Mechanical Engineering, Technion City, Haifa, Israel
*Corresponding author e-mail: tartak@technion.ac.il

ABSTRACT

Efficiency and power of the hybrid cycle combining fuel cell (FC) and internal combustion engine (ICE) was analyzed using finite-time and finite-speed thermodynamics (FTT and FST). The study shows that at high efficiencies beyond 70% the hybrid cycle has the potential of a significant power gain (up to 35%) over FC or ICE operation alone. Power-efficiency maps of the hybrid cycle are obtained for various conditions and properties of the selected FC and ICE. Thermochemical recuperation (TCR) was suggested for heat recovery from the FC & ICE, and onboard hydrogen production. TCR is found to be the favorite choice for waste heat recovery in the hybrid cycle. Vehicle weight, size and the travel range are functions of the specific power and the efficiency of the propulsion system. Hence, the results of the reported study are of high importance for transportation.

Keywords: Electrochemical reaction, Combustion, Finite-time thermodynamics, Finite-speed thermodynamics, Fuel cell

#92

THE ROLE OF HYDROGEN FOR THE DEFOSSILISATION OF THE GERMAN CHEMICAL INDUSTRY

[1*] Felix Kullmann, [1] Peter Markewitz, [1] Leander Kotzur, [1,2] Detlef Stolten
[1] Institute of Techno-Economic Systems Analysis (IEK-3), Forschungszentrum Jülich GmbH, Wilhelm-Johnen-Str., 52428 Jülich, Germany
[2] Chair for Fuel Cells, RWTH Aachen University, c/o Forschungszentrum Jülich (IEK-3)
*Corresponding author e-mail: f.kullmann@fz-juelich.de

ABSTRACT

Within the European Green Deal, the European industry is summoned to transform towards a green and circular economy in order to reduce CO_2-emisisons and reach climate goals. Special focus is on the chemical industry to boost recycling processes for plastics, exploit resource efficiency potentials, and switch to a completely renewable feedstock (defossilisation). Despite common understanding that drastic changes have to take place it is yet unknown how the industrial transformation should be accomplished. How does a cost-optimal defossilisation of the chemical industry in the context of national greenhouse gas (GHG) mitigation strategies look like? The central part of this investigation is based on a national energy system model to optimize the future energy system design of Germany. A replacement of fossil-based feedstocks by renewable feedstocks leads to a significant increase in hydrogen demand by +40% compared to a reference scenario. Without the import of hydrogen-based energy carriers, the entire hydrogen demand, including the demand for renewable raw materials, must be produced domestically. This leads to cumulative additional costs of the transformation that are 72% higher than those of the reference scenario. Fischer-Tropsch synthesis and the methanol-to-olefins route can be identified as key technologies for the defossilisation of the chemical industry.

Keywords: Energy systems analysis, Defossilisation, Industrial transformation, Chemical industry, Climate targets

#93

ASSESSMENT OF NATURAL HYDROGEN AND MANTLE HELIUM RESOURCES IN THE AFAR TRIANGLE, DJIBOUTI

Kadar Mohamed Hassan[1], Eric Deville[2], Alain Prinzhofer[3]*
[1] Djibouti Geothermal Energy Development Office (ODDEG), Djibouti
[2] IFP Énergies nouvelles, France
[3] GOE4U, Brésil
*Corresponding author e-mail: kadarmohamedhassan@gmail.com

ABSTRACT

The territory of the Republic of Djibouti is located in the Afar depression, at the meeting of three rifts: the Red Sea oceanic rift, the Gulf of Aden oceanic rift and the East African continental rift. In the extension of the Gulf of Aden, the opening of the Gulf of Tadjourah in the last million years was followed by the establishment of parallel NW-SE oriented depressions (Gobaad, Hanlé, Gaggade, Asal-Ghoubbet). This region is characterised by high heat flow, complex volcanic and tectonic activity and a dense network of faults favourable to the development of hydrothermal systems. This configuration is favourable to the exploration of multiple resources such as hydrothermal mineralisation, geothermal energy and natural hydrogen. A mission conducted by the authors of this presentation and engineers from the Djibouti Office for the Development of Geothermal Energy in March and April 2021 confirmed the presence of natural hydrogen at several sites and also revealed the presence of mantle helium on the shores of Lake Abbhé. Natural hydrogen emissions were detected at fumaroles and hot springs associated with hydrothermal systems at the edges of the Gobaad, Hanlé, Gaggade, Asal-Ghoubbet and Arta depressions, using the GA5000 sensor. Sampling and analysis by gas chromatography showed that the proportions of hydrogen could exceed 1500ppm in the Asal-Ghoubbet area. Analyses carried out at IFPEN show that the methane associated with the hydrogen is abiotic and could therefore result from the reaction of hydrogen with mantle CO_2 (Sabatier reaction). Helium emanations have been observed in particular on the banks of Lake Abbhé (Gobaad depression) in boiling hot springs (>100°C). Gas chromatography by 45-8 Energy showed helium contents exceeding 200 ppm. Isotopic analyses carried out at IFPEN on the same samples show an R/RA isotopic ratio of 7, which is a characteristic value for helium of mantle origin (8+/-1). The measured values of natural hydrogen and helium correspond to surface indices. They allow the hypothesis of accumulations at greater depths to be made, but do not allow the resource to be evaluated. For this, a geological and geophysical exploration campaign followed by exploratory drilling is necessary. This is the purpose of the DjiboutHy exploration project, initiated by ODDEG, which aims to understand the mechanisms of hydrogen and helium genesis and accumulation in Djibouti. If the resource is confirmed, natural hydrogen and helium 3, by co-valorisation of geothermal energy, could represent an economic interest for Djibouti and contribute to the decarbonisation of its energy mix.
Keywords: Djibouti, Natural hydrogen, Mantle helium, Surface shows, Exploration, Resource

#98

TSUKUBA GREEN HOLONISM TOWN (II)—EXAMINING A PRELIMINARY ENERGY DEMAND–SUPPLY OUTLOOK

[1] Ichiro Sugimoto, [2] Kenji Morita, [2] Hiroyuki Mitsuishi, [3] Masayoshi Ishida*
[1] Laboratory of Energy & Human Life Science Inc., 3-6-2, Asahigaoka, Ikeda-city, Osaka, Japan
[2] Japan Automobile Research Institute, Environment Research Division, 2530, Karima, Tsukuba, Ibaraki, Japan
[3] University of Tsukuba, Faculty of Engineering, Information and Systems, 1-1-1, Tennoudai, Tsukuba, Ibaraki, Japan
*Corresponding author e-mail: ichiro@energy-and-humanlife.com

ABSTRACT

This study proposes a draft system design for a solar photovoltaic (PV)-based energy community as an example of “Tsukuba Green Holonism Town” in Japan, as described in the previous report, “Building A Carbon-Neutral Community,” and examines a preliminary energy demand-supply outlook in 2030. The energy outlook includes an allocation plan of zero-emission energy sources in the Ibaraki Prefecture and a set of residential electricity and heat demands estimated in winter, summer, and the other seasons. Japan decided to increase renewable energy sources (RES) from 18% in 2019 to 36%-38% energy mix in 2030, thus we are urged to deploy a considerable amount of RES in each region. The preliminary outlook identifies a particular problem in the PV-based energy community in Japan. Furthermore, an example of solving this problem is also suggested.

Keywords: Energy community, Renewable energy resource, Solar photovoltaic, Power-to-hydrogen and fuel cell

#100

TSUKUBA GREEN HOLONISM TOWN (I)—BUILDING A CARBON-NEUTRAL COMMUNITY

[1*] *Kenji Morita,* [2] *Ichiro Sugimoto,* [1] *Hiroyuki Mitsuishi,* [3] *Masayoshi Ishida*
[1] Japan Automobile Research Institute, Environment Research Division, 2530, Karima, Tsukuba, Ibaraki, Japan
[2] Laboratory of Energy & Human Life Science Inc., 3-6-2, Asahigaoka, Ikeda-city, Osaka, Japan
[3] University of Tsukuba, Faculty of Engineering, Information and Systems, 1-1-1, Tennoudai, Tsukuba, Ibaraki, Japan
*Corresponding author e-mail: kmorita@jari.or.jp

ABSTRACT

This study illustrates a concept of "Tsukuba Green Holonism Town" in Japan, comprising three basic policies: achieving carbon neutrality in the community, balancing the energy demand and supply, and changing the lifestyle, work style, and mobility style of residents and workers. Furthermore, this community is constituted of five functional categories: community facilities with nearby renewable energy sources (RES), energy dispatching station and energy networks, common facilities equipped with fuel cells (FC), vehicle-to-microgrid integration facilities, household demand installed RES or FC, household demand with both controllable and uncontrollable appliances. Japan and other OECD countries are taking on the considerable challenge of reducing greenhouse gas emissions to zero by 2050, thus we must push for more robust green policies and decarbonization breakthroughs immediately. The workgroup of Tsukuba 3E Forum has been developing the concept of Tsukuba Green Holonism Town, which implements a carbon-neutral community using demand response methods in harmony with residents, workers, household FCs, and electric vehicles. An example of cooperative scenarios among the functional categories for a rainy week is also described.

Keywords: Carbon-neutral community, Balancing the energy demand and supply, Hydrogen and demand response

#108

DESIGN AND OPTIMIZATION OF GREEN HYDROGEN-BASED HYBRID ENERGY SYSTEM

[1,2] *Ceren Ceylan, Yılser Devrim*[2]
[1] Yıldız Technical University, Mechanical Engineering-Energy, Istanbul, Turkey
[2] Atılım University, Energy System Engineering Department, Ankara, Turkey
*Corresponding author e-mail: yilser.devrim@atilim.edu.tr

ABSTRACT

Hydrogen (H_2) is widely used in many industries because it can be used as a chemical raw material with its high mass-energy density and can be converted back into electricity via fuel cells. H_2 energy systems seem to be one of the most effective solutions for providing a better environment and sustainability. Green H_2, produced by renewable energy-assisted electrolysis without greenhouse gas emissions, has been of great importance in recent years. In this study, a hybrid energy system including Photovoltaic (PV), Wind Turbine (WT), Proton Exchange Membrane Fuel Cell (PEMFC), and electrolyzer is compared for grid-connected and off-grid operating conditions. In the grid-connected system, electricity generated from PV and WT is used directly to meet electricity demand, while excess electricity is used for green H_2 production. In the off-grid connected system, electricity generated from PV and WT was used for H_2 production. Produced H_2 and O_2 were used to generate electricity by PEMFC. While 20186 kWh energy & 3273 m^3 H_2 were generated in an on-grid connected system, 95145 kWh energy & 17942 m^3 H_2 and 83511 kWh energy & 14370 m^3 H_2 were generated in two different configurations in the off-grid connected system. The Levelized Cost of Energy (LCOE) for the on-grid connected system and the off-grid system for two different designs were determined as 0.307 $/kWh, 0.341 $/kWh and 0.349 $/kWh, respectively. The hybrid system design was simulated using MATLAB software and it was examined which hybrid energy system configuration would be the most economical to meet the load.

Keywords: Green hydrogen, Hydrogen production, Hybrid energy system, Renewable energy

#121

OPTIMAL CONFIGURATION OF ENERGY STORAGE AND HYDROGEN PRODUCTION AT RENEWABLE ENERGY SITES IN A POWER SYSTEM WITHOUT FOSSIL FUELS IN JAPAN

[1,2*] *Kosuke Harada,* [2] *Kuniaki Yabe,* [2] *Yasuhiro Hayashi*
[1] ENEOS, 8 Chidori-cho, Yokohama-shi, Kanagawa, Japan
[2] Waseda University, Address, City, Japan
*Corresponding author e-mail: harada.kosuke@eneos.com

ABSTRACT

In an electric power system consisting solely of non-fossil power sources, the capacity of storage batteries and hydrogen production facilities that should be attached to renewable energy power plants depends on the cost of these facilities and the cost of connecting them to the grid. In this study, assuming that a large amount of renewable energy will be introduced into the Japanese power system in 2050, the capacity and annual operation of storage batteries, water electrolysis equipment, hydrogen tanks, and transmission facilities that minimize costs were investigated. The results showed that solar photovoltaic (PV) plants require more variability mitigation equipment than wind farms. At a transmission cost of 1.2 JPY/kW/h, the optimal Li-ion battery capacity and transmission capacity for PV are 9.1 times and 0.18 times that for wind farms, respectively, and only PV is equipped with a 5 MW hydrogen production unit and 15 kNm^3 of hydrogen storage.
Keywords: Renewable energy, Hydrogen, Carbon neutrality, Sector coupling, Linear programming

#146

THE ROLE OF HYDROGEN FOR A GREENHOUSE GAS-NEUTRAL GERMANY BY 2045

[1*] *Thomas Schöb,* [1] *Peter Markewitz,* [1] *David Franzmann,* [1] *Heidi Heinrichs,* [1] *Leander Kotzur,* [1] *Jochen Linßen,* [1,2] *Detlef Stolten*
[1] Forschungszentrum Jülich GmbH, Institute of Energy and Climate Research, Techno-economic Systems Analysis (IEK-3), Wilhelm-Johnen-Straße, 52425 Jülich, Germany
[2] RWTH Aachen University, Chair for Fuel Cells, c/o Forschungszentrum Jülich GmbH, Institute of Energy and Climate Research, Techno-economic Systems Analysis (IEK-3), Wilhelm-Johnen-Straße, 52425 Jülich, Germany
*Corresponding author e-mail: t.schoeb@fz-juelich.de

ABSTRACT

Germany's transition to greenhouse gas-neutrality by 2045 requires a dynamic change in all sectors of its energy system. Despite several studies already depicting possible pathways for this transformation, the role of hydrogen in this process remains unclear. In this study we utilize a combination of energy system models to examine the usage and production of hydrogen during this transition in detail. Our results show that 412 TWh of hydrogen are needed in the year 2045, mostly in the industry and transport sector. Particularly, the use of hydrogen in industry is essential as there are no cost-effective alternatives for achieving greenhouse gas neutrality. Furthermore, we illustrate that domestic hydrogen production through electrolysis provides 53% of the needed hydrogen in 2045 and the remaining share is imported from other European countries or Northern Africa via pipelines or ships. Additionally, seasonal storage of hydrogen and hydrogen gas turbines play an important role in balancing the intermittent nature of variable renewable energy sources. In summary, hydrogen usage and production are crucial for a greenhouse gas-neutral Germany and should be integral part of the transformation strategy.
Keywords: Energy system modeling, Greenhouse gas-neutrality, Germany, Hydrogen demand, Hydrogen imports

#148

INTEGRATION OF A RENEWABLE METHANOL PRODUCTION PROCESS WITH A LOW CO_2 EMISSIONS CRGT POWER PLANT

[1*] *Vittorio Tola,* [1] *Francesco Lonis*
[1]University of Cagliari, Department of Mechanical Chemical and of Materials Engineering, Via Marengo 2, Cagliari, Sardinia, Italy
*Corresponding author e-mail: vittorio.tola@dimcm.unica.it

ABSTRACT

Power-to-liquids (PtL) technologies are an interesting way for storing the excess of renewable electricity into liquid fuels. Methanol is well-known as hydrogen carrier and energy feedstock, since it can be stored, transported and used more easily than hydrogen. The renewable methanol produced in PtL processes through the CO_2 hydrogenation process can feed a chemically recuperated gas turbine (CRGT) where the exhaust heat recovery boosts the plant performance. The hydrogen required for PtL is produced in an alkaline electrolyser, while the CO_2 is captured from the CRGT exhausts
Keywords: Methanol, CO_2 hydrogenation, Alkaline electrolysis, Chemically recuperated gas turbine, CO_2 capture

#172

VERTICALLY INTEGRATED PROJECTS AS A TRANSFORMATIVE PEDAGOGY FOR GREEN HYDROGEN STUDY ABROAD PROGRAMS

[1]Stewart F. Bauserman, [2]Johnny Nahui Ortiz, [3]Jose Cesar Ramos Saravia, [1]John W. Sheffield, [4]Matteo J. Mereu*
[1] Purdue University, School of Engineering Technology, West Lafayette, IN, U.S.A.
[2] Universidad Nacional de Ingeniería, Facultad de Ingeniería Ambiental, Lima, Peru
[3] Universidad de Ingeniería y Tecnología, Ingeniería de la Energía y Ingeniería Mecánica, Lima, Peru
[4] Purdue University, Mechanical Engineering Technology, West Lafayette, IN, U.S.A.
*Corresponding author e-mail: stew@purdue.edu

ABSTRACT
The introduction of transformative pedagogy provides for active learning in the incentivized, faculty-led, study abroad programs focused on green hydrogen projects. These study abroad programs utilize Purdue's Hydrogen Learning HUB, which is comprised of the Vertically Integrated Projects, Collaborative Online International Learning, Hub of Intercultural Learning, and Strategic Doing educational programs. Two faculty-led study abroad programs have been developed, one in Peru during Spring Break and one in Europe during a 4-week summer term. The Peruvian program is focused on two open-pit mines, the Falchani Lithium and the Quellaveco Copper projects, for green hydrogen technology integration into the mining operations. American Lithium Corporation is developing the Falchani mine located in the Andes Mountains. The Falchani mine is the world's sixth-largest hard rock lithium deposit. The Quellaveco mine, which is being developed by Anglo American Perú, in partnership with the Mitsubishi Corporation, is one of the world's largest copper deposits. The summer study abroad focuses on remote island communities, such as the Orkney Islands, as an ideal candidate for evaluation of green hydrogen technology integration into remote communities on islands. Currently, the community-based renewable energy systems on the Orkney Islands generate more than 130% of the electric energy consumed.
Keywords: Green hydrogen, Transformative pedagogy, Vertically integrated projects

#175

FUEL CELL-BATTERY HIBRIDIZATION FOR AN UNMANNED SURFACE VEHICLE POWERPLANT

[1]Diego Tejada-Guzmán, [1]Laura Vargas, [1]Eduardo M. López, [1]Fernando Isorna, [2]Víctor García, [2]Alberto Giménez, [2]Manuel Martínez, [2]Luis Domenech, [2]Fernando Sánchez, [2]Jordi Renau*
[1] Instituto Nacional de Técnica Aeroespacial (INTA), Área de Energías Renovables, Ctra. S. Juan- Matalascañas, km. 34, 21130 Mazagón-Moguer (Huelva), Spain
[2] Cardenal Herrera University – CEU Universities, C/ San Bartolomé 55, Alfara del Patriarca (Valencia), Spain
*Corresponding author e-mail: dtejguz@inta.es

ABSTRACT
Remote Piloted Vehicles are in the aim of the experts because of its wide usability. The main disadvantage of battery based technologies are their low endurance operation time due to high energy demand coming from propulsion system. This paper proposes a way to overcome this problem by means of a fuel cell (FC) and batteries hybrid system. The hybrid system designed consists in a 500W fuel cell and a 3S-3P battery in active configuration to deliver enough energy to feed the different loads onboard during at least 7h mission. The final target system increase of the total mission time and reliability of the whole system.
Keywords: Hybrid system, Fuel cell, Batteries, Hydrogen, Stack

#176

NUMERICAL INVESTIGATION OF THERMAL PERFORMANCE OF HYDROGEN - FUELLED MICRO-COMBUSTOR WITH TRAPEZOIDAL RIB

[1*] *Abdelbasset Lachraf,* [2] *Mohamed Si Ameur*
[1]Laboratory of the Industrials Energy Systems Studies, Mechanical Engineering Department, Faculty of Technology, University of Batna 2, Batna 05000, Algeria
[2] Laboratory of the Industrials Energy Systems Studies, Mechanical Engineering Department, Faculty of Technology, University of Batna 2, Batna 05000, Algeria
*Corresponding author e-mail: a.lachraf@univ-batna2.dz

ABSTRACT
The miniaturization movement in the recent years motivated the development of micro-combustion-based power generators. The micro-thermophotovoltaic (MTPV) relies on converting the heated micro-combustor radiation into electricity using PV cells. Enhancement of heat transfer and wall temperature distribution in a MTPV combustor is strongly influenced by the combustor structure. In this regard, a novel planar micro-combustor geometrical configuration based on creating a stable recirculation zone near the chamber wall using trapezoidal rib, is proposed. This work numerically investigated the flow and flame behavior in the proposed micro-combustor. It also studied the effect of hydrogen to air mixing ratio and the inlet velocity on the wall temperature distribution. The results shows that the wall temperature is increased by 3.4% to 9.24% with the increase of the inlet velocity and decreases for lean and rich hydrogen/air mixture by 0.33% to 3.92%. The average outer wall temperature is higher than that without ribs. The chemical reaction products locked in the recirculation zones formed around the ribs that acts just like an igniter and the flame is more stable and continuous. The proposed structure is found to have a better performance in terms of the thermal parameters of mean weighted average and non-uniformity index.
Keywords: Micro-combustion, Heat transfer enhancement, Hydrogen, Temperature distribution.

#179

PERFORMANCE ANALYSIS AND COMPARISON ON ENERGY STORAGE DEVICES IN HYDROGEN-BASED INTEGRATED ENERGY SYSTEMS

[1] *Ke Shao,* [1*] *Xiangxiang Dong,* [2] *Jie Zhang,* [1] *Zhanbo Xu,* [1] *Jiang Wu*
[1] MOE KLINNS Lab of Xi'an Jiaotong University, Xi'an, Shaanxi Province 710049, China
[2] Tongfang Co., Ltd., Beijing 10083, China
*Corresponding author e-mail: gavin1014@stu.xjtu.edu.cn

ABSTRACT
Storage devices play a very important role in the efficient utilization of renewable supply, since energy can be flexible scheduled by storage in time horizon and thus improve the energy utilization efficiency. It is important to plan, schedule, and coordinate storage devices together with other energy devices in energy systems. This paper proposes a bi-level planning and operation optimization problem of hydrogen-based integrated energy systems. The optimal combination and capacities of storage devices can be obtained at the upper level. The optimal scheduling strategy of the system is obtained at the lower-level, and a scenario tree-based algorithm is used to solve the lower-level problem with the system uncertainty. The effectiveness of the developed method is demonstrated using numerical case studies. It is also found that the combination of hydrogen and water tanks is most efficient in saving cost.
Keywords: Hydrogen-based integrated energy system, Storage devices, Bi-level programming problem

#186

ANALYSIS OF TRANSPORT OPTIONS FOR LIQUID HYDROGEN IN GERMANY

[1, 2*] *Toni Busch,* [1]*Theresa Groß,* [1]*Jochen Linßen,* [1, 2]*Detlef Stolten*
[1] Forschungszentrum Jülich GmbH, IEK-3, 52425 Jülich, Germany
[2] RWTH Aachen University, Templergraben 55, 52056 Aachen, Germany
*Corresponding author e-mail: t.busch@fz-juelich.de

ABSTRACT
A wide range of studies have analyzed the transportation of liquid hydrogen (LH_2) over long distances. This study aims to investigate the role of LH_2 in the downstream process of a greenhouse gas neutral energy supply system. The high volumetric energy density and high level of purity are two features that distinguish LH_2 from gaseous pipeline transport. An integrated energy system model covering the sectors electricity, hydrogen, and methane for Germany in a carbon neutral scenario for 2045 has been enhanced by means of liquid hydrogen transportation via inland vessel, truck, and rail. The results of the energy systems optimization highly depend on the amount and spatial distribution of the LH_2 demands: LH_2 demands can be either served by imports and the distribution by single means of transportation as well as combination of multiple means of transportation (intermodal) or even by the inland liquefaction of gaseous hydrogen (GH_2). The promising applications of LH_2 transportation in future energy systems are currently underrepresented in the discussion around options for hydrogen distribution.
Keywords: Liquid hydrogen, Hydrogen transportation, Integrated infrastructure analysis, transportation costs, Domestic hydrogen distribution

#201

NOVEL TEG HEAT EXCHANGER IN CU-CL CYCLE OF HYDROGEN PRODUCTION

[1*]*Amir Mohammadi* [1]*Ehsan Armoudli,* [1]*Ofelia A. Jianu*
[1]Mechanical Automotive and Materials Engineering, University of Windsor, 401 Sunset Avenue, Windsor, Canada
*Corresponding author e-mail: mohamm63@uwindsor.ca

ABSTRACT

The looming threat of global warming has elicited efforts to develop reliable sustainable energy resources. Hydrogen as a clean fuel is deemed an appealing solution to problem of the storage of power from renewable energy technologies. Among current thermochemical hydrogen generation methods, the thermochemical copper-chlorine (Cu-Cl) cycle is of high interest owing to lower temperature requirements. However, this method faces challenges such as scaling up. Therefore, it is crucial to improve the performance of the cycle in terms of designing more efficient heat exchangers to surmount such obstacles. Present study investigates a novel heat exchanger comprising a thermoelectric generator (TEG) within the Cu-Cl cycle. This configuration enables electric power production, which could be utilized in the electrolysis step of the cycle. There are several heat recovery spots within Cu-Cl cycle where conventional heat exchangers could be superseded by TEGs. The performance of the proposed heat exchanger is numerically examined using commercially available finite element software, COMSOL Multhiphysics. Impact of operational conditions on the performance of TEG has been assessed to provide insights for better understanding of the design. Results indicate that maximum generated power is 41.3 W at the matching current. Average deviation from anticipated friction factor and Nusselt number are 0.31% and 16.77%, respectively.

Keywords: Thermoelectric generator, Hydrogen, Thermolysis, Heat transfer, Copper-chlorine cycle.

#204

INTEGRATION OF PEM ELECTROLYZER AND FUEL CELL TO A SOLAR-GEOTHERMAL COMBINED SYSTEM FOR A ZERO-ENERGY BUILDING: AN EXERGYECONOMIC ANALYSIS

[1*] *Ehsan Baniasadi,* [1] *Masoud Ziaei-Rad,*[1] *Mohammad Amin Behvand,* [2] *Nader Javani*
[1]University of Isfahan, Department of Mechanical Engineering, Faculty of Engineering, Hezar Jerib Ave., Isfahan, Iran
[2] Yildiz Technical University, Department of Mechanical Engineering, Yildiz Campus, Istanbul, 34349 Yildiz, Turkey
*Corresponding author e-mail: e.baniasadi@eng.ui.ac.ir

ABSTRACT

In this study, a novel system which generates cooling effect, heat, electricity, hot water and distilled water simultaneously for a green building is analyzed which operates based on solar and geothermal heat pump, proton exchange membrane (PEM) electrolysis, proton exchange membrane (PEM) fuel cell, photovoltaics, desalination system along with pressure exchanger. The results demonstrats that energy and exergy efficiencies in cooling mode are 13.27% and 32.44% respectively, and in heating mode are also 17.25% and 42.4%, respectively. The largest exergy destruction occurs in the photovoltaics and organic Rankine cycle. It is also worth noting that turbine and vaporizer have the highest portion in exergy losses of organic Rankine cycle. The unit exergy cost of cooling, and hot water, and the cost of produced distilled water and 84.5 $/GJ, 64 $/GJ and 67.63 c$/m^3$, respectively.

Keywords: Zero energy building, CCHPW System, Geothermal energy, Solar energy, Exergy-economic analysis

#210

EVALUATION OF HYDROGEN PRODUCTION PROCESSES FOR USE IN AUTOMOTIVE SECTOR

[1]Francisco Edvan Bezerra Feitosa, [2]Antonella Lombardi Costa
Universidade Federal de Minas Gerais, Departamento de Engenharia Nuclear, Campus UFMG, Escola de Engenharia, Av. Antônio Carlos, 6627, Belo Horizonte, MG, Brasil.
*Corresponding author e-mail: [1] feb.feitosa@gmail.com, [2] antonella@nuclear.ufmg.br

ABSTRACT

This article identifies and evaluates large-scale hydrogen production processes - those capable of providing hydrogen for an eventual automotive hydrogen program in a community and along highways - to answer the following research question: which of the production processes of hydrogen is more attractive for an eventual automotive hydrogen program? To answer this question, the MACBETH method – Measuring Attractiveness by the Category-Based Assessment Technique Method and the computational code M-MACBETH 3.2.O are used. The MACBETH is a method to support complex decision making, which allows evaluating alternatives or options, taking into account multiple criteria. Thus, this work used the computational code M-MACBETH 3.2.0 to evaluate ten hydrogen production processes and build some Rankings of attractiveness of hydrogen production processes, considering the following criteria: economic (invested capital and production cost), technical (the purity of the hydrogen produced) and environmental (the amount of energy used to produce one kilogram of hydrogen and the CO2 emissions to produce one kilogram of hydrogen). In the end, MACBETH built three Rankings considering three scenarios, which allow to conclude that: a) the hydrogen production process from natural gas reforming with CCS is the most attractive alternative when economic and financial aspects prevail over environmental aspects and technicians; b) the hydrogen production process by the electrolysis process using photovoltaic solar energy becomes more attractive when the environmental aspects prevail over the economic and financial aspects; c) the process of producing hydrogen by the electrolysis process using photovoltaic solar energy is also the most attractive process when using balanced weights of economic, financial, technical and environmental aspects, in the analysis taken for decision making in relation to hydrogen.

Keywords: Hydrogen, Gasification, Steam reforming, Electrolysis

#212

THE ROLE OF RENEWABLE HYDROGEN-BASED SYSTEMS TO ACHIEVE LOW-CARBON STATIONARY POWER APPLICATIONS

[1] Víctor Manuel Maestre, [1*] Alfredo Ortiz, [1,] Inmaculada Ortiz
[1] *Chemical and Biomolecular Engineering Department, University of Cantabria, Av. Los Castros 46, 39005, Santander, Spain*
*Corresponding author e-mail: ortizal@unican.es

ABSTRACT

Increasing the contribution of renewable energy sources (RES) to the final energy consumed is fundamental to achieving a low-carbon economy. In this context, the use of hydrogen as an energy carrier offers a clean and versatile alternative to boost RES penetration and ensure an uninterrupted energy supply. Moreover, stationary applications account for almost 75% of greenhouse gases (GHG) emissions globally associated with power generation. This study thoroughly analyzes the state of the art and presents an overview of the evolution of renewable hydrogen-based systems (RHS) from simulated case studies to pilot plants and commercial systems for large power generation, industrial parks, buildings, and critical infrastructures. Relevant techno-economic parameters such as levelized cost of energy (LCOE), loss of power supply probability (LPSP), self-sufficiency ratio (SSR), hydrogen roundtrip efficiency (HRE), or renewable fraction (f_{RES}) are evaluated. Subsequently, the main techno-economic barriers and challenges for the deployment of RHS are identified and discussed. Finally, a pilot plant implemented in the north of Spain in the frame of the SUDOE ENERGY PUSH project is presented as a case study of the application of RHS in buildings.

Keywords: Renewable hydrogen, Stationary applications, Fuel cell, Technical feasibility, Cost-competitiveness.

#237

CONTROL STRATEGIES FOR THERMAL COUPLING SYSTEM OF FUEL CELL AND METAL HYDRIDE TANK: A REVIEW

[1] Jiaxuan Liu, [1] Fusheng Yang, [1] Zhen Wu, [1] Zaoxiao Zhang*
[1]School of Chemical Engineering and Technology, Xi'an Jiaotong University, Xi'an, China
*Corresponding author e-mail: yang.fs@mail.xjtu.edu.cn

ABSTRACT
The utilization of hydrogen storage unit in distribute energy system (DES) attracts wide attentions, and storing hydrogen with metal hydrides (MH) have been explored as a promising way considering the high volumetric density and relative safety. To improve system efficiency and compactness, the thermal coupling of fuel cell (FC) and MH tank is proposed. However, the strong interactions in the system introduces challenges for meeting the power demand satisfactorily, thus various control strategies have been proposed. The aim of this study is to review the control strategies of thermal coupling system in multiple scenarios comprehensively. The literature survey illustrates that the traditional linear controller e.g. PID can realize a good tracking performance in some application, but the output may fluctuate with fast-changing signal, and nonlinear multi-input-multi-output (MIMO) controller is hence recommended in this case.
Keywords: Thermal coupling, Metal hydride, Fuel cell, Control strategies

#270

GREEN MILITARY SITE SUPPORTING PUBLIC HYDROGEN MOBILITY

[1] Mitja Mori, [1] Urban Ž. Baškovič, [1] Boštjan Drobnič, [2] Robert Šipec, [1*] Tomaž Katrašnik*
[1] University of Ljubljana, Faculty of Mechanical Engineering, Aškerčeva 6, Ljubljana, SI-1000, Slovenia
[2] Ministry of Defense of the Republic of Slovenia, Vojkova cesta 55, Ljubljana, SI-1000, Slovenia
*Corresponding author's e-mail: mitja.mori@fs.uni-lj.si and tomaz.katrasnik@fs.uni-lj.si

ABSTRACT
To support the energy transition in the defence sector, transport, and power generation sector at the local level simultaneously, a detailed virtual analysis was conducted with an aim to convert military sites from a conventional consumer of external energy vectors to an energy positive hub and at the same time ensure independent operation in case of emergency circumstances. This was achieved by coupling of green energy sources, where geographic conditions favour solar energy, and zero emission storage devices with the main energy storage being hydrogen, which is supported by the batteries. This approach enables multiple shifts of paradigms: a) development of a stand-alone green energy system for military sites, b) converting military sites to energy positive hub for powering military and civil vehicles with green energy vectors (cumulative on-site production of electricity and hydrogen exceeds the electricity consumption by over 50 %), c) achieving autonomous energy operation for several days or weeks depending on the sizing of the system and concept of operation (with normal energy consumption the site can be autonomous for 30 straight days during 60 % of the year and with some reduction in energy consumption 30 day autonomous operation can be achieved throughout the entire year), and d) achieving, on the yearly basis, low or in some cases net negative carbon footprint of military barracks including support of the mobility sector (carbon footprint can be reduced by as much as 70 % with respect to grey H2 production). Such an approach ensures higher robustness of energy supply and storage, construction of hydrogen mobility infrastructure, and the support of local communities through green hydrogen production.
Keywords: Green hydrogen, Military site, Mobility, Sector coupling, Carbon footprint

#286

PREDICTION OF HYDROGEN COMBUSTION USING DATA-DRIVEN APPROACH

[1] Kazuma Kunihara, [1*] Rahmat Waluyo, [2*] Muhammad Aziz*
[1]Department of Mechanical Engineering, The University of Tokyo, 7-3-1 Hongo, Bunkyo-ku, Tokyo 113-8656, Japan
[2]Institute of Industrial Science, The University of Tokyo, 4-6-1 Komaba Meguro-ku, Tokyo 153-8505, Japan
*Corresponding author e-mail: kunihara@iis.u-tokyo.ac.jp, maziz@iis.u-tokyo.ac.jp

ABSTRACT
A data-driven simulation approach is proposed in this study to minimize the development process and efforts of hydrogen combustion-based energy systems. For this purpose, both reacting and non-reacting large-eddy simulation of a turbulent diffusion type burner is conducted to generate the data, which will be trained further using an artificial neural network that predicts the reacting field from a cold flow field. The training data consists of a non-reacting flow field as an input value, from which the neural network should predict the reacting flow, and a reacting flow field is treated as the true value. In the training phase, the prediction of the reacting flow from the former non-reacting flow is compared with the latter reacting flow. In addition, a governing equation is considered in the comparison.
Keywords: Hydrogen combustion, Large eddy simulation, Reacting flow, Non-reacting flow, Artificial intelligent

#289

PERFORMANCE ANALYSIS ON THE NOVEL PEMFC ASSISTED GROUND SOURCE HEAT PUMP SYSTEM

[1] *Jinyoung Kim,* [2*] *Yongchan Kim*
[1]1Graduate School of Mechanical Engineering, Korea University 145 Anam-ro, Seongbuk-gu, Seoul, 02841 Republic of Korea
[2]Department of Mechanical Engineering, Korea University 145 Anam-ro, Seongbuk-gu, Seoul, 02841 Republic of Korea
*Corresponding author e-mail: yongckim@korea.ac.kr

ABSTRACT
In this study, the novel PEMFC-assisted ground source heat pump system (PAGSHPs) was investigated by transient simulation. The mathematical model was developed and simulated in TRNSYS software. The annual performance and ground temperature degradation during the 5 years were analyzed by the simulation results. The heating and cooling COP were evaluated as the annual performance of PAGSHPs. The performance of GSHPs was compared with that of PAGSHPs. As a result, the average heating COP of PAGSHPs was enhanced by 26.5% compared to the conventional system. However, the average cooling COP of PAGSHPs was degraded by 7.65% owing to high ground rise.
Keywords: Proton exchange membrane fuel cell, Ground source heat pump, Waste heat recovery.

#293

IMPROVED REACTOR DESIGN FOR A METAL HYDRIDE REFRIGERATION SYSTEM IN HYDROGEN POWERTRAINS

[1] *Alexander Wimmer,* [1] *Steffen Feierfeil,* [1*] *Inga Bürger,* [1] *Marc Linder*
[1]German Aerospace Center (DLR), Department of Engineering Thermodynamics, Pfaffenwaldring 38-40, Stuttgart, Germany
*Corresponding author e-mail: inga.buerger@dlr.de

ABSTRACT

By means of metal hydrides the so far unused potential energy of compressed hydrogen in a hydrogen powertrain can be utilised for air condition of the cabin. The main problem in the latest development is the low power to mass ratio of the reactor component. That is why in this work a new reactor design is proposed, which shows mayor improvements in the key factors for high power to mass ration. Special focus is set on the outer heat transfer to a heat transfer fluid. By numerical simulation optimal design and operations points could be identified for the new reactor design.
Keywords: Metal hydrides, Unused energy, Refrigeration, Power to mass ratio

#302

PILOT-SCALE HYBRID SYSTEM FOR CO_2/H_2 MIXTURE PRODUCTION – FIRST EXPERIENCES IN THE "TENNESSEE" PROJECT

[1*] *Łukasz Bartela,* [2] *Janusz Zdeb,* [3] *Jarosław Milewski,* [3] *Aliaksandr Martsinchyk,* [2] *Wojciech Smółka,* [2] *Łukasz Rybak*
[1]Silesian University of Technology, Department of Power Engineering and Turbomachinery, 18 Konarskiego Street, Gliwice 44-100, Poland
[2] Tauron Wytwarzanie S.A., 51 Promienna Street, Jaworzno 43-603, Poland
[3] Warsaw University of Technology, Institute of Heat Engineering, 21/25 Nowowiejska Street, Warsaw 00-665, Poland
*Corresponding author e-mail: lukasz.bartela@polsl.pl

ABSTRACT

Currently, in the Tennessee project realized by the Polish energy group Tauron Polska Energia, work on the construction of an installation that integrates MCFC modules with SOE modules is nearing completion. The installation is to enable highly effective production of the CO_2/H_2 mixture based on the process of high-temperature electrolysis and process of CO2 separation carried out in MCFC modules from flue gases generated in the coal-fired unit. The article summarizes the results of analytical work and describes the first experiments on the first trial runs of the installation.

Keywords: Solid oxide electrolyzer, Molten carbonate fuel cell, CO_2 separation, Hydrogen, Synthetic natural gas

#309

THERMODYNAMIC ANALYSIS OF AN INTEGRATED SYSTEM WITH SOLAR METHANE CRACKING AND CO-ELECTROLYSIS OF CO_2/H_2O FOR METHANOL AND ELECTRICITY PRODUCTION

[1*] *Aliya Banu*, [1] *Yusuf Bicer*
[1] Division of Sustainable Development, College of Science and Engineering, Hamad Bin Khalifa University, Qatar Foundation, Doha, Qatar
*Corresponding author e-mail: alba34159@hbku.edu.qa

ABSTRACT

Due to zero greenhouse gas emissions, hydrogen fuel production from methane cracking is a cleaner pathway than steam methane reforming. Co-produced carbon black is valuable and can be used in other industries. Using solar energy for the high-temperature requirement can further improve the sustainability of the process. This paper evaluates an integrated solar methane cracking where its products are utilized in fuel cells to generate electricity. The CO_2 produced in the system is co-electrolyzed with water to produce syngas which is further converted to methanol. The process is simulated in Aspen Plus®, and its energy and exergy efficiencies are evaluated by conducting a detailed thermodynamic analysis. The proposed system has an energy and exergy efficiency of 37.4% and 31.2%, respectively

Keywords: Methane cracking, Turquoise hydrogen, Solid oxide electrolyzer, Synthetic fuel, Methanol

#318

THERMODYNAMIC CONSIDERATIONS OF THE CO_X HYDROGENATION REACTION TO LIGHT OLEFINS USING CARBON-NEUTRAL FEEDSTOCK MIXTURES

Evridiki Mandela[1], *Georgios Varvoutis*[1,2*], *Athanasios Lampropoulos*[1], *Eleni Papista*[1], *Costas Athanasiou*[3], *Dimitris Ipsakis*[4], *Michalis Konsolakis*[4], *George Marnellos*[1,2]
[1] Department of Mechanical Engineering, University of Western Macedonia, Kozani, Greece
[2] Chemical Process and Energy Resources Institute, CERTH, Thessaloniki, Greece
[3] Department of Environmental Engineering, Democritus University of Thrace, Thrace, Greece
[4] School of Production Engineering and Management, Technical University of Crete, Chania, Greece
*Corresponding author e-mail: e.mandela@uowm.gr

ABSTRACT

Light olefins are considered the backbone of chemical industry, and a broad variety of derivatives, used in our daily lives, are produced from these building blocks. Notably, it is estimated that the $C_{2\text{-}4}^{=}$ demand will face an annual growth of 3.5% by 2030, as a combined result of global population growth and rising living standards. The current leading technology for light olefins production is the steam cracking of natural gas and/or crude oil fractions but this process is linked with a high carbon footprint. Concerns associated with the depletion of fossil fuels and the threat of global warming have recently initiated efforts to explore alternative pathways and feedstocks to produce light olefins through CO_X hydrogenation by employing either excess RES-powered electrolytic hydrogen combined with captured CO_2 industrial emissions or syngas mixtures generated through biomass gasification or biofuels reforming. Therefore, the present work aims to examine the thermodynamic aspects of the CO_X hydrogenation to light olefins at a range of temperatures and pressures of industrial practice by feeding several carbon-neutral CO_X-H_2 mixtures. For this end, the Aspen Plus software and the Gibbs free energy minimization method have been compiled in a series of simulation scenarios.

Keywords: Thermodynamic analysis, CO_X hydrogenation, Light olefins production, Industrial CO_2 capture, Bio-syngas

#330

PROCESS SIMULATION AND ASSESSMENT OF AN INTEGRATED POWER SYSTEM COMBINING OLIVE KERNEL PYROLYSIS, GASIFICATION AND SOLID OXIDE FUEL CELL

Athanasios Lampropoulos[*,1], *George Varvoutis*[1,4], *Evridiki Mandela*[1], *Stavros Spyridakos*[1], *Dimitris Ipsakis*[2], *Costas Athanasiou*[3], *Michalis Konsolakis*[2], *George E. Marnellos*[1,5]
[1] Department of Mechanical Engineering, University of Western Macedonia, Kozani, Greece
[2] School of Production Engineering and Management, Technical University of Crete, Chania-Crete, Greece
[3] Department of Environmental Engineering, Democritus University of Thrace, Xanthi, Greece
[4] Chemical Process & Energy Resources Institute, Centre for Research & Technology Hellas, Thessaloniki, Greece
*Corresponding author e-mail: alabropoulos@uowm.gr

ABSTRACT
The adverse impact of fossil fuels' on the environment and the increasing concerns regarding climate change, have intensified research efforts towards the exploitation of renewable energy sources (RES). Biomass can be utilized as a CO_2-neutral fuel in several energy conversion technologies. For instance, biomass gasification converts solids to syngas, which can be directly used as a fuel or as a valuable building-block toward synthetic liquid fuels and/or chemicals. The scope of the present study is the simulation of a combined process that exploits olive kernel (OK, 833 kg/day) for the production of electrical power and bio-oil. The integrated process includes: a) the slow pyrolysis of the olive kernel at 500 °C to solids (biochar, 252 kg/hr), liquids (336 kg/hr) and non-condensable gases (245 kg/hr), b) the autothermal gasification of biochar to syngas (1126 kg/hr) and c) the direct utilization of syngas in a solid oxide fuel cell (SOFC), for the cogeneration of electrical (1.35 MW_{el}) and thermal (1.1 MW_{th}) power. The combined process approaches a 50 % electrical efficiency, upon the raw biomass lower heating value (LHV). The integrated process was simulated using Aspen Plus® software and based on the experimental results of a previous study.
Keywords: Olive kernel, Pyrolysis, Gasification, SOFC, Co-generation of electricity and io-oil

#348

SYSTEM INTEGRATION AND VALIDATION OF HYDROGEN FUEL CELL NICHE VEHICLES AND RELATED REFUELLING INFRASTRUCTURE AT HYSA SYSTEMS / SOUTH AFRICA

Vladimir Linkov, Mykhaylo Lototskyy, Sivakumar Pasupathi*
University of the Western Cape, South African Institute for Advanced Materials Chemistry, HySA Systems Centre of Competence, Robert Sobukwe Road, Private Bag X17, Bellville 7535, South Africa
*Corresponding author e-mail: vlinkov@uwc.ac.za

ABSTRACT
An overview of HySA Systems activities related to the development, demonstration and implementation of hydrogen fuel cell vehicles and their refuelling infrastructure is presented. The activities are focused on the integration, prototyping and validation of niche vehicles, including forklifts and scooters, as well as their hydrogen refuelling infrastructure.
Keywords: Hydrogen South Africa, Niche vehicles, Refuelling infrastructure, System integration, Testing and validation

#352

MODELING AND DESIGN OPTIMIZATION OF CARBON-FREE HYBRID ENERGY SYSTEMS WITH THERMAL AND HYDROGEN STORAGE

[1]*Jacob Bryan,* [1] *Aiden Meek,* [1] *Seth Dana,* [1] *Md Sajedul Islam Sakir,* [1*] *Hailei Wang*
[1]Utah State University, Mechanical and Aerospace Engineering, 4130 Old Main Hill, Logan, UT, USA
*Corresponding author e-mail: hailei.wang@usu.edu

ABSTRACT
The study is focused on replacing all coal and natural gas electricity generation in the state of Texas with solar, wind, and nuclear power. As an integral part of the designed hybrid energy system, both thermal and hydrogen storages are used to minimize overproduction and allow for load following. The Dymola system model uses wind speed and solar irradiation data for 2020 to meet the real load data for Texas in 2020. An optimization algorithm is developed to find an optimum design point, aiming to minimize the system's levelized cost of electricity (LCOE) while meeting the demand at all times of the year. The optimized LCOE of the system was $73.04/MWh, which results from 61 Natrium nuclear power plants, 5317 3.2-MW wind turbines, and 307.9 km2 of solar panels. Most of the demand is met by nuclear power with the rest being a near even split between wind and solar. While this optimized LCOE is greater than the current LCOE, it provides carbon-free electricity for the entire state of Texas. Although the stored hydrogen in salt caverns contributed only to a small portion of the total electricity production, it provides a large amount of green hydrogen to future clean energy markets.
Keywords: Hydrogen, Hybrid energy system, Nuclear, LCOE, Dymola/Modelica

#363

FUEL CELL POWER SYSTEM DESIGN AND IMPLEMENTATION BASED ON MULTI-LAYER CONVERTER

[1*] *Hossein Bagherian Farahabadi,* [1] *Amirhossein Pahnabi,* [1] *Reza Youneszadeh,* [1] *Mohammad Ali Alirezapouri*
[1] Northern Research Center for Science & Technology, Malek Ashtar University of Technology, Iran
*Corresponding author e-mail address: bagherian@mut.ac.ir

ABSTRACT
Power conditioning subsystem is considered as one of the main parts of fuel cell power systems. DC/DC converters play the main role in the power conditioning subsystem and fuel cell hybridization with other electric power sources. The load voltage is regulated by DC/DC converters and in some cases the fuel cell current changes and loading level is controlled by current-controlled DC/DC converters. Designing converters in multi-layer topology have some advantages including input current ripple reduction. Due to the current division among the layers, lower current rating semiconductor devices can be used. Also, failing one layer doesn't leads to complete system outage and the other layers can deliver a fraction of the nominal power. In this paper a fuel cell power system based on a 16 kW PEM fuel cell stack and a multi-layer DC/DC boost converter is designed and implemented. The power system is modeled and analyzed in MATLAB/Simulink software environment. The power system is implemented to verify the analysis and simulation results.
Keywords: PEM fuel cell, Multi-layer, DC/DC Converter, Power system.

#373

OFFSHORE WIND ENERGY PROSPECTS FOR POWER-TO-DIRECT AIR CAPTURE AND POWER-TO-GAS

* *Muhammad Faisal Shehzad, Haris Ishaq, Curran Crawford*
Institute for Integrated Energy Systems at University of Victoria (IESVic), Department of Mechanical Engineering, University of Victoria, BC V8P 5C2, Canada
*Corresponding author e-mail: mshehzad@uvic.ca

ABSTRACT
Direct air capture of carbon dioxide (CO_2) is technically a feasible solution for reducing atmospheric CO_2 concentrations at scale, building on decades of global research. However, powering such systems even partially with CO_2-intensive fossil fuels results in more CO_2 emissions. This paper presents a novel energy management strategy (EMS) to further explore modular offshore wind energy off Canada's West Coast via power-to-direct air capture and power-to-gas systems. The system architecture includes a 15MW wind turbine paired with a hydrogen energy storage system, i.e. hydrogen production and storage, and direct air capture (DAC) units. Hydrogen production from wind generation is stored and used to deliver the thermal loads of the DAC system. In addition to meeting DAC thermal loads, any excess produced hydrogen is used to meet hydrogen demand for external consumers, such as hydrogen as a fuel for fuel cell vehicles. The effectiveness of the proposed EMS is shown through extensive simulations with different seasonal conditions.
Keywords: Offshore wind energy, Direct air capture, Hydrogen storage, Power-to-gas, Energy storage system

#379

EXERGY ANALYSIS OF REVERSIBLE SOFC COUPLED WITH ORGANIC RANKINE CYCLE AND HYDROGEN STORAGE FOR RENEWABLE ENERGY STORAGE

[1] *Uday Raj Singh,* [1*] *Satya Sekhar Bhogilla*
[1] Department of Mechanical Engineering, Indian Institute of Technology Jammu, Jammu, 181221, India
*Corresponding author e-mail: satya.bhogilla@iitjammu.ac.in

ABSTRACT
A novel renewable energy storage system based on reversible solid oxide fuel cell (SOFC) with integrated organic Rankine cycle (ORC), metal hydride hydrogen storage (MHHS) and absorption refrigeration cycle are proposed in the present study. The system utilizes the waste heat generated from the SOFC unit into the ORC evaporator to produce power using the turbine. After that, the rejected heat is being used for heating application and produces a cooling effect by implementing the single-effect absorption chiller. A part of high-quality exhaust heat from SOFC is transferred to the MHHS for the desorption process to facilitate the release of hydrogen. Exergy analysis of the trigeneration system and evaluation of the exergy destruction rates of system components is carried out. Furthermore, a detailed parametric study is conducted to study the influence of critical parameters such as current density, SOFC temperature and turbine inlet pressure on exergy efficiency and exergy destruction rates. It has been observed that the maximum value of trigeneration energetic efficiency of 74% is obtained at SOFC temperature of 800°C and current density of 0.8 A/cm². Moreover, maximum net electrical exergy efficiency is 67.39%, maximum heating exergy efficiency is 73.1%, maximum cooling exergy efficiency is 66.48%, and maximum ORC exergy efficiency obtained is 16.63%.
Keywords: Solid oxide fuel cell, Exergy analysis, Trigeneration, Organic Rankine cycle, Metal Hydride

#389

SCIENTIFIC AND TECHNOLOGICAL SYNERGIES CONNECTING ELECTROLYSERS, FUEL CELLS AND ELECTROCHEMICAL COMPRESSORS FOR HYDROGEN USE

[1*] *Sonya Calnan*, [1,2] *Rutger Schlatmann*
[1]PVcomB, Helmholtz-Zentrum Berlin für Materialien und Energie GmbH, 12489 Berlin, Germany
[2] Hochschule für Technik und Wirtschaft Berlin, Wilhelminenhofstraße 75A, 12459 Berlin, Germany
*Corresponding author e-mail: sonya.calnan@helmholtz-berlin.de

ABSTRACT
Electrolysers, electrochemical compressors and fuels cells will be crucial to supporting the role of green hydrogen in the energy, transport and manufacturing sectors. In this contribution we discuss several scientific and technological synergies between these three types of electrochemical cells and their benefits towards fostering the wider deployment of these devices are outlined. The identified synergies can also be extended to the same type of electrochemical cells based on different dual use (energy and materials) chemicals for example ammonia.
Keywords: Hydrogen, Fuel cell, Electrolyser, Electrochemical compressor

#398

PRELIMINARY ASSESSMENT OF THE GREEN HYDROGEN PRODUCTION POTENTIAL IN KAZAKHSTAN

[1] *Saniya Danenova*, [2] *Yerdaulet Abuov*, [2]*Akmaral Tleubergenova*,[2,3,*]*Woojin Lee*
[1] Department of Mechanical and Aerospace Engineering, School of Engineering and Digital Sciences, Nazarbayev University, Nur-Sultan 010000, Republic of Kazakhstan
[2] Department of Civil and Environmental Engineering, School of Engineering and Digital Sciences, Nazarbayev University, Nur-Sultan 01000, Republic of Kazakhstan
[3] Green Energy and Environment Laboratory, National Laboratory Astana, Nazarbayev University, Nur-Sultan 01000, Republic of Kazakhstan
*Corresponding author e-mail: woojin.lee@nu.edu.kz

ABSTRACT
Hydrogen has been considered a clean energy source, playing a crucial role in the energy transition. Due to its low-carbon intensity, green hydrogen appears to be an exciting solution to reduce greenhouse gas (GHG) emissions and increase secure energy supply. This study is the first attempt to evaluate the green production of hydrogen in Kazakhstan. At this stage, we have used the GIS tool to quantify solar, wind, and biomass resources in Kazakhstan. Most prospective areas for solar-based hydrogen include Jambyl, Kyzylorda, and Turkestan with hydrogen potential of 3800-4100 t/km^2/year, while Jambyl, Kyzylorda, and Central Kazakhstan regions favored the production of wind-based hydrogen with a hydrogen potential of 16 000-18 800 t/km^2/year. Southern Kazakhstan is also prospective for biomass-based hydrogen energy production (up to 47 t/km^2/year). Based on the hydrogen production estimated from the regions, Kazakhstan could be a supplier of new energy carriers globally, significantly contributing to future hydrogen energy system development.
Keywords: Renewable sources, Electrolysis, Gasification, Hydrogen energy system

#401

OPTIMIZATION OF A STAND-ALONE PV SYSTEM FOR EFFICIENT HYDROGEN PRODUCTION USING AN ALKALINE WATER ELECTROLYZER

[1*] *Victor Arturo Martinez Lopez*, [2] *Hesan Ziar*, [3] *Miro Zeman*, [4] *Olindo Isabella*
[1, 2, 3, 4] Delft University of Technology, Faculty of Electrical Engineering, Mathematics and Computer Science, Photovoltaic Materials and Devices, Mekelweg 4, 2628CD, Delft, The Netherlands
*Corresponding author e-mail: V.A.MartinezLopez@tudelft.nl

ABSTRACT
We present the analysis of the size and angle configuration of a solar photovoltaic (PV) plant connected to an alkaline electrolyzer without electrical storage nor support from the grid. Our approach is based on using the available energy in the most efficient way. To reach our objective, we allocated the available PV power to the stack and auxiliary components, then determined the produced hydrogen in one year. By defining 4 indicators, we determine that the PV plant should be oversized 1.6 times the rated power of the electrolysis stack. The orientation analysis of the PV modules shows that the optimal angles determined for maximum PV yield are not the same if other indicators are used and many of them are in conflict.
Keywords: Optimization, Energy efficiency, Green hydrogen

#411

EFFECT OF THE ADDITION OF HYDROGEN-CONTAINING GAS ON INDICATED AND EFFECTIVE PARAMETERS OF A GASOLINE ENGINE

[1*] *Jonas Matijošius,* [2] *Yurii Gutarevych,* [2] *Yevheniy Shuba,* [1] *Alfredas Rimkus,* [2] *Oleksander Syrota,*
[1]Vilnius Tech, J. Basanavičiaus str. 28, Vilnius, Lithuania
[2] National Transport University, Mykhaila Omelianovycha-Pavlenka Str. 1, Kyiv 01010
*Corresponding author e-mail: jonas.matijosius@vilniustech.lt

ABSTRACT
The article presents the results of a study of the effect of the addition of hydrogen-containing gas on the indicator and effective indicators of a gasoline engine. Experimental and numerical analysis studies of the combustion process in a gasoline engine when operating without additives and with the addition of different quantities of hydrogen-containing gas have been carried out. As a result, it was found that the addition of a hydrogen-containing gas leads to a reduction in the duration of the combustion process and an improvement in engine performance. The addition of hydrogen-containing gas leads to an increase in the indicated efficiency of the engine, the heat utilization factor and an increase in the indicated power. As a result of bench tests, an increase in the effective power and a decrease in the brake specific fuel consumption of the engine were found.
Keywords: Hydrogen, Hydrogen-containing gas, HHO, Combustion process, Indicated parameters, Gasoline engine.

#412

HYDROGEN AND OXYGEN (HHO) GAS INFLUENCE ON ENGINE CHARACTERISTICS WHILE FUELED ON PETROL ANT BIOETHANOL LEAN MIXTURES

[1*] *Gabrielius Mejeras,* [1,2] *Alfredas Rimkus,* [1,2] *Jonas Matijošius*
[1]Vilnius Tech, J. Basanavičiaus str. 28, Vilnius, Lithuania
[2]Vilnius College of Technologies and Design, Antakalnio str. 54, Vilnius, Lithuania
*Corresponding author e-mail: gabrielius.mejeras@vilniustech.lt

ABSTRACT
As ecological requirements getting stricter and the new manners of decreasing emissions of pollutants are being researched. One of them is to focus the usage none or small count of carbon fuels as a fuel for internal combustion engine. Therefore, usage perspective of bioethanol with HHO gas as an additive fuel to petrol lean mixtures, is presented in this research. Ecological (CO, CO_2, HC, NO_x) and energetic (M_b, B_f, BTE) parameters were measured when using petrol ant bioethanol mixtures (E10 and E70) enriched with HHO gas. Numerical analysis was also performed to better explain the combustion process of the fuel mixtures ecological and energetical parameters. Experimentation was done by using spark ignition engine changing the ignition timing from 16 ° to 42 ° BTDC and changing stoichiometric mixture (λ = 1.0) to a lean (λ = 1.1; 1.2;1.3; 1.4). Hydrogen and oxygen gases are produced using mobile electrolysis unit – HHO gas generator. It was concluded that for all air / fuel ratios tested the maximum torque was reached with 70% bioethanol additive to petrol, HHO gas has positive effect when mixtures are lean. The NO_x emission's increased, however CO, CH and CO_2 was lower when HHO was supplied.

Keywords: Petrol, Bioethanol, Hydrogen, Combustion.

#428

EXPERIMENTAL STUDY ON SPRAY CHARACTERISTICS OF INTERNAL MIXED HYDROGEN-ASSISTED FUEL INJECTION SYSTEM

[1] *Zenghui Liu,* [1*] *Tao Qiu ,* [1] *Yan Lei*
[1] Department of Automotive Engineering, Beijing University of Technology, Beijing 100124, China
*Corresponding author e-mail: qiutao@bjut.edu.cn

ABSTRACT
Hydrogen-assisted diesel injection is suitable for low-power and high-power-to-weight ratio in-cylinder piston direct injection engines. The jet characteristics of hydrogen-assisted diesel direct injection have an important effect on engine performance. The effects of fuel injection duration and mixture duration, hydrogen pressure and fuel/hydrogen premix time on spray penetration distance and diffusion area were qualitatively analyzed by high-speed photography on a constant volume chamber test bench. The results show that increasing the fuel injection duration increases the penetration distance and decreases the spray projection area. Increasing hydrogen pressure will increase both penetration distance and spray projection area. Increasing the duration of air injection will increase the penetration distance and decrease the spray area. The spray area increases with the increase of fuel/hydrogen premixing time, and tends to be stable when the premixing time is 3ms, which has no effect on the spray penetration distance.

Keywords: Piston engine, Hydrogen-assisted injection system, Direct injection, Diesel, Spray characteristics

#435

ANALYSIS OF AN INTEGRATED GAS TURBINE-LOCOMOTIVE ENGINE USING SUSTAINABLE FUEL BLENDS WITH HYDROGEN

[1] Shaimaa Seyam, [1] Ibrahim Dincer, [1] Martin Agelin-Chaab*
[1] Clean Energy Research Laboratory (CERL), Faculty of Engineering and Applied Science Ontario Tech University 2000 Simcoe Street North, Oshawa, Ontario, L1H 7K4, Canada
*Corresponding author e-mail: Shaimaa.seyam@ontariotechu.net

ABSTRACT

Greenhouse gas emissions have led to the imminent global warming crisis, which has motivated scientists and engineers to search for creative solutions for this problem. Rail transportation is known to emit greenhouse gases because of its reliance on fossil fuels. This paper investigates an integrated design of a locomotive engine to replace the traditional internal combustion engines. The integrated system consists of a gas turbine with double compressors and double turbines, two fuel cells, and an energy recovery system including two thermoelectrical generators and an absorption refrigeration system. The proposed engine is analyzed thermodynamically to examine its performance using methane and hydrogen fuel blends. It was found that the integrated engine can generate 9 MW of total power, which is threefold of the traditional locomotive engines with 70.6% of thermal efficiency and 42% of exergetic efficiency.

Keywords: Locomotive engine, Fuel cells, Energy recovery system, Thermodynamic analysis.

#1443

AN APPLICATION AND EVALUATION OF BLENDING BIOGAS AND HYDROGEN INTO THE NATURAL GAS FOR COMBUSTION APPLICATIONS

[1] Merve Ozturk, [2,1] Ibrahim Dincer*
[1] Yildiz Technical University, Faculty of Mechanical Engineering, Mechanical Engineering Department, Istanbul, Turkey
[2] Clean Energy Research Laboratory, Ontario Tech. University, Faculty of Engineering and Applied Science, Ontario, Canada
*Corresponding author e-mail: merveoz@yildiz.edu.tr

ABSTRACT

In this study, an integrated system is developed for environmentally benign and efficient combustion of natural gas in domestic applications. For this purpose, natural gas is blended with biogas and renewable hydrogen to combat fossil fuel usage and greenhouse gas emissions released to the environment. Different blending ratios are analyzed with Aspen Plus software and combustion emissions are investigated. While CO_2 emission and reactor heat rate are 6.48 kg/h and 27 kW when using only natural gas. These values decrease to 6.35 kg/h and 22 kW for 60%-40% natural gas-biogas blend and 5.06 kg/h and 18 kW for 40%-40%-20% natural gas-biogas-hydrogen blend, respectively. In the case of this triple blending, the natural gas consumption reduces from 2.46 kg/h to 0.98 kg/h.

Keywords: Hydrogen, Renewable energy, Biogas, Natural gas, Blend, Emissions, Performance assessment

#1456

COMPARATIVE ANALYSIS OF A MULTI-GENERATION SYSTEM USING DIFFERENT CONVENTIONAL AND NANO BASEDWORKING FLUIDS

[1] Tahir Abdul Hussain Ratlamwala, [1] Hafsa Javed, [1] Sana Naseem, [1] Khurram Kamal*
[1]National University of Sciences and Technology, Islamabad, Pakistan
*Corresponding author e-mail: tahir.ratlamwala@pnec.nust.edu.pk

ABSTRACT

The aim of the research is to study a system that uses both non-renewable and renewable energy sources, fulfilling the energy requirements by using fossil fuels but also reducing the use of fossil fuels which are damaging the environment in hindsight by the introduction of a renewable energy system. The system provides a total of six different outputs, which are Electricity Generation, Desalination of Water, Heating of space, Cooling of space, Heating of Water and Waste Heat for Industrial Purposes. The performance of the system is studied through detailed energy and exergy analyses. Further the effects of variation in geothermal fluid's mass flow rate, pressure and quality on system outputs are evaluated. Additionally, multiple fuels including nano-based fuels with varying calorific values are evaluated and it is found that the fuels with highest calorific values provide the best possible system outputs.

Keywords: Nano fluids, Multigeneration, Exergy

#1472

SIMULATION OF PEMFC INTEGRATED TRILATERAL CYCLE (TLC) IN MATLAB/SIMULINK ENVIRONMENT

[1] Khurram Kamal, [1] Afzal Sheikh, [1] Muhammad Nouman Saleem, [1] Atif Naseer, [1] Tahir Abdul Hussain Ratlamwala, [2]Asad Ali Zaidi*

[1]National University of Sciences and Technology, Islamabad, Pakistan

[2]Department of Mechanical, Faculty of Engineering Science and Technology, Hamdard University, Pakistan

*Corresponding author e-mail: khurram.kamal@pnec.nust.edu.pk

ABSTRACT

Depletion of Petroleum reserve and their catastrophic global warming have shifted the focus of engineers towards the renewable energy source. Fuel cell is a portable, sustainable and renewable electrochemical device which has the potential to emerge has the major source of energy. Electrical Power, Waste Heat, water are the three products of the Fuel Cell. Electrical power is utilized by external circuit and Waste heat is removed via removal of water and external cooling. This Paper present the modelling of Ballard Mark V fuel cell and its Waste Heat Recovery Trilateral Cycle (TLC). Comparative analysis for the selection of Working Fluid of TLC was carried out using REFPROP library. Simulink model of the TLC Cycle and Fuel Cell is developed, and the thermal analysis of each model is carried out individually. Thermal Analysis showed that Fuel Cell has an electrical power of 4.3kW with thermal efficiency of 50%. Hence, 4.3 kW waste heat from fuel cell was utilized as an input heat and 391.4 W power was produced by TLC with an efficiency of 6.1%.

Keywords: Trilateral Cycle, PEMFC, Simulink

#1476

CO-GENERATION OF ELECTRICITY USING WASTE HEAT FROM HYDROGEN FUEL CELL IN A VEHICLE: A SIMULINK MODEL

[1] Khurram Kamal, [1] Adeem Ahmed Shaikh, [1]Muhammad Usama Shaikh, [1]Samita Khan, [1]Azka Jawed, Ammad Yousuf Tariq, [1] Tahir Abdul Hussain Ratlamwala, [2]Asad Ali Zaidi*

[1]National University of Sciences and Technology, Islamabad, Pakistan

[2]Department of Mechanical, Faculty of Engineering Science and Technology, Hamdard University, Pakistan

*Corresponding author e-mail: khurram.kamal@pnec.nust.edu.pk

ABSTRACT

This paper discusses the use of Proton Exchange Membrane Fuel Cell (PEMFC) as the source of energy for installation in vehicles. The paper includes a Simulink model for a vehicle with a Thermo-Electric Generator (TEG), also showing the fuel cell and the method used for a stable energy output from it. Considering the parameters for an automobile, especially weight and dimensional constraints, the paper is the study of waste heat recovery from a 50 to 70°C temperature difference produced by the fuel cell. The study has been done for a generalized scalable model of PEMFC, containing 20 cells per stack. The stacks are connected in parallel to keep the output voltage at a constant level. It was observed that under dynamic conditions an average of 10.85% power regeneration occurred. This regeneration percentage is directly proportional to the number of cells TEG modules used. Therefore, the study can be scaled to a variety of PEMFC models. However, increasing the number of cells does not affect the stack temperature significantly but provides a large area for heat transfer.

Keywords: Fuel cells, PEMFC, Simulink, TEG

#1479

PERFORMANCE ASSESSMENT OF A CALCIUM-IRON BROMIDE CYCLE BASED MULTIGENERATION SYSTEM

Fatih Sorgulu[1] and Ibrahim Dincer[2,1]*

[1]Faculty of Mechanical Engineering, Yildiz Technical University, Besiktas, Istanbul, Turkey

[2]Faculty of Engineering and Applied Science, Ontario Tech. University, Oshawa, Ontario, Canada

*Correspondence e-mail: fatihs@yildiz.edu.tr

ABSTRACT

In this study, a performance assessment of a novel solar energy-based multigeneration system integrated with a thermochemical cycle is performed. A steam generator is also integrated to reach high temperatures which are required for the thermochemical cycle. While 550 °C is reached with solar tower, the temperature is increased to 750 °C, which is the maximum temperature of the cycle, with the steam generator. Hydrogen is produced by a calcium-iron bromide cycle and is blended with natural gas. The blend is supplied both to the boiler of the organic Rankine cycle and a community to utilize in combi boiler and gas cooker. The reverse osmosis and multi-effect distillation units are integrated to produce fresh water for the community which consists of one thousand houses. 9.3 MWh electricity is supplied by organic Rankine cycle with 41.27 million m^3 hydrogen and natural gas blend. Furthermore, a total of 7.2 million m^3 of the blend is utilized for household appliances including gas cookers and combi boilers.

Keywords: Efficiency, Hydrogen, Natural gas, Renewable energy, Solar tower

#1504
HYDROGEN POWERED VESSELS AT SEA: FUEL CELL & BATTERY UPSCALING

[1*] *Christer Helleland,* [2] *Fionn Iversen,* [3]*Svein Olav Halstensen*
[1]NORCE, Nygårdsgaten 112, 5008, Bergen, Norway
[2]NORCE, Nygårdsgaten 112, 5008, Bergen, Norway
[3]NORCE, Sørhauggata 128, 5527, Haugesund, Norway
*Corresponding author email: chel@norceresearch.no

ABSTRACT

There is today a strong effort in developing fuel cell / battery systems for ship propulsion to achieve zero-emission maritime transport, in accordance with UN sustainability goals and the Fit For 55 plan to achieve the climate goals agreed by the EU Council and the European Parliament. Critical for successful implementation of fuel cell / battery systems are system design and control during operation. Fuel cells and batteries have ideal operating ranges. Use outside of this range will cause degradation, impacting system lifecycle. Fuel cell / battery systems are used for transport today but applying such systems for maritime transport requires significant upscaling. Cars typically have a power of 100 to 300 kW, while ocean going ships require tens of MW of power to handle the loads required. To achieve such system capacity, systems are assembled with multiple fuel cells and batteries in stacks. A better understanding of the effect of such upscaling, and system dynamics with respect to load, is therefore required for successful implementation of fuel cell / battery systems for maritime transport. This paper discusses fuel cell types, methods and models applicable for this purpose.

Keywords: PEM fuel cell, Battery, Upscaling, Marine vessel hybrid system.

#1522
THERMODYNAMIC ANALYSIS OF A NEW GEOTHERMAL ENERGY BASED INTEGRATED PLANT FOR COMPRESSED HYDROGEN PRODUCTION

[1*]*Fatih Yilmaz,* [1]*Murat Ozturk*
[1]Isparta University of Applied Sciences, Faculty of Technology, Department of Mechatronics Engineering, Isparta, Turkiye
*Corresponding author e-mail: fatiyilmaz7@gmail.com

ABSTRACT

The main aim of this newly designed geothermal energy-based combined plant is to conduct the thermodynamic performance investigation for clean and sustainable power, hydrogen, heating, cooling, and hot water. For this aim, the Kalina cycle, an ORC, a double effect cooling system, two thermoelectric generators, a hot water generator, and finally, a hydrogen generation and storage unit are thermally integrated with a geothermal source. Each subsystem is examined in detail from the thermodynamic point of view and parametric analyzes are carried out. According to the analysis findings, the energy and exergy efficiency of the whole system is determined as 39.63% and 36.14%.

Keywords: Energy, Hydrogen, Multigeneration, Geothermal.

#1523
MODELING OF A SUSTAINABLE INTEGRATED PLANT WITH S-CO_2 AND T-CO_2 CYCLES FOR HYDROGEN GENERATION

[1*]*Fatih Yilmaz,* [1]*Murat Ozturk,* [2]*Resat Selbas*
[1]Isparta University of Applied Sciences, Faculty of Technology, Department of Mechatronics Engineering, Isparta, Turkiye
[2]Isparta University of Applied Sciences, Faculty of Technology, Department of Mechanical Engineering, Isparta, Turkiye
*Corresponding author e-mail: fatiyilmaz7@gmail.com

ABSTRACT

The primary goal of this proposed work is to examine the solar energy-combined multigeneration model in order to produce heating, power, hydrogen, and clean water in a comprehensive way from the thermodynamic aspect. This plant consists of mainly five sub-unit that is heliostat field, supercritical Brayton cycle, transcritical Rankine cycle, multi-effect desalination unit, and PEM electrolyzer. Looking at analysis results, the amount of the hydrogen rate of this combined plant is 0.001179 kgs^{-1}. Also, the capacity of the electrical power is 1194 kW. To finish, the whole energetic and exergetic performance of the modeled plant is 44.63% and 13.74%, respectively.

Keywords: Energy, Exergy, Hydrogen, Thermodynamic, Solar

#1524

SMALL DRONE CONVERSION TO LONG ENDURANCE HYDROGEN FUEL CELL POWERED DRONE

Sayem Zafar, Shaaban Ali, Peter Dawson
Abu Dhabi Polytechnic (IAT), Aircraft Technology Department, Al Ain, UAE
*Corresponding author e-mail: sayem.zafar@adpoly.ac.ae

ABSTRACT

A study is conducted to investigate the integration of a hydrogen fuel cell power system to a small drone at Abu Dhabi Polytechnic in collaboration with Lockheed-Martin. The proposed hydrogen fuel cell power is to replace the existing battery of the fuel cell. The drone used for this study is Lockheed-Martin's *Indago 3* is used for the current study. The drone has a total weight of 2.5 kg and dimensions of 0.9 m by 0.9 m. *Indago 3* is used for this study since it is small, light-weight, portable and accessible to researchers. Analyses are conducted using data acquired through manufacturer data sheet, simulations and ground tests. Using the available drone power and weight data, the endurance of the drone using the hydrogen fuel cell was determined. Data simulations are conducted for the maximum required power of 510 W for all four motors. The flight endurance of the UAV improved when hydrogen fuel cell power system is used. The UAV endurance increased from 32 min to 108 min. The research study shows the usefulness of hydrogen fuel cell power system for a small drone as an alternative to the batteries to enhance the flight time of the drone. Finally, the paper also establishes the effectiveness of using renewable energy sources for mobile applications.

Keywords: Drone, Hydrogen fuel cell, Flight time, Renewable energy

#1550

ENERGY MANAGEMENT OF GREEN HYDROGEN-BASED POWER-TO-POWER GENERATION SYSTEMS

[1,3] Alexandros Kafetzis, [2] Stella Chatzigavriel, [1] Panos Seferlis, [3] Kyriakos Panopoulos*
[1]Aristotle University of Thessaloniki, Department of Mechanical Engineering, Thessaloniki, Greece
[2] Horizon S.A., Serres, Greece
[2] Centre for Research and Technology Hellas, Chemical Process and Energy Resources Institute, Thessaloniki, Greece
*Corresponding author e-mail: akafetzi@certh.gr

ABSTRACT

Post-2030 decarbonization targets, enable energy storage as a key element in the energy mix of future sustainable energy systems in Europe. Storage is supported by the high penetration of renewable energy sources (RES) in the European energy landscape. One of the most efficient, zero emission fuels is hydrogen produced by RES via electrolysis. Hydrogen production and storage is combined with fuel cells and batteries to comprise an integrated Power-to-Power (P2P) system. Such systems offer efficient, reliable, and cost-effective energy delivery that is quick in release and of high density, aspects that are necessary to counter the RES power intermittency. Stochastic RES profiles, dynamic response of sub-components, and multiple decisions inside a constantly changing environment are major challenges in P2P systems' operation. The Energy Management Strategy (EMS) developed in this work and employed in the control framework of the P2P systems ensures their efficient operation. The EMS supervises the optimal distribution of power production and consumption. A series of applications of pilot P2P systems with different characteristics showcase the system's performance, resilience and replicability potential through certain key performance indicators (KPIs).

Keywords: Energy storage, Green hydrogen, Control, Renewable energy, Energy management

#1553

HYDROGEN AND FRESHWATER PRODUCTION FROM TIDAL ENERGY

[1] Cihad Çelik, [2] Murat Emre Demir*
[1,2]İstanbul Technical University, Faculty of Naval Architecture and Ocean Engineering, Maslak, İstanbul, Turkey
*Corresponding author e-mail: celikciha@itu.edu.tr

ABSTRACT

This study presents a concept of a renewable energy system based on hydrogen generation by coupling of an electrolyser to a tidal generator. The proposed energy conversion system has two main energy requirements. The first one is for the electrolyser and the other is for the reverse osmosis unit. High-fidelity CFD simulations are performed on whether the preliminary designed turbine would provide sufficient power in OpenFOAM open-source package. Results show the importance of detailed design to understand the hydrodynamics characteristics of tidal turbines. Considering the maximum C_p at 3.5 TSR, the output power calculated as $44.67\ kWh$. The selected turbine's parameters do not meet the required power. In this case, the preliminary turbine design should be updated by increasing the swept area of it.

Keywords: Tidal power, Hydrogen storage, CFD, Reverse osmosis

#1555

DEEP LEARNING-BASED BINARY CLASSIFICATION OF ISLANDING CONDITIONS IN A HYDROGEN ENERGY-BASED DISTRIBUTED GENERATION SYSTEM

[1] *Alper Yılmaz*, [2*] *Gökay Bayrak*
[1,2] Bursa Technical University, Smart Grid Laboratory, Department of Electrical and Electronics Engineering, 16300, Bursa, Turkey
*Corresponding author e-mail: gokay.bayrak@btu.edu.tr

ABSTRACT

This paper presents a deep long short-term memory (DLSTM) with a binary-label classifier method proposed for binary classification of islanding and non-islanding events in a hydrogen energy-based distributed generator (DG) system. Deep learning (DL)-based method eliminated the lack of performance of conventional intelligent islanding detection methods that uses feature extraction, feature selection, and event classification. Besides, the proposed method has provided the need for a processing-intensive filtering process to reduce noise from the signal. The proposed islanding detection method has a 98.33% accuracy rate under no-noise, and 97.66% high-level noise conditions. In the proposed method, the non-detection zone (NDZ) is almost zero, and the detection time is under the defined IEEE 929-2000 standards. Experimental and simulative data results show that the LSTM-based islanding detection method outperforms the algorithms in recent studies in terms of noise immunity and accuracy.

Keywords: Hydrogen energy, Islanding detection, Long-short-term memory, Deep learning, Microgrid.

#1556

THD MINIMIZATION OF VEHICLE-TO-GRID (V2G) IN FUEL CELL EVS WITH A DEVELOPED ELLIPTIC IIR FILTER

[1*] *Gökay Bayrak*, [2] *Alper Yılmaz*
[1,2] Bursa Technical University, Smart Grid Laboratory, Department of Electrical and Electronics Engineering, 16300, Bursa, Turkey
*Corresponding author e-mail: gokay.bayrak@btu.edu.tr

ABSTRACT

The popularity of fuel cell electric vehicles (FCEVs) and plug-in electric vehicles (PEVs) is a key factor in addressing the electricity demand. With vehicle-to-grid (V2G) applications, these vehicles can act as distributed generators. Total harmonic distortion (THD) in the connection of electric vehicle charge stations (EVCSs) capable with V2G technology with the grid should be fulfilling the values specified by international electrical standards. Although V2G topologies are improved, the use of a suitable filter is necessary to improve the power quality (PQ) of the system. Since analog filters bring additional losses to power losses caused by inverter and converter, software-based digital filters are also needed. Due to the implementation of the infinite impulse response (IIR) filter includes fewer parameters, it requires less memory and has less computational complexity. In this study, a low-pass elliptical IIR filter design is realized in real-time with the converter using LabVIEW infrastructure. When imbalances occur in the grid voltage, reducing bandwidth using phase locked loop (PLL) will not be enough to keep the system stable. This problem solved by adding a proposed low-pass elliptical IIR filter to the system. The results obtained by using the filter are presented in the paper and the THD value was obtained as 0.82% for converter capable V2G.

Keywords: Vehicle-to-grid (V2G), Fuel cell electric vehicles (FCEVs), IIR filter design, THD minimization, Power quality

#1568

PV-FUEL CELL HYBRID SYSTEM MODELING AND ANALYSIS

[1] *Bihter Anlamaz*, [1,2] **Anil Can Turkmen*, [1] *Kursat Can Ata*, [1] *Cenk Celik*
[1] Kocaeli University Faculty of Engineering, Department of Mechanical Engineering, Kocaeli 41380, Turkey
[2] ACT Scientific Ltd., Budotek Teknopark, Istanbul, 34776, Turkey
*Corresponding author e-mail: anilcan.turkmen@hotmail.com

ABSTRACT

In this study, an analysis of the use of photovoltaic (PV) and fuel cell (FC) systems as a combined (hybrid) system is presented. unified system; It consists of a PV panel, electrolysis unit, hydrogen tank, and fuel cell. The electrical energy supplied from the PV panel is used for hydrogen production in the electrolysis unit. The stored hydrogen then drives the fuel cell, providing a regular supply of electricity. Fuel cell stack efficiency was found to be 65% in Antalya region and 58% in Sinop region.

Keywords: Photovoltaic, Fuel cell

#1587

EXPERIMENTAL STUDY ON HYDROGEN ENRICHED NATURAL GAS COMBUSTION IN INDUSTRIAL BURNER

[1,2]Sean Byrne,[2]Qarib Ullah,[2]Dipal Patel*
[1]BMM Heaters Ltd, Dormanstown, Redcar, United Kingdom
[2] Teesside University, School of Computing Engineering and Digital Technologies, Middlesbrough, United Kingdom
*Corresponding author e-mail: d.patel@tees.ac.uk

ABSTRACT
The effects of hydrogen enrichment with natural gas have been experimentally investigated in an industrial burner for heat production. The hydrogen content was varied from 0%, 30%, and 50% by vol in the fuel blend (hydrogen + natural gas) to examine the burner's performance, combustion, and emission characteristics. The emission characteristics were analysed by using a flue gas analyser and verified with a mass spectrometer. The experiments were performed on HEC (High Efficiency Combustion) range – TMG fully condensing industrial heater. The experimental study shows that flame thermal runaway occurs in the burner when deploying higher amount of hydrogen (i.e. ≥30% by vol.) in the blend and combustion instability increases. The required fuel flow rate for hydrogen blend increased to achieve the same power output as for natural gas. The most important influence of using hydrogen blend in combustion for industrial burner is the reduction of both CO and NOx. The study shows that CO, NO and NOx are reduced up to two times and more for 30% by vol. hydrogen blend with natural gas. The study also shows that the higher amount of hydrogen blend (i.e. ≥50% by vol.) will require a significant amount of modification to the burner's control.
Keywords: Industrial burner, Hydrogen, Emission, Combustion instability, Flames

#1597

INVESTIGATION OF SIMULTANEOUS HYDROGEN PRODUCTION AND DESALINATION OF SALINE WATER VIA ELECTRODIALYSIS PROCESS

*[1]Ragad AlShebli, [*1,2]Burak Yuzer, [1]Yusuf Bicer*
[1]Division of Sustainable Development, College of Science and Engineering, Hamad Bin Khalifa University, Qatar Foundation, Qatar
[2] Department of Environmental Engineering, Engineering Faculty, Istanbul University-Cerrahpasa, Istanbul, Turkiye
*Corresponding author e-mail: byuzer@hbku.edu.qa

ABSTRACT
Electrodialysis (ED) is an efficient process that desalinates brackish and saline water under the influence of the electrical field. The ions that present inside a solution moves through ion exchange membranes to the adjacent compartments called concentrate compartment. The main purpose of the ED process is to desalinate brackish water; besides this, a valuable energy carrier gas, hydrogen is generated at the cathode side of the ED cell in this study. However, due to the internal recirculation of the electrolyte solution from anode to cathode compartment, hydrogen gas reacts with oxygen gas and reforms water. In this study, the potential of hydrogen gas generation in an ED system while treating saline/brackish water, is experimentally investigated. The ion removal efficiencies are 68% and 67% for combined and separated processes, respectively. The hydrogen production rates of the ED system are 2.42 and 3.28 $mL/h.cm^2$ for combined and separated processes, respectively.
Keywords: Cogeneration, Energy Carrier, Hydrogen, Ion-exchange Membrane, Seawater

#1604

MATHEMATICAL MODELING AND DYNAMIC SIMULATION OF A PV-BASED HYDROGEN GENERATION AND STORAGE SYSTEM

[1]Gamze Soyturk, [1]Onder Kızılkan, [2]Mehmet Akif Ezan, [2]Can Ozgur Colpan*
[1]Isparta University of Applied Sciences, Faculty of Technology, Department of Mechanical Engineering, 32200, Isparta, Turkey
[2]Dokuz Eylul University, Faculty of Engineering, Department of Mechanical Engineering, Tinaztepe Campus, 35397, Izmir, Turkey
*Corresponding author e-mail: gamzeyildirim@isparta.edu.tr

ABSTRACT
Energy storage becomes a more critical issue for humanity to maintain a sustainable integration of renewable-based energy resources with the demand side. As an energy carrier, hydrogen can provide a large amount of energy storage with minimal loss over long periods. The current work focuses on designing and modeling a hybrid renewable energy-based system comprised of Photovoltaic (PV) cells, a battery bank, a PEM Electrolyzer for hydrogen generation, a compressor, and a pressurized hydrogen tank to meet the electricity demand of an off-grid house in Izmir. In the proposed system, solar energy was utilized to produce electricity through PV arrays. The produced energy was either used in the PEM electrolyzer for Hydrogen (H_2) production or stored in the batteries to meet the required energy during low solar radiation or nighttime. An energy management strategy was developed for the proposed hybrid system using the MATLAB software for carrying out the above-mentioned purposes. For the system component modeling, a one-dimensional mathematical approach was applied to investigate the dynamic behavior of the integrated system. The hydrogen generated by the electrolyzer was pressurized with a compressor and stored in pressure tanks at a pressure of 350 bar.
Keywords: PV, PEM electrolyzer, Energy management, Hydrogen storage.

#1606

A NEWLY DEVELOPED BRAYTON CYCLE-BASED COMBINED PLANT INCLUDING HYDROGEN PRODUCTION AND COMPRESSION: ENERGY AND EXERGY ANALYSES

*[1]*Yunus Emre Yuksel, [2]Murat Ozturk, [3]Ibrahim Dincer*
[1] Afyon Kocatepe University, Kirkgoz Campus, Afyonkarahisar, Turkey
[2] Isparta University of Applied SciencesCunur West Campus, Isparta, Turkey
[3] Ontario Tech. University, 2000 Simcoe Street North, Oshawa, Ontario, Canada
*Corresponding author e-mail: yeyuksel@aku.edu.tr

ABSTRACT
In this study, a novel multigeneration energy system based Brayton cycle is designed to generate power, compressed hydrogen, heating, drying and fresh water. The multigeneration system consists of the Brayton cycle, regenerative Rankine cycle, s-CO_2 power cycle, t-CO_2 power cycle, hydrogen production and compression plant, fresh water production plant and drying plant. In the evaluation part, energy and exergy analyses have been performed with a parametric analysis. The overall power production capacity of the system has been found as 13029 kW, and hydrogen production rate is 0.0624 kg/s. According to the thermodynamic analysis results, the overall energy and exergy efficiencies of the plant are 55.62% and 51.28%.

Keywords: Hydrogen production, Brayton cycle, Multigeneration, Thermodynamic analysis, Energy, Exergy, Efficiency

#1607

THERMODYNAMIC ANALYSIS OF A NEW COMPRESSED AIR ENERGY STORAGE-BASED COMBINED PLANT FOR MULTIGENERATION WITH HYDROGEN PRODUCTION

[1] *Murat Koc,* [2*] *Yunus Emre Yuksel,* [3] *Murat Ozturk*
[1]Isparta University of Applied Sciences, Technical Sciences Vocational School, Electricity and Energy Department, Cunur West Campus, Isparta, Turkey
[2]Afyon Kocatepe University, Bolvadin Vocational School, Electricity and Energy Department, Kirkgoz Campus, Afyonkarahisar, Turkey
[3]Isparta University of Applied Sciences, Faculty of Technology, Department of Mechatronics Engineering, Cunur West Campus, Isparta, Turkey
*Corresponding author e-mail: yeyuksel@aku.edu.tr

ABSTRACT
In this study, a novel compressed air energy storage-based combined plant for hydrogen production and other utilities is designed. Wind turbines and solar photovoltaic modules are the main drivers of the plant to compress the air. The multigeneration system is able to produce power, hydrogen, heating, and cooling. In the design step, each flow is enumerated and assigned thermodynamic balance equations. In order to evaluate the system performance, energy and exergy analyses are used. Then parametric analyses were performed in order to see the effects of the reference temperature and the charge-discharge pressure ratio. The study results show that the overall energy and exergy efficiencies of the multigeneration plant are 27.52% and 24.83%.
Keywords: Compressed air energy storage, hydrogen production, multigeneration, energy, exergy

#1608

A SYSTEM MODEL FOR SIMULATING A FUEL CELL BOAT

[1,2*] *S. Aykut Korkmaz,* [1] *Sera Ayten Çetinkaya,* [3] *Burak Göksu,* [2] *Olgun Konur, K. Emrah Erginer,* [4] *C. Özgür Çolpan*
[1] The Graduate School of Natural and Applied Sciences, Dokuz Eylul University, Izmir, Turkey
[2] Department of Marine Engineering, Faculty of Maritime, Dokuz Eylul University, Izmir, Turkey
[3] Department of Marine Engineering, Faculty of Maritime, Bulent Ecevit University, Zonguldak, Turkey
[4] Department of Mechanical Engineering, Faculty of Engineering, Dokuz Eylul University, Izmir, Turkey
*Corresponding author e-mail: aykut.korkmaz@deu.edu.tr

ABSTRACT
Fuel cell vehicles' minimal negative environmental effects, current technological advancements, and commercial manufacturing have opened the path for their employment in a variety of areas. The usage of fuel cell technology in marine transport has increased as the International Maritime Organization's (IMO) environmental regulations have been tightened. A simulation of a fuel cell propulsion system for use on boats will be constructed in this study. A fuel cell, a metal hydride hydrogen tank, a battery, and an electric motor will be represented as part of the system. The speed-power curve of the hull will be obtained for the design draft using a computational fluid dynamics tool. The field data from the ongoing project will be used to verify this system model.
Keywords: PEMFC, System simulation, Recreational boat, Fuel cell vehicles, CFD

#1610

MULTI-OBJECTIVE OPTIMIZATION OF AN INTEGRATED DOWNDRAFT BIOMASS GASIFIER AND SOLID OXIDE FUEL CELL SYSTEM

[1*] *Beyza Dursun,* [1] *Anil Erdogan,* [2] *C. Ozgur Colpan* [3] *Azize Ayol*
[1]The Graduate School of Natural and Applied Sciences, Dokuz Eylul University, Buca, Izmir, Turkey
[2] Faculty of Engineering, Department of Mechanical Engineering, Dokuz Eylul University, Buca, Izmir, Turkey
[3] Faculty of Engineering, Department of Environmental Engineering, Dokuz Eylul University, Buca, Izmir, Turkey
*Corresponding author e-mail: beyzanisandursun@gmail.com

ABSTRACT
In this study, multi-objective optimization of an integrated system that consists of a downdraft biomass gasifier and a solid oxide fuel cell was performed. For this purpose, the energy and exergy analysis of the proposed system was conducted to indicate the inlet and outlet conditions and irreversibility of the system components. Then, using economic analysis, the average specific cost, the unit exergy cost, and the operating cost of the system were found. Finally, a multi-objective optimization study is carried out using the two-stage Taguchi method to determine the optimum operating parameters of the system. Furthermore, high thermodynamic performance (energy, exergy efficiency) and low cost are taken as an objective functions.
Keywords: Downdraft biomass gasifier, Solid oxide fuel cell, Multi-objective optimization, Genetic algorithm

#1618

A STUDY ON EXERGETIC SUSTAINABILITY INDICATORS OF SOLAR METHANE CRACKING

[1,2*] *Aliya Banu,* [2] *Adnan Midilli,* [1] *Yusuf Bicer*
[1] Division of Sustainable Development, College of Science and Engineering, Hamad Bin Khalifa University, Qatar Foundation, Doha, Qatar
[2] Division of Hydromechanics and Hydraulic Machines, Department of Mechanical Engineering, Yildiz Technical University, Istanbul, Turkey
*Corresponding author e-mail: alba34159@hbku.edu.qa

ABSTRACT
In this study, exergetic sustainability indicators of solar methane cracking for hydrogen production have been analysed. For this purpose, solar methane cracking system is considered a cleaner process for production of hydrogen fuel from natural gas. To evaluate the system comprehensively, a detailed exergy analysis is performed, and indicators based on exergetic sustainability are defined and calculated. The system has an exergy efficiency of 53% and a recoverable exergy ratio of 34%. Further improvements to the system can lead to enhanced sustainability.
Keywords: Exergetic sustainability indicators, Turquoise hydrogen, Thermodynamic modelling, Methanol, DME

#1620

SOLAR ASSISTED HYDROGEN PRODUCTION VIA PV/T ASSISTED SMALL SCALE TRANSCRITICAL POWER CYCLE WITH DIRECT STEAM GENERATION

[1*]*Gamze Soyturk,* [1]*Onder Kızılkan,* [2]*Mehmet Akif Ezan,* [2]*Can Ozgur Colpan*
[1]Isparta University of Applied Sciences, Faculty of Technology, Department of Mechanical Engineering, 32200, Isparta, Turkey
[2]Dokuz Eylul University, Faculty of Engineering, Department of Mechanical Engineering, Tinaztepe Campus, 35397, Izmir, Turkey
*Corresponding author e-mail: gamzeyildirim@isparta.edu.tr

ABSTRACT
The objective of the proposed study is to examine the performance of an integrated hydrogen generation system based on solar energy. For this purpose, CO_2, a natural fluid that does not harm the environment, was used as the working fluid. The system is comprised of the Photovoltaic/thermal (PV/T) panels, a pump, a condenser, a turbine, a Proton Exchange Membrane Electrolysis Cell (PEM-EC), and hydrogen and oxygen storage tanks. MATLAB and EES software programs are utilized to perform the performance assessment of the system. According to the analysis made on data for 17th August of İzmir, the net power generation from the PVT panels was calculated as 2696 W, the net power generation from the transcritical CO_2 Rankine cycle was 73.03 W, and the hydrogen production was 0.514 g/h.
Keywords: PV/T, CO_2, Transcritical CO_2, Hydrogen, PEM electrolyzer

#1622

DEVELOPMENT AND PERFORMANCE ASSESSMENT OF INTEGRATED RENEWABLE ENERGY SYSTEM WITH HYDROGEN STORAGE FOR AUTONOMOUS AND MOBILE 3D PRINTING SYSTEM

**Shoukat Alim Khan, *Muammer Koc*[1,2]
[1]Division of Sustainable Development (DSD), Hamad Bin Khalifa University (HBKU), Qatar Foundation (QF), Education City, Doha, Qatar
[2] University of Karabük, Turkey
*Corresponding author e-mail: shoukat.alimkhan@gmail.com; mkoc@hbku.edu.qa

ABSTRACT
3D concrete printing technology provides an ideal solution for resilient infrastructure development in critical and emergency situations; however, access and energy are critical challenges in such conditions. This study presented the design of an integrated renewable energy system with hydrogen storage for a unique mobile and autonomous 3D printing system for construction printing. The system has been designed to fulfil the off-grid energy requirement, such as material synthesis, printing, computation, communication, and surveillance/monitoring. The designed energy system has been analysed to produce a 3D printed structure with two different local materials; Construction and Demolishing Waste (CDW) based geopolymer concrete and direct printing of local materials. Due to the energy-intensive process and higher energy requirement for the pre-processing of waste to produce geopolymers, the designed system is more favourable for the direct printing of local materials. With the designed steady-state standard operating conditions the designed integrated system of 5.36kW can print 2.86m^3 of the final structure from direct printing of local material and 0.22m^3 of geopolymer based concrete structure in 24 hours. The analyse feasibility and production capacity of the designed system, and the overall performance of the system are also analysed for varying solar irradiance (I) conditions.
Keywords: 3D construction, Integrated renewable energy system, Hydrogen storage, Mobile 3D printing.

#1624

NEGATIVE EMISSIONS TECHNOLOGY FOR CLEAN ENERGY GENERATION: HYDROGEN PRODUCTION VIA DIRECT AIR CAPTURE OF CO_2

[1]*Ahmed Sodiqa,*[2] *Muftah El-Naasb and* [1]*Abdulkarem Amhamed**
[1]Qatar Environment and Energy Institute (QEERI), Hamad Bin Khalifa University, Doha, Qatar.
[2]Gas Processing Center (GPC), Qatar University, Doha, Qatar.
*Corresponding author e-mail: aamhamed@hbku.edu.qa

ABSTRACT

Direct air capture (DAC) has been reported as one of the negative emissions technologies (NETs) to deliver the needed carbon dioxide removal (between 100 and 1000 $GtCO_2$) from the atmosphere by the year 2100 to keep the global warming at ~1.5 °C more than the pre-industrial era. This is necessary to avoid catastrophic climate change challenges that may occur if the current global mean temperature reaches 2 °C above the pre-industrial era. As interesting as DAC is in achieving the desired carbon removal objectives, the cost of DAC is still very high if the captured CO_2 is not utilized to produce high-value commodities. Hydrogen is the next generation energy, more and more research are being carried out to solve the problems associated with its storage. However, a more convenient pathway to utilize hydrogen is using other compounds as hydrogen carriers, which comes with selecting compounds that release hydrogen easily when perturbed and have high value ratio such as platform chemicals. Formic acid is a hydrogen carrier with a high value ratio that is comparable to ethylene glycol and acrylic acid. Its production from CO_2 via electrochemical technique is well established in the literature, although most of the reported CO_2 feedstock is not from DAC. In our group, we are carrying out research activities to utilize captured CO_2 from DAC for formic acid production as a hydrogen carrier. In this presentation, Qatari as well as global strategies in climate change mitigation will be presented. The strategies will involve direct air capture of CO_2 via traditional heating, ventilation and air conditioning (HVAC) systems (mainly the air conditioning system) and the conversion of captured CO_2 to formic acid for hydrogen generation.

#1625

THERMODYNAMIC ASSESSMENT OF A NEW SMALL MODULAR REACTOR FOR HYDROGEN AND ELECTRICITY

[1*] *Ieeba Khan,* [2] *Farrukh Khalid*
[1]Indian Institute of Technology, Delhi, India
[2] Department of Mechanical Engineering, Istinye University, Topkapi Kampüsü, Teyyareci Sami, Sk. No.3, 34010, Zeytinburnu, Istanbul, Turkey
*Corresponding author e-mail: farrukh.khalid@ontariotechu.net

ABSTRACT

In this paper, a technological assessment of a small modular nuclear reactor system for hydrogen and electricity is presented. Energy and exergy analyses are being used to make the technological assessment by evaluating the efficiencies namely, energy and exergy efficiencies. A three-step thermochemical cycle based on aluminum is being used for hydrogen production. Heat and electricity from the nuclear reactor are being used to run the thermochemical cycle. Simulation results show that one can produce 2.2 tonnes of hydrogen daily with an electric input of 190 MW.

Keywords: Energy, Hydrogen, Thermochemical, Integrated system, Thermodynamic

#1626

DESIGN OF A NEW HELICAL METHANE FIXED BED- REACTOR

**Andre Bolt, Ibrahim Dincer and Martin Agelin-Chaab*
Clean Energy Research Laboratory (CERL), Faculty of Engineering and Applied Science, Ontario Tech. University, 2000 Simcoe Street North, Oshawa, Ontario L1H 7K4, Canada
* Corresponding author's email: Andre.Bolt@ontariotechu.ca

ABSTRACT

In this study, the design of a new fixed-bed reactor is proposed and examined through computational fluid dynamics. The design follows a unique helical design to maximize the amount of surface area that is exposed and to reduce the need for gas recycling. The heat distribution through the reactor is measured using the surface temperature before and after cooling takes place. Additionally, the mole ratio of all of the species used in the reaction is measured along the length of the reactor. The numerical simulations reveal that less than 1 kW of cooling is sufficient to significantly reduce the temperature of the reactor and that an H_2 conversion of approximately 84% can be achieved.

Keywords: Hydrogen, Natural Gas, Methane, CFD, Reactor analysis.

Track 10.

Power to Gas

#63

GREEN HYDROGEN PRODUCTION IN HYDROPOWER STATION

[1]El Manaa Barhoumi, [2]Ikram Ben Belgacem, [3]Paul C. Okonkwo, [1]Manaf Zghaibeh*

[1] Department of Electrical and Computer Engineering, Dhofar University, Salalah, Oman

[2] Laboratoire de Génie Mécanique, Ecole Nationale d'Ingénieurs de Monastir, Université de Monastir, Monastir, Tunisia

[3] Department of Mechanical and Mechatronics Engineering, Dhofar University, Salalah, Oman

*Corresponding author e-mail: ebarhoumi@du.edu.om

ABSTRACT

The development of green hydrogen production processes is highly praised due to its advantages in environment protection and economy growth. Within this framework, this paper discusses the feasibility of hydrogen production in small hydroelectric power stations. The system is based on the conversion of water fall energy into electrical power and hydrogen gas. The water is stored in tanks located at adequate level. When valves are opened, the falling water is used to run small hydro-turbines to produce electrical energy. The produced electrical energy is converted into hydrogen through electrolysis process. Therefore, the produced hydrogen will be used for refuelling fuel cell vehicles or any other applications. A hydropower station daily capacity of 108 000 cubic meter allows to produce 847 584 kg of hydrogen per year. The total capacity of the hydropower station is 21.18 MW. The estimated cost of the project depends on the cost of civil works, hydro turbines, electrolysers, water, and hydrogen tanks.

Keywords: Green hydrogen, Hydropower, Levelized cost

#66

FUTURE ECONOMIC PERSPECTIVE OF POWER-TO-GAS SYSTEM BASED ON MOLTEN CARBONATE ELECTROLYZER

*[1]Dayan Monzer, [1]*Chakib Bouallou*

(MINES ParisTech, PSL - Research University, CES - Centre d'Efficacité Energétique des Systèmes), 60 Boulevard Saint Michel, 75006 Paris, France

*Corresponding author e-mail: chakib.bouallou@mines-paristech.fr

ABSTRACT

A Power-to-gas system based on high-temperature electrolysis is a feasible and environmental approach to convert low-carbon electrical energy into chemical energy stored in the form of synthetic gas (H_2 & CO). The most desirable application is to convert the syngas into synthetic fuel. The overall process is currently being studied using two different electrolyzers: Solid Oxide Electrolyzer and Molten Carbonate Electrolyzer. This work focuses on the Power to Methane technology using high-temperature Molten Carbonates electrolysis cells (MCEC). It aims to investigate the economic feasibility of the overall process in the methane production. For this purpose, a rigorous parametric study is conducting by developing a VBA excel code to acquire a better knowledge of the cost drivers of the methane production cost. This overall study revealed that if more effort is put into reducing cell and operating costs, this technology might become competitive with conventional methane production technologies. A perspective towards the future revealed that the operating cost, mainly represented by the renewable electricity cost, could attain the required target. However, estimating the time required to have an economically competitive power-to-gas plant is challenging due to the lack of data on the MCEC cell cost and its roadmap.

Keywords: Power-to-gas, Molten carbonate electrolysis cell, Economic assessment

#76

A NOVEL COMBINED BIOMASS-BASED HYDROGEN/AMMONIA PRODUCTION AND RENEWABLES MULTI-GENERATION SYSTEM

[1,2]Du Wen, [2]Muhammad Aziz*
[1] Department of Mechanical Engineering, The University of Tokyo, 7-3-1 Hongo, Bunkyo-ku, Tokyo Japan
[2] Institute of Industrial Science, The University of Tokyo, 4-6-1 Komaba, Meguro-ku, Tokyo 153-8505, Japan
*Corresponding author e-mail: maziz@iis.u-tokyo.ac.jp

ABSTRACT
In this study, a novel integrated renewable multi-generation system is designed to provide constant baseload electricity (20 MW). Biomass-based hydrogen production is involved to facilitate short-term energy storage and negative carbon. Ammonia is seen as a long-term energy storage method to store excess hydrogen. The maximum energy and exergy efficiencies are 46.7% and 66.1%, respectively. The total energy outputs of solar and wind subsystems are 44,779 kWh and 103,391 kWh, respectively. The annual ammonia yield is 28,764 t and the annual carbon capture is 97,866 t.
Keywords: Solar, Wind, Biomass, Hydrogen, Ammonia

#111

TOWARDS ELECTRIFYING CEMENT PRODUCTION BY ELECTROCHEMICALLY-ENHANCED DISSOLUTION OF CACO3 DURING WATER ELECTROLYSIS UNDER A PH-GRADIENT

[1]Rémy Rouxhet, [1]Renaud Delmelle, [1]Joris Proost*
[1]Université catholique de Louvain, Division of Materials and Process engineering, 1348 Louvain-La-Neuve, Belgium
*Corresponding author e-mail: remy.rouxhet@uclouvain.be

ABSTRACT
The cement industry, which accounts for 7-8% of worldwide CO_2 emissions, is essential to decarbonize but challenging especially due to its high process emissions, high temperature heat requirements and low maturity of decarbonization solutions. A new electrochemical path to produce calcium hydroxide, a precursor of cement, has been proposed recently. This technology is based on a new design of a water electrolyser working in tri-phase environment. It has the potential to electrify cement production while at the same time producing valuable gases, but is still at a very early stage of development (TRL-3). In this paper, lab-scale experiments in a 200mL cell were performed to have a better understanding of the electrochemical system. The development of a pH gradient between the anode and the cathode has been quantified for different electric charges applied. Due to acidification of the anode side, the dissolution of calcium carbonate is enhanced. A solubility ten times higher than at neutral pH has been observed. At the same time, the migration of Ca^{2+} and OH^- ions to respectively the cathodic and anodic side has been demonstrated as well, thereby opening the way for an electrochemically-enhanced $Ca(OH)_2$ precipitation.
Keywords: Electrolysis, Electrification, Cement, Hydrogen

#125

BUTADIENE PRODUCTION VIA THE DIRECT DEHYDROGENATION OF N-BUTANE IN MEMBRANE REACTORS: A TECHNO-ECONOMIC ANALYSIS

[1]Camilla Brencio, [1,2]Martina Maruzzi, [2]Giampaolo Manzolini, [1,3]Fausto Gallucci*
[1]Inorganic Membranes and Membrane Reactors, Sustainable Process Engineering, Department of Chemical Engineering and Chemistry, Eindhoven University of Technology, De Rondom 70, Eindhoven, 5612 AP, NL
[2]Group of Energy Conversion Systems, Department of Energy, Politecnico di Milano, Milano, Italy
[3]Eindhoven Institute for Renewable Energy Systems (EIRES), Eindhoven University of Technology, PO Box 513, Eindhoven 5600 MB, the Netherlands
*Corresponding author e-mail: F.Gallucci@tue.nl

ABSTRACT
The direct dehydrogenation of butane (BDH) is emerging as an attractive on-purpose technology for the direct production of 1,3-butadine. However, its product yield is hindered by the high rate of carbon deposition associated to the high temperature required for the highly endothermic reaction. In this work, we evaluated the use of membrane reactor with H_2-selective membranes, to increase the yield of the dehydrogenation process at milder operating conditions. The novel proposed membrane reactor (MR)-assisted BDH technology is compared from a techno-economic point of view with the benchmark technology. The results of this analysis reveal that the membrane reactor technology allows to maintain same production capacity as the benchmark technology, working at milder operating conditions and most importantly lowering the required shale gas-based feedstock; this will result in an overall plant efficiency almost 20% higher in the MR-assisted plant, being equal to 37.7% with respect to the one of the benchmark case, which is 50.92%. This work demonstrates that MR-assisted technology is a valuable alternative to the conventional BDH technology, reducing of almost 20% the final cost of production of 1,3-butadiene, due to the lower installation costs and the higher energy efficiency.
Keywords: Butane dehydrogenation process, Butadiene production, Membrane reactors, Hydrogen removal, Techno-economic analysis

#141

NOVEL EMERGENCY GAS-TO-POWER MH-STORAGE AND FUEL CELL SYSTEM: MODELING AND EXPERIMENTAL VALIDATION

[1,]David Michael Dreistadt, [1,2]Julián Puszkiel, [1]José M. Bellosta von Colbe, [1]Giovanni Capurso, [3]Gerd Steinebach, [3]Stefanie Meilinger, [1]Thi Thu Le, [2]Myriam Covarrubias Guarneros, [1,2]Thomas Klassen, [1,2]Julian Jepsen*

[1]Institute of Hydrogen Technology, Helmholtz-Zentrum hereon GmbH, Max-Planck-Straße 1, D-21502 Geesthacht, Germany

[2]Helmut Schmidt University, Holstenhofweg 85, 22043 Hamburg, Germany

[3]Hochschule Bonn-Rhein-Sieg, Institut für Technik Ressourcenschonung und Energieeffizienz, Grantham-Allee 20, 53757 Sankt Augustin, Germany

*Corresponding author e-mail: David.Dreistadt@hereon.de

ABSTRACT

A gas-to-power (GtoP) system for power outages is digitally modeled and experimentally developed in this work. The design includes a solid-state hydrogen storage system based on TiFeMn as a hydride forming alloy (5 tanks, total capacity: 110 g H_2) and an air-cooled fuel cell (maximum power: 1.6 kW). In an emergency use case of the system, hydrogen is supplied to the fuel cell, and the waste heat coming from the exhaust air of the fuel cell is used for the endothermic dehydrogenation reaction of the metal hydride. This GtoP system shows fast, stable, and reliable responses from 149 W to 596 W under constant and dynamic conditions. The developed model is based on a network approach, and it is validated under static and dynamic power load scenarios, showing excellent agreement with the experimental results.

Keywords: Gas to power, Hydrides, Hydrogen storage, Fuel cell, Modeling, Hydrogen

#188

PROCESS IMPLICATIONS OF ELECTRIFYING AMMONIA PRODUCTION

[1]Antoine Dechany, [2]Vladimir Galvita, [2]Kevin Van Geem, [1]Joris Proost*

[1] Université catholique de Louvain, Division of Materials and Processes Science, Place Ste Barbe 2, Louvain-la-Neuve, Belgium

[2] Universiteit Gent, Laboratory for Chemical Technology, Technologiepark 125, B-9025, Ghent, Belgium

*Corresponding author e-mail: antoine.dechany@uclouvain.be

ABSTRACT

The current ammonia production plants - Steam Methane Reforming (SMR) and Haber-Bosch (HB) - are responsible for 1.2% of global CO_2 emissions. As more sectors are shifting to electrification, so does the NH_3 industry as shown by the amount of studies focusing on electrolysers and Pressure Swing Adsorbers (PSA) to replace SMR. Haber-Bosch itself is being questioned as a new alternative technology is emerging: Chemical Looping (CL). Such transformations imply changes to the current process. This work assesses such implications by comparing 2 alternative scenarios with the conventional case. In terms of emissions, the electrification is clearly benefic with a cut of 74-95% when using wind energy. The replacement of SMR by electrolysers and PSA also improves the energy efficiency, as >60% of the energy consumption in conventional plants originates from the compressors and heat integration. Finally, the combination of Alkaline Electrolysers (AE) and CL is determined as the most suitable for small-scall flexible and economical installations.

Keywords: Ammonia synthesis, Hydrogen production, Electrolysis, Electrification, Green hydrogen

#207

SENSITIVITY ANALYSIS OF INDEPENDENT PARAMETERS FOR FORMATION OF NO_x EMISSION IN HYDROGEN ENRICHED COMPRESSED NATURAL GAS ALONG WITH EXHAUST GAS RECIRCULATION BY SUPPORT VECTOR MACHINE

[1,2]*Anas Rao*, [1] *Yongzhen Liu*, [1*]*Fanhua Ma*
[1] State Key Laboratory of Automobile Safety and Energy, Tsinghua University, Beijing, 100084, China
[2]Department of Mechanical Engineering, University of Engineering & Technology Lahore, Pakistan
*Corresponding author e-mail: anasrao986@gmail.com

ABSTRACT

The utilization of hydrogen fuel in internal combustion engine is one step towards the implementation of zero-carbon foot print. The main drawback is higher PPM of NOx emission. Numerous techniques are applied by different researchers to bring NOx emission under EURO-VI emission standards. The experiments have been performed at different spark timings (0 to 60°CA bTDC), hydrogen percentages (0 to 40%) in CNG fuel, EGR rates (0 to 35.8%), MAP (65 to 178 kPa), speed (700 to 2000 rpm) at *lambda* = 1.0. The simulation of NO_x emission has been conducted by support vector machine. The sensitivity analysis has been carried out for the selection of best combination of input variables for the formation of NOx emissions that are: controllable parameters (MAP, hydrogen fractions in CNG, EGR rate, spark timing & RPM) and combustion parameters (maximum pressure, IMEP, adiabatic flame temperature, HRR & COV). The minimum mean absolute percentage error is 7.6996% & MRE is 57.05 corresponding to the best combination (RPM-MAP-ST-EGR-P_{max}/T_{ad}).
Keywords: Hydrogen enriched compressed natural gas, NOx emission, Support vector machine

#229

CO_2 METHANATION OVER BIMETALLIC NICKEL-NOBLE METAL CATALYSTS

[1]*Anastasios I. Tsiotsias*, [1]*Nikolaos D. Charisiou*, [2]*Giovanni D. Ferrante*, [2*]*Cristina Italiano*, [2]*Antonio Vita*, [3]*Victor Sebastian*, [1*]*Maria A. Goula*
[1] Laboratory of Alternative Fuels and Environmental Catalysis (LAFEC), Department of Chemical Engineering, University of Western Macedonia, GR-50100 Kozani, Greece
[2] CNR-ITAE, Institute for Advanced Energy Technologies “Nicola Giordano”, Via S. Lucia sopra Contesse 5, 98126, Messina, Italy
[3] Chemical and Environmental Engineering Department, Instituto de Nanocienza de Aragón (INA) and Instituto de Cienza de Materiales de Aragón (ICMA), Universidad de Zaragoza-CSIC, Zaragoza, Spain
*Corresponding author e-mail: mgoula@uowm.gr; cristina.italiano@itae.cnr.it

ABSTRACT

The CO_2 methanation reaction was investigated over bimetallic Ni-NM catalysts supported on Pr-doped CeO_2, where NM represents a noble metal (NM = Ru, Pt, Rh, Pd and Ir). 10% Ni and 1% NM were loaded over a mesoporous Pr-CeO_2 support via co-impregnation and directly reduced at 400°C, without prior calcination. The prepared catalysts were characterized via XRD, N_2-physisorption and HAADF-STEM along with EDS mapping. The addition of 1% Ru and Rh was shown to improve the dispersion of the metallic Ni phase and reduce pore blockage upon impregnation. Catalytic activity evaluation revealed that the addition of 1% Ru led to a remarkable increase in the catalytic activity, especially at lower temperatures. Pt and Ir addition led to minor changes in activity, whereas Rh and Pd incorporation surprisingly reduced CO_2 conversion. The most active 1% Ru, 10% Ni/ Pr-CeO_2 catalyst was shown to be particularly stable over a 50h time-on-stream experiment at 325°C, with CO_2 conversion and CH_4 selectivity values at 80% and 99.5% respectively.

Keywords: Power-to-Gas, Synthetic natural gas, CO_2 methanation, Bimetallic catalysts, Noble metals

#249

HYDROGEN AS ENERGY STORAGE FOR RESOLVING ELECTRICITY GRID ISSUES IN INDONESIA

[1]Arif Darmawan, [2]Muhammad Huda, [1] Eniya Listiani Dewi, [1]Abdul Hamid Budiman, [1]Abdul Hadi, [1]Kurniawan, [3]Muhammad Aziz*

[1]National Research and Innovation Agency, Tangerang Selatan, Indonesia.
[2] The Center of Certification Indonesian State Electric Company (PT PLN) Jakarta Selatan, Indonesia.
[3] Institute of Industrial Science, The University of Tokyo, Japan
*Corresponding author e-mail: arif.darmawan@brin.go.id

ABSTRACT

According to many studies, economic growth is closely correlated with energy consumption. Specifically, electricity is required in the regional development to support all residential, government, or private agencies and industrial sectors. Unfortunately, because of unexpected low demand due to a complex economic system, the increase in power generation is predicted to result in an oversupply. Power-to-Gas is a vital part of a future renewable energy system to convert water into hydrogen. Surplus electricity can be utilized by adopting this technology via the electrolysis of water to produce hydrogen; therefore, it can be stored or converted into other energy carriers. The pre-feasibility of investing in hydrogen production is investigated in the Java-Bali grid of the Indonesian power system, considering volatilities and future uncertainties in the region as background. Some scenarios are evaluated for different parameters such as electricity demand projection, electrolyzer cost and efficiency, including plant capacity factor. With a very large electrolyzer, operating with an efficiency of about 70% for about 8000 hours per year, the annual hydrogen production potential would be 600-900 Mt of hydrogen, assuming 50-80 kWh could produce 1 Kg of H_2. A proper approach to the cost reduction in raw material procurement, power generation, and related H_2 facilities should be taken and established. Therefore, the overall H_2 production cost can be minimized. Further investigation will be conducted for storage scenarios, including distribution strategies.
Keywords: Hydrogen, Power-to-Gas, Surplus electricity, Electrolyzer

#343

AN MINLP-BASED OPTIMAL DESIGN AND SCHEDULING OF A POWER TO GAS SYSTEM INTEGRATED MICROGRID: A CASE STUDY FROM TURKEY

[1,2] Handan Akülker, [2,3,4] Erdal Aydın*

[1]Ondokuz Mayıs University, Department of Chemical Engineering, Kurupelit, 55139, Samsun,
[2] Boğaziçi University, Department of Chemical Engineering, Bebek, 34342, İstanbul, Turkey
[3] Koç University, Department of Chemical and Biological Engineering, Sarıyer, 34450, İstanbul, Turkey
[4] Koç University, Tüpraş Energy Center, Sarıyer, 34450, İstanbul, Turkey
*Corresponding author e-mail: eaydin@ku.edu.tr

ABSTRACT

A microgrid is a power network section including distributed generators, storage systems, and loads. A "*Power to Gas*" (PtG) system is a rising technology that produces synthetic methane (or similar gas) by using electricity and carbon dioxide extracted from the flue gases. Recently, Turkey has been preparing to make strict sanctions on energy producers to decrease the greenhouse gas emissions due to the Paris Agreement. Additionally, it is struggling with the outage of imported natural gas. Accordingly, PtG systems may handle both the problems of natural gas shortages and carbon dioxide emissions. This study aims to propose methods to optimally design and schedule a PtG system integrated microgrid by Mixed-Integer Nonlinear Programming (MINLP). PtG system is assumed to be installed, whereas other equipment, consisting of renewable and non-renewable sourced generators and a battery, is nominated as selection candidates. Two different integrated gasification combined cycle generators and one combined heat and power generator are selected to be installed. The model does not prefer to choose renewable sourced generators, such as wind turbines and solar panels, for the investigated location due to fixed and maintenance costs, weather conditions, and demand levels.

Keywords: Power to Gas, Microgrid, Carbon dioxide emission, MINLP, Optimal design and scheduling

#359

HEAT SOURCE FREE CO_2 METHANATION OVER HYDROGEN STORAGE ALLOY

[1,2,3*] *Keito Sawahara,* [3,4] *Ryota Gemma,* [1,2]*Hajime Kawanami*
[1]University of Tsukuba, Degree Programs in Pure and Applied Sciences, 1-1-1 Tennodai, Tsukuba Ibaraki, Japan
[2]National Institute of Advanced Industrial Science and Technology (AIST), 1-1-1 Higashi, Tsukuba, Ibaraki, Japan
[3]Tokai University, Graduate School of Engineering, 4-1-1 Kita-kaname, Hiratsuka, Kanagawa, Japan
[4]Tokai University, Department of Applied Chemistry, 4-1-1 Kita-kaname, Hiratsuka, Kanagawa, Japan
*Corresponding author e-mail: k-saw@star.tokai-iu.jp

ABSTRACT

Recently, CO_2 methanation has gained attention for mitigating global warming. In our previous study, it has been demonstrated that the methanation of CO_2 takes place by mechanochemical reaction under H_2+CO_2 atmospheric conditions if a small amount of hydrogen storage alloys like $LaNi_5$ are present. It has also been found that the $LaNi_5$ partially decomposed into La-oxides, hydroxides, carbonate, and metallic Ni formed metal/oxide nanostructure complex during the reaction. However, the impact of this decomposed structure on the CO_2 methanation itself has not been revealed yet. In this study, we attempted *in-situ* measurements of gas composition during the mechanochemical CO_2 methanation using ball mill connected with quadrupole mass spectrometer (QMS).

Keywords: Methanation, CO_2, $LaNi_5$, Hydrogen storage alloys

#402

INTEGRATED PLANNING TOOL FOR COST AND 3D STRUCTURAL PLANNING FOR OFFSHORE WIND FARMS FOR THE GENERATION OF H_2

Martin Hayduk [1], *Romy Sommer* [1], *Oliver Kühn* [2], *Florian Beuß* [2], *Wilko Flügge* [3], *Johannes Gulden* [1*]
[1]University of Applied Sciences Stralsund, Institute of Renewable Energy Systems (IRES),
Zur Schwedenschanze 15, 18435 Stralsund, Germany
[2]Fraunhofer Institute for Large Structures in Production Technology (IGP),
Albert Einstein Str. 30, 18059 Rostock, Germany
[3]University of Rostock, Chair of Manufacturing Technology,
Albert Einstein Str. 30, 18059 Rostock, Germany
* Corresponding author email: johannes.gulden@hochschule-stralsund.de

ABSTRACT

The planning of new offshore wind farms (OWP) is characterized by increasing complexity. In addition to technical factors like water depth, ground conditions, wind development, and others, there is also an increasing range of design options in the wind farm concept. This concerns in particular the integration of hydrogen into the value chain for offshore wind power. For the wind farm planner, the decision, whether a decentralized electrolysis is directly implemented at the wind farm or a centralized electrolysis is built at the harbor edge, is crucial. Again, the influencing factors are manifold. The cable length for shore connection, the potential storage and offtake of hydrogen close to the harbor edge, the hydrogen transport via pipelines or ships have to be considered.

To address this complexity, a planning tool is being developed that enables an evaluation of offshore wind farm options. The core of the tool is a holistic cost model for the installation of offshore wind farms for hydrogen production. Based on this, an interactive 3D planning tool is developed, which enables the flexible structural planning of new wind farms based on GIS data to be displayed in a VR environment. The interactive adjustment of the wind farm changes the cost drivers of the cost model. In addition, the land connection and associated transport routes are selected in the 3D model and transferred to the cost model. The wind farm planner directly sees the impact of changes on the total costs. Thus, the system helps in the design and structural planning of new offshore wind farms as well as the conversion planning of existing offshore wind farms for hydrogen generation. Here we present the first results of this ongoing project.

Keywords: Planning tool, Offshore wind farm, Hydrogen

#406

METHANATION OF CO_2 OVER LANI$_5$/V LAYERED FILM

[1]Shuichi Kaneta, [1]Haruya Baba, [2]Sota Yamada, [1,2]Ryota Gemma*

[1] Graduate School of Engineering, Tokai University, 4-1-1 Kitakaname, Hiratsuka, Kanagawa, 259-1292, Japan

[2] Department of Materials Science, Tokai University, 4-1-1 Kitakaname, Hiratsuka, Kanagawa, 259-1292, Japan

* Corresponding author email: sh.knt99.udon.180315@gmail.com

ABSTRACT

In this study, the effect of underlying V film on the CO_2 methanation on $LaNi_5$ surface was investigated using a quadrupole mass spectrometer, using a stacked film of LaNi-based thin film as a catalyst layer on top of a V layer as a hydrogen supply layer. It was confirmed that CO_2 methanation over thin film samples can be experimentally observed. Also, the underlying V layer was found to absorb hydrogen, thereby possibly prevented severe oxidation of La and concomitant phase decomposition of the $LaNi_5$ upper layer in to La oxide and Ni.

Keywords: CO_2 methanation, Hydrogen, Hydrogen storage alloys

#407

CO_2 METHANATION OVER SURFACE MODIFIED LANI$_5$ FILMS WITH PD

[1]Haruya Baba, [1]Shuichi Kaneta, [2]Sota Yamada, [2]Ayataka Motoshige, [1,2]Ryota Gemma*

[1] Graduate School of Engineering, Tokai University, Kitakaname 4-1-1, Hiratsuka City, Kanagawa, 259-1292, Japan

[2] Department of Material Science, Tokai University, Kitakaname 4-1-1, Hiratsuka City, Kanagawa, 259-1292, Japan

*Corresponding author e-mail: bbharukb@icloud.com

ABSTRACT

Recent increase in the concentration of carbon dioxide (CO_2) in the atmosphere has led to global warming. For mitigating the increase in atmospheric CO_2, CO_2 methanation using hydrogen (H_2) has been proposed. In this study, we attempted to convert CO_2 into methane using $LaNi_5$ alloy thin films prepared by DC magnetron sputtering. The surface was decollated with palladium (Pd) islands, which is known as a hydrogen dissociation catalyst. Monitoring of gas species in the reaction chamber by quadrupole mass spectroscopy revealed successful methane generation over the film sample. The findings from such thin film samples with artificially formed interfaces as attempted in this study can be translated to the design of catalysts in powder form, in search of more efficient methanation catalysts.

Keywords: Thin Film, $LaNi_5$, Methanation, Palladium

#417

PRELIMINARY DESIGN AND FLOWSHEETING OF A SABATIER BASED POWER-TO-GAS SYSTEM WITH INTEGRAL HEAT RECOVERY AND DOWNSTREAM SYNGAS CLEANING

R.Capata[a], R.Melli[b], E.Sciubba[c]

a: roberto.capata@uniroma1.it; b: xpertsystems@mpessrl.it; c: enrico.sciubba@unicusano.it

ABSTRACT

The present global energy scenario -and the consequences of the invasion of Ukraine- forces researchers, designers and policymakers to face the technical and economic challenges of an unavoidable and urgent mitigation of global Greenhouse gas (GHG) emissions. Such emissions from anthropogenic sources have been continuously growing since the beginning of the industrial revolution. The perturbing potential of these GHG emissions on the natural atmospheric concentration cycle might trigger, or at least hasten, an amplification of the global climate change.

Besides continuous efforts to improve the efficiency of combustion processes and the recourse to "CO_2 neutral" secondary fuels, the only feasible path -at least in the so-called "transition phase" towards a less unsustainable energy scenario- is the implementation of CO_2 capture and storage solutions. Since Thermodynamics teaches us that in the energy conversion arena "there is no free lunch", technical feasibility must be combined with economical positive returns, and thus the energy community must address the problem of the high CO_2 sequestration costs.

Sabatier based power-to-gas systems are potential answers for this issue, and this paper describes the modelling, process design and simulation of a CO_2 methanation plant based on the Sabatier reaction. To cure one of the problems of this technology, namely its low overall conversion efficiency, an exergy-based optimization of the thermal recovery within the system boundary was introduced. The results of our study demonstrate the great technical and economic potential of this solution as an H_2-mediated "energy storage" and CO_2 capture facility.

Keywords: CO_2 methanation, Hydrogen Cyclic Storage, Energy Recovery, Sustainable Energy

#438

POWER TO X: THE CRUCIAL SOLUTION ON THE WAY OF TUNISIAN ENERGY TRANSITION AND SUSTAINABLE DEVELOPMENT

[1]S. Salhi, [1*]E. Znouda, [1*]C. Bouden*
[1]Université de Tunis El Manar, Ecole Nationale d'Ingénieurs de Tunis, LR - 11-ES16 (LR – MOED – ENIT), 1002, Tunis, Tunisie
*Corresponding author e-mail: sana.salhi@enit.rnu.tn; essia.znouda@enit.utm.tn; chiheb.bouden@enit.rnu.tn

ABSTRACT
This paper investigates the importance of Power to X (PtX) implementation in the Tunisian Electricity System. The considered technologies are electrolysis and methanation. Electrolysis converts the overflow of renewable electricity into chemical energy by storing electrons in the form of stable chemical bonds. Therefore Hydrogen gas (H_2) is produced. A defined percentage of H_2 is directly conducted to the natural gas pipelines while the rest is associated to CO_2 molecule to produce Methane gas (CH_4 is the major constituent of natural gas). This process is called methanation. This research study is based on Osemosys (Open Source Energy Modeling System) modelling and simulation. Different scenarios of renewable energy development schemes (Business as usual, optimistic and pessimistic scenarios) are also developed and discussed. The obtained results show that green Hydrogen gained from renewable energy sources via electrolysis can stand for the key to net-zero emissions and sustainable development target in Tunisia.
Keywords: Power to X; Green hydrogen; Zero CO_2 emissions; Osemosys

#1500

METHODS STUDY OF ECONOMIC AND TECHNICAL ANALYSIS OF POWER-TO-GAS INTEGRATED ENERGY SYSTEM

[1]Honglin Wang*
[1]The University of Sydney, Department of Electrical Engineering, Sydney, Australia
*Corresponding author e-mail: hwan5836@uni.sydney.edu.au

ABSTRACT
The application of power-to-gas technology can effectively solve the problem of power abandonment of renewable energy. However, the economics of power-to-gas technology will affect whether the technology can be applied in practical projects. Existing literature has massive technical and economic analysis methods of power-to-gas technology. This paper re-analyzes the existing methods, proposes a modeling method for simplifying power-to-gas integrated energy system, and introduces the return on investment into the economic evaluation of the system.
Keywords: Power to gas technology, Integrated energy system, P2G, Power generation economics

#1536

INFLUENCE OF BIOGAS COMPOSITION TO CATALYTIC METHANATION PROCESS

[1,2]Jan Kulas, [1]Lukáš Polák, [1]Aleš Doucek*
[1] ÚJV Řež, plc., Department of Hydrogen Technologies, Hlavní 130, Husinec-Řež, Czech Republic
[2] University of Chemistry and Technology, Department of Gaseous and Solid Fuels and Air Protection, Technická 5, Prague, Czech Republic
*Corresponding author e-mail: jan.kulas@ujv.cz

ABSTRACT

It is expected that generation of electricity from renewable energy sources will significantly increase in the next decades. As a basic assumption for successful integration of renewable energy, any large-scale and long-term energy storage system will be needed. Power-to-Gas (P2G) technology is often mentioned as a promising solution. The surplus of electricity can be used for electrolytic hydrogen production. In the second step, the synthetic natural gas (SNG) is produced via catalytic hydrogenation of carbon dioxide. Experiments based on direct biogas methanation show, that this technology provides an effective way of production storable and transportable energy medium. Once national SNG quality requirements are met, the existing natural gas infrastructure give a massive energy storage system.
Keywords: Power-to-Gas, Methanation, Biogas, Synthetic natural gas, Biogas upgrading

#1616

TECHNO-ECONOMIC PERFORMANCE ASSESSMENT OF A REACTOR SYSTEM USED FOR POWER-TO-METHANE PLANT

[1,2,3*]*Alper Can Ince*, [4]*C. Ozgur Colpan*, [5]*Ali Keles*, [1]*Mustafa Fazil Serincan*, [2,3]*Ugur Pasaogullari*
[1]Gebze Technical University, Faculty of Engineering, Mechanical Engineering Department, Gebze, Kocaeli, 41400, Turkey
[2]Center for Clean Energy Engineering, University of Connecticut, Storrs, CT 06269-5233, United States
[3]Department of Mechanical Engineering, University of Connecticut, Storrs, CT 06269-4602, United States
[4]Dokuz Eylul University, Faculty of Engineering, Mechanical Engineering Department, Buca, Izmir, 35397, Turkey
[5]GKE Energy R&D Center, Milas, Muğla, 48200, Turkey
*Corresponding author e-mail: alper_can.ince@uconn.edu

ABSTRACT

The interest in methane production from the utilization of electricity and hydrogen, also well-known as power-to-methane (PtM), has increased significantly in the last decades. A typical PtM system mainly consists of an electrolyzer (for hydrogen production) that is powered by a renewable power production technology, such as a solar PV module, a CO_2 source and a chemical reactor for methane production. In this study, the sizing of a PtM system is first performed based on the operating strategy that relies on the avoidance of hydrogen storage and selection of appropriate hydrogen content of syngas and catalyst loading in the reactor. Then, thermodynamic analysis is performed for this system. Finally, cost analysis is conducted for new reactor installation considering sizing and thermodynamic performance of the system. The combined simulation shows that the electrical efficiency is found as 50-55 % according to various operating conditions. The syngas production rate decreases even though the methane content of syngas increases when the operating pressure of the reactor decreases. Moreover, the total investment cost decreases from 4,354,200 $ to 3,470,200 $ when the reactor pressure increase from 1 bar to 7 bar.

Keywords: Power-to-methane, Syngas, Cost analysis, Economic model, Methane reactor

Track 11.

Hydrogen Safety

#8

COMPUTATIONAL INVESTIGATION OF PREMIXED HYDROGEN-AIR FLAMES STABILIZED IN DIVERGING ANNULAR CHANNEL

*[1] *Ali Cemal Benim, Björn Pfeiffelmann*
Duesseldorf University of Applied Sciences, Faculty of Mechanical and Process Engineering, Center of Flow Simulation (CFS), Muenstersrasse, 156, D-40476 Duesseldorf, Germany
*Corresponding author e-mail: alicemal@prof-benim.com

ABSTRACT

Atmospheric, laminar, premixed flames of hydrogen and air are computationally investigated in an annular diverging channel. This used configuration closely resembles the one that was recently used in a series of experimental studies to obtain the burning velocities and quenching distances for premixed flames of different fuels, including hydrogen. Three different equivalence ratios are considered. Global and detailed reaction mechanisms are adopted to describe the combustion process. For ensuring an adequately fine resolution of the flame fronts, local adaptive grid refinement techniques are applied to track the flame front. The goal of the current analysis is the validation of the applied prediction procedures by comparing them with the experimental results. To this purpose, the predicted burning speeds and quenching distances are compared with the measured values.

Keywords: Hydrogen Combustion, Premixed Flame, Flame Speed, Quenching Distance, Computational Fluid Dynamics

#55

MESH-INDEPENDENT LARGE-EDDY SIMULATION WITH ANISOTROPIC ADAPTIVE MESH REFINEMENT FOR HYDROGEN DEFLAGRATION PREDICTION IN LARGE-SCALE VENTED VESSELS

[1*] *Lucian Ivan,* [2] *Mohamad Khalil,* [2] *Clinton P.T. Groth,* [1] *Zhe Liang*
[1] Canadian Nuclear Laboratories, 286 Plant Road, Chalk River, Canada
[2] University of Toronto Institute for Aerospace Studies, 4925 Dufferin Street, Toronto, Canada
*Corresponding author e-mail: lucian.ivan@utoronto.ca

ABSTRACT

The use of high-fidelity simulation methods based on large-eddy simulation (LES) are proving useful for understanding and mitigating the safety hazards associated with hydrogen release in nuclear facilities. However, accurate modeling of turbulent premixed hydrogen flames via LES can require very high resolution to capture both the large-scale turbulence and its interaction with the flame fronts. Standard meshing strategies can result in impractically high computational costs, especially for thin hydrogen flame fronts. The use of a recently formulated integral length scale approximation (ILSA) subfilter-scale model in combination with an efficient anisotropic block-based adaptive mesh refinement (AMR) technique is examined herein for performing LES of hydrogen flames in large-scale vented vessels. The proposed LES methodology has already been applied to simulations within closed vessels. The anisotropic AMR method resolves the flame fronts. The grid-independent properties of the ILSA model ensure that numerical errors associated with implicitly-filtered LES techniques in regions with varying spatial resolution, and hence filter widths as well, are avoided and therefore, formally converged LES solutions are allowed. The final paper will provide a detail description of the computational framework along with an assessment of the capabilities of the combined approach based on comparisons between predictions and experimental data.

Keywords: Large-Eddy Simulation, Adaptive Mesh Refinement, Integral Length Scale Approximation, Large-Scale Vented Vessels, Hydrogen Release In Nuclear Plants

#252

FAULT ANALYSIS AND SAFETY PROTECTION OF ON-BOARD HYDROGEN SUPPLY SYSTEM

[1]Xiujuan Cao, [1]Xingzi Yu, [2]Donghai Hu, [1*] Caizhi Zhang
[1] School of Automotive Engineering; The State Key Laboratory of Mechanical Transmissions; Chongqing Automotive Collaborative Innovation Centre, Chongqing University, Chongqing, China, 400044
[2] School of Automotive and Traffic Engineering, Jiangsu University, Zhenjiang 212013, China
*Corresponding author e-mail: czzhang@cqu.edu.cn

ABSTRACT

Fuel cell vehicle hydrogen supply system is an important part of fuel cell vehicle driving. Ensuring the safety of hydrogen supply system is very important for fuel cell vehicles. At present, the main safety problems in hydrogen supply system of fuel cell include hydrogen leakage, overtemperature and overpressure. In this paper, the fault tree is used to analyze the explosion caused by internal faults in the hydrogen system, and the safety protection for the hydrogen supply system is carried out. As the monitoring equipment of hydrogen supply system, hydrogen controller plays an important role in ensuring the safety of on-board hydrogen supply system. The safety status of hydrogen supply system is verified by hydrogen controller test.

Keywords: Hydrogen Supply System, Hydrogen Controller, Solenoid Valve, Fault Tree, Labview

#257

SAFETY STUDY AND CFD SIMULATION OF HYDROGEN LEAKS AND DISPERSION WITHIN SEMI ENCLOSED SPACE OF HYDROGEN FACILITY

[1*] Daniel Prasetyo, [2] Alberto Costilla Alvarez, [3] Alberto Frisa Rubio, [4] Aurora Garcia Jimenez
[1] CIRCE - (Research Centre for Energy Resources and Consumption), Avenida Ranillas, Edificio Dinamiza 3D, Zaragoza, Spain
*Corresponding author e-mail: dprasetyo@fcirce.es

ABSTRACT

Safety study and Computational Fluid Dynamics (CFD) simulation are conducted to analyze hydrogen leakage in semi -closed space of hydrogen facilities and installation in the framework of Cervera H24NEWAGE project. The goal of this study is to evaluate the hydrogen dispersion from release sources inside the building and to give detailed analysis of gas dispersion by using CFD in all areas, especially in some areas where there are highly potential leakages and inadequate flow ventilation due to some obstacles which could impede air recirculation in the zone. This study is useful to understand the dispersion of hydrogen release inside the building in order to implement best safety engineering practice for the new hydrogen facilities. In this study, hydrogen release is calculated by using UNE 60079-10 and considering other international standards such as API 505, and EIGA Doc 15/21. CFD simulations of different combinations of hydrogen release are done by varying pressure and opening area of release source with four air ventilation systems in operation. Velocity of air and concentration of hydrogen are calculated from the CFD model to hydrogen dispersion inside the building.

Keywords: Hydrogen Safety, Hydrogen Leakage, CFD Simulation, Air Ventilation

#280

TOWARD THE CONTINUOUS SENSING OF LEAKED HYDROGEN BY A QUAD-ROTOR DRONE

[1*]Takafumi Suga and [1*]Kazuo Matsuura
[1]Ehime University, Bunkyo-cho, Matsuyama, Ehime, 790-8577, Japan
*Corresponding author e-mail: matsuura.kazuo.mm@ehime-u.ac.jp

ABSTRACT

Hydrogen is expected to leak in a variety of situations, from production to consumption. To realize a hydrogen sensing system that is more flexible and quicker than conventional systems, we have proposed a new drone-based system for hydrogen sensing with a small hydrogen sensor of the semiconductor type. Initially, quad-rotor drones were thought to be unsuitable for hydrogen leak detection because hydrogen is pushed away from the drone by propeller downwash. However, recent CFD (Computational Fluid Dynamics)-analyses and experiments detecting hydrogen at a drone have shown that hydrogen leak detection is possible even under the propeller downwash. In particular, it has been found that the flow rises from the leak source to the propeller outside the propeller downwash. In this study, we investigate the mechanism of hydrogen sensing by the quad-rotor drone through direct measurement of hydrogen dispersion around the drone. For this purpose, hydrogen leak experiments were conducted and the path of hydrogen dispersion around the drone was analyzed by twenty hydrogen sensors installed on a lattice constructed around the drone. These results substantiate, for the first time as long as the authors know, the hydrogen sensing mechanism mentioned above and support that reliable drone sensing can be achieved.

Keywords: Hydrogen Safety, Sensing, Drone, CFD Analysis, Smoke-Visualization

#296

RISK EVALUATION OF HYDROGEN DISPERSION FROM COMPRESSED HYDROGEN (H_2) STORAGE VESSELS

[*1] Rafiziana Md. Kasmani, [2]Arshad Ahmad, Norafneeza Norazahar , Aishah Abd.Jalil, Tuan Amran Tuan Abdullah, Mohd. Fadzhir Ahmad Kamaroddin
Centre of Hydrogen Energy (CHE), Universiti Teknologi Malaysia, 81310 Johor Bahru, Johor, Malaysia.
*Corresponding author e-mail: rafiziana@utm.my

ABSTRACT

Demand for hydrogen fuel increases with the introduction of fuel cell electric vehicles, giving increased pressure to minimize refueling station footprints and lower costs while maintaining safety and performance. Compressed gas hydrogen (H_2) storage is a viable approach to assuring sufficient hydrogen capacity at commercial fuelling stations. Due to the high pressure at which hydrogen is usually stored and dispensed, consequence analysis for risk assessment and power reduction is very crucial. In this regard, the present study aims at simulating hydrogen dispersion along with consequence analyses for such events as jet fire using ALOHA model. Dispersion consequence modeling was performed, followed by the evaluation of the effect of environmental (i.e., stability, ambient temperature, surface roughness, wind speed, and humidity) and process (i.e., vessel temperature and pressure, and leakage diameter) parameters on maximum size flammable vapor cloud and maximum level jet fire radiation on the ground. The size of flammable vapor cloud (consequence dispersion index) and the maximum flux of radiation were affected by process parameters more than ambient parameters. Leakage diameter was found to have the highest impact on the operational parameters.

Keywords: Dispersion Hydrogen, Consequences, ALOHA

#323

OPTIMIZATION OF ROOM TEMPERATURE HYDROGEN SENSING CAPABILITY OF Pd THIN FILMS

* *Viney Dixit,* [1]*Deepshikha Jaiswal-Nagar,* [1]*Aditya Jayakumar,* [1]*Sarath Jose*
[1]Indian Institute of Science Education and Research, Thiruvananthapuram, School of Physics, Maruthamala P.O, Vithura, Trivandrum - 695551, Kerala, India.
*Corresponding author e-mail: viney@iisertvm.ac.in

ABSTRACT

Hydrogen being a colourless, odourless and tasteless gas, leak detection is somewhat very difficult using normal human senses. It has been reported that Pd-based nanostructure materials could be helpful in improving the response time and sensitivity of the hydrogen sensors due to the strong affinity of Pd towards hydrogen. Following this, in the present work we have synthesized palladium thin films of various base resistances by tuning the film thickness and inter particle separation, using the home-made sputtering nanocluster deposition system. Resistance based hydrogen gas sensing measurements were carried out in house-built gas sensor characterization system. The responses of these films on exposure to H_2 were such that they were dependent on their baseline resistance. These films were able to detect hydrogen to a limit as low as 1000 ppm. At larger interparticle separation, the films showed a resistive character which further increased on hydrogen exposure. On the other hand, the films that were in the metallic regime, showed a drop in resistance in similar conditions of hydrogen exposure. We could obtain films which showed conductive nature that transformed into highly resistive films via films of intermediate resistance by decreasing the time of deposition. Resistance vs temperature measurements of all the synthesized films were measured on Hall effect measurements system. The temperature dependence of these films showed a metallic and resistive response.

Keywords: Hydrogen Sensor, Thin Films, Hall Effect Measurements.

#384

INVESTIGATIONS ON THE DEFLAGRATION-TO-DETONATION PHENOMENA BY MEANS OF NUMERICAL SIMULATIONS WITH DETAILED CHEMISTRY AND AUTOMATED MESHING

[1*] *Pietro Scienza,* [1] *Marius-Gabriel Cojocaru,* [2] *Nitesh Attal,* [2] *Gaurav Kumar*
[1] Convergent Science GmbH, Hauptstrasse 10, 4040 Linz, Austria,
[2] Convergent Science Inc., Madison, WI, 53719, USA

*Corresponding author e-mail: pietro.scienza@convergecfd.com

ABSTRACT

When it comes to storing and transporting hydrogen, safety is key. Using Computational Fluid Dynamics (CFD) simulations in the design and verification of hydrogen storage and transportation devices has become the norm. Accurate CFD models for explosions and hydrogen venting involve complex meshing solutions applied in several iterations to refine and accurately capture the flame and shock positions. To this end, the current work builds on the study of the deflagration-to-detonation transition (DDT) phenomena by proposing and validating against experiments a novel simulation approach. This approach couples automated mesh generation and mesh refinement techniques with detailed chemistry to reduce the overall time to solution. The proposed method is coupled with different combustion modeling approaches, including the eddy dissipation concept and the homogeneous reactor model, as part of the validation study. The numerical simulations are centred around the analysis of DDT in hydrogen-rich enclosures that include a number of obstacles arranged in either a symmetrical or staggered manner. The influence of the layering of the gas species inside the enclosures that leads to homogenous or inhomogeneous conditions is discussed in parallel to the effects of the overall hydrogen fraction.

Keywords: Hydrogen Safety, Deflagration-to-Detonation Transition, CFD.

#408

ASSESSMENT OF OVERPRESSURES RESULTING FROM HYDROGEN EXPLOSIONS USING ARTIFICIAL NEURAL NETWORKS

*[1]Tabassum Abbasi, *[2]Tasneem Abbasi, [2]Abbasi S. A.*
[1]University of Petroleum and Energy Studies, School of Engineering, India
[2]Pondicherry University, Centre for Pollution Control and Environmental Engineering, Pondicherry, India
*Corresponding author email: t.abbasi.cpe@pondiuni.edu.in

ABSTRACT

One of the main safety aspects to be addressed in the wide-scale use of hydrogen to meet energy needs is the possibility of vapour cloud explosions (VCEs) arising from the leakage of hydrogen storage vessels. The blast waves from hydrogen VCEs can cause considerable damage to life and property. Currently, the means to estimate hydrogen VCE overpressures is to use the models used for hydrocarbon VCE overpressure assessment, or from CFD studies. These methods are not suitable for hydrogen as the properties and behaviour of hydrogen is dramatically different. Moreover, a hydrogen vapour cloud carries much greater risk of suffering VCE even in total absence of confinement, unlike vapour clouds of other substance which require partial confinement. This paper reports a novel approach to modelling overpressures resulting from hydrogen VCEs, using artificial neural networks (ANNs). The inputs to the ANN model are the volume of the cloud, the concentration of hydrogen in the cloud and the location at which the overpressure due to the VCE is to be estimated. The output is the overpressure. The model was trained and validated using experimental data from hydrogen explosions. The performance of the model was evaluated from the RMSE and R^2 of the observed versus predicted values. The R^2 of over 0.9 in the training and validation of the ANN model indicates its accuracy and demonstrates the potential for use of ANNs for predicting overpressures resulting from hydrogen explosions.

#422

IS THE TEMPERATURE MEASURED AT ONBOARD COMPRESSED HYDROGEN STORAGE' IN-TANK VALVE REPRESENTATIVE OF THE TANK TEMPERATURE?

[1] Beatriz Acosta Iborra, [1] Pietro Moretto, [1,2] Rafael Ortiz Cebolla*
[1]European Commission- Joint Research Centre, Westerduinweg 3, Petten, the Netherlands
[2]Go Ahead Engineering S.L., El Puerto de Santa Maria, Spain
*Corresponding author e-mail: beatriz.acosta-iborra@ec.europa.eu

ABSTRACT

The work presented here describes the experimental methods, results and conclusions of a study on temperature measurements delivered by the temperature sensor of the in-tank valve at on-board compressed hydrogen storage systems. The goal of this study was to determine whether temperatures measured by this device are representative of the gas temperature distribution inside the storage tanks. Specifically during fueling and defueling, non-homogeneous temperature distribution within the tank can take place. In these cases, the sensor may not detect local temperature surpassing the operational limits of minimum –40°C and maximum 85°C, leading to potentially unsafe situations.

Keywords: Hydrogen Fueling, On-Board Hydrogen Storage, In-Tank Valve Thermistor.

#429

FRETTING WEAR OF ELASTOMER MATERIALS IN HYDROGEN

[1] Géraldine Theiler, [2] Andreas Hausberger,*
[1]Bundesanstalt für Materialforschung und -prüfung (BAM), 12203 Berlin, Germany
[2] Polymer Competence Centre Leoben GmbH (PCCL), 8700 Leoben, Austria
*Corresponding author e-mail: Geraldine.theiler@bam.de

ABSTRACT

Safety and reliability are the major challenges to face for the development and acceptance of hydrogen technology. It is therefore crucial to study deeply material compatibility, in particular polymer materials that are directly in contact with hydrogen. This paper presents an experimental study on the fretting wear behavior of two types of cross-linked hydrogenated acrylonitrile butadiene rubbers against 316L steel ball in hydrogen environment. Furthermore, aging experiments were conducted for 7 days under static conditions in 100 MPa hydrogen. The influences of hydrogen pressure as well as the aging exposure on the fretting behavior are discussed by means of surface analyses and well as material properties.

Keywords: Fretting Wear, Elastomers, Hydrogen, High-Pressure

#436

METAL NANOPARTICLE DECORATED ZnO NANORODS FOR HYDROGEN SENSOR APPLICATIONS

[1*]*Sadullah Öztürk*, [2]*Arif Kösemen*, [3]*Necmettin Kilinç*, [4]*Zafer Ziya Öztürk*
[1]İstanbul University-Cerrahpasa, Institute of Nanotechnology and Biotechnology, İstanbul, TURKEY
[2]Mus Alparslan University, Department of Physics, 49100 Mus, TURKEY
[3]Inonu University, Department of Physics, 44280, Malatya, TURKEY
[4]Gebze Institute of Technology, Department of Physics, 41400, Kocaeli, TURKEY
*Corresponding author e-mail: sadullahozturk@iuc.edu.tr

ABSTRACT

In this study, ZnO nanorods, functionalized with Cr, Co, Ni and Cu metal nanoparticles are synthesized and the structural, electrical and hydrogen gas sensing properties are examined. ZnO nanorods with approximately 90 nm in diameter and 1 μm in length are produced by using hydrothermal method on ZnO seed layer coated glass substrate. Then Cr, Co, Ni and Cu metal acetate solutions are separately coated on ZnO nanorods by using spin coating method. It is obtained from structural characterization that the fabricated bare and metal functionalized ZnO nanorods are vertically aligned and have c–axis orientation. The FESEM images show metal nanoparticles with size below 20nm on ZnO nanorods. The electrical and hydrogen gas sensing characteristics of gold electrodes coated bare and metal functionalized ZnO nanorods are measured from room temperature to 200 °C. The highest sensitivity and good selectivity were observed for Ni nanoparticles decorated ZnO nanorods.

Keywords: ZnO nanorods, Hydrogen, Gas Sensor, Nanoparticle, Decoration

#1475

THE EFFECT OF CRYSTAL STRUCTURE AND METAL ELECTRODES ON GAS DETECTION IN TiO_2 NANOTUBES H_2 SENSORS

[1*] *Lutfi Bilal Tasyurek*, [1] *Esme Isik*, [2] *Ibrahim Isik* [3]*Necmettin Kilinc*
[1] Department of Optician, Malatya Turgut Ozal University, 44700, Malatya, Turkey
[2] Department of Electrical Electronics Engineering, Faculty of Engineering, Inonu University, 44280, Malatya, Turkey
[3] Department of Physics, Faculty of Science & Arts, Inonu University, 44280, Malatya, Turkey
*Corresponding author e-mail: bilal.tasyurek@ozal.edu.tr

ABSTRACT

In this study, the effects of various metal electrodes and various crystal structures on hydrogen (H_2) gas sensors based on titanium dioxide (TiO_2) nanotubes were investigated. For the production of TiO_2 nanotubes, anodization method consisting of an electrolyte containing 0.5wt% NH_4F in 85% pure glycerol solution was applied. Scanning electron microscope (SEM) images of the obtained TiO_2 nanotubes were examined. In order to see the effect of different crystal structures of TiO_2, amorphous, anatase and rutile phases were obtained by annealing of samples. Each of the Ti/TiO_2 nanotubes/metal (Pd, Pt, Au, and Ag) gas sensors, obtained by coating with palladium (Pd), platinum (Pt), gold (Au) and silver (Ag) electrodes, was tested at room temperature at 1% H_2 concentration depending on three different phases.

Keywords: Titanium Dioxide, Nanotubes, Hydrogen Sensor, Anodization, Metal Electrode

#1482

DETERMINATION OF SAFETY DISTANCE AND THE STRUCTURAL DAMAGE VULNERABILITY RESULTED FROM VAPOR CLOUD EXPLOSION (VCES)

[1]Aminu Ismaila, [2*]Rafiziana Md Kasmani, [2]Ahmad Termizi Ramli
[1] Department of Physics, Ahmadu Bello University Zaria, Nigeria
[2] Energy Management Group, School of Chemical and Energy Engineering, Universiti Teknologi Malaysia, 81310 Skudai, Johor, Malaysia
*Corresponding author e-mail : rafiziana@utm.my

ABSTRACT
International Atomic Energy Agency (IAEA) specifies the principal requirements for the protection and mitigation strategies of safety-related plant components, within the vicinity of the nuclear plant. However, safety issues related to pressurized hydrogen release are of concern since a small leak in a hydrogen system could ignite easily, support a flame that is difficult to detect, and lead to catastrophic fire and explosion. In this work, three correlations used to determine the vapor cloud explosion prediction, i.e., Trinitrotoluene (TNT), TNO Multi-energy and Baker-Strehlow-Tang (BST) to estimate the failures and consequences of the accidental release of hydrogen in a hypothetical nuclear power plant. The data was compared to simulation results from FLACS dispersion model. It was shown that the consequential damage of explosion overpressure is strongly dependant on the global load of flammable gas volume and plant layout. In this work, 5000 m^3 of hydrogen explosion is sufficient to produce blast load wave for total plant destruction. It can be said that, for a safety consideration, a physical distance of 200 m between the explosion source and the target outer walls could be sufficient to protect against the explosion hazards.
Keywords: Blast Load Wave, Failure and Consequence Analysis, Hydrogen Explosion, Nuclear Plant, Safety Distance

#1514

ASPECTS OF RISKS USING MAGNESIUM HYDRIDE FOR ZERO EMISSION MOBILITY

[1*] Bjørn Axel Gran, [2] Kjell Løvold, [1] Stefano Deledda
[1] Institute for Energy Technology, Norway
[2] Hydrogen Storage AS, Norway
*Corresponding author e-mail: bjorn.axel.gran@ife.no

ABSTRACT
The maritime sector has an increased focus on zero emission mobility solutions. One new initiative using hydrogen, is based upon storing hydrogen as magnesium hydride (MgH_2). Since in a such solution, continuous heating is required to desorb H_2, hydrogen storage in MgH_2 is considered a safer solution compared to compressed or liquified H_2. Indeed, if by accident there is a rupture of the metal container, the endothermic desorption of hydrogen will cool down MgH_2 and, as soon as heating is stopped, no hydrogen will be released. Institute for Energy Technology (IFE) was asked by a client to evaluate the safety benefits of magnesium hydride. This included to conduct a preliminary risk assessment and comparing the findings with similar risk assessments on the use of hydrogen and ammonia solutions related to use as a maritime fuel. The work also included compiling an overview of applicable rules and guidelines applicable in Norway, and an overview of relevant past incidents. This paper summarises on that work. One conclusion from the work is that the risk and safety assessments should not only include technical aspects, but also human, organisational and operational factors.
Keywords: Magnesium Hydride, Hydrogen Storage, Risk Assessment, Human Factors, Organisational Factors

#1519

HYDROGEN SENSING PROPERTIES OF ULTRATHIN PT-CO ALLOY FILMS

[1,2]M Erkovan, [3]C. Deger, [1,2]S Cardoso, [4*]N. Kilinc
[1]Instituto de Engenharia de Sistemas E Computadores – Microsistemas e Nanotecnologias (INESC MN) Lisbon, 1000-029, Portugal
[2]Instituto Superior Tecnico (IST), Universidade de Lisboa, 1040 001 Lisbon, Portugal
[3]Marmara University, Physics Dept. 34722, Ziverbey, Istanbul, Turkey
[4]Inonu University, Department of Physics, 44280, Malatya, Turkey
*Corresponding author e-mail: necmettinkilinc@gmail.com

ABSTRACT
In the present work, ultrathin Pt_xCo_{1-x} (x=1, 0.75, 0.5 and 0.25) alloy films are fabricated using co-sputtering with approximately 2nm in thickness. The stoichiometry, structural and electrical resistivity characterization of the thin films are obtained from EDX, RBS and XPS measurements. The structural characterization of the thin films showed smooth coverage of the surface, in a fcc crystalline plane (111). The resistive properties of the films are tested towards an hydrogen gas sensor between 25 °C – 150 °C in the gas concentration ranging from 0.5% to 5%. The surface scattering phenomenon could explain the hydrogen gas sensing mechanism of ultrathin PtxCo1-x alloy thin films. PtCo alloy thin films show better response time than bare Pt thin films.
Keywords: Platinum, Platinum-cobalt alloys, Thin films, Hydrogen sensor, Gas Sensor

#1534

AN EXPERIMENTAL APPARATUS FOR IN-SITU STUDIES OF HYDROGEN INGRESS, DISSOLUTION AND PRECIPITATION AT CONTROLLED TEMPERATURE AND APPLIED TENSILE STRESSES

*[1] Julien Lang, [1] Michael Gharghouri, [1] Helmut Fritzsche
[1]Canadian Nuclear Laboratories, 286 Plant Road, Chalk River, Canada
*Corresponding author e-mail: julien.lang@cnl.ca

ABSTRACT

This manuscript presents the design and utilisation of a unique environmental chamber allowing specimens to be heated and cooled, under tensile load and controlled atmosphere, while in a neutron beam, offering a unique opportunity for in-situ neutron diffraction experiments. The chamber was built to gain insight into the impact of parameters such as tensile stress, temperature and exposed atmosphere on the hydrogen solubility of materials and on the mechanisms relating to delayed hydride cracking, hydrogen embrittlement and hydrogen ingress.

The investigation presented in this work shows the chamber's performance up to 450°C and 275 MPa applied tensile stress. The effect of tensile stresses and temperature on hydrogen solubility in Zr-2.5Nb is presented for a sample nominally charged to a hydrogen concentration equivalent of 500 wppm (mg/kg). Due to kinetic factors, no significant effect of tensile stress on the hydrogen solubility of our samples was found for temperatures up to 300°C and at tensile stresses up to 275 MPa.

Keywords: Hydrogen, Tensile Stress, Ingress, Dissolution, Precipitation

#1560

NUMERICAL INVESTIGATIONS ON FLASHBACK LIMITS OF PREMIXED METHANE-HYDROGEN-AIR LAMINAR FLAMES

*[1]Tahsin Berk Kıymaz, [1]Emre Böncü, [1]Dilay Güleryüz, [2]Mehmet Karaca, [3]Barış Yılmaz, [4]Christophe Allouis, *[1,5]İskender Gökalp*
[1]Middle East Technical University, Mechanical Engineering Department, Ankara, Turkey
[2]Middle East Technical University, Aerospace Engineering Department, Ankara, Turkey
[3]Marmara University, Mechanical Engineering Department, İstanbul, Turkey
[4]STEMS-CNR, Naples, Italy
[5]ICARE-CNRS, Orléans, France
*Corresponding author e-mail: igokalp@metu.edu.tr

ABSTRACT

Premixed laminar methane-hydrogen combustion contains a potential flashback risk, which may be detrimental for home appliances. The present study investigates the effect of hydrogen addition to methane-air premixed laminar flames with two-dimensional transient computations performed by the CFD code OpenFOAM. The effect of wall temperature on flame flashback propensity is examined. After a stabilized flame is achieved, flashback conditions are approached by gradually decreasing the inlet premixture bulk velocity. At flame flashback velocities, flame symmetry is found to be broken because of the oscillations at the flame leading edge. Flashback tendency is found to be increasing with increasing wall temperature and increasing hydrogen addition rate. Flashback limits for 600K wall temperature case are calculated as 0.368 m/s, 0.68 and 0.99 m/s for 0 mol%, 10 mol% and 20 mol% of H_2 additions to CH_4-air mixture respectively. For 300K wall temperature case, they are calculated as 0.165 m/s, 0.265 m/s and 0.44 m/s for 0 mol%, 10 mol% and 20 mol% of H_2 additions to CH_4-air mixture respectively.

Keywords: Laminar premixed flames, Flame flashback, Hydrogen, Numerical simulations, OpenFOAM

Track 12.

Codes, Standards and Regulations

#25

THE GERMAN HYDROGEN RCS ROADMAP

[1*] *Elena Hof,* [2] *Reinhold Wurster*
[1]NOW GmbH, Fasanenstr. 5, 10623 Berlin, Germany
[2] Ludwig-Bölkow-Systemtechnik GmbH, Daimlerstr. 15, 85521 Ottobrunn, Germany
*Corresponding author e-mail: reinhold.wurster@LBST.de

ABSTRACT
In the exercise of developing a German Roadmap for Hydrogen Regulations, Codes and Standards (RCS), the identification of current developments and existing gaps and the preparation of recommendations has been performed. The following ongoing international RCS activities were reviewed: ISO, IEC, CEN, CENELEC, EU and UN ECE / WP29. Focus was primarily on hydrogen and fuel cell applications for road transport and stationary applications and to a lesser extent on trains / airports.
It became obvious that the development of standards and regulations and in particular the coordination between the two is complex and requires a concerted approach and substantial efforts. For this reason, a roadmap strategy paper has been prepared, in which a roadmap and timeline has been developed. As an appropriate instrument to achieve a successful implementation of all regulatory and normative requirements while involving all actors and stakeholders, the establishment of an H_2 RCS coordination platform has been considered.
Keywords: RCS Roadmap, RCS Platform, AFID, GTR13

#213

EUROPEAN REGULATORY FRAMEWORK FOR HYDROGEN UNDERGROUND STORAGE

[1*] *Sara Martínez,* [1] *Jesús Simón,* [2] *Arnaud Reveillere,* [2] *Flore Ostapoff*
[1]Foundation for the Development of New Hydrogen Technologies in Aragon (FHA), Parque Tecnológico Walqa Ctra. N-330a, km. 56622197 Huesca, Spain
[2] Geostock, 2, rue des Martinets 92500 Rueil-Malmaison, Paris, France
*Corresponding author e-mail: smartinez@hidrogenoaragon.org

ABSTRACT

Renewable hydrogen, when combined with large-scale underground storage in aquifers, depleted fields, or salt caverns, enables energy transport over time while balancing the impacts of variable energy production from renewable sources. Although hydrogen storage in salt caverns has been practised since the 1970s in Europe, it has not yet been implemented anywhere in depleted fields or aquifers. The HyStories [1] project aims to provide technical developments applicable to depleted aquifers or fields, to conduct techno-economic feasibility studies and to provide information on underground hydrogen storage to decision-makers in administration and industry. In this context, the legal framework for underground hydrogen storage at European level was analysed in terms of the existence, or otherwise, of regulatory barriers, as well as the extent to which these barriers may affect the development of underground hydrogen storage projects. The starting point of this analysis of the legal framework for UHS was the existing national regulations for the mature underground natural gas storage industry and more than 39 experts from 17 different countries were involved in the project. Thus, this study compares the different country-specific approaches and offers a series of recommendations to avoid legal barriers to the deployment of UHS in geological formations across Europe.

Keywords: Hydrogen, Underground, Storage, Regulatory

#258

TESTING OF BLENDED GREEN HYDROGEN IN GAS PIPELINES: CONSIDERING THE END-USERS LIMITS

[1*] *Ali Ekhtiari,* [2] *Liam Nolan,* [1] *Eoin Syron*
[1]School of Chemical & Bioprocess Engineering, University College Dublin, Ireland
[2]Gas Networks Ireland, Dublin, Ireland
*Corresponding author e-mail: mohammad.ekhtiari@ucd.ie

ABSTRACT

Gas networks play a vital role in the global energy infrastructure. In Ireland, the natural gas transmission pipelines transport about 50 GWh, twice as much energy as power grids. The gas grids provide a reliable and secure energy supply for electricity generation as a backup when renewable energy is not available. The European Commission in the Green Target Plan set out the goal of net-zero carbon by 2050. The decarbonisation of gas networks incorporating hydrogen generated from surplus renewable power is a potential solution for the storage of excess renewable energy especially so in Ireland with huge available wind resources. The main objective of this research is to ensure a reliable and safe supply of adequate energy to residential end-users while decarbonising the gas network. Dealing with varying hydrogen blends poses significant challenges for gas network operators to ensure hydrogen concentration meets the limits of end-user devices. This experimental research investigates the effects of various hydrogen concentrations on common existing end-user devices found in the Irish gas network. The project examines the potential range of hydrogen blends that may be incorporated into the Irish gas network from 2-20% Hydrogen. This research work provides a detailed account of the tests and experiments carried out as part of this project in the UCD Integrated Energy Lab and the Hydrogen Innovation Centre of Gas Network Ireland. This includes modelling of pressure drop in an example of distribution pipe rig, combustion and ignition temperature, and comparing the accuracy of meters before and after blending hydrogen through the pipelines. This study investigates how much the addition of hydrogen impacts the operation of appliances in the residential segment, also provides reference data for all relevant parties. The outcomes from this practical research allow for a complete costing of the necessary network and appliance upgrades to accommodate blended hydrogen in the gas network.

Keywords: Green Hydrogen, Gas Networks, Energy Storage, Hydrogen Blend

#338

HYDROGEN FUEL QUALITY FOR TRANSPORT: NPL ACCREDITATION ISO 17025, REFERENCE MATERIALS, PROFICIENCY TESTING AND NEW SAMPLING SYSTEM

[1*]*Thomas Bacquart,* [1]*Abigail Morris,* [1]*Niamh Moore,* [1]*Mathew Hookham,* [1]*Yoana Hristova,* [1]*Robbie Wilmot,* [1]*Femi Omoniyi,* [1]*Arul Murugan*
[1] National Physical Laboratory, Teddington, United Kingdom
*Corresponding author e-mail: thomas.bacquart@npl.co.uk

ABSTRACT

The enforcement of regulation on hydrogen fuel quality is a need supported by car manufacturer, policy makers and end users. Several laboratories in Europe and worldwide are becoming able to measure hydrogen fuel quality according to ISO 14687. However, it is currently difficult to evaluate the quality of these laboratories. Lack of gas calibrants, reference material and inter-laboratory comparison is a barrier for European commercial laboratory to prove their competences and obtain accreditation ISO 17025. National Physical Laboratory (NPL) has ISO 17025 accreditation and developed reference materials for hydrogen fuel quality. Based on experience in the previous proficiency testing on hydrogen fuel quality, NPL propose a new proficiency testing scheme and guidance on common issues. NPL will present new results on stability of contaminant in sampling container and advice for hydrogen fuel sampling. The presentation will provide advanced results and good practices to ensure reliability and accuracy of hydrogen quality analytical laboratory.

Keywords: Hydrogen Quality, Fuel Cell Hydrogen Vehicles, ISO14687, Gas Analysis, Proficiency Testing

#368

METROLOGY FOR HYDROGEN VEHICLE 2: ACHIEVEMENTS AND PROGRESSES

[1*] *Thomas Bacquart,* [2] *Marc de Huu,* [3] *Karine Arrhenius,* [4] *Thor Anders Aarhaug,* [5] *Jaana Viitakangas,* [1]*Arul Murugan*

[1] National Physical Laboratory, Hampton Rd, Teddington Middlesex, TW11 0LW, United Kingdom
[2] Federal Institute of Metrology METAS, Lindenweg 50, 3003 Bern-Wabern, Switzerland
[3] RISE, Research Institutes of Sweden, Box 857, 501 15 Borås, Sweden
[4] SINTEF Industry, Richard Birkelandsvei 2B, 7034, Trondheim, Norway
[5] VTT Technical Research Centre of Finland, VTT, P.O. Box 1000, 02044, Finland
*Corresponding author e-mail: thomas.bacquart@npl.co.uk

ABSTRACT

Hydrogen fuel cells are an alternative power supply for electric drive trains and could represent 32 % of fuel demand by 2050. To deploy fuel cell electrical vehicles, there is current regulatory barriers (ISO 14687, OIML recommendations) that requires accurate measurements. The European funded project MetroHyVe has provided solutions and improvements in the four measurements challenges (flow metering, quality control, quality assurance and sampling). New challenges arised due to increase of hydrogen economy, therefore a new European project MetroHyVe 2 started in 2020 and its objectives will provide perspectives for the hydrogen economy to solve all regulatory barriers (ISO 14687, ISO 19880-8, ISO 19880-1, ISO 21087, OIML R139-1) and new measurement challenges (flow metering, quality control, sampling and fuel cell stack testing). The presentation will provide a comprehensive overview of the project achievements. The achievements around primary standard for flow metering (light and heavy duty), worldwide inter-laboratory comparison for hydrogen fuel quality, hydrogen sampling inter-comparison and fuel cell stack testing recommendations will be highlighted.

Keywords: Hydrogen Fuel Quality, ISO 14687, Flow Metering, Metrology, Regulations

#1563

SAFE ENERGY RELATIONS: UNFOLDING THE PRECAUTIONARY PRINCIPLE WITH THE ADVENT OF HYDROGEN TECHNOLOGIES

[1*] *Ayşe Şehnaz Kart* [2]*İskender Gökalp*

[1] Middle East Technical University, Science and Technology Policy Studies, Ankara, Turkey
[2] Middle East Technical University, Mechanical Engineering, Ankara, Turkey
* sehnazkart@gmail.com , igokalp@metu.edu.tr

ABSTRACT

Proposals on the inclusion of hydrogen as an energy vector into the large-scale energy socio-technical system has gained considerable momentum along with the effects of the climate crisis and the COVID-19 pandemic. This study examines the conflict between various dimensions of decarbonization with hydrogen agenda within the conceptual framework of international environmental law and policies. Firstly, we carry out a general due diligence of the technical, economic, and legal aspects of the hydrogen economy particularly in Europe. Subsequently, via textual analyses of European Union's strategic documents, the incompatibility of the hydrogen risk chain with the hydrogen value chain is revealed. Finally, as one remedy to this incompatibility; the precautionary principle, its relation to science, technology and society studies, and its possible policy applications in the context of hydrogen technologies are discussed.

Keywords: Hydrogen, Decarbonization, Risk, Precautionary Principle, Environmental Law and Policy.

Track 13.

Hydrogen Strategies and Policies

#95

HYDROGEN ROADMAP ASSESSMENT FOR COLOMBIA UNDER AN INTERNATIONALLY COMPARATIVE FRAMEWORK

[1]*Paula Riveros-Melo*, [1]*John Sanchez C.*, [1]*Martha Cobo-Angel*, [1*]*Cesar Barraza-Botet*
[1]Universidad de La Sabana, School of Engineering, Energy, Materials and Environment Laboratory, Km. 7 Autopista Norte de Bogotá, Chía, Cundinamarca, Colombia
*Corresponding author e-mail: cesar.barraza@unisabana.edu.co

ABSTRACT

Hydrogen roadmaps and national strategies have been used to evaluate scenarios and define pathways to include hydrogen as an energy vector in different countries. Aiming to become one of the early adopters of hydrogen in Latin America, Colombia has recently issued its hydrogen roadmap that sets goals for the near and long term. The aim of this study is to develop an assessment matrix to evaluate the hydrogen roadmaps of several countries and to propose a framework to compare them with Colombia's. To design the matrix, the key elements proposed by the International Energy Agency (IEA) were considered to evaluate the selected roadmaps. As an initial result, the analysis showed that the Colombian hydrogen roadmap contains several of the main aspects that a roadmap well-established should have. However, it should be improved by including more detailed information related to the use of the natural resources, setting milestones for the proposed goals, and designing policies aligned to the country's commitments to the Paris Agreement. As a result, the authors recommend the roadmap to be complemented by an actionable National Hydrogen Strategy containing the aspects identified in this work.

Keywords: Roadmap; Hydrogen, Policy, Comparative Assessment, National Strategy.

#104

CREATING A GLOBAL HYDROGEN ECONOMY: REVIEW OF INTERNATIONAL STRATEGIES, TARGETS, AND POLICIES WITH A FOCUS ON JAPAN, GERMANY, SOUTH KOREA AND CALIFORNIA

[1*] *Vishnu Vijayakumar, Lewis Fulton, Mahdi Shams, Daniel Sperling*
[1] Institute of Transportation Studies, University of California, Davis, California, US
*Corresponding author e-mail: vvijayakumar@ucdavis.edu

ABSTRACT

Motivated by increasing emphasis on decarbonization, hydrogen is enjoying unprecedented political and business momentum. This paper reviews the status of hydrogen strategies and progress in major global economies investing in hydrogen, and then focus on four jurisdictions (Japan, Germany, S. Korea and California) that have been among the most aggressive, though in different ways. Japan, Germany and S. Korea are more focused on developing a sustainable hydrogen supply chain. In contrast, California has been more focused on spurring hydrogen demand, especially in the transportation sector. Japan's strategy involves forging partnerships to import "blue" hydrogen while Germany has focused on "green" hydrogen production, along with plans to leverage its extensive natural gas pipelines for hydrogen distribution. Japan anticipates the power sector to be the largest consumer of hydrogen, while others expect the transportation and industry sectors to be the prime movers of future hydrogen demand. Japan, S. Korea and Germany will likely import a substantial portion of their future hydrogen supplies, while California has the potential for low-cost hydrogen production but establishing the distributional infrastructure continues to be a challenge. In all four jurisdictions, investments are still small and there exists huge opportunities for cooperation to develop a self-sustaining global hydrogen market.

Keywords: GHG Emissions, Sector Coupling, Blue and Green Hydrogen, Hydrogen Economy

#113

SUSTAINABILITY ANALYSIS OF HYDROGEN PRODUCTION PROCESSES

Andrea Mio[a,c], Elena Barbera[b], Alessandro Massi Pavan[a,c], Alberto Bertucco[b,d], Maurizio Fermeglia[a,c]*
[a] Department of Engineering and Architecture, University of Trieste, Italy
[b] Department of Industrial Engineering (DII), University of Padova, Italy
[c] Center for Energy, Environment and Transport Giacomo Ciamician, University of Trieste, Italy
[d] Centro Studi "Levi Cases" for Energy Economics and Technology, University of Padova, Italy
**Corresponding author e-mail:* elena.barbera@unipd.it

ABSTRACT

Hydrogen is a versatile energy carrier and storage medium that may be employed in a variety of applications. It may be produced using different processes, each one generating a peculiar hydrogen identified by a color. In this work, process simulation is used to obtain material and energy balances for each process investigated, as well as for the evaluation of capital and maintenance costs. Process simulation outcomes are then used for to estimate three key performance indicators focusing on sustainability issues: the energy return of energy invested, the levelized cost of hydrogen and the life cycle assessment. We compared several hydrogen generation processes, each denoted by a unique color code: (i) green hydrogen, produced by electrolysis of water using electricity from renewable sources, (ii) yellow hydrogen, produced by electrolysis using grid electricity, (iii) grey hydrogen, produced from natural gas using steam reforming and (iv) blue hydrogen, like grey one, but with carbon capture and sequestration (CCS). From the results obtained it is possible to conclude that the most sustainable hydrogen production methods is the so-called green hydrogen, produced by water electrolysis.

Keywords: Hydrogen Production, EROEI, LCOH, LCA

#194

ASSESSING RENEWABLE HYDROGEN PRODUCTION CAPACITY ON A REGIONAL BASIS

[1,2] Gonzalo Puig-Samper, [1,3] Felipe Campos-Carriedo, [1] Diego Iribarren, [1,3] Javier Dufour*
[1] IMDEA Energy, Systems Analysis Unit, 28935, Móstoles, Spain
[2] Universidad Autónoma de Madrid, Chemical Engineering Department, 28049, Madrid, Spain
[3] Rey Juan Carlos University, Chemical and Environmental Engineering Group, 28933, Móstoles, Spain
*Corresponding author e-mail: javier.dufour@imdea.org

ABSTRACT

Local renewable hydrogen production is being promoted by European countries. In this sense, the deployment of renewable hydrogen requires evaluating whether countries or regions could achieve specific future hydrogen production and environmental targets. Within this context, this work proposes a linear optimisation model to find the most suitable production mix at the regional level in terms of costs, while respecting an exogenous environmental constraint. The model was applied to the case study of Spanish regions, analysing the potential contribution to meeting the Renewable Energy Directive II (RED II) target for the transport system in 2030. According to the results, production mixes would vary strongly depending on the region, and only one of the assessed regions would fail to meet the hydrogen demand from renewable sources. It was found that the overall national demand could be fulfilled using indigenous renewable sources, and renewable hydrogen hubs were identified with a regional scope.

Keywords: Environmental Impact, Levelised Cost, Linear Optimisation, Regional Assessment, Renewable Hydrogen

#226

BLUE H_2 PERSPECTIVE IN ENERGY TRANSITION OF COLOMBIA

[1*] *Sara Domínguez Cardozo,* [2] *Bernay Cifuentes Vanegas,* [3] *Felipe Bustamante Londoño,* [4] *Néstor Sánchez,* [5*] *Martha Cobo*

[1,3] Universidad de Antioquia UdeA, Faculty of Engineering, Calle 70 No. 52-21, Medellín, Colombia
[2] Universidad de la Salle, Bogotá, Faculty of Engineering, Chemical Engineering Program, Carrera 2 No. 10-70, Bogotá, Colombia
[4,5] Universidad de La Sabana, Faculty of Engineering, Campus Universitario Puente del Común, Chía, Colombia
*Corresponding author e-mail: martha.cobo@unisabana.edu.co

ABSTRACT

Latin America is starting its transition towards sustainable energy alternatives. In particular, given its abundant natural resources and fossil fuel reserves, hydrogen (H_2) could play a leading role in Colombia. This contribution presents an analysis of the potential of blue H_2 in Colombia, considering it a possible promoter for the H_2 economy. The study focuses on the natural resources available to produce blue H_2 in the context of the recently launched H_2 Road Map and Energy Plan to 2050. Results indicate that the production of low-emission blue H_2 in Colombia, mainly from coal, besides allowing a more sustainable use of non-renewable resources would open the way to green H_2, and could supply up to 10% of global demand of blue H_2 by 2050. However, implementation of a clear public policy and a more detailed roadmap for the inclusion of blue H_2 in the energy matrix is required for the establishment of a H_2 economy in the country.

Keywords: Carbon Footprint, Blue Hydrogen, Coal, Gasification, Natural Gas.

#228

COLOMBIA'S GREEN HYDROGEN: SOLAR AND WIND POWER CAPACITY SCENARIOS

*David Rodríguez-Fontalvo, Nelly M. Cantillo, Néstor Sánchez, Martha Cobo**
Universidad de La Sabana, Facultad de Ingeniería, Campus del Puente del Común, Chía, Cundinamarca, Colombia.
*Corresponding author e-mail: martha.cobo@unisabana.edu.co

ABSTRACT

Producing green hydrogen (H_2) with solar and wind energy as main sources is one of the main objectives in Colombia's national strategy for decarbonizing the national energy mix. This contribution studies the role of solar and wind H_2 projects in the Colombian energy mix to meet the H_2 demand for 2030, 2040 and 2050 established on the national H_2 strategy for different scenarios. For creating each scenario, different parameters such as installed capacity of each technology, the resource-to-H_2 efficiency and distribution of the electricity produced to generate H_2 (D_{H2}) were varied. Particularly in Scenario 3, which assumed a D_{H2} of 16.7 %, the solar and wind capacities will need to be 204,749 MW and 88,970 MW, respectively. This scenario was identified as a route to achieve the yearly goal proposed in Colombia's national strategy. This work exposes the implications that H_2 demand exerts on electricity supply and project installations from renewable sources, and is an approach to the green H_2 requirements within the Colombian context. Furthermore, this analysis can guide the required strategies and incentives to successfully integrate green H_2.

Keywords: Green Hydrogen, Installed Capacity, Onshore Wind Parks, Offshore Wind Parks, Photovoltaics.

#267

HYDROGEN ENERGY RESEARCH AND DEVELOPMENT IN KAZAKHSTAN: CURRENT STATUS

[1*] *Saule Zholdayakova,* [1] *Botakoz Suleimenova*
[1] KMG Engineering LLP, D.Kunayev St, Nur-Sultan city, Republic of Kazakhstan
* Corresponding author e-mail: s.zholdayakova@niikmg.kz

ABSTRACT
Constant energy demand and environmental pollution have become a global concern. Central Asia Caspian countries are shifting their focus on alternative fuels, particularly hydrogen energy, while having significant fossil fuel resources. This study is a review of work and procedures done in Kazakhstan toward achieving a net zero emission future. Current studies and projects are summarized showing the condition of hydrogen production, storage and application. In this case, the organization of hydrogen supply chain and consumption, providing national funding, fruitful partnership, assessment of risks and outcomes should be taken into consideration, although it is the very first step of Kazakhstan to hydrogen energy.
Keywords: Hydrogen Energy, Central Asia Caspian Countries, Decarbonization Challenges

#298

DEVELOPMENT OF HYDROGEN ENERGY IN RUSSIA

[1,2*] *Dmitry Dunikov,* [1] *Vasily Borzenko*
[1]Joint Institute for High Temperatures of the Russian Academy of Sciences, Laboratory for Hydrogen Energy Technologies, 125412 Izhorskaya st. 13 bld. 2, Moscow, Russia
[2] National Research University "Moscow Power Engineering Institute", Krasnokazarmennaya 14, Moscow,Russia
*Corresponding author e-mail: h2lab@mail.ru

ABSTRACT

In August 2021 the Concept for the Development of Hydrogen Energy in Russia was released with a strategic goal to make Russia one of the global leaders in hydrogen production and export. It is a major step ahead, since from the collapse of the USSR there were no hydrogen energy program in Russia. The priorities for the development are low-carbon processes of hydrogen production from the fossils with CO_2-capture and water electrolysis using nuclear power. The Concept includes 3 stages with export targets at the end of each stage are 0.2 Mt H_2 in 2024, 2-12 Mt H_2 in 2035 and 15-50 Mt in 2050 H_2 depending on the development rate of the global low-carbon economy.
Keywords: Russian Federation, State policy, Concept for the Development of Hydrogen Energy

#304

FROM FOSSIL FUEL ENERGY TO HYDROGEN ENERGY: TRANSFORMATION OF FOSSIL FUEL ENERGY ECONOMIES INTO HYDROGEN ECONOMIES THROUGH SOCIAL ENTREPRENEURSHIP

[1*] *Jossie Esteban Garzón Baquero,* [1] *Daniela Bellon Monsalve*
[1] Universidad de Santander, Facultad de Ingenierías y Tecnologías, Instituto de Investigación Xerira, Bucaramanga, Colombia
*Corresponding author e-mail: jos.garzon@mail.udes.edu.co

ABSTRACT
Social entrepreneurship plays a crucial role in global sustainable development, enhancing the quality of life and preserving environmental, human, and social capital. However, when it relates to the energy transition, it faces numerous challenges and experiences conflicts in terms of costs, technological innovation, public policies. This study seeks to illustrate one of the new alternative energy schemes which could replace fossil fuels in the future: hydrogen. This transformation would result in significant social impacts, leading to the question, "how should it be done?" Social entrepreneurship can integrate socio-economic actors and agents and help them to devise and implement new forms of energy innovation. Therefore, a descriptive qualitative methodology was designed, that allows us to analyze the process of building entrepreneurship with a social vision and to propose a model that enables the transition from fossil economies to the hydrogen economies. Among the most significant results, stands out the importance of the support of the three primary axes of each country and the role of social entrepreneurship as a key element for the transition. The discussion contributes to the debate on the path that academia should lead, and the fundamental role of entrepreneurship based on social conscience as a driver of change.
Keywords: Hydrogen Economy, Social Entrepreneurship, Hydrogen Energy, Sustainable Development, Innovation.

#329

WAYS TO IMPROVE THE COMPETITIVENESS OF CHINA'S HYDROGEN ENERGY INDUSTRY

[1*] *Xiangyu Meng,* [2] *Alun Gu,* [1]*Mingyun Chen,*[1] *Xinguo Wu,* [2]*Jian Zhou,* [2]*Bin Liu,* [1,2**] *Zongqiang Mao*
[1]Tsinghua Innovation Center in Dongguan, Songshan Lake Hi-tech industrial Park, Dongguan, P.R. China
[2] Institute of Nuclear and New Energy Technology, Tsinghua University, Beijing, P.R.China
*Corresponding author e-mail: mengxy@tsinghua-dg.org
**Corresponding author e-mail: maozq@mail.tsinghua.edu.cn

ABSTRACT

At present, the development of China's hydrogen energy industry is beginning to take shape, and the high cost of hydrogen energy industry chain is the biggest obstacle to the development of hydrogen energy industry. Based on the analysis of the development background and current situation of hydrogen energy in China, this paper points out that the realization of economy of green hydrogen energy industry chain in China needs to start from the following four aspects: formulating policies, regulations and standards suitable for hydrogen energy; Promote the progress of hydrogen energy technology; Promote the localization and large-scale application of hydrogen energy technology, and strengthen international cooperation. The green hydrogen energy industry will also provide strong support for China to achieve the goal of carbon peak and carbon neutralization.

Keywords: Green Hydrogen, Economy, Sustainable Development

#377

H2-INDEX FOR THE EVALUATION OF HYDROGEN PROJECTS IN MEXICO

[1*] *G. Ramos-Sánchez,* [2] *R.G. González Huerta*
[1]Universidad Autónoma Metropolitana- I IPH Department, Mexico City, Mexico
[2] ESIQIE-IPN, Mexico City, Mexico.
*Corresponding author e-mail: gramos@xanum.uam.mx

ABSTRACT

Hydrogen projects are being implemented all around the world, although at first sight all projects in which Hydrogen is involved appear appealing, in some cases other alternatives such as electrification and efficiency growth are better suited. In this work we have developed a methodology for the analysis of Hydrogen projects that assign a quantitative value to its implementation viability. The H2-index is based on the evaluation of 6 factors, social benefits, economic benefits, environmental benefits, national development, efficiency, and technical viability. A weighted factor will help to decide, in a simple manner, whether a project should be promoted and, moreover, what areas should be strength in order to make the project not only viable but worth to be financed.

Keywords: H2 Projects Evaluation, H2-Index, Positive Impact of Projects.

#392

HYDROGEN POTENTIAL AS VECTOR FOR A BIOMASS-BASED DECARBONISATION OF TRANSPORT IN BRAZIL

[1,2] Suani T. Coelho, [1] Antonio Stuchi, [1,2] Danilo Perecin, [2,3] Karen L. Mascarenhas, [2] Julio Meneghini*
[1] Institute of Energy and Environment, University of São Paulo, Av Prof Luciano Gualberto, São Paulo, Brazil
[2] Research Centre for Greenhouse Gas Innovation, School of Engineering, University of São Paulo, Avenida Mello Moraes 2231, 05508-030, São Paulo, Brazil
[3] Institute of Psychology, University of São Paulo, Avenida Mello Moraes 1721, 05508-030, São Paulo, Brazil
*Corresponding author e-mail: suani@iee.usp.br

ABSTRACT

Hydrogen can be produced from biomass and eventually deliver largely needed negative emissions when combined with carbon capture and storage. The sugarcane industry in Brazil is well established and its main energy products – ethanol and electricity – are potential solutions but are still facing challenges related to decarbonisation. Aiming to contribute to the Brazilian matrix decarbonisation, this article estimates the hydrogen production potential for a current state-of-the-art sugarcane mill with an annexed distillery, based on 1G and 2G ethanol reforming, biogas reforming, and the use of surplus electricity for electrolysis-based process. This result is applied to the total sugarcane production in Brazil to compare the country's potential by using hydrogen in fuel cells to the equivalent in useful energy delivered by all fuels used in the transport sector. As a result, sugarcane-based hydrogen could deliver around 57% of total transport sector energy demand, compared to only 19% of current ethanol's contribution. In addition, ethanol is only used in passenger cars where pure electric vehicles are becoming increasingly competitive, and diesel oil consumption in the country is extremely high mainly for trucks; on another hand, hydrogen is more likely to play a role decarbonising these heavy vehicles. Hydrogen could become an option for the sugarcane industry to remain relevant under a battery electric-cars future and Brazil is well-positioned to develop a strategy around biomass-based hydrogen for heavy vehicles.

Keywords: Hydrogen, Biomass, Sugarcane, Transport Decarbonisation, Brazil

#1478

ARGENTINE ACTIVITIES IN THE FIELD OF HYDROGEN

Juan Carlos Bolcich
AAH (Argentine Hydrogen association)

Historical events in research, development and academic sector began in 1980, receiving a strong boost with the first visit of Prof. Veziroglu to Argentina in 1986. That same year, we took part in the 6th WHEC in Vienna, continuing our participation in the following WHECs uninterruptedly and the 12th WHEC took place in Buenos Aires, the capital of Argentina in 1998. In June 1996, the AAH (Argentine Hydrogen Association) was founded and the publication of a regular hydrogen bulletin was started in Spanish language (https://www.aah2.org/). In 1997, a Hydrogen Committee was created in IRAM (National Institute for Codes and Standards) to meet the ISO TC 197 Standard. Among the most outstanding current activities, the Province of Río Negro stands out with the signing of an agreement with the Australian company Fortescue Future Industries for the installation of a mega wind plant–green hydrogen to be applied in green ammonia production on the Atlantic Coast. The agreement above was announced at COP 26 in Glasgow with a projected investment of 8,400 million dollars. The plant will produce 1 million tons of ammonia per year. There is a strong will and desire to promote renewable energy and hydrogen, especially aimed at the towns within the province, where experts from all over the country have been invited to participate. Other projects are being analyzed with the participation of the Fraunhofer Institute in Germany. One of the main interests is the improvement of a railway that links the Atlantic and the Andes Mountains in north Patagonia, with an extension of 900 km destined to improve the service and that includes hydrogen trains. There is a strong drive for human resource training in middle schools, the National Technological University, as well as other universities and institutions. In 2020 YPF (Argentine National Oil & Gas Company) created a consortium of 40 companies to analyze and seek the investment of green hydrogen. The Argentine Chamber of Renewable Energies strongly promotes the incorporation of a greater number of wind and solar parks, currently reaching a capacity of 6,000 MW. Growth is limited by the availability of power grids. To overcome this restriction, we want hydrogen technologies to be taken into account for energy use, as well as P2X, such as fertilizer industries, refineries and metal treatments so as to take advantage of the large amounts of clean energy available in the south of our country. The National Economic and Social Council has undertaken actions to define the strategic plan and the implementation of hydrogen projects (started in 2021). The environmental situation and the reduction of greenhouse gas emissions is another important issue in Argentina.

#1535

COULD GREEN HYDROGEN AND ITS DERIVATIVE IMPROVE ENERGY SYSTEMS IN NORTH AFRICA, CASE OF MOROCCO, EGYPT AND TUNISIA

[1*] *Amin Lahnaoui,* [1] *Wilhelm Kuckshinrichs*
[1]Forschungszentrum Jülich, Institute of Energy and Climate Research, Systems Analysis and Technology Evaluation, 52425 Jülich, Germany
*Corresponding author e-mail: a.lahnaoui@fz-juelich.de

ABSTRACT

North Africa constitutes a strategic point at the door of Europe and the corridor of West Asia. Some common cultural aspects could facilitate collaboration to strengthen its position in the region in the energy sector. Adding to that an increasing concern regarding the environmental impact of the current energy system, and a big renewable resources potential, the region could build a more sustainable economy around new energy resources. However, opportunities and potentials do not automatically translate into successful and radical changes and it is therefore important, now that the hydrogen economy and its derivatives its peaking speed, to not overlook the structural change that should be done in local energy systems in favour of export-based economy. Looking back to the last 28 years, hardly any change has been made to the way energy mixes are defined and the importance of carbon sources in it and the energy economy. Therefore, it is important to analyse first the energy supply and what drives energy consumption to define where future sustainable energy systems should intervene locally.

Keywords: Energy System, LMDI Decomposition, Energy Supply, Green Hydrogen.

#1599

GREEN AMMONIA TO ADVANCE THE ENERGY TRANSITION IN CHINA: AN ANALYSIS FROM A COMPLEX SYSTEM ENGINEERING PERSPECTIVE

**Hanxin Zhao, Linda M. Kamp, Zofia Lukszo*
Faculty of Technology, Policy and Management, Delft University of Technology, Jaffalaan 5, 2628BX Delft, the Netherland
*Corresponding author e-mail: h.zhao-1@tudelft.nl

ABSTRACT

This paper discusses the development of future green ammonia supply chains in China with the theory of complex system engineering, taking account of technical system, actors and institutions in future energy systems featured socio-technical systems as a whole. The energy condition in China identified features a spatial imbalance between renewable energy supply and demand, which cannot be fully addressed by the current power system-centric solution. This calls for hydrogen to make a concerted effort in the energy transition. By comparing major hydrogen delivery options, we argue that green ammonia can play a feasible role for large-scale energy distribution and long-term energy storage. The development of green ammonia supply chains and direct use of ammonia are proposed to avoid large uncertainties and initial investment in the early stage. The market creation will be key in the supply chain development. A long-term bilateral contract between buyer and seller and a joint investment in an integrated supply chain by several stakeholders are advised to share risks and ensure capital recovery. In addition, government participation is crucial in the early development phase by setting regulatory and financial institutions to support the market creation and supply chain development.

Keywords: Hydrogen Economy, Green Ammonia, Supply Chain, China, Complex System Engineering

Track 14.

Hydrogen Industry, Commercialization and Marketing, Applications

#12

ANALYSIS OF THE HYDROGEN PURITY AT HYDROGEN REFUELLING STATIONS

[1, 2*] *Holger Janßen,* [1] *Michael Kröner,* [1] *Alexander Dyck,* [2] *Michael Wark,* [1] *Carsten Agert*
[1] German Aerospace Center (DLR), Institute of Networked Energy Systems, Carl-von-Ossietzky-Str. 15, 26129 Oldenburg, Germany
[2] Carl von Ossietzky University, Institute of Chemistry, Carl-von-Ossietzky-Str. 9-11, 26129 Oldenburg, Germany
*Corresponding author e-mail: Holger.Janssen@dlr.de

ABSTRACT

Contaminations in hydrogen have a strong impact on the long-term stability and thereby performance of proton exchange membrane (PEM) based fuel cells for mobile applications. While these influences have been intensively studied, particularly the purity of the hydrogen provided at public hydrogen refuelling stations (HRS) which is well-defined in ISO standards is rarely analyzed. We intend to take samples of hydrogen at HRS with a specially designed mobile refuelling module enabling the sampling at 70 MPa. With a method specifically developed and explicitly described in this paper, we seek to ensure that other sources of contamination can be excluded during the probe sampling. With analysis techniques able to determine concentrations of contaminants down to the parts per billion (ppb) level the hydrogen samples will be investigated in the laboratory. While single routes of contamination, such as the synthesis route, have been individually studied in detail elsewhere, the provision of hydrogen with different storage processes, as well as transport and compression at the HRS will be considered in these investigations as a holistic system. Finally, it can be stated whether the dispensed hydrogen meets the high-quality requirements of fuel cells for mobile applications.

Keywords: Contamination, Hydrogen Refuelling Station, Purity Analysis, Hydrogen Sampling

#80

INJECTION OF HYDROGEN INTO HIGH PRESSURE NATURAL GAS GRIDS: INVESTIGATION OF THE IMPACT ON MATERIALS AND EQUIPMENT AT RELEVANT ENVIRONMENT

[1,2*] *Vanesa Gil,* [1] *Javier Sánchez-Laínez,* [3]*Alberto Cerezo-Alarcón,* [3,4] *María Dolores Storch de Gracia,* [5] *Ekain Fernandez,* [5] *Virginia Madina*
[1]Foundation for the Development of New Hydrogen Technologies in Aragón, Parque Tecnológico Walqa Ctra. N-330A, km. 566, Cuarte, Huesca, Spain
[2]ARAID Foundation, Avda. de Ranillas 1-D, 50018 Zaragoza, Spain
[3]Redexis, C/ Mahonia 2, 28043 Madrid, Spain
[4]Universidad Politécnica de Madrid, 28040 Madrid, Spain
[5]Tecnalia, Parque Tecnológico de Bizkaia, Astondo bidea, Edificio 700, E-48160 Derio, Bizkaia, Spain
*Corresponding author e-mail: vgil@hidrogenoaragon.org

ABSTRACT

This work addresses the potential of hydrogen injection into the transmission high pressure natural gas grid as way to decarbonise the gas system and gas uses. To achieve this potential, knowledge gaps have to be covered considering the current know-how on how different concentrations of hydrogen gas could affect the infrastructure and its components. The activities are developed within the frame of HIGGS (FCH 2JU funded project, No. 875091). An R&D platform working at high pressure has been developed in HIGGS to achieve advance the knowledge on operation of hydrogen admixtures in the high-pressure natural gas grid, simulating the operational conditions from selected equipment, gas quality, etc. The admixture levels consider various hydrogen concentrations until reaching pure hydrogen. So far, the impact of H_2/NG blends with up to 20 %vol H_2 on steels and equipment has been studied through a mechanical and chemical characterization after been exposed to the blend. Membrane technology has also been tested for hydrogen recovery, using a Pd-based membrane prototype installed in the platform.

Keywords: Admixture, H_2 injection, Power to Gas, Gas transmission, Decarbonisation.

#118

SOLENCO POWER: HYDROGEN FOR THE DECARBONIZATION OF THE ENERGY SECTOR

[1] *Hugo Vandenborre*, [1*] *Francisco López*

[1]Solenco Power NV, Slachthuisstraat 112 box 2 - 2300 Turnhout, Belgium

*Corresponding author e-mail address: francisco.lopez@solencopower.com

ABSTRACT

Solenco Power NV (SP) is a fast-growing Belgian SME active in the energy storage sector, with systems that combine generation, storage, and usage of pressurized hydrogen. SP was founded in 2015, as a spinoff of Vandeborre Energy Systems NV, company with an extensive career in the hydrogen sector. SP was launched having as a first objective, the commercialization of an integrated hydrogen solution capable of absorbing excess of a renewable energy sources, when available, for hydrogen generation, store that hydrogen in a pressurized form for unlimited periods and use that hydrogen for the cogeneration of electricity and heat, when needed. For reaching that objective, since its foundation SP has matured this concept towards a product called Solenco Powerbox (SPB) [1] and its certification.

Keywords: Renewable energy, energy storage, seasonal storage, hydrogen, proton exchange membrane.

#166

GREEN HYDROGEN AS A FUNDAMENTAL ENERGY VECTOR FOR ALGERIA'S FUTURE SUSTAINABLE ENERGY AND INDUSTRIAL SYSTEMS (HYDROGEN AS A FUEL IN THE TRANSPORT SECTOR)

[1*]*Ahmed Abdelmouiz* , [2]*Abdelkader Hamdi*

[1]*Physics and Chemistry laboratory, University Amar Thelidji, Laghouat, Algeria*

[2] *Process engineering department, University of Amar Thelidji, Laghouat, Algeria*

*Corresponding author e-mail address: a.abdelmouiz@lagh-univ.dz

ABSTRACT

Growing human activity has resulted in a critical increase in global energy consumption; however, because the current primary sources of energy production are still fossil fuels, this industry is associated with the production of harmful byproducts that contribute to environmental deterioration and climate change. Renewable hydrogen has the potential to replace fossil fuels as a worldwide energy vector; however, for this to happen, dependable technologies for carbon-free production must be developed. The Production, separation, and storage of hydrogen for use as a major source of energy is a key component of the global green energy economy. Hydrogen is a potentially non-carbon-based energy source that is increasingly replacing reliance on fossil fuels. As an alternative fuel, hydrogen has the greatest promise for lowering greenhouse gas emissions, boosting engine efficiency, and providing fuel security. The present study's goal is to assess the economic competitiveness of alternative fuels. Based on the techno-economic parameters, a cost-benefit analysis of hydrogen-powered vehicles against gasoline-powered vehicles is performed. Results obtained indicate that improvements in manufacturing procedures will lead to a more competitive hydrogen-powered technology.

Keywords: Renewable, Electrolysis, Green Hydrogen

#200

AIR CARBON RECYCLING FOR AVIATION FUEL TECHNOLOGY

[1,2*] Vanesa Gil, [3] Kiyoharu Tadanaga, [4] Harald Gröger, [5,6] Stefan Wuttke, [7,2] Jonas Gurauskis, [8] Pedro Camargo, [9] Reinaldo Giudici, [10] Francesca Bonino, [11] Joke Hadermann

[1] Aragon Hydrogen Foundation, Parque Tecnológico Walqa Ctra. N-330A, km. 566, Cuarte, Huesca, Spain

[2] ARAID Foundation, Avda. de Ranillas 1-D, 50018 Zaragoza, Spain

[3] *Division of Applied Chemistry, Faculty of Engineering, Hokkaido University, 060-8628Sapporo, Japan*

[4] *Chair of Industrial Organic Chemistry and Biotechnology, Faculty of Chemistry, Bielefeld University, Universitätsstr. 25, 33615 Bielefeld, Germany*

[5] *BCMaterials, Basque Center for Materials, UPV/EHU Science Park, 48940 Leioa, Spain*

[6] *Ikerbasque, Basque Foundation for Science, 48013 Bilbao, Spain*

[7] *INMA, Instituto de Nanociencia y Materiales de Aragón (CSIC-Unizar), 50018 Spain*

[8] *Department of Chemistry, University of Helsinki, 00560 Helsinki, Finland*

[9] *Escola Politécnica da Universidade de São Paulo, Av. Prof. Luciano Gualberto trav.3, no. 380, 05508-010 São Paulo, Brazil*

[10] *Department of Chemistry, NIS and INSTM Reference Centre, University of Turin, Via G. Quarello 15, I-10135 and Via P. Giuria 7, I-10125 Turin, Italy*

[11] *Department of Physics, EMAT, University of Antwerp, Groenenborgerlaan 171, B-2020 Antwerp, Belgium*

*Corresponding author e-mail: vgil@hidrogenoaragon.org

ABSTRACT

The European Union and the Japan Science and Technology Agency awards 2.9M€ to 4AiCRAFT "Air Carbon Recycling for Aviation Fuel Technology", for helping the aviation sector to reach the EU 2050 climate-neutrality targets.

4AirCRAFT, a H2020 funded project in International Cooperation with Japan for Research and Innovation on alternative renewable fuels, offers a novel cascade reactor for sustainable aviation fuel synthesised from H_2 and CO_2. The conversion to high-density hydrocarbons will be achieved at mild conditions and based on an intensified cascade reactor.

Key to the process is the combination of highly efficient electro-, chemo- and bio- catalysts. Synergy between hybrid catalysts which are selectively embedded within advanced porous carriers including hierarchical scaffolds are expected to raise selectivity and energy efficiency. In this project the technology readiness level is raised from TRL 2 to 3.

Keywords: Hydrogen-based fuels, sustainable fuel, jet fuel, cascade synthesis, process intensification.

#214

GREEN HYDROGEN PRODUCTION FOR FCEV TRUCKS AT A REMOTE OPEN-PIT COPPER MINE

[1*]*Stewart F. Bauserman,* [2]*Johnny Nahui Ortiz,* [3]*Jose Cesar Ramos Saravia,* [1]*John W. Sheffield,* [4]*Matteo J. Mereu*
[1] Purdue University, School of Engineering Technology, West Lafayette, IN, U.S.A.
[2] Universidad Nacional de Ingeniería, Facultad de Ingeniería Ambiental, Lima, Peru
[3] Universidad de Ingeniería y Tecnología, Ingeniería de la Energía y Ingeniería Mecánica, Lima, Peru
[4] Purdue University, Energy Engineering Technology, West Lafayette, IN, U.S.A.
*Corresponding author e-mail: stew@purdue.edu

ABSTRACT

This paper presents the results of an international collaboration on the analysis of the production of green hydrogen for a fleet of fuel cell electric vehicle mining trucks for use in a remote open-pit copper mine in Peru. For this research, HOMER Pro® microgrid software was used to simulate, optimize, and analyze the renewable energy system integration into the operation of fueling a fleet of 300-tonne mining trucks for the copper mine based on a 30-year life of the remote mine. The optimization results shows that the electrolyzer provided a mean output of 29.4 kg/h per truck for an operational schedule of 8,097 h/y with 46.4 kWh/kg specific energy. The system architecture of the green hydrogen production microgrid includes wind turbines, AC-DC bidirectional power converters, a battery energy storage system, electrolyzers, and compressed hydrogen storage tanks. The two loads were the electric load for the balance of plant and the hydrogen load to fuel the fleet of mining trucks. To meet the two loads, the optimized microgrid powered one 1,505 kW electrolyzer having a specific energy of 46.4 kWh/kg resulting in a mean hydrogen output of 29.4 kg/h to fuel one 300-tonne mining truck.

Keywords: Green Hydrogen, Microgrid, FCEV, Mining Trucks, GW Scale

#285

CHIYODA'S APPROACH FOR HYDROGEN SUPPLY CHAIN BUSINESS WITH "SPERA HYDROGEN™" SYSTEM

[1*] *Osamu Ikeda,* [2] *Milesi Sara,* [1] *Masashi Nagai,* [1,3] *Takakazu Morimoto*
[1]Chiyoda Croporation, Hydrogen Business Department, 4-6-2 Minatomirai Nishi-ku, 2208765 Yokohama, Japan
[2] Chiyoda Corporation Netherlands BV, Parkstraat 83, 2514 JG Den Haag, Netherland
[3] Chiyoda Croporation, Frontier Business Devision, 4-6-2 Minatomirai Nishi-ku, 2208765 Yokohama, Japan
*Corresponding author e-mail: ikeda.osamu@chiyodacorp.com

ABSTRACT

Hydrogen is indispensable for decarbonisation through the expansion of renewable energy as its energy carrier. The organic chemical hydride method is key technology of hydrogen carrier to store and transport hydrogen under normal temperature and pressure in the liquid form by incorporating hydrogen atoms into the molecular structure of liquid organic hydrogen carrier (LOHC). Chiyoda started the development of innovative catalyst technology of LOHC method to establish hydrogen supply chain system since 2002, named "SPERA Hydrogen™" and the system has successfully demonstrated the international massive hydrogen supply chain from Brunei Darussalam to Japan in 2020. It is the only system that has completed the international demonstration of the entire value chain from production to utilization, and has moved to the commercialization stage. This system enable to storage and transport hydrogen safely, economically with its proven technology and existing petroleum infrastructure, and also has a high potential for cost reduction towards the future.

Keywords: Hydrogen, Storage, Transportation, LOHC, SPERA

#328

DEMONSTRATING THE LIQUEFIED HYDROGEN SEABORNE SUPPLY CHAIN TO JAPAN AND DEVELOPMENT OF FUTURE COMMERCIALIZATION

[1*]*Taku Hasegawa,* [1]*Yoshichika Taira,* [1]*Naoki Maruyama,* [1]*Norio Ueda,* [1]*Yasuhiro Yoshino,* [1]*Kenji Yoshimura,* [1]*Motohiko Nishimura and* [1]*Eiichi Harada*
[1] Kawasaki Heavy Industries, Ltd., 1-15-5, Kaigan, Minato-ku, 105-8315, Tokyo, Japan
*Corresponding author e-mail: hasegawa_taku@khi.co.jp

ABSTRACT
To achieve the target for Nationally Determined Contributions in Japan, hydrogen will play a vital role in the energy system, both CO2 reduction and energy security. In October 2020, the Japanese government announced the carbon-neutrality until 2050 and launched 14 important pillars. Hydrogen was selected as one of these pillars as the important energy for decarbonization. Introducing large-mass-hydrogen-energy is expected to expand hydrogen application or solution to energy issues of Japan. Under these circumstances, imported CO2-free-hydrogen will be one of the solutions for energy security and CO2 reduction if the hydrogen is affordable.
Kawasaki Heavy Industries, Ltd. (KHI) presented the concept of the "Hydrogen Energy Supply Chain (HESC)" in 2010. The HESC requires several vital technologies such as hydrogen production, hydrogen liquefaction, liquefied hydrogen storage, and transportation. In January 2022, World's first liquefied hydrogen carrier, "Suiso Frontier," arrived in Port of Hasting and successfully shipped first cargo to Japan. For future commercialization, the success of the operation of "Suiso Frontier" and the scaling up of each facility are important to achieve affordable hydrogen. KHI will present the current situation of the HESC project and hydrogen related projects.
***Keyword**:* Liquefied hydrogen, Seaborne transportation, Liquefied hydrogen supply chain, Suiso Frontier, Hydrogen utilization

#350

OPTIMIZATION OF A PREMIXED CHARGE HYDROGEN ENGINE IN ARGON POWER CYCLE

[1*] *Taisei Chiba,* [2] *Taku Tsujimura,* [1] *Mihiro Kobayashi,* [2] *Yasumasa Suzuki,* [1] *Daisaku Swada,* [1] *Chen Zhili,*
[1]Tokai University, Hiratsuka city. 259-1292, Japan
[2] National Institute of Advanced Industrial Science and Technology, Koriyama city. 963-0298, Japan
*Corresponding author e-mail: chiba-taisei@aist.go.jp

ABSTRACT
Hydrogen is attracting attention as a future fuel for automobiles and power generator because it does not emit carbon dioxide (CO_2) during the utilization phase. For example, when hydrogen is adapted as a fuel to a stationary engine generator, it is expected to be able to operate with higher thermal efficiency and cleaner exhaust emissions than those of conventional engines. Further improvement in efficiency is expected by adapting argon (Ar) gas with high specific heat ratio, to the working gas of hydrogen engines. The objective of this study is to optimize operating conditions of Ar power cycle of a spark ignition premixed hydrogen engine for achieving high efficiency and high power. In this study, the effect of Ar concentration added to the working gas on hydrogen combustion characteristics and engine performance was investigated with a single-cylinder test engine. The result shows that thermal efficiency was greatly improved as Ar concentration in the working gas was up to 40 mol% in comparison with the air cycle. On the other hand, some technical issues relating abnormal combustion were revealed.
Keywords: Hydrogen Engine, Argon Addition, High Thermal Efficiency

#365

MODIFIED WSGG GAS RADIATION MODEL FOR ANY MIXTURE OF H_2/CH_4 FUEL FOR HIGH-TEMPERATURE INDUSTRIAL FURNACES

[1*] *Benjamin Le Creurer,* [1] *Fouad Ammouri*
[1]Air Liquide – Innovation Campus Paris, 1 Chemin de la Portes des Loges 78350, Les Loges-en-Josas, France
*Corresponding author e-mail: benjamin.le-creurer@airliquide.com

ABSTRACT
Energy transition will push more and more the use of hydrogen for mobility and to heat industrial furnaces with other fuels where radiation has the major contribution. Consequently, the need for adequate radiation model parameters to account for gas radiation from mixtures of hydrogen/methane combustion in high-temperature furnaces is of major importance. The proposed model is a modified weighted sum of grey gases (WSGG). The model validation is presented for a 1D gas column and also on a 2D domain with walls.
Keywords: Industrial Furnaces, H_2/CH_4 Mixture, Thermal Gas Radiation, Numerical Modelling

#387

HYDROGEN-METHANE MIXTURE STORAGE IN DEPLETED RESERVOIRS: AN OPTION FOR CONVERTING DECOMMISSIONED OFFSHORE PLATFORMS

[1] Anna Chiara Uggenti, [1] Giorgio Rech, [1] Raffaella Gerboni, [1] Andrea Carpignano, [2] Amedeo Aliberti, [3] Andrea Tortora, [2] Gabriele Ballocco*

[1]Politecnico di Torino, Energy Department, Corso Duca degli Abruzzi 24, Torino, Italy
[2] RAMS&E s.r.l., Via Livorno 60, Torino, Italy
[3] Environment Park S.p.A. Via Livorno 60, Torino, Italy
*Corresponding author e-mail: raffaella.gerboni@polito.it

ABSTRACT

With several oil or natural gas offshore reservoirs depleting in different areas of the world, the producing platforms which insist on them are becoming a challenge for companies and governments: on one side they represent infrastructures that are ageing, and that most legislative frameworks impose to remove, while on the other side they represent a valuable opportunity for supporting the energy transition, thanks to their position, technical and structural characteristics.

The paper presents the outcomes of a basic design to reuse a natural gas production platform under decommissioning to inject and extract alternatively and seasonally a mixture of 10% hydrogen and methane in a depleted reservoir. The reuse brings along the idea of removing the equipment that are not useful anymore from the various platforms decks while preserving those major components that can still be fruitfully exploited: typical examples are represented by wellheads and separators. The exploitation of a depleted reservoir is a delicate matter and deep knowledge of the specific features of each reservoir is mandatory to dimension the single components. This paper focuses on the engineering philosophy of this kind of reconversion providing guidelines, included environmental and HSE safeguards to be considered.

Keywords: Reuse, H_2+CH_4 Mixtures, Platform Conversion, Safety, Temporary Storage

#388

REAL-WORLD ENERGY MEASUREMENTS AND LOCAL HYDROGEN COST AS INPUT PARAMETERS FOR REGIONAL VEHICLE FLEET OPTIMIZATION

[1] Rittmar von Helmolt, [1] Martin Rothbart, [2] Hans Beck, [2] Florian Bindges [3] Loic Lerminiaux*

[1]AVL List GmbH, 8020 Graz, Austria
[2] Strategy Engineers GmbH & Co. KG, 80335 Munich, Germany
[3] Güriş İnşaat & Mühendislik A.Ş., 06830 Gölbaşi, Ankara
*Corresponding author e-mail: rittmar.vonhelmolt@avl.com

ABSTRACT

When changing vehicle fleets from Diesel to a zero-emission alternative, the change involves the vehicle but also the fuel supply chain. For an informed decision on choosing vehicles fuelled by either hydrogen or direct electricity, this is a decisive factor which needs to be predicted as accurately as possible for a quite long time in the future, ideally for the lifetime of the intended infrastructure. For supply of green hydrogen, we have considered scenarios that incorporate either a local or domestic production or an import of hydrogen. The hydrogen is assumed to be transported in pressure vessels from the point of generation to the filling station. Also, possible alternative routes via Ammonia or LOHC are indicateded.

We furthermore describe a method for TCO optimization for a regional vehicle fleet, which is based on real-world measurements on the vehicle. Measurements have been done on a bus fleet in daily operation with focus on the thermal energy flow, and monitored for an extended period of 2 years in order to cover a wide range of climate and traffic conditions. These data are the basis for a simulation for an operation of battery electric as well as hydrogen vehicles, and the layout of respective infrastructures.

Keywords: Hydrogen Transport Cost, Hydrogen Bus Fleet, Regional hydrogen cost, Vehicle TCO, Fleet Monitoring and Simulation

#442

FRAUNHOFER HYDROGEN LABS: UNIQUE TEST INFRASTRUCTURE FOR THE ENTIRE HYDROGEN VALUE CHAIN

[1] Vincent Köhler, M.Sc; [2] Kevin Schalk, M.Sc.; [3]Moritz Kühnel, Dr.-Ing.; [4*] Johannes Höflinger, Dr. Ing.; [5] Sebastian Schmidt, Dr.-Ing.*

[1,4] Fraunhofer Institute for Wind Energy Systems IWES, Hydrogn Lab Görlitz, Am Haupttor 06237 Leuna Germany

[2] Fraunhofer Institute for Wind Energy Systems IWES, Hydrogn Lab Bremerhaven, Am Seedeich 45, 27572 Bremerhaven, Germany

[3] Fraunhofer Institute for Wind Energy Systems IWES, Hydrogn Lab Bremerhaven, Am Haupttor 06237 Leuna Germany

[5]Fraunhofer Institute for Machine Tools and Forming Technology (IWU), Reichenhainer Str. 88, 09126 Chemnitz, Germany

*Corresponding author e-mail: vincent.koehler@iwes.fraunhofer.de; Johannes.hoeflinger@iwes.fraunhofer.de

ABSTRACT

The three Fraunhofer Hydrogen Labs in Bremerhaven, Leuna and Görlitz, aim to provide digitally cross-linked research infrastructure with testing capacities for hydrogen technologies with over 27 MW electrical power supply. The focus of the test fields is to investigate the efficiency and performance of electrolysers powered by renewable energy, building on the combined expertise of the Fraunhofer Institute for Wind and Energy Systems in collaboration with the Institute for Machine Tools and Forming Technology (IWU) and Center for Chemical-Biotechnological Processes (CBP). These integrated research facilities will enable evaluation and appraisal as the key basis for driving the market ramp-up of hydrogen technologies.

All three hydrogen Labs are digitally interconnected and cover the whole green hydrogen process: starting from renewable power generation with on- and offshore wind turbines, the optimization of electrolysis and manufacturing of electrolysers, as well as storage, transport, and electricity generation from green hydrogen. Therefore, the Fraunhofer Hydrogen Labs can offer a worldwide unique spectrum of pilot plants, covering the complete value creation chain of the hydrogen economy.

Keywords: Hydrogen, Electrolyser, Storage, Fuel Cell

#1442

USE OF HYDROGEN FOR GREEN STEEL PRODUCTION

[1] Pablo Duarte, [2] Stefano Maggiolino, [3] Jorge Martinez, [4] Enrico Malfa*

[1]Sr. Consultant, Tenova, Castellanza, Italy

[2] President & CEO, Tenova HYL, Monterrey, Mexico

[3] Commercial director, Tenova HYL, Monterrey, Mexico

[4] R&D Director, Tenova

*Corresponding author e-mail: jorge.martinez@tenova.com

ABSTRACT

Among the various approaches for decarbonization of the steelmaking industry, two main routes should be considered, based on the intensive use of hydrogen (H_2) (CDA) and capture and use of CO_2 (CCU). One consists of the progressive conversion of the BF-BOF facilities to direct reduction-electric arc furnace (DRI-EAF). The second alternative is the production of hot metal (HM) by installing a gas-based direct reduction plant feeding DRI to an open slag bath furnace (DRI-OSBF). Schemes for liquid steel production with reduced or practically nil carbon input by using H_2, its equivalent cost for DRI production and the reduction of CO_2 emissions are analysed.

Keywords: Hydrogen, Direct Reduction, Energiron process, Electric Arc Furnace, Open Slag Bath Furnace.

#1448

GREEN HYDROGEN PRODUCTION USING GEOTHERMAL POWER GENERATION (1) PROJECT IN MOKAI, NEW ZEALAND

[1] *Kenichi Ando,* [1] *Toshihiro Hisaeda,* [1*] *Chiaki Nagai,* [1] *Nobuyoshi Sasaki,* [1] *Shoichi Ichikawa,* [1] *Yukio Mashimo,* [2] *Aya Inagaki*
[1]Obayashi Corporation, Green Energy Division, 2-15-2 Konan, Minato-ku, Tokyo, Japan
[2] Halcyon Power, 54 Tuwharetoa Street, Taupo, New Zealand
*Corresponding author e-mail: nagai.chiaki@obayashi.co.jp

ABSTRACT
For reducing greenhouse gases, the introduction of machines (Mobility and Power plants) that operate on hydrogen as a fuel has been under way. For hydrogen to be produced in a carbon-free way, water electrolysis using renewable energy is one of the methods implemented in the industry. Since continuous power generation is not committed from solar and wind power, stable production of hydrogen can be challenging as well. Therefore, we considered the efforts to stably produce green hydrogen by water electrolysis using geothermal power generation, and in 2021, New Zealand's first megawatt-class hydrogen production plant using geothermal power generation started its operation. This report describes the hydrogen production equipment, its operating conditions, and the utilization of hydrogen produced.
Keywords: Green Hydrogen, Geothermal Power Generation, Supply Chain

#1451

GREEN HYDROGEN PRODUCTION USING GEOTHERMAL POWER GENERATION (2) PROJECT IN OITA, JAPAN

[1*] *Hitoshi Nagatsugu,* [1] *Kiyoshi Shima,* [1]*Tsuyoshi Ito,* [1] *Moriya Kajiki*
[1]Obayashi Corporation, Green Energy Division, 2-15-2 Konan, Minato-ku, Tokyo, Japan
*Corresponding author e-mail: nagatsugu.hitoshi@obayashi.co.jp

ABSTRACT
Japan has the third-largest geothermal resource in the world. Geothermal power generation is one of the renewable energy sources being an excellent energy source with a stable supply. Unfortunately, however, commercialization has been delayed due to several reasons. Because geothermal power generation facilities are in mountainous areas, the capacity of the power grid is often insufficient. In addition, since the development period is rather long, the capacity of the commercial power grid to apply for the feed-in tariff (FIT) gets filled earlier by other renewable energy projects which require a mere short development period. Accordingly, there exists difficulty for geothermal power to be connected to the transmission line. Therefore, we considered promoting the use of green hydrogen and establishing its economic efficiency along with the development of geothermal power generation. This project demonstrated a scheme in which hydrogen produced by geothermal power in Oita Prefecture is transported to various parts of Kyushu by land.
Keywords: Green Hydrogen, Geothermal Power Generation, EMS, Hydrogen Transport System, Supply Chain

#1468

ANALYSIS OF HYDROGEN COMBUSTION AS FUEL TO PREHEAT AIR IN POWER GENERATION PLANTS IN MICROMIX INJECTION TECHNOLOGY

[1] *Germán Jiménez,* [2] *Ernesto Cantillo,* [2] *Ronald Howard,* [1] *Lesme Corredor,* [1] *Arturo González-Quiroga,* [1*] *Victor Pugliese*
[1]Universidad del Norte, Mechanical Engineering Department, Barranquilla, Colombia
[2] Gecelca S.A., Barranquilla, Colombia
*Corresponding author e-mail: vpugliese@uninorte.edu.co

ABSTRACT
Hydrogen represents a viable alternative as fuel for future power generation plants. Different uses include but are not limited to partial substitution of coal in boilers, an energy source for preheating air, and fuel for starter-diesel boilers. The objective of power generations plants is to reduce emissions to fulfill national and international commitments before 2050. To speed up the use of hydrogen in established power plant generation systems, it is necessary to evaluate the current combustion technology and its flexibility to handle hydrogen due to the large difference in hydrogen thermophysical properties compared to other fuels such as natural gas or diesel. One of the main components that are calling the attention of researchers is the injection-mixing technology. The micromix hydrogen combustion injector allows a fast and intense mixing of hydrogen and air. As a result, micro flames are developed, and the residence time of the NOx-forming reactants is reduced. This study aims to evaluate the effect of air-fuel ratio on flame structure and stability in a micromix hydrogen combustion injector.
Keywords: Micromix Burner, Hydrogen, Combustion, Flame Temperature

#1483

EXTENSION OF LEAN LIMIT USING HYDROGEN ADDITION FOR GASOLINE DIRECT INJECTION ENGINE AND EMSSION REDUCTION

[1] *Jerome Stanley M*, [1] *Leenus Jesu Martin M*, [2] *Edwin Geo Varuvel*
[1]Green Vehicle Technology Research Centre, Department of Automobile Engineering, SRM Institute of Science and Technology, Kattankulathur, Tamilnadu, India.
[2*]Department of Mechanical Engineering, Faculty of Engineering and Natural Sciences, Istinye University, Istanbul, Turkey
*Corresponding author e-mail: vedwingeo@gmail.com

ABSTRACT
The effect of hydrogen induction (0-5 liter per minute) in to the intake manifold of the small bore Gasoline Direct Injection (GDI) Engine is investigated experimentally. The intake manifold is slightly modified to accommodate the hydrogen induction system, where premixed mixture of hydrogen and air is formed in the intake manifold; attaining the excess air ratio of 1.0 to 1.2. With the increment of hydrogen fraction the fuel leaning (Gasoline) is attained and achieving economical fuel consumption rate. The decrement in torque characteristics is compensated with the increase of hydrogen fraction. The hydrogen induction improves the combustion rate and mean effective pressure; shortens the flame propagation, maximize the heat release rate and peak pressure attainment. On the emission side consistent decrease in CO and HC emission; and increase of NO_x emission since the mean gas temperature has increased. The cycle to cycle variation during the lean operating condition at 1.2 shows the combustion stability and effective flame propagation.
Keywords: Hydrogen Induction, Small Bore, Gasoline Direct Injection

#1490

HYDROGEN AS FUTURE ENERGY CARRIER FOR MOBILITY

[1*] *Thomas von Unwerth,*
[1]Chemnitz University of Technology, Faculty of Mechanical Engineering, Department Advanced Powertrains), Reichenhainer Str. 7, 912 Chemnitz, Germany
*Corresponding author e-mail: Thomas.von-unwerth@mb.tu-chemnitz.de

ABSTRACT
Many countries around the world are turning towards climate friendly energy usage. One of the main options appreciated is seen in electricity won from renewables and then used in a direct way for stationary and mobile applications. Taking into account that there's still a big lack for electric energy storage, hydrogen as an energy carrier more and more plays an important role. Producible via many different ways from almost any primary energy with different sizes of carbon footprints, it can be stored in large quantities, transported by pipelines, road or sea and can be used in a lot of applications.
In the future, when global transformation of energy systems towards hydrogen economy proceeds, hydrogen production is located especially in the sun-favoured regions and transport lines are established, the use of hydrogen will also become increasingly interesting for mobile applications. The amounts needed are relatively low, compared to other energy intensive sectors and can be provided as energy feedstock.
Of course, using hydrogen for mobility results in a lower overall efficiency than using directly electric energy for a vehicle with a battery. However, seeing the overall global picture in a time where hydrogen will be a very common energy carrier, available almost all around the world, it will show its full potential with many advantages in terms of storage, comfort, dynamic availability and many more. Relating to mobility that means short filling durations, long ranges with all known convenience from conventional mobility, particularly important for light and heavy-duty vehicles. Therefore, research work still has to be carried out towards a production of large quantities of vehicles. The main topics in terms of durability, RCS, certification and reduced costs will be addressed in the new Hydrogen Innovation Centre at Chemnitz.Please carefully follow the guidelines in the current template and prepare your short paper in MS Word. The abstracts should be submitted via Microsoft's Conference Management Toolkit (CMT). Please create a user account on the submission site. Make sure that your paper is free of technical, grammatical and typographical errors. Please ensure using a plagiarism software that the similarity index is less than 20% with no more than 1% from any source (excluding the references). The abstract (maximum 200 words) should briefly state the content, methods, and results only.
Keywords: Electromobility Hydrogen, Fuel Cells

#1495

LARGE SCALE LOW-CARBON HYDROGEN EXPORT FROM QATAR TO THE ASIA-PACIFIC, AND EUROPE - TECHNO-ECONOMIC ASSESSMENT

[1*] *Ahmad Sleiti,* [1] *Wahib Al-Ammari,* [1] *Mohammed Al-Khawaja*
[1]Qatar University, College of Engineering, Department of Mechanical & Industrial Engineering), Doha, Qatar
*Corresponding author e-mail: asleiti@qu.edu.qa

ABSTRACT

Low-carbon hydrogen is projected to have significant contribution to the global near-term and long-term energy mix. However, there are only few studies that investigate the economic feasibility of blue hydrogen export especially in the Middle East region. Therefore, this study presents a techno-economic assessment (TEA) for the hydrogen production and overseas transportation from Qatar to Asia-Pacific and European countries. Two different pathways for transportation were assessed; liquefied hydrogen (LH2) pathway, and ammonia (NH3) pathway. The assessment boundaries extended from the hydrogen production stage from natural gas source with carbon capture process to the distribution stage before the end-use. The TEA was carried out in terms of the specific energy consumption, levelized cost of hydrogen, and CO_2 intensity for each pathway stage. In addition, the effect of some proposed improvements for the LH2 pathway was presented. The results show that based on the current hydrogen liquefaction and storage technologies, the overall LCOH for LH2 pathway (5.17 $/kg-H2) is higher than that of NH3 pathway (4.76 $/kg-H2) by about 8.61% at a capacity of 600 tons per day and shipping distance of about 14000 km. However, for the improved LH2 pathway, the LCOH of LH2 is reduced to 4.46 $/kg-H2, which is 6.3% lower than of NH3 pathway under the same conditions. It is found that the LCOH of blue hydrogen (5.71 $/kg-H2) with transportation distance up to 14000 km is lower than that of domestic green hydrogen (6.87 $/kg-H2) by about 17%.

Keywords: Hydrogen and Ammonia Pathways, Blue Hydrogen, Low-Carbon Hydrogen, Levelized Cost of Hydrogen, LCOH.

#1496

PROGRESS AND PERSPECTIVES IN USING HYDROGEN-ENRICHED BIOGAS FROM WASTE TO ENGINE IN AGRICULTURE

[1*] *Sami Ayad,* [1] *Carlos Belchior,* [2] *Inoussa Tougri,* [3] *Robert Amoah,*[4] *Isaac Bryant*
[1] Department of Mechanical Engineering, Federal University of Rio de Janeiro, Rio de Janeiro, Brazil
[2] École Polytechnique de Ouagadougou (EPO), Ouagadougou, Burkina Faso
[3] Department of Agricultural Engineering, University of Cape Coast, Cape Coast, Ghana
[4] Department of Environmental Science, University of Cape Coast, Cape Coast, Ghana
*Corresponding author e-mail: samiayad@ufrj.br

ABSTRACT

This paper reviews the progress and perspectives in using hydrogen-enriched biogas, produced from agricultural wastes as fuel to power internal combustion engines. There is a direct link between a country's capacity for economic growth and its energy consumption, which in turn, is strongly correlated with its pollutant emissions. In response, many countries aim to exploit and include biofuels in their respective energy matrices to address energy insecurity and environmental concerns, foreign exchange savings, and fomenting growth in the rural sector. One way of realizing this potential is producing biogas through the fermentation or anaerobic digestion of organic, biodegradable waste. However, biogas has limitations when used as a fuel in internal combustion engines. In this context, hydrogen addition is one way of solving the drawbacks associated with biogas. Hydrogen enrichment of biogas has been shown to increase the engine's efficiency, mixture's lean operating limit, improving combustion stability, increase the mixture's laminar speed, and decrease carbon emissions. As a result, biological generation of hydrogen (biohydrogen) from renewable biomass presents the opportunity to simultaneously reduce fossil fuel dependence, decrease carbon dioxide emissions, and recover bioenergy. In addition, in some countries the thermal generation of hydrogen from renewable biomass is a viable option due to the abundance of solar energy.

Keywords: Biogas, Biohydrogen, Hydrogen Enrichment, Waste to Engine, Agriculture

#1513

A CFD STUDY ON HYDROGEN ADDITION TO THE METHANE-AIR MIXTURES

[1-2*] *Eren Çolak, İlhami Karagül* [2],
[1]Hacettepe University, Mechanical Engineering Department, , Ankara, Turkey
[2] GKE Energy R&D Center, Muğla,Turkey
*Corresponding author e-mail: eren.colak@gke.com.tr

ABSTRACT
Hydrogen can be an alternative fuel to control the environmental affects of the hydrocarbon fuels. Since hydrogen flame temperature and, flame speed is higher than the methane flame it is an important alternative to the hydrocarbon fuels, which can replace hydrocarbon fuels fully or partially in near future. In this study CFD study of a reactive flow of the Hydrogen-Air-Methane mixture is investigated to understand the combustion characteristics of the mixture. 5-20% H_2 is added to the CH_4-Air mixture (16% CH_4) and temperature-specie fields are compared with the CH4-Air mixture combustion. Study conducted with turbulent flow conditions and with Eddy Dissipation Concept. It is found that hydrogen addition to the mixture increases the flame temperature, water production and decreases the CO_2 concentration along the flow in each H_2 percentage increase between 5-20% hydrogen addition.
Keywords: CFD, Methane, Hydrogen, Combustion, OpenFOAM.

#1531

PREDICTION OF CARBON DI OXIDE AND OTHER EMISSIONS CHARACTERISTICS OF LOW CARBON BIOFUEL-HYDROGEN DUAL FUEL ENGINE - A MACHINE LEARNING APPROACH

[1*]*Femilda Josephin Joseph Shobana Bai and* [2]*Edwin Geo Varuvel*
[1*]Department of Computer Engineering, Faculty of Engineering and Natural Sciences, Istinye University, Istanbul, Turkey
[2]Department of Mechanical Engineering, Faculty of Engineering and Natural Sciences, Istinye University, Istanbul, Turkey
*Corresponding author e-mail: femij80@gmail.com

ABSTRACT
The transportation sector is a major emitter of carbon dioxide emissions. It is a known fact that carbon dioxide is the cause of global warming which has resulted in extreme weather conditions as well as climate change. In this study a combination of different methods of expediting the CO_2 emission from a single cylinder common rail direct injection (CRDI) engine has been explored. The methods include use of low carbon content biofuels (lemon peel oil (LPO) and camphor oil (CMO), inducing hydrogen in the intake manifold and zeolite based after-treatment system. The emissions were found to reduce even further and at full load condition the lowest CO2 (39.7% reduction) and smoke (49% reduction) emissions were observed with LPO blend and hydrogen induction. The NO emission with hydrogen induction increases for both the blends, however, it was seen that the zeolite-based treatment system was effective in reducing the emission as well. As compared to baseline diesel, the maximum reduction in NO emission was 23% at full load with LPO blend, hydrogen induction and after-treatment system.
Unfortunately, a lot of experimental research in the engineering field takes a long time and costs a lot of money. The number of experimental trials can be minimized by applying predictions using the available experimental data. Machine learning approaches can aid in the development of rapid and reliable data-based models that can supplement a traditional physical model. The goal of this work is to investigate if a data-based model can help to predict engine emission characteristics including CO, NO_x, Smoke, BTE, and HC more accurately.
In machine learning, ensemble methods are strategies for creating numerous models and then combining them to obtain better results. In most cases, ensemble approaches provide more accurate results than a single model. In the present work, ensemble learning algorithms like XGBoost, LightGBM, CatBoost, Random Forest (RF) are used for the prediction of emissions. The brake power and BSEC are the input parameters to these algorithms from which CO, NO_x, Smoke, BTE, and HC are predicted under various combination of additives. The CatBoost model has produced high accuracy predictions which was followed by XGBoost, RF and LightGBM models. The predicted and actual values are compared each other and the performance of the algorithms were analysed using the evaluation metrics like R-Square(R^2), Mean Absolute Error (MAE), Mean Square Error (MSE) and Root Mean Square Error (RMSE).
Keywords: Hydrogen, Low Carbon Biofuel, After Treatment, Machine Learning, Ensemble Learning

#1552

EVALUATION OF KINETIC MODELS VIA COMPUTATIONAL OPTIMIZATION TECHNIQUES FOR DIRECT SYNGAS-TO-OLEFINS PROCESS

[1*] *Kerem Bülbül*, [2] *Abdullah Zahid Turan*, [1] *Alper Sarıoğlan*, [2] *Gamze Behmenyar*, [2] *Özlem Ataç*
[1]Istanbul Technical University, Faculty, Department of Chemical Engineering, ITU Ayazaga Campus, 34469, Maslak, Istanbul
[2] TUBITAK Marmara Research Center, Energy Institute, Kocaeli, Turkey
*Corresponding author e-mail: che.kerembulbul@gmail.com

ABSTRACT
In this study, kinetics of Fischer-Tropsch (FT)-to-olefins was thoroughly investigated on activated carbon supported Fe-Cu-K catalyst. Among the evaluated methods, it was observed that the Runge-Kutta method gave better results. In general, the model that pertain to study of Fernandes introduced fewer errors than the Wang et al.'s model. In the simulations based on the Fernandes model, the H_2 values were estimated within error limits in between 2% and 8% validated for 7 distinct experiments. CO, on the other hand was estimated more accurately with the error limits in the ranges of 4-7% for high gas hourly space velocity (GHSV) values. However, error band of the model in the latter case was increased up to 30% for low GHSV values. Regarding hydrocarbon products, an average error value of 30% was obtained for ethylene while the best estimations were obtained for propylene with an error of 0.46% and 13.27%.
Keywords: Kinetics, Fischer-Tropsch, Advanced Optimization, Multi-Objective Generic Algorithm

#1595

DRIVE CYCLE SIMULATION OF A SMALL-SIZED FUEL CELL ELECTRIC VEHICLE

[1,2*] *Eda Alpaslan*, [1] *Mustafa Umut Karaoğlan*, [1] *Can Ozgur Colpan*
[1]Mechanical Engineering Department, Dokuz Eylul University, Buca, Izmir, Turkey
[2] The Graduate School of Natural and Applied Sciences Dokuz Eylul University, Buca, Izmir, Turkey
*Corresponding author e-mail: edaa.alpaslann@gmail.com

ABSTRACT
Environmental concerns such as global warming and air pollution have increased mainly due to the high energy consumption all over the world. In order to reduce the greenhouse gas and pollutant emissions from transportation sector, fuel cell vehicles offer a clean and highly energy-efficient alternative. In fuel cell vehicles, an energy storage unit such as a battery and/or a supercapacitor (SC) is required in high power demands such as accelerating, uphill and start-up conditions. In this study, a mathematical model a fuel cell vehicle including both a supercapacitor and a battery was developed and its drive cycle simulation was conducted to determine the vehicle performance. As a result of the drive cycle simulation, FCEVs equipped with battery and supercapacitor as storage units, energy efficiency has increased according to the developed simulation algorithm.
Keywords: Fuel Cell Vehicle, Drive Cycle Simulation, Battery, Supercapacitor

#1615

DECARBONIZING HARD INDUSTRIAL AND COMMERCIAL THERMAL LOADS

[1*] *Dean Moretton*
[1]Hydrogen Technologies Inc
*Corresponding author e-mail: dean@hydrogenTechnologiesInc.com

ABSTRACT
Join us on a journey to the decarbonized future of industrial and commercial thermal loads. This roadmap presentation charts a carbon-free tomorrow paved with metrics-based CO_2 reducing solutions. Participants will explore the stoichiometric reaction ratio of H_2 and O_2 in a vacuum to create superheated steam. The condensing steam transfers energy from the tube side of the heat exchanger to yield working fluid as low as 60°C and/or steam above 400°C at pressures as high as 40 bar. This exothermic energy released during H_2O formation decarbonizes industrial and commercial process steam and hot water using a GHG-free solution. The journey concludes by highlighting financial incentives for the hydrogen economy from G20 Nations and *directions* to GHG-free funding that supports CO_2, NOX, SOX and other GHG eliminating projects.
Keywords: Hydrogen, Oxygen, Zero GHG Emission

Track 15.

Hydrogen Economy, Logistics, Infrastructure

#17

ASSESSMENT OF THE SOCIO-ECONOMIC COSTS AND BENEFITS OF INCREASED USE OF BIOMETHANE AND HYDROGEN IN EUROPE

Jan Michalski, Matthias Altmann, Ulrich Bünger, Jan Zerhusen*
Ludwig-Bölkow-Systemtechnik GmbH (LBST), Daimlerstr. 15, 85521 Ottobrunn, Germany
*Corresponding author e-mail: jan.michalski@lbst.de

ABSTRACT
This paper presents selected results from the study "Impact of the use of the biomethane and hydrogen potential on trans-European infrastructure" which has been conducted by Trinomics, Ludwig-Bölkow-Systemtechnik GmbH (LBST) and E3Modelling (E3M) for the European Commission. The major objective of the study was to analyse the impact of biomethane and hydrogen on the gas sector in Europe until 2050 from technical, economic and regulatory perspective. In general form the system perspective, the optimal system design strongly depends on the anticipated GHG emission reduction targets. Among the analysed cases the scenario with a strong focus on hydrogen technology appears to be a robust compromise where the advantages of higher system flexibility overcompensate the disadvantages of lower energy efficiency in comparison to the electricity-focused scenario. Based on the study's results, strategies for fully decarbonized gas system by 2050 should be developed describing cost-effective transition pathways in the medium-term (2030) and towards the long-term (2050) target situation of full decarbonisation.
Keywords: Energy System, Gas Infrastructure, Decarbonization, Modelling

#62

THE HYDROGEN SCIENTIFIC ASPECTS IN ROMANIA

[1] Ioan Iordache, [1] Mihai Varlam, [1] Elena Carcadea, [1] Dorin Schitea, [1] Mihaela Iordache*
[1] National Research and Development Institute for Cryogenics and Isotopic Technologies -ICSI, Uzinei Str., Rm. Vâlcea, Romania
*Corresponding author e-mail: iordache.ioan@icsi.ro

ABSTRACT
This work presents the latest advances of hydrogen and fuel cell research and development from Romania.
The presentation focuses more on National Hydrogen and Fuel Cell Centre (NHFCC) researchers' activities as a part of national policy and program issues. This centre is a research and development facility with the mission to implement, develop and disseminate hydrogen-based technologies in Romania, as well as to support national priority policies in the field of energy and environment. It has an exceptional infrastructure for the entire process chain of the new energy revolution (production, storage, transport, and utilization). The researchers are focused on the development of technologies, products and services that contribute to achieve an "economy of hydrogen" in Romania.
Keywords: Romania, National Hydrogen and Fuel Cell Centre

#101

MUCILAGE IN THE MARMARA SEA VERSUS BLACK SEA's H_2S; HYDROGEN ENERGY PRODUCTION OPPORTUNITIES

[1] Erhan Atay, [2] Sudi Apak*
[1] Trakya University,Economics Department, Edirne,Türkiye.
[2] Istanbul Esenyurt University,Ind.Eng. Dept,Istanbul,Türkiye
*Corresponding author e-mail: erhanatay@trakya.edu.tr

ABSTRACT
Hydrogen energy is among alternative solutions to energy shortage regarding the aspects of being environmentally clean, economic and efficient. In this context, Turkey's energy demand, which cannot be met by our country and will not be able to be met by local resources in the 2020s. Therefore, Turkey should turn to renewable energy sources as soon as possible, especially hydrogen energy to be obtained from the Black Sea, as well as a new type of energy that can be obtained by turning the mucilage crisis in the Sea of Marmara into an opportunity. In addition, the conversion of these organic wastes in the Marmara Sea into hydrogen energy as a renewable energy source will be an innovative and high added value solution method.
Our aim in this study is to bring up the hydrogen energy potential in the Black Sea and Marmara Sea's mucilage crises to investigate the contribution of hydrogen energy to our economy by eliminating the energy deficit.
Keywords: Hydrogen economy, Marmara Sea, Mucilage, H_2S, Black Sea

#112

FABRICATION OF PLATINUM-COBALT NANOWIRES BY CENTRIFUGAL ELECTROSPINNING METHOD AS ELECTROCATALYSTS FOR PEMFC

[1]*Chen-Yu Wu*, [1*]*Min-Hsing Chang*
[1]Department of Mechanical and Materials Engineering, Tatung University, Taipei, 104, Taiwan
*Corresponding author e-mail: mhchang@gm.ttu.edu.tw

ABSTRACT
The centrifugal electrospinning method is employed to fabricate platinum-cobalt (PtCo) bimetallic nanowires as electrocatalysts for proton exchange membrane fuel cell (PEMFC). The influences of system parameters on the nanowire morphology are explored systematically including the rotating speed of spinneret, applied voltage, and atomic ratio of Pt and Co in the nanowires. The electrochemical performance of the PtCo nanowires is evaluated by performing cyclic voltammetry (CV) tests to characterize the electrochemical active surface area (ECSA). The accelerated degradation tests (ADT) are also conducted to examine the durability of the PtCo nanowires. The membrane electrode assembly (MEA) using PtCo nanowires as cathode electrocatalysts is also made and the fuel cell performance is tested and compared with conventional MEA using Pt/C catalysts. It is found that under the condition of rotating speed 1600 rpm, collecting distance 12 cm, applied voltage 13 kV, and atomic ratio of Pt:Co = 4:1, PtCo nanowires can be produced successfully with good morphology and the mean diameter is 76 nm. The corresponding ECSA is 11.69 m^2g^{-1} and the ADT results show the resultant PtCo nanowires exhibit better durability than conventional Pt/C catalysts.
Keywords: Centrifugal electrospinning method, PtCo nanowires, Electrocatalyst, PEMFC

#117

ECONOMICAL PREPARATION AND CHARACTERIZATION OF DUAL-IONS CONDUCTING FUEL CELL

[1] *Yu-Tse Lu*, [1] *Wei-Cheng Huang*, [2] *Shing-Hoa Wang*, [1*] *Horng-Yi Chang*
[1] Department of Marine Engineering, National Taiwan Ocean University, Keelung 202301, Taiwan
[2] Department of Mechanical and Mechatronic Engineering, National Taiwan Ocean University, Keelung 202301, Taiwan
*Corresponding author e-mail: hychang@mail.ntou.edu.tw

ABSTRACT
The composite powders consisted of oxygen ion conductive $(La_{0.75}Sr_{0.2}Ba_{0.05})_{0.175}Ce_{0.825}O_{1.891}$ (LSBC) and proton conductive $BaZr_{0.1}Ce_{0.7}Y_{0.2}O_{3-\delta}$ (BZCY) were prepared by solid state reaction and sintered to be a composite membrane. The inter-diffusion was found between LSBC and BZCY. The conductivity of LSBC-BZCY single membrane exhibited slightly non-ohmic behavior in air but obviously non-ohmic diode behavior at 500°C in Ar/H_2. It indicated that the Schottky barrier could be designed at low to intermediate temperatures. The microstructure of sintered LSBC-BZCY surface fluctuated with convex and concave regions. The convex region was hard LSBC and the concave region was soft BZCY by micro-hardness and elemental measurement. The LSBC-30%BZCY let the two phases single membrane possess dual-ions conduction to obtain the power density of 20.51 mW/cm^2. The elemental distribution difference abruptly for Ba, Ce and O occurred at grain boundaries of LSBC/BZCY may correspond to the inter-diffusion and Schottky barrier results. The dual-ions composite membrane was proven single layer fuel cell possibly by this economical design process.
Keywords: composite membrane, dual-ions conduction, Schottky barrier, economical design

#132

ANALYSIS OF ECONOMIC EFFICIENCY ON INTERNATIONAL HYDROGEN SUPPLY CHAINS TO JAPAN

[1*] *Yuki Ishimoto,* [1] *Michio Hashimoto,* [2] *Eiji Ohira*
[1] Kyoto University, Graduate School of Advanced Integrated Studies in Human Survivability, Higashi-Ichijo-kan, Yoshida-Nakaadachicho 1, Sakyo-ku, Kyoto, Japan
[2] New Energy and Industrial Technology Development Organization, Smart Community and Energy Systems Department, Fuel Cell and Hydrogen Technology Office, 1310 Omiya-cho, Saiwai-ku, Kawasaki City, Kanagawa 212-8554 Japan
*Corresponding author e-mail: ishimoto.yuki.4j@kyoto-u.ac.jp

ABSTRACT
In order to achieve carbon neutrality, hydrogen is one of the key technologies to decarbonize the whole energy system. Several countries especially Japan are planning to import low carbon hydrogen using international supply chains setting their hydrogen strategy. There could be a wide variety of combinations among the technology option to make the supply chains. LCOEs using the international hydrogen transport chains are analyzed in this study to consider economic efficiency and to find effective clues for cost reduction in the international hydrogen transport chains. As preliminary results, we have found that the transportation cost that includes liquefaction, storages and international seaborne transport is improved by about 40% considering the advantages of large-scale facilities and that lignite gasification technologies with carbon capture have a competitive edge under the current assumption. For the time being, blue hydrogen could be an affordable option until the cost of green hydrogen decreases to the similar level. (<200 words)
Keywords: Hydrogen carriers, International supply chains, Economic analysis

#135

ON THE FUTURE ROLE OF HYDROGEN AS STORAGE FOR ELECTRICITY

[1*] *Reinhard Haas,* [1] *Marlene Sayer,* [1]*Amela Ajanovic*
[1] TU Wien, Energy Economics Group, 1040 Wien, Austria
*Corresponding author e-mail: haas@eeg.tuwien.ac.at

ABSTRACT
Increasing electricity generation from variable renewable energy sources, such as wind and solar, has led to interest in additional short-term and long-term storage capacities. The core objective of this paper is to investigate the costs and the future market prospects of different electricity storage options, such as short-term battery storage, and long-term storage as pumped hydro, as well as hydrogen. The method of approach is based on formal economic framework with a dynamic component to derive scenarios up to 2040. The major conclusion is, that the economic prospects of storage are in general not very bright. For all market-based storage technologies it will become hard to compete in the wholesale electricity markets. The core problem of virtually all categories of storage are low full-load hours. However, any new storage capacity should be constructed only in a coordinated way and if there is a clear sign for new excess production, in this case from variable renewables.
Keywords: Storage, Hydrogen, Pumped hydro storage, Battery, Economics

#153

NUMERICAL MODEL AND EXPERIMENTAL VALIDATION OF ULTRA-LEAN AIR-HYDROGEN COMBUSTION IN CATALYTIC MONOLITHS

[1]*Francesco Battistella,* [1]*Alessandro Donazzi,* [1]*Antonino Ravidà,* [1*]*Gianpiero Groppi,* [1]*Gianluca Valenti*
[1]Politecnico di Milano, Dipartimento di Energia, Via Lambruschini 4/A, 20156 Milano, Italy
*Corresponding author e-mail: gianpiero.groppi@polimi.it

ABSTRACT
Hydrogen plays an important role in the energy transition. The exploitation of hydrogen in gas turbines, as well as in other combustion processes, is promising but it may favor the formation of nitrogen oxides due to its high adiabatic flame temperature. The catalytic combustion of ultra-lean air-hydrogen mixtures solves the issue and improves the stability of the reaction at partial loads. The present work develops a numerical model for the design of catalytic combustors able to process ultra-lean air-hydrogen mixtures. The model simulates the catalytic combustion in a honeycomb monolith. Such tool is useful for the sizing of innovative combustors for micro-gas turbines for power generation. The numerical model solves mass and energy balances in a two-dimensional domain describing a single channel of the monolith. The channel is modelled as a cylinder, while the outer radius describes the catalyst surface. A validation of the numerical model is performed with experimental data obtained on a dedicated test bench at low inlet temperature and pressure. Comparing the simulated results with the experimental measurements, a 0.6% difference in outlet bulk temperature is obtained. Ultimately, useful recommendations are provided for combustor designers, based on the estimations of the numerical model in different operating conditions.
Keywords: Hydrogen, Catalytic combustion, Ultra-lean mixture, Numerical model, Micro-gas turbines

#185

OPTIMIZATION OF A HYDROGEN SUPPLY CHAIN: A CASE STUDY FOR ITALY

[1,2*] *Renato Luise,* [1] *Annabelle Brisse,* [3] *Pietro Quaglia,* [2] *Catherine Azzaro-Pantel*
[1]European Institute for Energy Research, Emmy-Noether Straße 11, Karlsruhe 76131, Germany
[2] Université de Toulouse, Laboratoire de Génie Chimique, CNRS, INPT, UPS, 6 Allée Emile Monso, 31400 Toulouse, France
[3] Polytechnic of Turin, Corso Duca degli Abruzzi, 24, Turin, Italy
*Corresponding author e-mail: Renato.luise@eifer.eu

ABSTRACT
Although hydrogen has been identified as key for a zero-carbon energy system, the design and deployment of the hydrogen supply chain (HSC) is a challenging issue, in particular due to the various ways to produce, condition, store and transport hydrogen. Hydrogen demand is expected to increase rapidly as several new sectors (e.g. mobility, heat and buildings) in addition to the conventional industrial ones realize its applications.
The paper addresses the emerging issue of how to design, organize and size the HSC. The problem involves a single optimization framework, where the total cost of the HSC is minimized, with a multi-period (2020-2040) mixed-integer linear programming (MILP) formulation that is implemented in the General Algebraic Modelling System (GAMS) environment, using CPLEX as a solver. The superstructure used for HSC modelling is split into six echelons, i.e., primary energy source, H_2 production, conditioning and centralized storage, distribution, conditioning and decentralized storage, and finally usage.
A case study for Italy has been developed, leading to a final hydrogen cost of 4.6€/kg in 2045. Various key performance indicators (KPIs) have been identified for the optimal solution obtained: centralization degree of the HSC, form of hydrogen (i.e. liquified, compressed), transport mode (gaseous or liquid H_2 trucks, H_2 pipeline) and economic parameters (i.e. investment, operation and maintenance costs).
Keywords: Hydrogen supply chain, Optimization model, GAMS, Mixed integer programming, Decentralization

#191

LIFE CYCLE COSTING APPROACHES OF FUEL CELL AND HYDROGEN SYSTEMS: A LITERATURE REVIEW

[1*] *Yuki Ishimoto,* [2] *Christina Wulf,* [2] *Wilhelm Kuckshinrichs*
[1]The Institute of Applied Energy, Shimbashi SY Bldg., 1-14-2 Nishi-shimbashi, Minato-ku, Tokyo 105-0003, Japan
[2] Forschungszentrum Jülich, Institute of Energy and Climate Research—Systems Analysis and Technology Evaluation (IEK-STE), D-52425 Jülich, Germany
*Corresponding author e-mail: ishimoto@iae.or.jp

ABSTRACT
A comprehensive literature review on the papers using life cycle costing (LCC) approaches to fuel cell and hydrogen (FCH) related technologies was carried out as one task in the European project SH2E in order to develop an LCC guideline. The papers to be reviewed were extracted from two major literature databases, SCOPUS and Web of Science. The extracted papers were briefly reviewed to decide if the paper is to be reviewed later in detail. The numbers of papers to be reviewed in detail were finally 155. The selected papers were reviewed from the various viewpoints, in particular, the objectives, the scope, the entity of assessment, stakeholder involvement, depth of assessment, mass and energy balances of the systems, the facilities considered, calculation methods, discounting (social vs private) or EoL treatment etc. The overall trend of LCC approaches, methods and indicators will be clarified, in order to establish the LCC guidelines.
Keywords: Life cycle costing, Hydrogen, Fuel cell

#217

SERIES SYSTEM WITH HYDROGEN RECOVERY

[1]Jenn-Kun Kuo, [1*] Tzu-Hsiang Lin
[1]Department of Mechanical and Electro-Mechanical Engineering, National Sun Yat-sen University, Kaohsiung, 80424, Taiwan
*Corresponding author e-mail: jenn.kun@gmail.com

ABSTRACT

This study uses MATLAB/Simulink simulation to build a series PEM fuel cell system with a 10 kW fuel cell stack as the base unit and active hydrogen recovery for efficiency calculations and to simulate the power requirements of various systems by connecting different numbers of fuel cell stack series system. The fuel cell system is cascaded in 10 kW units to achieve high-power supply commercial requirements. This allows for cost savings, efficient space utilization, and medium to large series power generation system installations. The results show that the efficiency of each stack in series can be increased by about 7% when the pressure is increased from 1.1 bar to 1.8 bar, because the fuel cell system efficiency can be increased by increasing the air pressure. The temperature of the fuel cell stack increases and the efficiency of the system also increases, and the best efficiency is achieved when the stack temperature reaches 65°C. However, when the temperature increases to 75°C, the efficiency of the fuel cell system decreases. However, when the temperature increases to 75°C, the system performance decreases because the proton exchange membrane dehydrates at high temperatures, which affects the conduction rate. The optimum operating temperature of the fuel cell stack is 60°C to 75°C. The active hydrogen recovery ratio of the 20 kW PEM fuel cell system is 14.1% at 360 seconds of operation, 11.8% at 30 kW of operation, and 10.65% at 40 kW PEM fuel cell stack.

Keywords: Proton exchange membrane fuel cell, Active hydrogen recovery, Stack series system, Purge valve, Efficiency

#225

THE TECHNO-ECONOMIC EVALUATION OF HYDROGEN PRODUCTION COST TOWARDS ANION EXCHANGE MEMBRANE ELECTROLYZER

[1,2] Bowen Yang, [1,2] Ruofan Zhang, [1,2] Cunman Zhang
[1] School of Automotive Studies, Tongji University, Shanghai 201804, China
[2] Clean Energy Automotive Engineering Center, Tongji University, Shanghai 201804, China
*Corresponding author e-mail: zhangcunman@tongji.edu.cn

ABSTRACT

With the significant development of electrolyzer technology, blueprint of economical and long-run hydrogen production adopted by this technology inspires great interest. The economic competence of electrolyzer needs further investigation to answer their current and future viability with technology development of ultimate performance as well as the decisive impactor to affect hydrogen production cost. Economically and technically, this research is originally established with a combination of crucial technology features including current density, overpotential, and ohmic resistance, acquired from the polarization curve to make the techno-economic analysis of anion exchange membrane electrolyzer technology. A cell-stack-system level on materials and fabrication is performed based on the bottom-up study to give an optimal investigation. It reveals the possibility for future hydrogen cost reduction and points out how the internal technical factors act on achieving a more cost-competitive hydrogen production. With consideration of the service lifetime together, this research exhibits the potential economic benefits from multiple dimensions of technological progress.

Keywords: Hydrogen economy, Electrolyzer technology, Hydrogen production

#238

CHARACTERISTIC AND PERFORMANCE OF $Ce_{0.6}Mn_{0.3}Fe_{0.1}O_2$ FOR SOLID OXIDE FUEL CELLS ANODE ELECTRODE

[1] *Ko-Yun Chao*, [1] *Debabrata Mohantya*, [1,2*] *I-Ming Hung*, [3] *Tai-Nan Lin*
[1] Department of Chemical Engineering and Materials Science, Yuan Ze University, Taoyuan, Taiwan
[2] Hierarchical Green-Energy Materials Research Center, National Cheng Kung University, Tainan, Taiwan
[3] Nuclear Fuels and Materials Division, Institute of Nuclear Energy Research, Taoyuan, Taiwan
*Corresponding author e-mail: imhung@saturn.yzu.edu.tw

ABSTRACT
The catalytic activity of $Ce_{0.6}Mn_{0.3}Fe_{0.1}O_{2-\delta}$ (CMF) for electrode reaction was reasonably high for SOFC anode application. In this study, we investigated the characteristic and electrochemical performance of CMF for solid oxide fuel cell (SOFC) anode in comparison with that of the conventional Ni-based anode. CMF anode powder was prepared by citric acid-EDTA complexing method with a fluorite structure and single phase, which was confirmed by XRD analysis. The average size of primary particle is about 200 nm, which was observed by SEM, and it sintered and aggregated to large secondary particle after calcination at 1000°C. The secondary particle size distribution, which was analysed by Dynamic Light Scattering (DLS), is in the range of 10-95 μm with D_{50} particle size of 27 μm.
Keywords: Solid oxide fuel cells (SOFC), Anode, Sol-Gel Method, Fluorite structure

#241

SYNGAS PRODUCTION VIA CHEMICAL LOOPING DRY REFORMING OF METHANE USING IRON-BASED OXYGEN CARRIERS

[1] *Po-Cheng Tsou*, [1*] *Rei-Yu Chein*, [2] *Wei-Hsin Chen*
[1] Dept. of Mechanical Engineering, National Chung Hsing University, Taichung City, Taiwan
[2] Department of Aeronautics and Astronautics, National Cheng Kung University, Tainan, Taiwan
*Corresponding author e-mail: rychein@dragon.nchu.edu.tw

ABSTRACT
In this study, the iron-based oxygen carrier was used for the syngas production via chemical looping dry reforming of methane (CL-DRM). The effect of the content of F_2O_3 supported by Al_2O_3 on the reduction stage during the CL-DRM was examined for various reaction temperatures was experimentally studied. It was found that higher Fe_2O_3 content and reaction temperature were required to obtain high CH_4 and CO_2 conversions and avoid carbon deposition. The experimental results indicated that 100% CH_4 and CO_2 conversion can be obtained from 30wt% Fe_2O_3 oxygen carrier and reaction temperature of 1000°C. At lower Fe_2O_3 contents and temperatures, Fe_2O_3 has low reactivity and high carbon deposition leading to poor CL-DRM performance. The experimental results also indicated that iron-based oxygen carrier was suitable for reducing CO_2 into CO and carbon.
Keywords: Iron-based oxygen carrier, Syngas, Chemical looping dry reforming of methane (CL-DRM), CH_4 and CO_2 conversions

#243

MODELING FOR THE DEVELOPMENT OF HEAVY DUTY REFUELING PROTOCOLS

[1*] *Arnaud Charolais*, [1] *Fouad Ammouri*, [1] *Elena Vyazmina*, [2] *Alexander Grab*[2], [2] *Antonio Ruiz*, [3] *Alexander Kvasnicka*, [3] *Christian Spitta*, [4] *Rony Tawk*, [4] *Quentin Nouvelot*, [4] *Nicola Benvenuti*, [4] *Thomas Guewouo*
[1] Air Liquide, R&D, Jouy-en-Josas, France
[2] Nikola Corporation, Phoenix, Arizona, USA
[3] ZBT GmbH, Duisburg, Germany
[4] Engie, Stains, France
*Corresponding author e-mail: arnaud.charolais@airliquide.com

ABSTRACT
The road transport sector is in need of new technologies to help it emit less greenhouse gases, as the world's emissions should be halved before 2030 and ultimately be part of a net-zero society. To that goal, hydrogen is envisioned to be used as the fuel powering road vehicles, in particular for heavy duty (HD) applications. To achieve the replacement of the current fossil fuel vehicle fleet, a network of hydrogen refueling stations (HRS) should be installed, with the ability to provide safe and rapid fillings to ensure the widest adoption of this clean technology worldwide. The FCH JU project PRHYDE aims to develop a dedicated HD refueling protocol for type III and IV tanks with 350, 500 and 700 bar nominal working pressures (NWP). For this purpose, the SOFIL code, modeling the physical variables in the tanks during filling, is used in the frame of the project. The current paper compares SOFIL to experimental data for HD type IV tanks.
Keywords: Heavy duty, Hydrogen, Refueling, Protocol, Modeling

#260

INFLUENCE OF THE TURBULENCE MODEL IN THE CFD SIMULATION OF HYDROGEN TANK FILLING BY AN IMPINGING OBLIQUE JET

Julien Martin[1], Quentin Nouvelot [1], Vincent Ren [2], Guillaume Lodier [2], Pierre Carrere [2], Arnaud Charolais [2], Fouad Ammouri [2], Elena Vyazmina [2], Alexander Grab[3], Antonio Ruiz[3]*
[1]ENGIE LAB Crigen,4 Avenue Joséphine Baker, 93240 Stains, France
[2] Air Liquide, Innovation Campus Paris, 1, Chemin de la Porte des Loges, 78350 Jouy-en-Josas, France
[3] Nikola Corporation, Phoenix, Arizona, USA
*Corresponding author e-mail: julien.martin2@engie.com

ABSTRACT
During a hydrogen tank filling, high temperatures can be generated inside the vessel with a vertical or/and horizontal thermal stratification that can potentially further increase the temperature of the gas and the tank wall. European funded project PRHYDE study this phenomena as it can have an influence on the choice made during refueling protocol development. CFD tools can help predict this thermal stratification within the tank by providing complete and detailed 3D information on the flow characteristics and temperature distribution. The eddy viscosity turbulence model (Boussinesq hypothesis) approach is most often used since it gives the best compromise between the number of grid cells and equation solving time. This hypothesis is reasonable for turbulent shear flows without big curvature and swirl. These models show their limitations when the anisotropy of the turbulence significantly affects the mean flow. This paper compares several turbulence models (Eddy viscosity and RSM model) for the case of hydrogen tank filling with a turbulent tilted impinging jet and compare simulation results with experimental results generated in the European funded project PRHYDE.

Keywords: Hydrogen storage, tank filling, turbulence model, impinging jet, stratification

#295

FORMABILITY AND PERFORMANCE TESTING OF STAINLESS-STEEL BIPOLAR PLATE FOR AIR-BREATHING PEMFC

[1] Chen-Yu Chen, [2] Nai-Hsien Wu, [3] Kuan-Jen Huang*
[1]National Chiayi University, College of Science and Engineering, Department of Mechanical and Energy Engineering, No.300, Syuefu Rd., Chiayi City 60004, Taiwan (R.O.C.)
[2]National Cheng-Kung University, College of Engineering, Department of Aeronautics and Astronautics, No.1, Ta-Hsueh Rd., East District, Tainan City 701, Taiwan (R.O.C.)
[3]National Cheng-Kung University, College of Engineering, Department of Aeronautics and Astronautics, No.1, Ta-Hsueh Rd., East District, Tainan City 701, Taiwan (R.O.C.)
*Corresponding author e-mail: aeroshower@msn.com

ABSTRACT
In this study, the formability of the metallic bipolar plates for PEMFCs were studied via DYNAFORM software and LS-DYNA and the performance and the electrochemical impedance the air-breathing PEMFC with the stamped metallic bipolar plates were tested analyzed. The simulation results show that the optimum stamping parameters for the SS316L are the flow channel depth of 0.8 mm, punch and die radius of 0.4 mm, stamping speed of 250 mm/s, blank thickness of 0.2 mm and the binder pressure of 200 kN. The maximum error between the real stamped flow channel depth and the target depth is 12.8%. With the stamped SS316L bipolar plate, which has an active area of 150×54 mm^2, the air-breathing in this work has the maximum power density of 187.19 mW/cm^2 at an operating temperature of 45°C, a torque of 30 kgf-cm, a hydrogen stoichiometric ratio of 1.5 and a relative humidity of 100%.

Keywords: Proton exchange membrane fuel cell, Stainless steel bipolar plate, Stamping fabrication process, Performance test

#310

PROTON-CONDUCTING SOLID OXIDE FUEL CELLS WITH NLSCF CATHODE

[1*]*S. W. Lee*, [2]*W. Y. Huang*, [3]*Y. C. Huang*, [4]*C. J. Tseng*
[1] Institute of Materials Science and Engineering, National Central University, Taoyuan, Taiwan
[2] Department of Mechanical Engineering, National Central University, Taoyuan, Taiwan
*Corresponding author e-mail: swlee@g.ncu.edu.tw

ABSTRACT
The electrochemical performances of the solid oxide fuel cells (SOFCs) fabricated with Nd-doped LSCF (NLSCF) perovskite cathodes, thin BCZY electrolytes, and BCZY–Ni anodes by tape casting, spin coating, and co-firing are evaluated at 600–800 ℃. Material analysis, such as SEM, TEM, and XRD, confirmed that no detectable second phase remains in the NLSCF cathode, indicating that the calcined NLSCF nanopowders have good compatibility with the fabrication of anode-supported fuel cells in this study. It can be clearly seen that the NLSCF cathode is highly porous and adhered well to the BCZY electrolyte. Fuel cell testing with the NLSCF cathode exhibits a maximum power density of ~407.6 mW/cm^2 at 800 ℃, which is significantly higher than those of cells with a powder derived LSCF cathode. The significantly lower polarization resistance elements extracted from electrochemical impedance spectroscopy (EIS) further suggested that the NLSCF cathode has superior catalytic activity for the oxygen reduction reaction and better oxygen ionic transport in the cathode reactions. The performance improvement of NLSCF cathode can be explained in terms of trade-off between electrocatalytic activity, oxygen ionic and electronic conductivity of the NLSCF. This study shows that NLSCF nanopowder would be a promising cathode material for proton conducting SOFCs.
Keywords: Nd-doped LSCF, Nanopowder, Cathode, Oxygen reduction reaction, P-SOFC

#351

TRANSACTIVE MOBILITY WITH HYBRID ELECTRIC AND HYDROGEN CHARGING INFRASTRUCTURES

[1,2*] *Hossam A.Gabbar*
[1]Faculty of Energy Systems and Nuclear Science, Ontario Tech University, 2000 Simcoe St. North, Oshawa L1G0C5, ON, Canada
[2]Faculty of Engineering and Applied Science, Ontario Tech University, 2000 Simcoe St. North, Oshawa L1G0C5, ON, Canada
*Corresponding author e-mail: hossam.gaber@ontariotechu.ca

ABSTRACT
Mobility is supported by transportation infrastructures based on energy networks to meet mobility demands. Transportation electrification enables mobility with more penetration of electric vehicles (EVs) and hydrogen-based fuel cell vehicles (HVs), besides internal combustion vehicles. The charging infrastructures should support mobility based on hybrid transportation technologies. The complex and expensive transition to transportation electrification infrastructures can be alleviated by implementing transactive mobility, which will provide cost management of different layers within the mobility services infrastructures. This paper presents an integrated framework for transactive mobility in view of hybrid charging infrastructures. The interface between transactive energy and charging infrastructures will be modeled and formulated by the transactive mobility model.
Keywords: Transactive mobility (TM), transactive energy (TE), hybrid charging stations (HCSs), hydrogen vehicle (HV), transportation electrification

#367

HYDROGEN TRANSPORTATION OPTIONS AND CHALLENGES

[1,2*] *Mohammad Anwar Omid*, [3] *Muammer Koç* , [2*] *Ömer Necati Cora*
[1] Kabul Polytechnic University, Faculty of Electromechanics, Department of Auto-Mechanical Engineering, Kabul, Afghanistan
[2] Karadeniz Technical University, School of Engineering, Department of Mechanical Engineering, Trabzon, Turkey
[3] Hamad bin Khalifa University, College of Science and Engineering, Sustainable Development Division, Doha, Qatar
*Corresponding author e-mails: ma.omid@kpu.edu.af; oncora@ktu.edu.tr

ABSTRACT
In this study, different types of hydrogen transportation and delivery options have been evaluated comparatively. Various kinds of hydrogen transportation options including cryogenic tankers, tube trailers, ships, trains, novel transportation options, in addition to existing pipelines have been reviewed. Major findings such as cost-efficiency, technical and logistic challenges and problems, advantages and solutions of each option are outlined along with the further research and development needs.
Keywords: Hydrogen energy, Transportation, Hydrogen infrastructure, Hydrogen pipeline, Hydrogen delivery

#397

ECONOMIC AND ENVIRONMENTAL EVALUATION OF FUELING OPTIONS FOR HYDROGEN FUEL CELL HEAVY-DUTY VEHICLES

[1*] *Amgad Elgowainy,* [1] *Krishna Reddi*
[1]Argonne National Laboratory, 9700 S Cass Ave, Lemont, IL 60439, USA
*Corresponding author e-mail: aelgowainy@anl.gov

ABSTRACT
Hydrogen fuel cell electric vehicles have the advantage of faster fueling and longer driving range compared to battery electric vehicles, especially for medium and heavy-duty vehicles (M/HDVs). Argonne National laboratory developed cost and energy/emissions estimates of various options for fueling hydrogen fuel cell HDV fleets, considering various hydrogen supply chain (e.g., gaseous vs. liquid). In general, liquid hydrogen sourcing provides a significant cost advantage for large fleets with high fueling rates, compared to gaseous hydrogen supply to fueling stations. However, the hydrogen liquefaction is an energy intensive process that affects life-cycle energy use and greenhouse gas emissions, depending on the electricity generation mix used for liquefaction. The contribution of refueling station to total hydrogen cost at dispenser is between \$2-5/kg_{H2}, depending on daily and hourly fueling demand and speed, but can be reduced to \$1/kg_{H2} when considering large fleets and high production volume of fueling components. The fueling station cost contribution can be further reduced to <\$1/kg_{H2} by considering low-pressure liquid hydrogen storage onboard the fuel cell M/HDVs.
Keywords: Hydrogen, Fuel cell, Refueling cost, Greenhouse gas, Heavy-Duty vehicle

#409

ANALYSIS OF THE DEMAND OF HYDROGEN AS FUEL FOR TRANSPORT IN THE UAE

[1,2] *Maram Awad,* [3] *Ali Bouabid,* [3] *Andrei Sleptchenko,* [1,2] *Ali Almansoori,* [1,2*] *Ahmed Alhajaj*
[1] Research and Innovation Centre on CO2 and H2, Khalifa University of Science and Technology, PO Box 127788, Abu Dhabi, United Arab Emirates
[2] Department of Chemical Engineering, Khalifa University, P.O. Box 127788, Abu Dhabi, United Arab Emirates
[3] Department of Industrial and Systems Engineering, Khalifa University, P.O. Box 127788, Abu Dhabi, United Arab Emirates
*Corresponding author e-mail: ahmed.alhajaj@ku.ac.ae

ABSTRACT
With the growing emphasis on building a green economy with low carbon footprint, UAE is gradually building a hydrogen economy through introducing hydrogen fuel for transport. Although hydrogen sources are abundant in the UAE, the supply-chain model is not in place. Given the cost sensitivity of hydrogen in relation to volumes produced, large consumption is essential to reduce the cost. In this work, we developed a system dynamics model that allow us to design a roadmap for deployment of hydrogen network in the UAE. We examined different policy incentives that inaugurate hydrogen fuel stations at a reasonable price in the UAE market.
Keywords: Hydrogen network, Green transport, System dynamics, Analysis, Demand

#439

GRID BASED RISK ASSESSMENT OF A HYDROGEN SUPPLY CHAIN

[1*]*Ebru Geçici,* [1]*Mehmet Güray Güler,* [1]*Ahmet Erdoğan*
[1]Department of Industrial Engineering, Faculty of Mechanical Engineering, Yıldız Technical University, Istanbul, Turkey
*Corresponding author e-mail: egecici@yildiz.edu.tr

ABSTRACT
Today's energy recourses are not supposed to be sufficient to fulfill increased energy demand in the near future, thus researchers and governments look forwards to alternative energy sources. Hydrogen energy is one of these alternative energies. To increase the use of hydrogen energy, it is essential to establish a good hydrogen supply chain (HSC), which provides the transmission of hydrogen from production facilities to the users. There are several key issues which must be addressed in establishing a good HSC like capital cost and operating costs, environmental effects like CO_2 emission, and risks. Although minimizing the total costs or total CO_2 emissions can be appropriate for a country, minimizing the cumulative risk may result in an unbalanced risk load between cities or grids of a country. In this study we analyze establishing the HSC of Turkey and showed that minimization of total risk yields low risks in grids with low population and grids with higher populations have to cope with larger risks.
Keywords: Hydrogen Supply Chain, Risk Analysis, Multi-objective Supply Chain

#1458

ANALYSIS OF A HYDROGEN SUPPLY CHAIN WITH RANDOM DEMAND: A CASE STUDY

[1] Busenur Türkali Özbek, [1] Mehmet Güray Güler*
[1] Department of Industrial Engineering, Faculty of Mechanical Engineering, Yıldız Technical University, İstanbul, Turkey
*Corresponding author e-mail: busenur.turkali@std.yildiz.edu.tr

ABSTRACT
Today, energy sources that are used intensively especially in vehicles are generally non-renewable energy sources and they are on the verge of depletion with increasing demand. To cope with this, countries have turned to hydrogen, which is seen as a clean and renewable energy source. However, due to the uncertain future demand, it is also difficult to design a good hydrogen supply chain. To overcome this, a stochastic hydrogen supply chain model is proposed in this study and the Marmara region of Turkey is used as a case study.
Keywords: Hydrogen supply chain, Stochastic, Renewable energy source

#1470

ASSESSMENT OF HYDROGEN DELIVERY OPTIONS

[1] Eveline Weidner, [2] Francesco Dolci, [3] Rafael Ortiz Cebolla, [4] Alessandro Arrigoni*
[1-4] European Commission Joint Research Center, Westerduinweg 3, 1755 LE Petten, Netherlands
*Corresponding author e-mail: Eveline.Weidner@ec.europa.eu

ABSTRACT
The transport of hydrogen will be a key enabler for the widespread use of renewable hydrogen in Europe. To achieve the goals of the European Hydrogen Strategy [1] it is important to understand whether it is cost effective to produce renewable hydrogen where renewable electricity is cheap and then to transport the hydrogen to the customer, or it is better to produce the renewable hydrogen close to the demand location. JRC has performed a comprehensive study regarding the transport of hydrogen, in terms of costs and energy demand. The study reveals that there is no single optimal hydrogen delivery solution across every transport scenario. The most cost effective way to deliver renewable hydrogen depends on distance, amount, final use, and whether there is infrastructure already available. For distances compatible with the European territory, compressed and liquefied hydrogen solutions, and especially compressed hydrogen pipelines, offer lower costs than chemical carriers do. Chemical carriers become more competitive the longer the delivery distance (due to their lower transport costs) and open up import options from suppliers located, for example, in Chile or Australia.
Keywords: Hydrogen delivery, Hydrogen export, Hydrogen import

#1485

TECHNO-ECONOMIC AND PROCESS SIMULATION OF SMALL-SCALE HYDROGEN PRODUCTION FROM NH_3 DECOMPOSITION

[1]Mostafa El-Shafie*
[1] Gifu University, Environmental and Renewable Energy Systems Division,
Graduate School of Engineering, 1-1 Yanagido, Gifu, 501-1193, Japan.
*Corresponding author e-mail: mostafaelshafie81@gmail.com

ABSTRACT
In this study, two proposed configuration plants were designed and simulated for the production of high-purity hydrogen at a rate of 25 kg_{H2}/day from blue ammonia. In configuration A, hydrogen was generated in a membrane reactor, while in configuration B, NH3 decomposition and H2 separation were carried out in an integrated catalytic membrane reactor. The performance of both hydrogen production plants was evaluated under different operating conditions. A pure palladium membrane with a thickness of 20 μm was utilized for pure hydrogen production. Configuration B was more energy efficient than configuration A. The hydrogen flow rate was evident with the increase in feeding pressure from 0.1 MPa to 0.3 MPa. The total H_2 production cost of configuration A was 5.33 €/kg_{H2} and that of configuration B was 5.05 €/kg_{H2}. Since the proposed plant configurations generated hydrogen and nitrogen, the total cost of production was distributed between them. The final H_2 and N_2 separation costs of configuration A was 4.21 €/kg_{H2} and 0.95 €/kg_{H2}, and configuration B was 3.94 €/kg_{H2} and 0.90 €/kg_{H2}. It can be also considered that the ammonia synthesis pathway controlled the ammonia prices and subsequently the hydrogen production cost.
Keywords: Hydrogen separation, Ammonia decomposition, Energy efficiency, Permeation rate

#1525

TECHNO-ECONOMIC ANALYSIS OF 350 BAR LOHC-SUPPLIED HYDROGEN REFUELING STATIONS FOR HEAVY DUTY VEHICLE FLEETS

[1*] *Stefan Aschbrenner,* [2] *Tobias Eissler,* [3] *Marius Schneider,* [4] *Christopher Voglstätter*
[1,2,3,4] Fraunhofer Institute for Solar Energy Systems ISE, Heidenhofstrasse 2, 79110 Freiburg, Germany
*Corresponding author e-mail: stefan.aschbrenner@ise.fraunhofer.de

ABSTRACT

The cost of hydrogen at a refueling station depends mostly on two factors, the hydrogen production itself and the hydrogen supply chain. For both there are different options with LOHC that are in the focus of several scientific discussions. The aim of this work is to contribute to this discussion a techno-economic comparison of a 350 bar Liquid Organic Hydrogen Carrier (LOHC)-supplied hydrogen refueling station (HRS) with a standard HRS. The analysis was focused on supplying hydrogen for a fleet of busses or trains with a total daily hydrogen demand of around 1.2 t/d. A dehydrator required to release the hydrogen from the LOHC as well as other standard components of an HRS were dynamically modelled and optimised depending on various demand profiles of the vehicle fleets using the inhouse simulation software H2ProSim. The results show specific refueling costs (HRS only) of between 2.1 €/kg and 3.3 €/kg for the LOHC-HRS scenarios investigated and a minimum of 0.89 €/kg can be obtained for a standard HRS. This cost difference is mainly caused by the high energy cost of the dehydrator and the added CAPEX. Furthermore, a smart demand management on the vehicle side can lead to significant cost reductions for the HRS infrastructure.

Keywords: Hydrogen refueling station, LOHC, Compressed hydrogen, Refueling cost

#1562

EVALUATION OF POTENTIAL HYDROGEN PRODUCTION METHODS IN TURKEY BY USING A HYBRİD METHOD BASED ON PYTHAGOREAN FUZZY AHP AND INTERVAL TYPE-2 FUZZY TOPSIS

[1]*Aytaç Yıldız,* [2*] *Yunus Demir,* [3] *Gürkan Işık*
[1,2] Department of Industrial Engineering, Bursa Technical University, 16310, Bursa, Turkey
[3] Department of Business Development, Valuable Touch Energy Services, 41275, Kocaeli, Turkey
*Corresponding author email: yunus.demir@btu.edu.tr

ABSTRACT

Hydrogen is a promising energy storage and generation alternative to ensure that renewable energy sources are available to meet all energy needs in the long term. Many factors should be considered for sustainability of the environment while designing a hydrogen supply chain which consists of different production, storage, and transportation methods. Hydrogen energy is a new and innovative area especially for developing countries, so there can be high uncertainty during the decision process because of lack of expertness. In this study, available hydrogen production alternatives of Turkey are evaluated by using an integrated Pythagorean fuzzy AHP and interval type-2 fuzzy TOPSIS based methodology by considering technical, economic, environmental, and social aspects.

Keywords: AHP, Hydrogen production, Interval type-2 fuzzy set, Pythagorean fuzzy set, TOPSIS

#1632

WHAT IS THE KEY ROLE OF HYDROGEN ENERGY IN METAVERSE

[1*] *Feride Cansu İskenderoğlu,* [2] *Hüseyin Turan Arat,* [3] *Mustafa Kaan Baltacıoğlu*
[1] İskenderun Technical University, Faculty of Engineering and Natural Science, Mechanical Engineering Department, Hatay, Turkey
[2] Sinop University, Faculty of Engineering and Architecture, Mechanical Engineering Department, Sinop, Turkey
[3] İskenderun Technical University, Faculty of Engineering and Natural Science, Mechatronics Engineering Department, Hatay, Turkey
*Corresponding author e-mail: mkaan.baltacioglu@iste.edu.tr

ABSTRACT

With the increase in digitalization, the demand for energy is increasing day by day. Web 3 version, IoT technologies, social media platforms, rapidly increasing online worlds with online games and the popularization of crypto technologies make people dependent on energy. One of the most important problems of crypto and metaverse technology is the insatiable use of electricity. The current research uses a PEM fuel cell system as a renewable energy source to meet the electricity demand required for crypto mining. The required amount of hydrogen and equipment for the fuel cell system are explained.

Keywords: Metaverse, Coin mining, Cryptocurrency, PEMFC, Hydrogen

Track 16.

Environmental Impact and Sustainable Development

#21

DESULFURIZATION PERFORMANCE OF SBA 15 SUPPORTED CALCIUM BASED MIXED METAL OXIDE SORBENTS

[1*]Arzu Kanca, [1]Zeynep Koseoglu, [1]Osman Nuri Ata
[1] Ataturk University, Engineering Faculty, Chemical Engineering Department, 25240, Erzurum, Turkey
*Corresponding author e-mail: akanca@atauni.edu.tr

ABSTRACT

Syngas is a mixture of CO and H_2 formed during the gasification process of coal and biomass. Additionally, H_2S is undesired gasification products of fossil fuels with high sulfur content. H_2S causes serious problems, such as catalyst poisoning and pipeline corrosion during production process of fuel from syngas. Hot gas desulfurization (HGD) enables to reduce the sulfur contents of the gasification products by eliminating thermal losses of endothermic syngas processes. This study aims to develop regenerable sorbents to remove H_2S from hot flue gas. Unsupported and SBA 15 supported Ca-based binary mixed metal oxides (CaO-CuO, CaO-FeO, CaO-MnO, CaO-ZnO) were synthesized as sulfur sorbents by wet impregnation method. The crystal structure of sorbents was determined by X-ray diffraction (XRD), while BET analysis was used to determined the surface area and pore size distribution of the Ca based mixed metal oxide sorbents. The initial results of the XRD and BET analysis revealed the mixed metal oxide formation and high surface area of SBA 15 supported sorbents, respectively. Desulfurization performance of the sorbents was examined by gas chromatography analyzer equipped with Flame Photometric Detector. The best desulfurization performance with breakthrough sulfur capacity of 22.72 g S/100 g sorbent and 46.65% capacity usage ratios was obtained for CaO-CuO adsorbent.

Keywords: Desulfurization, Ca-Based Sorbents, SBA 15, Mixed Metal Oxide

#36

LIFE CYCLE GHG EMISSIONS OF A GASOLINE AND FUEL CELL VEHICLE WITH VARIOUS HYDROGEN PRODUCTION PATHWAYS

[1*]Samane Ghandehariun, [1]Shayan Sadeghi, [2]Amir Mohammad Ghandehariun
[1]Sustainable Energy Research Group (SERG), School of Mechanical Engineering, Iran University of Science and Technology, Tehran, Iran
[2]Faculty of Engineering, Ferdowsi University of Mashhad, Mashhad, Iran
*Corresponding author e-mail: samane_ghandehariun@iust.ac.ir

ABSTRACT

Moving towards a cleaner transportation is necessary for a more sustainable future. Hydrogen, as a clean energy carrier, can play an important role. It can be used in fuel cell vehicles (FCV) or in internal combustion engines. In this paper, a life cycle assessment of a FCV with 5 different fuel cycles including steam methane reforming (SMR), coal gasification, photovoltaics, solar thermal and grid electrolysis is conducted for Iran. Also, the FCV is compared with a conventional gasoline vehicle. It is concluded that for all of the considered pathways, the FCV is more environmentally benign than the gasoline vehicle, except when its hydrogen is produced from the electrolysis of water using national grid electricity. The total greenhouse gas (GHG) emissions of the FCV with grid electrolysis are found to be 0.465 kg CO_2 eq./km, which is 56% higher than those of a gasoline vehicle. It is also shown that the material production and manufacturing phase of the FCV's vehicle cycle is the main contributor to the total GHG emissions of the vehicle. The glider, hydrogen tank and fuel cell stack manufacturing have the most impacts on the environment. A FCV powered by clean hydrogen produced from electrolysis of water with the electricity produced from photovoltaics produces 0.135 kg CO_2 eq./km which is less than half of the emissions associated with a gasoline vehicle.

Keywords: Fuel Cell Vehicle, Hydrogen Production, Life Cycle Assessment, Greenhouse Gas Emissions

#38

STEAM METHANE REFORMING INTEGRATION AND INCREASE OF CARBON DIOXIDE PRODUCTION

[1*] *Marcelo Tagliabue*
[1] Air Liquide Argentina S.A., Av. Larrabure 115, Campana (2804), Bs. As., Argentina
*Corresponding author e-mail: marcelo.tagliabue@airliquide.com

ABSTRACT
The present work is a study of the efficiency optimization of a Hydrogen (H_2) production plant through natural gas reforming and contributes to preserving the environment.
This work was a theoretical and practical study with the objective to see how a stream of non-condensable usually vented to the atmosphere (rich in carbon dioxide (CO_2) and H_2) and coming from the stripper of the CO_2 liquefaction plant could be added to the feed of the steam Methane reforming (SMR) plant. In order to reduce the emissions of CO_2 and other compounds responsible of the greenhouse, and to reduce the consumption of natural gas, keeping hydrogen production.
In the second stage, once made the theoretical study of the impact on the SMR when this feed is added, it was decided to proceed to the experimental work to learn how the major variables of the process were affected. The practical results of the test were very encouraging. In a third stage, in order to increase the profits of the business unit and mainly to continue reducing the emissions of CO_2 to the environment, a non-utilized active (a CO_2 production plant burning natural gas to produce it) was used to capture CO_2 from the SMR flue gases vented into the atmosphere. Thus, about 25 tons/day of CO_2 are recovered for the CO_2 local market, reducing emissions into the atmosphere in the same amount.
This technique is very favorable for the industry since the stream rich in CO_2 is a waste. However, the practical use of this technique has some disadvantages, which must be known in advance to do not commit costly errors. The aforementioned possible drawbacks were solved by adding a suitable NOX filter as well as, a formulation of the monoethanolamine (MEA) solution suitable for O_2 present. As a result, production could be increased by around 25Tn / day of CO_2.
Keywords: H_2, CO_2, Recovery, SMR, Optimization.

#43

WELL TO WHEEL COMPARISON OF FUEL CELL BUSES BASED ON MULTIPLE HYDROGEN PATHWAYS WITH BATTERY & IC ENGINE BUSES IN INDIA

[1*]*Sachin Chugh,* [1]*Chinmay Chaudhari,* [1]*Tarun Jindal,* [1]*Alok Sharma,* [1]*G.S Kapur, S.S.V. Ramakumar*
[1]Research & Development Centre IndianOil Corporation Ltd, Faridabad, India
*Corresponding author e-mail: chughs@indianoil.in

ABSTRACT
Global developments pertaining to electric vehicles are catalyzing the interests in hydrogen as an energy carrier coupled with energy converter like fuel cells for both stationary & mobility applications. The present study provides Well-to-Wheel (WTW) analysis based on GREET life cycle assessment model customized for Indian conditions. The study compares hydrogen produced from various sources (reforming of methane, methanol & bio-methane, solar and biomass/coal gasification etc.) for powering 9/12 meter fuel cell bus with electricity generated from current grid mix in India and I.C. engines. WTW results indicate CO_2 equivalent emissions of 1458 g km^{-1} for PEM fuel cell based heavy duty bus powered by hydrogen from steam methane reforming. These emissions are observed to be lower by 48% and 80% respectively when compared with diesel and electricity-based drivetrains. The study also reveals that solar based electrolysis and biomass gasification in India are among the least CO_2 intensive pathway (671 and 877 g km^{-1} of CO_2). On energy front, the fuel cell based on NG reforming is reported to be 25% and 60% more efficient than diesel and electricity pathways.
Keywords: Life cycle analysis, CO_2 equivalent emissions, Hydrogen fuel cell bus, battery electric bus

#59

A PARAMETRIC NUMERICAL ANALYSIS OF LAMINAR HYDROGEN DIFFUSION FLAMES

Ayse Korucu [1], Ali Cemal Benim [2]*
[1]Izmir Institute of Technology, Faculty of Mechanical Engineering, Gülbahçe 35430 Urla / İzmir, Turkey
[2]Duesseldorf University Appl. Sci., Mech. & Process Eng., Center of Flow Simulation (CFS), Muensterstr., 156, 40476 Duesseldorf, Germany
*Corresponding author e-mail: alicemal@prof-benim.com

ABSTRACT
Atmospheric, laminar, diffusion flames of hydrogen and air are numerically investigated. A detailed hydrogen combustion reaction scheme, in combination with the extended Zeldovich mechanism for the thermal nitrogen oxide formation are used. For comparison purposes, a global mechanism is also applied. The numerical procedure is first validated by comparisons with results of other authors. Subsequently, parametric studies are performed to find optimal solutions with respect to the related to the operation parameters of such flames to achieve minimum low nitrogen oxide emission levels. The question that are addressed include the Reynolds number effect on nitrogen emissions, and the interaction of neighbouring flames, when they are applied in an array. For ensuring an adequately fine resolution of the flame fronts, local adaptive grid refinement techniques are applied to track the flame front. For preliminary results the radiative heat loses has assumed to be insignificant however it should be taken into the account for the further analyses. The maximum temperature is predicted to be ~2040 K which is higher than the reported adiabatic stoichiometric flame temperature, 2023 K for the exit velocity of 0.5 m/s. The radial mole fractions of N_2 and H_2 at the centerline are observed to be 0.66 and 0.41 respectively at the axial distance of 10 mm. Furthermore, the width of the high temperature region of the flame is observed to be ~6.5 mm.
Keywords: Hydrogen combustion, Laminar diffusion flame, Thermal nitrogen oxide formation, CFD

#115

HYDROGEN CERTIFICATION OF ORIGIN IN COLOMBIA

[1] Juan Camilo Moreno, [1] Martha Cobo, [1] Nestor Sanchez*
[1]Group of Energy, Materials, and Environment. Universidad de La Sabana, Faculty of Engineering, Department of Chemical and Biochemical Processes. km 7 Autopista Norte Bogotá-Chía, Campus Universitario Puente del Común. Chia, Colombia
*Corresponding author e-mail: nestor.sanchez1@unisabana.edu.co

ABSTRACT
Hydrogen (H_2) has been widely recognized as a crucial alternative regarding an imminent energy transition, due to its use as an energy vector and its environmental innocuousness at usage. Steam Methane Reforming (SMR) is the most common H_2 production method, and standardizing its emissions is key to ensure long term benefits from using H_2. This work aims at comparing several existing standards and proposing an emission reduction target for Colombia. SMR has an average carbon footprint of 10.74 kg CO_2-eq/kg H_2. Additionally, it was found that existing standards concur on an emission reduction target of 60%. Factoring Colombia's low emission factor in energy production, as well as its existing piping system, it was concluded that this target is achievable and, due to the advantages of complying with international standards, it is recommendable to institute it in future regulations.
Keywords: Greenhouse Gases, Hydrogen, Life Cycle Assessment, Steam Reforming

#137

PROSPECTS OF RENEWABLE HYDROGEN IN TRANSPORT

[1] Amela Ajanovic, [1] Reinhard Haas, [1] Marlene Sayer*
[1]Vienna University of Technology (TU WIEN), Energy Economics Group, Gusshausstr. 25-27/370-3,1040 Vienna, Austria
*Corresponding author e-mail: ajanovic@eeg.tuwien.ac.at

ABSTRACT
Hydrogen is often discussed as an energy carrier of the future. In this paper economic and environmental benefits of hydrogen use in passenger car mobility are analysed in comparison to the conventional vehicles. In spite of many hypes over the last decades, fuel cell vehicles are still a rarity on the streets. However, with the pressing environmental problems and possibility to use hydrogen as a fuel for mobility as well as storage for surplus electricity from renewable energy sources, role of hydrogen in the future energy and transport system is becoming more important.
Keywords: hydrogen, fuel cell vehicles, mobility, costs, emissions

#151

HYDROGEN PRODUCTION FROM OLIVE OIL MILL WASTEWATER THROUGH STEAM REFORMING IN MULTIFUNCTIONAL REACTORS

*Cláudio Rocha, Miguel Angel Soria, Luís Miguel Madeira**
LEPABE, Dept. of Chemical Engineering, Faculty of Engineering-University of Porto, Rua Dr. Roberto Frias s/n, 4200-465 Porto.
*Corresponding author e-mail: mmadeira@fe.up.pt

ABSTRACT
Steam reforming technology integrating a membrane reactor and/or CO_2 capture for H_2 production from olive mill wastewater (OMW) was developed. The objective is to use a multifunctional reactor combining OMW reforming (using a stable/active catalyst) and the simultaneous products removal from the reaction zone in a single device: H_2 through an H_2-selective membrane and CO_2 through a CO_2 sorbent. Thus, the benefits of using different multifunctional reactors (sorption-enhanced reactor (SER), membrane reactor (MR) and sorption-enhanced membrane reactor (SEMR)), comparatively to the traditional reactor (TR), were assessed in this work in terms of H_2 production through the steam reforming of OMW (OMWSR). Using a SEMR, an H_2 yield enhancement of ≈ 44 % was observed compared to the TR – H_2 production of ≈ 11.5 mol_{H2}/mol_{OMW} in the SEMR.
Keywords: Olive mill wastewater; Steam reforming; CO_2 sorbent; H_2-selective membrane; Multifunctional reactors.

#152

BIOMASS GASIFICATION FOR GREEN HYDROGEN PRODUCTION: A REVIEW

[1]Sameer Usmani, [2]Liyuan Fan, [3]Ahmad Saud Masood
[1] PhD, College of Engineering and Computer Science, Australian National University, Australia
[2] Lecturer, College of Science and Engineering, James Cook University, Australia
[3] Department of Civil, Environmental and Land Planning Engineering, Politecnico di Milano, Italy

ABSTRACT
Hydrogen is one of the most promising alternative energy resource to achieve a sustainable energy future. Now, hydrogen is mainly derived from the thermo-catalytic process using natural gas and coal. Hydrogen production cost is currently high and not sustainable and the focus has been shifted to green hydrogen production. Syngas which is produced from biomass gasification, with a substantial content of hydrogen, is one of the best alternative pathway for green hydrogen production. Green hydrogen production price is estimated to drop to a mark that can offer carbon neutral energy with a reasonable price. However, green hydrogen production from biomass needs further improvement, gasification involves several challenges such as unstable biomass supply, gas cleaning, heavy carbon rich oil formation, minerals and ash, tar and soot formation. This work will review the recent development of biomass gasification for green hydrogen production, discuss the technical challenges, and point out the future direction for affordable green hydrogen production from biomass gasification. Further, different biomass resources will be analysed with a substantial focus in Oceania and South-East Asian countries to give a directive guide for green hydrogen production from regional supply of biomasses.
Keywords: Green Hydrogen, Gasification, Biomass

#197

THE INTERNATIONAL ENERGY AGENCY'S HYDROGEN TECHNOLOGY COLLABORATION PROGRAMME FOR WHEC-2022

[1] Paul Lucchese, [2] Marina Holgado Dones*,*
[1]CEA, Paris-Sacla, Batiment 446, BP 191, 91191 Gif Sur Yvette, France
[2] ARIEMA Energía y Medioambiente SL, Ronda de Poniente, 15, 1ª planta Izda., 28760. Tres Cantos, Madrid, Spain
*Corresponding author e-mail: marina.holgado@ieahydrogen.org, technicalsecretariat@ieahydrogen.org

ABSTRACT

The International Energy Agency's Hydrogen Technology Programme (Hydrogen TCP) works for a future based on clean sustainable energy supply of global proportions through the development of a hydrogen economy with the goal of accelerating hydrogen implementation and widespread utilization to optimize environmental protection, improve energy security and promote economic development internationally, the Hydrogen TCP relies on an international network of hydrogen experts. Through collaborative R,D&D projects called Tasks, experts from 24 different countries, 5 companies, and 3 entities carry out research addressing all stages of the hydrogen value chain. Tasks' results are collected in Final Reports, which are made publicly available through the Hydrogen TCP website. In this Conference, the Hydrogen TCP could present its role in the international hydrogen network, briefly introduce current and planned activities (including Open Tasks on topics such as "Energy Storage and Conversion based on Hydrogen", "Data and Modelling" and "Underground Hydrogen Storage" and Tasks in Definition on topics such as "Offshore Hydrogen Value Chains", "Renewable Hydrogen Production", "Hydrogen from Nuclear Energy", "Safety and RCS of Large Scale Hydrogen Energy Applications", "Hydrogen in the Mining, Mineral Processing, and Resource Sectors" and "Hydrogen Export Value Chains" and, most importantly how to join and benefit from this international network of experts in hydrogen technologies.

Keywords: International, Collaboration, Research, Hydrogen, Network

#266

SUSTAINABILITY ASSESSMENT OF A PROTON-EXCHANGE MEMBRANE FUEL CELL STACK AS A BASIS FOR THE DEVELOPMENT OF ECO-DESIGN GUIDELINES

[1] Mitja Mori, [2] Diego Iribarren, [3] Julie Cren, [3] Elise Monnier, [1] Rok Stropnik, [1] Andrej Lotrič, [1] Mihael Sekavčnik, [4] Darío Cortés, [4] Lara Giménez, [5] Laurent Rey, [2,6] Gonzalo Puig-Samper, [2,7] Felipe Campos-Carriedo, [2] Eleonora Bargiacchi, [2,7] Javier Dufour, [3*] Emmanuelle Cor*
[1] University of Ljubljana, Faculty of Mechanical Engineering, Aškerčeva 6, Ljubljana, SI-1000, Slovenia
[2] IMDEA Energy, Systems Analysis Unit, E-28935 Móstoles, Spain
[3] Univ. Grenoble Alpes, CEA, LITEN, F-38054 Grenoble, France
[4] Aragon Hydrogen Foundation, E-22197 Huesca, Spain
[5] SYMBIO, F-73370 Le Bourget-du-Lac, France
[6] Universidad Autónoma de Madrid, Chemical Engineering Department, E-28049 Madrid, Spain
[7] Rey Juan Carlos University, Chemical and Environmental Engineering Group, E-28933 Móstoles, Spain
*Corresponding author e-mail: emmanuelle.cor@cea.fr

ABSTRACT

The eGHOST project is the first milestone for the development of eco-design criteria in the European hydrogen sector. In the framework of this project, a life cycle sustainability assessment (LCSA) of a proton-exchange membrane fuel cell (PEMFC) stack was performed to estimate its potential environmental, economic, and social impacts. This assessment supports the identification and development of future sustainable design criteria that could be incorporated at early stages of the product development. The methodologies applied in the framework of the LCSA include environmental life cycle assessment (LCA), life cycle costing (LCC), and social life cycle assessment (S-LCA). Environmental (climate change, acidification, eutrophication, and resource use), economic (e.g., total production cost) and social (child labour, contribution to economic development, health expenditure, etc.) life-cycle indicators are evaluated for the product at the manufacturing phase, leading to the identification of sustainability hotspots. The results will support the development of future eco-design guidelines adapted to current and future fuel cells and hydrogen (FCH) technologies.

Keywords: eco-design, hydrogen, proton exchange membrane fuel cell, life cycle assessment, life cycle cost, social impacts

#283

THE ENERGY-ENVIRO-ECONOMIC EVALUATION AND MULTI-OBJECTIVE OPTIMIZATION OF THE HYDROGEN PRODUCTION PROCESS FROM COAL-BIOMASS CO-GASIFICATION CONSIDERING UNCERTAINTY IN CARBON PRICES

[1] Han Yang, [1] Min Dai, [1] Fusheng Yang, [1]Yunsong Yu, [1]Zhen Wu, [1]Zaoxiao Zhang*
[1] School of Chemical Engineering and Technology, Xi'an Jiaotong University, Xi'an, Shaanxi, China
*Corresponding author e-mail: yang.fs@mail.xjtu.edu.cn

ABSTRACT
Hydrogen has attracted more and more attention due to its advantages of low environmental impact and high energy density. However, the current hydrogen production process based on coal is usually accompanied by high energy consumption and CO_2 emission. Therefore, it is particularly important to develop efficient and clean hydrogen production technology. Based on this, a poly-generation system based on the co-gasification of coal and biomass coupled with carbon capture was proposed. Carbon dioxide emissions pricing is employed as an approach to mitigate climate change. Therefore, the impact of carbon prices on co-gasification system is analyzed, and the energy-enviro-economic evaluation of the system is carried out. Besides, the trade-off between exergy efficiency, annual gross profit and annual carbon emissions is conducted by multi-objective optimization. The results show that the system can be operated successfully under the optimum settings, achieving green and efficient hydrogen production while obtaining high economic benefits.
Keywords: Hydrogen production, Carbon price, Multi-objective optimization, Co-gasification

#314

EFFECTIVE METHODS TO REDUCE NOX EMISSION IN A HYDROGEN FUELED GAS TURBINE ENGINE.

Lohith A Vashishta, Amit Kumar Thakur

ABSTRACT
The rapid progress in the development of the aviation sector has been a direct contributor for the emission of NOx in earth's atmosphere, which is the cause for many serious environmental problems. Hydrogen has proved to be efficient in eliminating emissions such as carbon dioxides and carbon monoxide but fails to eliminate nitrogen oxides. So, based on the factors that influence the formation of NOx, the possible NOx abatement techniques for hydrogen fueled gas turbines are discussed along with a new method that works on the principle of nitrogen absence combustion, where the combustion takes place only with oxygen excluding other elements that are present in the air. This involves an addition of some components into the aircraft and other modifications to be made on the engine. Also, by considering this method a new type of cooling system can be employed in the aircraft's engine. The feasibility of this method is also discussed by keeping in mind its benefits and challenges.
Keywords: Nitrogen oxides, NOx, Hydrogen, Hydrogen fueled aircrafts, Nitrogen absence combustion, zero-emission, oxygen separation.

#315

LCA AND CRITICALITY ANALYSIS OF WATER ELECTROLYSIS TECHNOLOGIES

[1] Jan Christian Koj, [2] Ansgar Taubitz, [2] Ole Zelt [2], [1] Wilhelm Kuckshinrichs, [3] Klaus Görner*
[1]Forschungszentrum Jülich, Institute of Energy and Climate Research - Systems Analysis and Technology Evaluation (IEK-STE),
52425 Jülich, Germany
[2] Wuppertal Institute for Climate, Environment and Energy – Division Future Energy and Industry Systems,
42103 Wuppertal, Germany
[3] Gas- und Wärme-Institut Essen, 45356 Essen, Germany
*Corresponding author e-mail: j.koj@fz-juelich.de

ABSTRACT
Water electrolysis technologies enable the decarbonization of the industry, energy and transport sectors. Significant increases of electrolysis deployment are expected and will cause extensive material requirements. The current study investigates to which extent prospective electrolysis deployment affects raw material demand in relation to production volumes and reserves as well as environmental impacts related to further construction materials. The methods life cycle assessment and criticality analysis are used to exploit sustainability potentials of three water electrolysis technologies (AEC, PEMEC, and SOEC). LCA revealed minor contributions to climate change caused by materials required for plant construction. Clear changes of environmental impacts up to the year 2050 are given for SOEC as their life time significantly increases and material demand decreases. The work on the criticality analysis identified nine different raw materials, which are considered potentially critical and are required for water electrolysis plant construction. The expected demand for iridium and platinum, nickel, lanthanum and yttrium are particularly critical. Graphite, potassium, titanium and zirconium, on the other hand, do not exhibit raw material criticality. Results show different electrolysis technologies are likely to be used in parallel. Possible risks in the future raw material supply will thus be spread and mitigated overall.
Keywords: Hydrogen, water electrolysis, Power-to-Gas, Life Cycle Assessment, criticality analysis

#394

ENVIRONMENTAL EVALUATION OF THE PRODUCTION AND LIQUEFACTION OF GREEN HYDROGEN

[1] Jimena Incer-Valverde, [1] Sudheep Senthilkumar, [1] George Tsatsaronis, [1]Tatiana Morosuk*
[1] Technische Universität Berlin, Institute for Energy Engineering, Marchstr.18, 10587 Berlin, Germany
*Corresponding author e-mail: jimena.incervalverde@tu-berlin.de

ABSTRACT
Climate change and energy transition towards clean energy has been the most widely discussed topic in recent years. Hydrogen is seen as a key energy vector towards decarbonization. However, many questions remain about how environmentally friendly hydrogen really is. The proper quantification of the environmental impact of green hydrogen production and liquefaction chain represent an important question yet to be studied. This research is the only Life Cycle Assessment (LCA) study that complements its results with an exergoenvironmental analysis, an exergy-based environmental analysis, to produce green hydrogen via PEM electrolysis and further liquefaction to transport green liquid hydrogen. An LCA model, with the supply of wind-based electricity was developed using cradle to gate as the system boundary. The LCA models were created and simulated using the software GaBi version 9. Global warming potential, acidification potential, eutrophication potential and water footprint were evaluated in the study. For the exergoenvironmental analysis, a previous paper by the authors simulated the system and calculated the exergy analysis with the aid of Aspen Plus ®, and the exergoenvironmental analysis was calculated with the aid of Engineering Equation Solver. The environmental profile is dominated by the source of electricity in the production stage of hydrogen, whereas the use and end of life (EoL) were not considered in the scope of this study. According to the study, production stages are of significant environmental importance. The turbomachinery in the liquefaction system has the highest exergoenvironmental impact associated with the exergy destruction of the system. The future research will focus on the use phase and the EoL phase when extending the system boundary to include cradle-to-grave.
Keywords: Green hydrogen production, Green hydrogen liquefaction, Life Cycle Assessment, Exergoenvironmental analysis, Environmental Impact

#403

IMPROVE PHOTOCATALITYC HYDROGEN PRODUCTION WITH TI-NI AS NANOCOMPOSITE

[1*] *Alejandro Pérez-Larios*, [2]*Carolina Belver*, [2]*Jorge Bedia*, [3]*Rodolfo Zanella*, [4]*J.L. Rico*
[1] Universidad de Guadalajara, Centro Universitario de los Altos, Depto. Ingenierías, Laboratorio de Investigación en Materiales, Agua y Energía, Tepatitlán de Morelos, Jalisco, México. 47600.
[2] Universidad Autónoma de Madrid, Campus Cantoblanco, Facultad de Ciencias, Sección de Ingeniería Química, Madrid, España.
[3] Universidad Nacional Autónoma de México (UNAM), Centro de Ciencias Aplicadas y Desarrollo Tecnológico, Ciudad de México, México.
[4] Universidad Michoacana de San Nicolás de Hidalgo, Facultad de Ingeniería Química, Laboratorio de Catálisis, Morelia, Michoacán, México,
*Corresponding author e-mail: alarios@cualtos.udg.mx

ABSTRACT
The effect of Ni into the titanium oxide matrix as photocatalysts in the generation of hydrogen from water is herein reported. Ti–Ni nanocomposite and pure titania were synthetized by sol-gel. The Ni content was 0, 1, 3, 5, and 10 wt.%. The solids were characterized by Scanning electron microscope-energy dispersive spectrometer (SEM-EDS), N_2 physisorption, X-ray difrraction (XRD), ultraviolet visible spectroscopy (UV–Vis), spectroscopy Raman, X-ray photoelectron spectroscopy (XPS) spectroscopy and High resolution transmission electron microscope (HRTEM). The results showed that the mixed oxides show larger specific surface areas (73–186 m^2 /g) compare to that of pure TiO_2 (64 m2 / g). The XRD patterns of the Ti-Ni samples resemble that of anatase and segregation of Ni was not observed by this technique. The band gap energies of these solids vary from 3.05 to 2.85 eV which are smaller than that of pure TiO_2 (3.2 eV). The Ti-Ni oxides showed an enhancement in the hydrogen production (~4056 μmol/h) compare to that of TiO_2 (190 μmol/h) when using UV light. Furthermore, the photocatalytic activity of titania (110 μmol/h) for this reaction was also smaller than those observed for the Ti-Ni mixed oxides (~4213 μmol/h) under UV light.
Keywords: Photocatalysis, Energy, Hydrogen production, nanocomposites, TiO_2-NiO

#432

ENERGY SUPPLY IS THE MAIL GOAL OF SUSTAINABLE DEVELOPMENT

[1*]*Mubariz Nuriyev*, [1]*Saleh Mövlamov*
The State Statistical Committee of the Republic of Azerbaijan, Centre of Scientific research and statistical innovations, Baku-AZ1136,Inshaatchilar Avenue,81
*Corresponding author e-mail: mubariz.nuriyev@stat.gov.az , saleh.movlamov@stat.gov.az

ABSTRACT
The article highlights the important role of the energy sector in the socio-economic life of the country over the years, and also examines the impact of energy security reforms on the efficient use of energy resources. At the same time, energy security, meeting the needs of the economy and the population in energy, and replacing non-renewable resources with alternative energy sources were studied as the goal of sustainable development.
Per capita production, per capita consumption, etc. the use of units of measurement of economic physics in the analysis of indicators makes it possible to more accurately predict the goals and objectives of sustainable development. Therefore, the study was used energy intensity, energy efficiency, etc., which are integral indicators of economic physics. With the help of time series and relevant methods, as well as simple statistical models, were analyzed the country's GDP, energy consumption, population size until 2050. Was investigated for the sustainable development of the economy, the efficient use of energy resources, the application of new technological innovations, the transformation of economic activities to low energy consumption and the prevention of environmental pollution.
Keywords: econophysics, energy security, energy consumption, environmental protection, ecological investment.

#1444

A COMPARATIVE LIFE CYCLE ASSESSMENT OF HYDROGEN PRODUCTION USING THE SPECTRUM OF HYDROGEN COLORS

Huseyin Karasu, Ibrahim Dincer
Clean Energy Research Laboratory (CERL), Faculty of Engineering and Applied Science, Ontario Tech. University, 2000 Simcoe Street North, Oshawa, Ontario L1H 7K4, Canada
*Corresponding author e-mail: huseyin.karasu@ontariotechu.net

ABSTRACT

In this study, a comparative life cycle assessment (LCA) of hydrogen production is presented using the spectrum of hydrogen colors. The main hydrogen colors are studied depending on their varying energy sources and hydrogen production processes. The aim of the study is to investigate the environmental impacts of main hydrogen colors. The study results are illustrated in 6 different impact categories namely; global warming potential (GWP), ozone layer depletion potential (ODP), human toxicity potential (HTP), photochemical oxidation potential (POP), acidification potential (AP), and eutrophication potential (EP). The results show that brown hydrogen is the opposite of green hydrogen in the hydrogen spectrum, and it is the most environmentally harmful hydrogen type. Brown hydrogen emits 0.325 kg of CO_2 eq per 1 kg of hydrogen production while green hydrogen produce only 0.0072 kg of CO_2 eq per 1 kg of hydrogen production. Grey hydrogen is the second most harmful hydrogen type after brown hydrogen, with a value of 0.178 kg of CO_2 eq per 1 kg of hydrogen production. Turquoise hydrogen with a value of 0.079 kg of CO_2 eq per 1 kg of hydrogen production. Green hydrogen is the most environmentally friendly and sustainable option among the studied hydrogen production options.

Keywords: Hydrogen production, Life cycle assessment, Hydrogen colors, Environmental impact, Global warming.

#1480

REDUCTION OF HYDROGEN CARBON FOOTPRINT IN EUROPE VIA INTERNATIONAL SHIPPING

[1] Alessandro Arrigoni, [1] Eveline Weidner, [1] Francesco Dolci, [1] Rafael Ortiz Cebolla, [2] Umberto Eynard, [2] Fabrice Mathieux*
[1] European Commission Joint Research Center, Westerduinweg 3, 1755 LE Petten, Netherlands
[2] European Commission Joint Research Center, Via E. Fermi, 2749, 21027 Ispra, Italy
*Corresponding author e-mail: alessandro.arrigoni-marocco@ec.europa.eu

ABSTRACT

Green hydrogen is expected to play an important role in European decarbonisation efforts. This work investigates whether shipping green hydrogen within Europe could be a better climate solution than producing it locally. Three options for delivering hydrogen are analysed: hydrogen compression, liquefaction, and chemical bonding to other molecules (i.e., using ammonia, liquid organic compounds, methanol, or synthetic natural gas as hydrogen carriers). A distance compatible with the European territory was considered: i.e., production in Portugal and end-use in the Netherlands. The life cycle greenhouse gas emissions of shipped hydrogen are compared to the emissions arising from producing hydrogen locally, via either steam methane reforming or electrolysis powered by the electric grid. Preliminary results show that all the delivery options would guarantee in 2030 a supply of hydrogen with a lower global warming potential than locally produced hydrogen. Liquefaction appears to be the least greenhouse gas intense delivery solution, thanks to the lower volumes transported and the lack of an energy intensive transformation process at the delivery site. Nevertheless, much of the infrastructure for large scale hydrogen delivery does not yet exist, and therefore assumptions on technologies and emissions are subject to a high degree of uncertainty. Different delivery conditions (e.g., distances, means of transportation) can also alter the GHG emission ranking. Moreover, the present analysis was limited to the global warming impact, but an assessment of the overall environmental consequences is necessary to avoid shifting the burden from one environmental issue to another.
Keywords: Hydrogen delivery; Greenhouse gas emissions; Life cycle assessment

#1492

HOT GAS DESULFURIZATION PERFORMANCE OF SBA-15 SUPPORTED/MIXED METAL OXIDES (Cu, Fe, Mn, and Zn)

[1*] Arzu Kanca, [2] Gülcan Korkmaz
[1, 2] Ataturk University, Engineering Faculty, Chemical Engineering Department, 25240, Erzurum, Turkey
*Corresponding author e-mail: akanca@atauni.edu.tr

ABSTRACT
The main components of the synthesis gas formed during gasification is H_2 and CO. In addition to these gases, it contains H_2S due to the sulfur contents of organic matters. Since H_2S causes corrosion of system equipment and catalyst poisoning, it should be removed from flue gas stream. Furthermore, since fuel production from synthesis gas is an endothermic process and cooling of syngas causes energy loss, desulfurization should be carried out at high temperature. This study aims to determine the hot gas desulfurization performance of unsupported and SBA-15 supported MeO-MeO (Me: Cu, Fe, Mn, and Zn) sorbents. Sorbents prepared by wet impregnation method were characterized by X-ray diffraction (XRD) technique and Brunauer, Emmet ve Tellere (BET). In the characterization part, metal oxide formation was indicted by XRD findings, while BET results showed that SBA-15 supported CuO-ZnO sorbent has the largest surface area. Finally, desulfurization performance of sorbents was analyzed by gas chromatography equipped with a fixed bed quartz reactor at 800°C. Ar balanced simulated coal gas including 330 ppm H_2S, 9% H_2, 13.5% CO, and 4.5% CO_2 was used as the flue gas. The results of the desulfurization experiments revealed that the sorbents including MnO indicated the similar good sulfidation performance among the unsupported sorbents, while the best desulfurization performance was obtained for FeO-MnO among SBA 15 supported sorbents.
Keywords: Hot gas desulfurization, SBA 15, mixed metal oxide

#1516

THE EFFECT OF HYDROGEN AND AMMONIA COMBUSTION ON PERFORMANCE AND EMISSIONS

[1*] Kubilay Bayramoğlu, [2]Abdullah Bahlekeh, [3]Kemal Masera
[1]Dokuz Eylul University, Maritime Faculty, Marine Engineering Department, Buca, Izmir, Turkey
[2]Ege University, Mechanical Engineering Department, Bornova, Izmir, Turkey
[3]Aston University, Mechanical Biomedical and Design Engineering Department, Birmingham, UK
*Corresponding author e-mail: kubilay.bayramoglu@deu.edu.tr

ABSTRACT
The co-combustion of traditional methane gas and alternative fuels importance to reduce emissions in combustion has been increased in recent years. In this study, the effects of the combustion of methane-hydrogen and methane-ammonia-hydrogen fuel mixture on system performance and emissions were numerically investigated. Firstly, the effects of methane and 5%, 10% and 15% hydrogen mixture were investigated. Then, methane and 5% fixed hydrogen ratio with 5% ammonia, 10% ammonia and 15% ammonia mixtures were examined. As a result of the study, combustion chamber temperature, carbon and NO_x emissions are presented comparatively for each case. In addition, the Sandia D model used in the study is presented by verifying with the literature data. The findings obtained in the study showed that increasing hydrogen and ammonia increased NO_x emissions while decreasing CO_2 emissions.
Keywords: Hydrogen, Ammonia combustion, Flame, Emissions

#1549

LIFE CYCLE ASSESSMENT OF DIFFERENT HYDROGEN CONVERSION TECHNOLOGIES FROM BIOMASS GASIFICATION

[1*] *Mehmet Utku Öztürk,* [2*] *Azize Ayol,* [1] *Özgün Tezer*[1]
[1] Dokuz Eylul University, The Graduate School of Natural and Applied Sciences, Buca, 35390, Izmir, Turkey
[2] Dokuz Eylul University, Faculty of Engineering, Department of Environmental Engineering, Buca, 35390, Izmir Turkey
*Corresponding author e-mail: azize.ayol@deu.edu.tr

ABSTRACT
Gasification of different types of biomass in a lab scale up-draft fixed bed gasifier is evaluated from the environmental effect perspective through Life Cycle Assessment (LCA). Biomass is an energy source which has a lot of potential for electricity generation, and it is considered as an environmentally friendly renewable energy source. Gasification of the biomass has been considered as a significant renewable energy production alternative to fossil fuels. Biomass through gasification forms a syngas which includes H_2, CH_4, CO and as a solid by-product biochar is produced at high temperatures. In this study, LCA is used as a tool for assess the different environmental impact categories of the energy production from green waste and biological treatment sludge gasification studies, with the cradle to grave approach. Different hydrogen conversion technologies via LCA have been also assessed. LCA calculations were performed by using SimaPro 9.1 software and experimental data collected from LCA database and a lab scale gasifier operated in Dokuz Eylul University, Turkey.
Keywords: Life Cycle Assessment, Biomass, Gasification, Green Waste, Treatment Sludge, Hydrogen Conversion

#1589

LIFE CYCLE AND ECONOMIC ASSESSMENT OF HYDROGEN FUEL CELL BUSES

[1*] *Alireza Khoshnevisan,* [1] *Pouria Ahmadi,* [2] *Nader Javani*
[1]School of Mechanical Engineering, College of Engineering, University of Tehran, P.O. Box 11155-4563, Tehran, Iran
[2]Faculty of Mechanical Engineering, Yildiz Technical University, 34349, Istanbul, Turkey

ABSTRACT
Converting Intercity buses to hydrogen buses is an effective approch for a sustainable public transportation systems. In the current study, a life cycle analysis of hydrogen fuel cell and diesel buses are conducted, using real-world driving cycles. In this study, hydrogen buses are compared to diesel buses in terms of both life cycle emissions and life cycle cost. The results indicate that hydrogen buses can be economically comparable to diesel buses. Meanwhile, teing environmentally benign, makes them a promising solution for the considered situations in Canada.
Keywords: Life cycle assessment, Fuel cell, Electric Vehicles, Hydrogen

#1611

TOWARDS ETHICAL ENERGY STORAGE MATERIALS – COBALT FREE CATHODE ACTIVE MATERIAL LKMNO

* *Karolina Charzewska, Olga Surma, Gabriel Moskal, Agnieszka Węgrzyn, Marcin Molenda*
Jagiellonian University, Faculty of Chemistry, Department of Chemical Technology, Gronostajowa 2, 30-387 Kraków, Poland
*Corresponding author e-mail: karolina.charzewska@student.uj.edu.pl ; k.charzewska55@gmail.com

ABSTRACT
The replacement of fossil fuels by renewable energy sources will require batteries capable of storing significant amounts of energy. The effects of scientific studies on this subject are not limited to the research sphere, but have real economic, political and social consequences: independence from the supply of raw materials from distant areas or reduction of human rights violations in the case of conflict elements. Ethical and ecological supply of the elements is regulated by the EU and the US, among others – all of this must be taken into the consideration when proposing new materials for Li-ion cells. Based on these premises, this article is focused on the production of cobalt free and low-nickel lithium-ion cells using improved cathode material LKMNO. Its 3D spinel structure is capable of fast cation-mediated anionic redox reaction making it stable, reversible and efficient cathode material to use.
Keywords: energy storage; Li-ion batteries; cobalt-free cathode materials; defect spinel; green chemistry

Track 17.

Social Dimensions

#71

TEACHY - A FLAGSHIP PROJECT FOR TEACHING FUEL CELL AND HYDROGEN TECHNOLOGY

[1, 2]*Ioan Iordache*, [2]*Virgil Dumbrava* , [3]*Robert Steinberger-Wilckens*, [3]*Naser Al-Mufachi*, [4]*Aravind Purushothaman Vellayani*, [5]*Massimo Santarelli*, [6]*Yegor Brodnikovskyi*, [7]*Lars N. Cleeman*, [8]*Karel Bouzek*, [9]*Jan Van Herle*, [10]*Jean-Luc Delplancke*, [11]*Florence Druart*, [12]*Vladimir Molkov*, [13]*Olaf Jedicke*,

[1] The National R&D Institute for Cryogenic and Isotopic Technologies – ICSI, Str. Uzinei 4, Rm. Valcea, Romania
[2] University POLITEHNICA of Bucharest, Spl. Independentei Str. 313, Bucharest, Romania
[3] Centre for Fuel Cell and Hydrogen Research, School of Chemical Engineering, University of Birmingham, Edgbaston B15 2TT, UK
[4] University of Groningen, 9700 AB Groningen, the Netherlands
[5] Politecnico di Torino, Str. Corso Duca degli Abruzzi 24, Torino, Italy
[6] National Technical University of Ukraine 'Kyiv Polytechnic Institute', Str. Prosp. Peremohy 37, Kyiv, Ukraine
[7] Denmark Technical University, Str. Anker Engelunds Vej 1, Lyngby, Denmark
[8] University of Chemistry and Technology, Prague; Technická 5; 16628 Prague 6; Czech Republic
[9] Ecole Polytechnique Federale de Lausanne, Rte Cantonale, 1015, Lausanne, Switzerland
[10] Universite libre de Bruxelles, Av. Franklin Roosevelt 50, 1050 Brussels, Belgium
[11] Grenoble Institute of Technology, Av. Félix Viallet 46, Grenoble, France
[12] Ulster University, St. York 25-51, Belfast, United Kingdom
[13] Karlsruhe Institute of Technology, Karlstraße 6, Karlsruhe, Germany
*Corresponding author e-mail: iordache.ioan@icsi.ro

ABSTRACT

The TeacHy project (Teaching Fuel Cell and Hydrogen science and engineering across Europe) is funded by the Fuel Cell & Hydrogen Joint Undertaking (FCH2 JU), as part of the Horizon 2020 Programme. The TeacHy educational material and MSc course modules have been developed for blended learning delivery and will be available through the partnering universities. 12 partners from 11 European countries have contributed to the successful development of 20 modules.

#193

SOCIAL LIFE CYCLE ASSESSMENT OF A SOLID OXIDE ELECTROLYSIS CELL STACK

[1,2] *Felipe Campos-Carriedo*, [1,3] *Gonzalo Puig-Samper*, [1] *Eleonora Bargiacchi*, [1] *Diego Iribarren*, [1,2*] *Javier Dufour*

[1] IMDEA Energy, Systems Analysis Unit, 28935, Móstoles, Spain
[2] Rey Juan Carlos University, Chemical and Environmental Engineering Group, 28933, Móstoles, Spain
[3] Universidad Autónoma de Madrid, Chemical Engineering Department, 28049, Madrid, Spain
*Corresponding author e-mail: javier.dufour@imdea.org

ABSTRACT

The relevance of Fuel Cells and Hydrogen (FCH) systems as decarbonisation solutions has grown significantly during the past decade. However, a sustainable life-cycle performance of FCH systems should be guaranteed. In this sense, while the focus is typically placed on their economic and environmental performance, scarce attention is usually paid to the social dimension, which should be assessed to avoid burden shifting. In this work, a Social Life Cycle Assessment (S-LCA) of a 5 kW Solid Oxide Electrolysis Cell (SOEC) stack was carried out within the context of the eGHOST project. The system boundaries include the extraction of materials, the manufacturing of components and the final assembly of the stack parts (balance of plant excluded). Design parameters such as current density, degradation and lifetime were defined considering 2030 targets, when this type of electrolysers is expected to be commercially mature. Inventory data (including working hours) were adapted accordingly from literature sources, while trade information from the UN Comtrade database was used for the regionalisation of the supply chain. Modelling and evaluation were performed using openLCA and the PSILCA database and method. Overall, stainless steel production in Spain arose as the main social hotspot under most of the evaluated indicators.

Keywords: Hydrogen, Life Cycle Assessment, Solid Oxide Electrolysis, Social Impact, Sustainability

#239

ASSESSING PUBLIC ACCEPTANCE ON HYDROGEN ECONOMY IN JAPAN: A COMPARISON OF PAST SURVEY IN 2015

[1] Jiazhen Yap,[1] Benjamin McLellan*
[1]Graduate School of Energy Science, Kyoto University, Kyoto, 606-8501, Japan
*Corresponding author e-mail: yap.jiazhen.76z@st.kyoto-u.ac.jp

ABSTRACT

Hydrogen and Japan have a long, shared history, dating back to 1974 with the start of a green initiative known as the Sunshine Project. Since then, the Japanese government has actively sought to realise a hydrogen society by using hydrogen as an energy carrier in transportation, residential power systems, and industrial applications. Despite the continuous effort by the Japanese government, it remains to be seen whether hydrogen can achieve large-scale deployment. Assessing society's acceptance of a hydrogen economy is important to understanding social support and ultimately avoiding unwillingness for hydrogen technology and infrastructure deployment. This study aims to analyze the current attitude of Japanese society towards the realization of a hydrogen economy through a community survey. Given recent global interest, the results will be compared with a similar survey conducted in 2015 to see if there has been any recent changes. The questionnaire survey was designed to analyze responses under four main aspects: awareness of various energy resources and environmental policy; perception of hydrogen economy; knowledge of hydrogen technology and infrastructure; and acceptance towards the establishment of hydrogen infrastructure in the community.

Keywords: Hydrogen Economy, Survey, Public Acceptance, Japan

#1473

GREEN HYDROGEN, AN ECONOMIC PARADIGM SHIFT – NEW PERSPECTIVES FOR THE GLOBAL SOUTH?

[1] Andreas Stamm, [1] Rita Strohmaier, [1] Ece Oyan, [1] Katharina Thoms*
[1]German Development Institute – Deutsches Institut für Entwicklungspolitik (DIE), Bonn, Germany
*Corresponding author e-mail: andreas.stamn@die-gdi.de

ABSTRACT

Hydrogen is a key element for the energy system of the future. International experts and organizations [1] forecast a rapidly increasing demand for green hydrogen in the coming decades, especially in Europe and Japan. This opens new opportunities for developing countries to position themselves beneficially in a new international division of labour. Costa Rica has locational advantages for the production of hydrogen with renewable energies. It makes sense for the country not to focus exclusively on opportunities to develop a new export sector, which may not generate very good income and employment opportunities in the future. Rather, more comprehensive strategies should be developed combining export revenues and

Keywords: Green Hydrogen, Developing Countries, Development Potentials, Decarbonisation, Employment Creation

#1474

GREEN HYDROGEN IN COSTA RICA – PERSPECTIVES OF AN ECONOMIC PARADIGM SHIFT FOR A SMALL DEVELOPING COUNTRY

[1] Andreas Stamm, [1] Katharina Thoms, [2] Fernando Lizana*
[1]German Development Institute – Deutsches Institut für Entwicklungspolitik (DIE), Bonn, Germany
[2] Instituto Costarricense de Electricidad (ICE), San José, Costa Rica
*Corresponding author e-mail: andreas.stamn@die-gdi.de

ABSTRACT

Hydrogen is a key element for the energy system of the future. International experts and organizations [1] forecast a rapidly increasing demand for green hydrogen in the coming decades, especially in Europe and Japan. This opens new opportunities for developing countries to position themselves beneficially in a new international division of labour. Costa Rica has locational advantages for the production of hydrogen with renewable energies. It makes sense for the country not to focus exclusively on opportunities to develop a new export sector. Rather, Costa Rica should actively seek to create additional benefits domestically through the usage of hydrogen. In transport and certain industries, there are opportunities to lower greenhouse gas emissions while significantly reducing the import of fossil resources and creating job opportunities.

Keywords: Green Hydrogen, Developing Countries, Development Potentials, Decarbonisation, Employment Creation

#1477

TURKEY'S POTENTIAL TO PRODUCE GEOTHERMAL-BASED GREEN HYDROGEN: INSIGHTS FROM INSIDE

[1*] *Ece Oyan*
[1]German Development Institute - Deutsches Institut für Entwicklungspolitik (DIE)
Tulpenfeld 6 53113 Bonn, Germany
*Corresponding author e-mail: ece.oyan@die-gdi.de

ABSTRACT

As a country with high renewable energy potential but still very much dependent on fossil fuel imports, green hydrogen can yield many opportunities to the Turkish economy. This study aims to examine Turkey's potentials in producing geothermal-based green hydrogen. For such an analysis, different stakeholders like private sector, scholars, policymakers, civil society organizations and locals will be interviewed and the results will be analyzed based on techno-economic, political-economic, environmental and societal impacts argued by the interviewees.

Keywords: Green hydrogen, Geothermal, Turkey

#1631

EFFECTS OF SOCIAL MEDIA PLATFORMS ABOUT ATTENDANCE TO WHEC 2022 CONFERENCE

[1*] *Feride Cansu İskenderoğlu,* [2] *Mustafa Kaan Baltacıoğlu,* [3] *Hüseyin Turan Arat*
[1] İskenderun Technical University, Faculty of Engineering and Natural Science, Mechanical Engineering Department, Hatay, Turkey
[2] İskenderun Technical University, Faculty of Engineering and Natural Science, Mechatronics Engineering Department, Hatay, Turkey
[3] Sinop University, Faculty of Engineering and Architecture, Mechanical Engineering Department, Sinop, Turkey
*Corresponding author e-mail: mkaan.baltacioglu@iste.edu.tr

ABSTRACT

In recent years, it has become very important to examine the positive or negative factors affecting participation in Scientific Conferences and to determine the right strategies. In this study, it is aimed not only at academic research focusing on the motivating and hindering factors in the literature, but also to expand the existing academic knowledge in terms of social media platforms, together with the data obtained from the social media platforms of the WHEC2022 conference. In addition to new and established factors affecting conference attendance, an interactive management and organizational strategies are proposed. An increase of 3.2% was observed in the WHEC2022 conference participation with the social media strategy used. Research findings are important for conference administrators in addressing the higher-importance social media strategies that affect conference attendance and the factors that affect them.

Keywords: Social Media, Hydrogen Energy, Attractions, Effects, Conference

#1635

GREEN HYDROGEN PRODUCTION FOR ESKIL OIZ HEATING

[1*]*Yasin Öğütcü,* [2*]*Bahattin Tanç,*

Iskenderun Technical University, Energy Institute, Energy Systems Engineering, Hatay, Turkey

*Corresponding author e-mail: yasinogutcu.96@gmail.com

ABSTRACT

Energy need is a major concern than ever before. The increasing demand and developing technology in every field within the industry have increased the demand for energy. Therefore, the gradual depletion of fossil fuels, which has been used as an energy source, pushed people to seek new energy sources. Energy from fossil fuels was polluting the environment depending on the amount reducing the resources since it was consumed from the volume of the limited resource. The energy source of the future is seen as alternative energy sources, as they can be adapted to any area where energy is needed, from transportation to lighting. Among these, gas that contains the highest energy is hydrogen and can be produced by renewal. It comes to the fore in the choice of energy source. As Green Hydrogen, the production of hydrogen with solar energy and the use of the produced hydrogen in heating the Industrial Zone have been studied theoretically. As a result, hydrogen can be produced with zero emission with a solar power plant to be built in the vicinity of the OIZ, which is planned to be built in Eskil, and the heating of the OIZ can be provided with Green Hydrogen.

Keywords: Energy, Green Hydrogen, Solar Energy, Heating, Hydrogen Production

HOSPITALITY
MORE THAN JUST A WORD
True hospitality comes from the heart.
From a genuine desire to make sure our guests always feel totally at home.
BUSINESS CLASS
TURKISH AIRLINES
Products and services are subject to change depending on flight duration and aircraft.
STAR ALLIANCE
25 YEARS

BAU

Bahçeşehir University

TEMSA
MOTORLU ARAÇLAR
Sabancı Üniversitesi

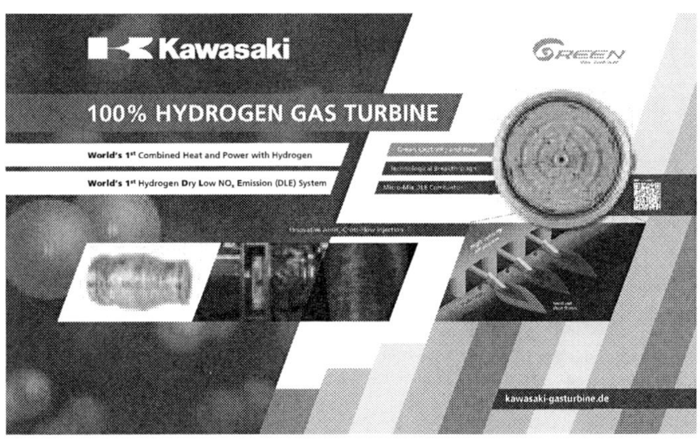

Kawasaki
GREEN
100% HYDROGEN GAS TURBINE
World's 1st Combined Heat and Power with Hydrogen
World's 1st Hydrogen Dry Low NO_x Emission (DLE) System
kawasaki-gasturbine.de

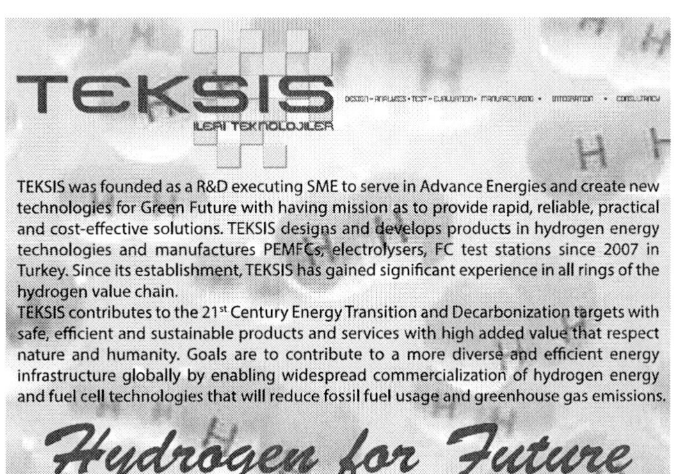

TEKSIS
ILERI TEKNOLOJILER
DESIGN • ANALYSIS • TEST • EVALUATION • MANUFACTURING • INTEGRATION • CONSULTANCY
TEKSIS was founded as a R&D executing SME to serve in Advance Energies and create new technologies for Green Future with having mission as to provide rapid, reliable, practical and cost-effective solutions. TEKSIS designs and develops products in hydrogen energy technologies and manufactures PEMFCs, electrolysers, FC test stations since 2007 in Turkey. Since its establishment, TEKSIS has gained significant experience in all rings of the hydrogen value chain.
TEKSIS contributes to the 21st Century Energy Transition and Decarbonization targets with safe, efficient and sustainable products and services with high added value that respect nature and humanity. Goals are to contribute to a more diverse and efficient energy infrastructure globally by enabling widespread commercialization of hydrogen energy and fuel cell technologies that will reduce fossil fuel usage and greenhouse gas emissions.
Hydrogen for Future

BCSMÜHENDİSLİK

Fakir
HAUSGERÄTE

İTÜ
İSTANBUL TEKNİK ÜNİVERSİTESİ
1773

Sistem Al
ALÜMİNYUM

Westfälische Hochschule
Gelsenkirchen Bocholt Recklinghausen
University of Applied Sciences

YILDIZ TEKNİK ÜNİVERSİTESİ
1911

KUTEM

OZ Energy

FIRAT UNIVERSITY 1975

NATIONAL HYDROGEN ASSOCIATION TURKEY

International Association for Hydrogen Energy

International Journal of Hydrogen Energy

IHTEC 2023

www.ihtec2023.org

7th International HYDROGEN TECHNOLOGIES Congress

10-12 May 2023

Fırat University, Elazığ, Turkey

Contact

Association Secretary:
Fatma Taşçı - 0 533 726 72 55 - fatma.tasci@hidrojenteknolojileri.org
www.hidrojenteknolojileri.org

Organization Secretariat

BROS
Congress, Incentive and Events

Esentepe Mah. Sağlam Fikir Sok. Esen Palas Apt. A Blok No:2 D:9 Esentepe / İstanbul / Turkey
Tel: +90 212 296 66 70 / Fax: +90 212 296 66 71
www.brosgroup.net e-mail: hatice.cilek@brosgroup.net

National Hydrogen Association Turkey
Ontario Tech University
International Association for Hydrogen Energy

Main Sponsors

Republic of Turkey Ministry of Energy and Natural Resources
TENMAK – Turkish Energy, Nuclear and Mineral Research Agency
Turkish Airlines – A Star Alliance Member

Platinum Sponsors

BAU Bahçeşehir University
FuelPositive – Fuel For A Mindful World
INOGEN Enerji Teknolojileri Energy Technologies

Gold Sponsors

Enerjisa Üretim
Temsa Motorlu Araçlar
Sabancı Üniversitesi
Üsküdar Belediyesi

Silver Sponsors

Kawasaki – Kawasaki Gas Turbine Europe GmbH
Teksis
WHTC 2023

Bronze Sponsors

BCS Mühendislik
Fakir Hausgeräte
İTÜ
Sistem Alüminyum
Westfälische Hochschule – Gelsenkirchen Bocholt Recklinghausen University of Applied Sciences

Other Sponsors

KUTEM
OZ Energy

www.whecistanbul.org
info@whecistanbul.org

International Association for Hydrogen Energy (IAHE)
5794 SW 40 St. #303
Miami, FL 33155, USA

ISBN 978-1-7138-5770-9
9 781713 857709

CURRAN ASSOCIATES INC.
proceedings.com